PROPERTY OF

MACMILLAN
DICTIONARY
OF
LIFE SCIENCES

SECOND EDITION

EDITED BY

E.A. MARTIN, MA

MACMILLAN PRESS
LONDON

First published 1976; second edition 1983 by
THE MACMILLAN PRESS LTD
London and Basingstoke

Associated companies in Auckland, Delhi, Dublin, Gaborone, Hamburg, Harare, Hong Kong, Johannesburg, Kuala Lumpur, Lagos, Manzini, Melbourne, Mexico City, Nairobi, New York, Singapore, Tokyo

Paperback of second edition 1985
Reprinted 1985

British Library Cataloguing in Publication Data

A Dictionary of life sciences — 2nd. ed.
  1. Biology — Dictionaries
  I. Martin,E.A.
  574′.03′21   QH302.5

ISBN 0–333–34867–2
ISBN 0–333–38647–7 Pbk

Prepared for automatic typesetting by
Market House Books Ltd Aylesbury

Printed and bound in Great Britain by
Anchor Brendon Ltd, Tiptree, Essex

This book is a companion to The Macmillan Press's
A Dictionary of Physical Sciences, edited by
John Daintith, and *A Dictionary of Earth Sciences,*
edited by Stella E. Stiegeler
Series editor: Alan Isaacs, PhD

Contributors

J.S. de Belleroche, BA, MSc, DIC, PhD
G.W. Bennett, BSc, MSc, DIC, PhD
S.J. Coles, BSc
Eve Daintith, BSc
Indrajit Das, MSc, DPhil, ARIC
S.B. Holmes, MA, MIBiol
N. Maclean BSc, DPhil
Shirley McCready BSc, DPhil
R.A. Prince, MA
Judith H. Pybus, MA, DPhil
Cherril S. Smith, BSc, PhD
D.J. Taylor, BSc, PhD
Peter Thompson, BSc, MIBiol
S.D. Wratten, BSc, MA, PhD

Preface to the Second Edition

This dictionary was first published in 1976. Its success, in schools and universities both at home and abroad, has provided the stimulus to update and expand it.

In this new edition we have increased the text by some 300 new entries, most of which reflect recent advances in genetics, molecular biology, microbiology, and immunology. Existing entries that relate to these topics have been revised and updated. There has been a small reduction in the coverage of the more traditional aspects of biology. This reflects the shift in emphasis in biology teaching away from classical zoology and botany and enables the new material to be accommodated without making the book considerably larger and therefore more expensive.

I should like to thank Drs Maclean, McCready, and Wratten for their help in preparing this new edition.

E.A.M., 1983

Key to Symbols

Asterisks before words in the text denote cross-references to entries that will provide additional information. Entries are defined under the most commonly used term, with synonyms shown in brackets.

A

aardvark. *See* Tubulidentata.

abaxial. Designating the surface of a leaf or other lateral organ that is developmentally furthest from the apex of the axis that bears it (the *lower* (or *dorsal*) surface of such organs). *Compare* adaxial.

abdomen. 1. The part of the body cavity of vertebrates in which the stomach, intestine, liver, kidneys, etc., are suspended (*compare* thorax). In mammals the abdomen is clearly separated from the thorax by the diaphragm.
2. The posterior region of the body of arthropods, often consisting of a series of similar segments.

abducens nerve. *See* cranial nerves.

abiogenesis. *See* spontaneous generation.

abiotic environment. *See* biotic environment.

abomasum. The fourth chamber of the stomach of ruminants. *See* Ruminantia.

abortive transduction. *Transduction of bacterial genes into a new host cell by a viral vector that is not followed by integration of the new genes into the genome of the recipient cell. The transduced genes may, however, persist for a time in the cell as a plasmid, conferring on the recipient bacterium new but transient genetic properties.

abscisic acid (ABA). A plant growth substance (see formula) previously known as *dormin* or *abscisin II.* (Abscisin I is a similarly acting, but chemically unrelated and less effective, substance.)

ABA has been implicated in abscission (e.g. leaf fall and fruit drop), leaf senescence, seed dormancy (e.g. in cotton and apple), bud dormancy (e.g. in birch), apical dominance (where it may inhibit lateral bud growth), and inhibition of flowering of long-day plants under short-day conditions. In all its roles it appears to be inhibitory, and it may be that the relative balance (environmentally controlled) between ABA and the growth promoters (auxins, gibberellins, and cytokinins) determines response.

abscission. The organized separation of a plant organ from the plant, as in leaf fall, fruit drop, and loss of unfertilized flowers. It is caused by the breakdown or separation of a layer of cells, the *abscission layer*, which forms part of an *abscission zone* at the base of the organ. A second, *protective layer* is left. Abscission is controlled by growth substances, probably by a balance between *auxins and *abscisic acid, the former usually inhibiting and the latter promoting the phenomenon. Gibberellins may also be involved.

absorption. 1. The uptake of liquid digested food from the alimentary canal into the bloodstream and lymph vessels. Absorption takes place mainly from the small *intestine, the inner surface of which is covered with small finger-like projections (*see* villus) that greatly increase the surface area over which absorption can occur.
2. The uptake of water and mineral salts by plant roots. The main regions of absorption are just behind the root tips where the *root hairs occur.

absorption spectrum. The spectrum obtained when radiation (light, ultraviolet radiation, etc.) from a source giving a continuous spectrum is passed through a substance. If the substance is in the gaseous state dark lines or bands appear in the spectrum in the same positions as the coloured lines that appear in the characteristic *emission spectrum* of that substance. If the substance is a solid or liquid the spectrum of the light transmitted through the substance consists of broad dark regions, which cannot be resolved into sharp lines. However a graph of the relative amounts absorbed by different wavelengths can be used to identify the presence of some biologically important substances. The chlorophylls have absorption peaks in the red and blue parts of the visible spectrum and therefore appear green (reflecting green light). Nucleic acids do not markedly absorb visible light and therefore appear colourless in solution; they do, however, have characteristic peaks at 260 nm in the ultraviolet absorption spectrum. Instruments designed to measure light absorption at different wavelengths, for purposes of identification or quantification, are called *spectrophotometers* or *colorimeters*.

abyssal. Designating or inhabiting the deep waters of an ocean (approximately below 2000 metres), where conditions are cold, dark, and still.

Acanthocephala. A phylum of elongated cylindrical pseudocoelomate parasitic worms. The adults inhabit the intestines of vertebrates, with arthropods as the intermediate hosts. They are characterized by a retractile spiny proboscis, which they use to cling to the host's gut wall. There is no mouth or digestive tract. *See also* Aschelminthes.

Acanthodii. The class of vertebrates containing the earliest jawed fishes, which appeared in the Silurian, were common in the Devonian, and became extinct in the Permian. They had paired fins and a heterocercal tail. The acanthodians show affinities to both the Osteichthyes and the Chondrichthyes and are sometimes placed in one or other of these classes.

Acari (Acarina). A large order of the Arachnida, containing the ticks and mites. They typically have small round bodies with the cephalothorax and abdomen fused and the segmentation obliterated. The order includes scavengers, e.g. *Megninia* (feather mite); ectoparasites, e.g. *Ixodes* (sheep tick); and blood suckers, e.g. *Eutrombidium* (velvet mite); the latter are important in spreading disease.

accessory cell. *See* subsidiary cell.

accessory chromosomes. *See* B chromosomes.

accessory nerve. *See* cranial nerves.

accommodation. 1. The reflex adjustments in the eye by which an image is brought to focus on the retina. The process may involve constriction of the pupil to increase the depth of focus (stopping down), as well as either moving the lens backwards or forwards (cephalopods, fish, and amphibians), changing the shape of the cornea (birds), or changing the curvature of the lens by the action of the ciliary body (amniotes).
2. (of sense organs). *See* adaptation.

acellular. Designating an organism, tissue, part, etc., consisting of a mass of protoplasm that has no size limit and is not divided into cells. For example, the multinucleate hyphae of fungi and the muscle fibres of animals are acellular.

acentric. (Designating) a chromosome or chromosome fragment without a centromere.

acetabulum. The socket in a tetrapod pelvic girdle that holds the ball-shaped head of the femur to form the hip joint.

acetylcholine (ACh). A neurotransmitter of the vertebrate and invertebrate peripheral nervous system that is the acetyl ester of *choline. Acetylcholine was the first chemical demonstrated to be a neurotransmitter: in 1920 Otto Loewi found that stimulation of the vagus nerve of a frog heart held in saline solution inhibited the beat of a second heart placed in the solution. The substance released by the first heart and responsible for the inhibition was later identified as acetylcholine.

ACh acts as a neurotransmitter at the synapses of parasympathetic nerves, sympathetic and parasympathetic ganglia, all preganglionic nerve endings of the ANS, and at the neuromuscular junction of all somatic motor nerves. There is also a small resting release of ACh from somatic motor nerve endings, detected as miniature end-plate potentials. ACh may also function as a neurotransmitter in certain parts of the central nervous system.

Nerve fibres or nerve endings that release ACh as a neurotransmitter are termed *cholinergic*.

acetyl coenzyme A. *See* coenzyme A.

acetylmuramic acid. An amino sugar, derived from D-glucosamine and lactic acid. It is a component of bacterial cell wall polysaccharides (*see* mucopeptide).

achene. A dry indehiscent monocarpellary uniovular *fruit.

A chromosomes. The main chromosome complement of a eukaryotic cell, excluding the supernumerary *B chromosomes.

acid-base balance. The maintenance of the acid:base ratio in the blood (*see* homeostasis). Blood contains carbonic acid and bicarbonate in the ratio of 1:20, which maintains the pH at 7.4. If this ratio is altered, as in respiratory acidosis (when carbonic acid accumulates in the blood), bicarbonate reabsorption by the kidney tubules is increased as a compensatory action to bring the ratio back to the required value.

acidic stains. *See* staining.

acoelomate. Designating any metazoan animal that lacks a coelom. The term is often restricted to the Platyhelminthes and Nemertina but may be extended to include the Nematoda, Rotifera, and a few other phyla.

Aconta. Eukaryotic algae that never produce flagella, comprising only the *Rhodophyta. *Compare* Contophora.

acorn worms. *See* Hemichordata.

acoustico-lateralis system. A system of receptors for the detection of movement and vibration in water, found in invertebrate chordates, fish, and aquatic amphibians. It consists of a series of sensory papillae (*neuromasts*) scattered or arranged in rows above the cranial nerves on the head or along the body (*lateral line system*). The structure and function of the neuromasts resembles that of the *macula of the tetrapod ear and the system is probably homologous with the inner ear.

acquired characteristics. *See* Lamarckism.

Acrania. *See* Cephalochordata.

Acrasiales. A group of fairly common soil fungi, the cellular slime fungi, whose plant body is a pseudoplasmodium (*see* plasmodium). The Acrasiales are of uncertain affinities but are usually classified as *Myxomycophyta.

Proflavin

acridine. One of a class of organic dyes that can act as *mutagens, causing deletions and additions of base pairs, especially in plasmids and other extrachromosomal DNA molecules. The flat acridine molecules intercalate between adjacent base pairs in DNA and cause unwinding of the helix. An example is proflavin (2,8-diaminoacridine; see formula).

acrocarp. A moss with an upright growth habit and terminal sex organs. *Compare* pleurocarp.

acrocentric. *See* centromere.

acropetal (in botany). Undergoing development from base to apex, i.e. with the oldest structure at the base, as of leaves and inflorescences. *Compare* basipetal, centripetal, centrifugal.

acrosome. *See* spermatozoon.

ACTH (adrenocorticotrophic hormone, corticotrophin). A straight-chain polypeptide hormone of 39 amino acid residues synthesized and secreted during most states of stress by the pars distalis of the mammalian pituitary gland. Its main action is on the growth and maintenance of the adrenal cortex and the stimulation of synthesis and release of corticosteroid hormones. ACTH also stimulates melanin production in pigment cells and lipolysis in fatty tissue, reflecting its similarity in structure to melanocyte-stimulating hormone and lipotrophin. Isolation of the hormone in the late 1950s revealed that the N-terminal 1–24 amino acids were common to all species studied and showed full biological activity. ACTH secretion is regulated by a specific hypothalamic hormone, *corticotrophin-releasing factor (CRF)*, and possibly also by vasopressin; ACTH release is further modulated by a negative feedback action of corticosteroids and ACTH itself by acting at both pituitary and hypothalamic levels.

actin. A protein characteristic of contractile systems, e.g. muscle and flagella. *See* striated muscle, smooth muscle.

actinomorphic (in botany). Showing *radial symmetry. The term is applied particularly to flowers whose parts are arranged in radial symmetry around the receptacle. *Compare* zygomorphic.

actinomycetes. A group of nonmotile Gram-positive eubacteria with a mycelial vegetative growth habit. The genus *Mycobacterium* has a transient mycelial growth phase, breaking into irregular rods, while the genera *Nocardia* and *Actinomyces* produce a more extensive mycelium, which fragments only when

growth ceases. *Streptomyces* and *Microspora* have a permanent mycelial growth and resemble fungi in producing reproductive conidia at the tips of the hyphae. Most actinomycetes are saprophytic, but some species of *Actinomyces*, *Streptomyces*, and *Nocardia* are parasites and can cause disease in animals (*actinomycosis*). Species of *Streptomyces* produce almost all the important antibiotics, excepting those of the fungus *Penicillium*.

actinomycin D. An antibiotic derived from the bacterium *Streptomyces*. It is widely used experimentally in cell biology because of its potent suppression of RNA synthesis, especially that of ribosomal RNA.

Actinopterygii. A subclass of the Osteichthyes containing the majority of living bony fishes, the ray-finned fishes, in which the fins are composed of a web of skin stiffened by approximately parallel rows of horny rays and lack a central axis. In most modern forms the scales are reduced or absent, the jaw suspension is *hyostylic, and there is usually a *swim bladder functioning as a hydrostatic organ. There are three subdivisions, the *Chondrostei, *Holostei, and *Teleostei. *Compare* Choanichthyes.

actinostele. *See* stele.

Actinozoa. *See* Anthozoa.

action potential. The transitory reversal of the potential across a nerve or muscle membrane from -70 mV to $+30$ mV (approximately). The action potential is the most easily observed manifestation of the passage of a nervous *impulse. *See also* resting potential.

action spectrum. A plot of the relative efficiencies of different wavelengths of radiation (usually light) in causing a reaction. The action spectrum for photosynthesis is shown in the diagram and corresponds closely with the absorption spectrum of the chlorophylls, indicating that the latter pigments are the primary

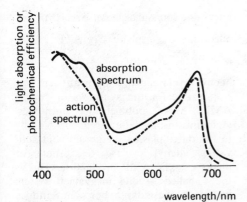

Light absorption spectrum and action spectrum of photosynthesis for a green plant

light-trapping molecules in photosynthesis.

active site. The region of an *enzyme with which the substrate reacts.

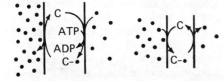

Fig. 1: Active transport   Fig. 2: Facilitated diffusion

Fig. 3: Exchange diffusion

Membrane transport systems

active transport. The transport of molecules across a biological *membrane against a concentration gradient (i.e. from a region of low concentration to one of high concentration). Active transport is mediated by a carrier (C), thought to be a protein or lipoprotein, which becomes saturated at high concentration levels. It also requires a source of energy, e.g. ATP (see Fig. 1), and is usually unidirectional (unlike passive diffusion, which is reversible). Active transport is responsible for the entry of amino acids into cells and for the exclusion of sodium from neurones to produce a resting potential across the cell membrane (*see* sodium pump).

Passive transport (i.e. without expenditure of energy) may occur reversibly by carrier-mediated systems. Two such systems are *facilitated diffusion*, which occurs along a concentration gradient (see Fig. 2), for example in the transport of glucose into red blood cells; and *exchange diffusion*, in which molecules are exchanged between one side of the membrane and the other (see Fig. 3), for example in the exchange of phosphate across the mitochondrial membrane.

actomyosin. A protein consisting of combined actin and myosin, formed transitorily during contraction of *striated muscle.

acyl glycerols. *See* glycerides.

adaptation. 1. Any change in an organ or characteristic of an animal or plant that makes it better suited to survive a particular environment. Adaptations eventually result in the evolution of new species.
2. The diminution with time of the frequency of the impulses evoked in a receptor by a constant stimulus. Adaptation may be a property of the accessory structures of a sense organ or of the receptor membrane. The rate and extent of adaptation of a receptor is related to its function: nonadapting receptors monitor the static aspects of a stimulus; rapidly adapting phasic receptors, responding to a change in the level of stimulation, are able to monitor dynamic aspects, i.e. the rate of change of a stimulus. Also called: **accommodation**.

adaptive enzyme. *See* inducible enzyme.

adaptive radiation. The evolutionary divergence of many forms of animals or plants from a single ancestral stock to fill many ecological niches. These forms can become new species or even, in time, new genera and families. For example, insects underwent adaptive radiation into types suited for flying, burrowing, aquatic life, parasitism, etc.; mammals, both placental and marsupial, evolved into carnivores, herbivores, burrowers, and aquatic, arboreal, and flying types. Flowering plants adapted to suit desert conditions, freshwater, marshland, and salt-marsh habitats, and into climbing, insectivorous, and parasitic modes of life.

adaxial. Designating the surface of a leaf or other lateral organ that is developmentally closest to the apex of the axis that bears it (the *upper* (or *ventral*) surface of such organs). *Compare* abaxial.

additive recombination. Gene *recombination achieved by insertion of a new sequence of DNA into an existing genome without any reciprocal loss of DNA. This is probably achieved by a special insertion sequence on the new DNA pairing up with a complementary sequence on the chromosome, followed by breaking and resplicing so as to include the new molecule as a colinear insert. The DNA bacteriophage lambda is believed to be integrated into the circular genome of *E. coli* by this mechanism. *See* insertion element.

NH$_2$

Adenine

adenine. A purine base (see formula) that is an essential constituent of the nucleic acids (*see* DNA, RNA) and also of such coenzymes as NAD and FAD. *See also* nucleotide, nucleoside.

adenohypophysis. *See* pituitary gland.

adenosine. A *nucleoside consisting of D-ribose and adenine linked with a β-glycoside bond.

adenosine diphosphate. *See* ADP.

adenosine monophosphate. *See* AMP.

adenosine triphosphate. *See* ATP.

adenovirus. *See* virus.

adenyl cyclase. An important enzyme responsible for the synthesis of *cyclic AMP. Most polypeptide hormones, including insulin, affect cells by binding to the outer plasma membrane and activating adenyl cyclase to initiate or increase cyclic AMP production. This is the so-called 'second messenger' system by which these large hormones induce changes in cellular gene expression.

adenylic acid. *See* AMP.

ADH (antidiuretic hormone). *See* vasopressin.

adipose tissue (fatty tissue). Tissue consisting of an aggregation of fat cells, in mammals occurring predominantly in subcutaneous tissue, the mesenteries, around the kidneys, and in the mediastinum. A typical fat cell contains a thin band of cytoplasm that has been displaced to the cell periphery by a single large fat droplet. While being present in all connective tissue, fat cells are not called adipose tissue unless aggregated in large masses. Adipose tissue represents a considerable energy source in both normal and starvation conditions; in some species it also provides insulation against heat loss and acts as shock-absorbing tissue, e.g. on the soles of the feet.

adjuvant. A substance that is not itself antigenic but, when mixed with an antigen, enhances antibody production. Adjuvant not only helps to produce antibody against small amounts of antigen but also prolongs the period of antibody production. Adjuvants for therapeutic use must be easily metabolizable and ultimately eliminated. Although the exact mode of action of adjuvants is uncertain, they are known to promote the persistence of antigen and to cause an inflammatory response that leads to a local influx of antibody-forming cells. *See also* Freund's adjuvant.

ADP (adenosine diphosphate). A nucleotide consisting of adenine, D-ribose, and two phosphate groups that is an important coenzyme in many biological reactions. It undergoes phosphorylation to ATP, which is required for many anabolic processes. In the mitochondria ADP is converted to ATP by *oxidative phosphorylation. The level of ADP with respect to that of ATP controls the balance of anabolic and catabolic processes occurring in the cell; the rate of oxidative phosphorylation is stimulated by high levels of ADP and depressed by high levels of ATP.

adrenal glands. A pair of compound endocrine glands in mammals, situated along the anterior surface of each kidney. The outer cortex region and the inner medulla region are derived from different embryonic tissues. The *adrenal cortex* originates from lateral mesoderm, in close association with the developing gonads, and consists of three distinct regions surrounded by a thick capsule. It synthesizes and secretes various steroid hormones (*see* corticosteroid). The outer *zona glomerulosa* produces mineralocorticoids and glucocorticoids, while the inner *zona reticularis-fasciculata* synthesizes mainly glucocorticoids, especially cortisol. In humans this zone also secretes small amounts of androgens and possibly oestrogens. The *adrenal medulla* differentiates from the neural crest into modified ganglion cells in close contact with the sympathetic nervous system; it consists chiefly of *chromaffin tissue and secretes the catecholamines adrenaline and noradrenaline under sympathetic stimulation. Adrenal tissues are present in all other vertebrates but considerable variation occurs in the arrangement and

Adrenaline

distribution of the steroid-producing and chromaffin tissues.

adrenaline (epinephrine). The main hormone secreted by the chromaffin tissue of the adrenal medulla in mammals and by the corresponding tissue in other vertebrates and in some invertebrates. It was first isolated in 1901, by Takamine, and synthesized in 1904, by Stolz (see formula). Adrenaline secretion is stimulated by the sympathetic nervous system under various conditions of stress, including pain, fear, muscular activity, and a fall in blood-sugar levels, and has been popularly named the 'fight, fright, flight, and frivolity hormone.' Its most important effects are on the dilation and constriction of blood vessels and on carbohydrate metabolism, which result in stimulated blood flow and higher blood-glucose levels. Adrenaline is also secreted at the endings of sympathetic nerves and may act as a neurotransmitter. *See also* catecholamines.

adrenergic. Designating a nerve fibre or nerve ending that releases adrenaline or noradrenaline as a neurotransmitter from the presynaptic membrane. Vertebrate postganglionic sympathetic neurones are adrenergic. *Compare* cholinergic.

adrenocorticotrophic hormone. *See* ACTH.

adsorption. 1. The attachment of bacteriophage particles to specific receptors on the host cell prior to injection of nucleic acid.
2. The binding of proteins to the surface of finely divided materials, such as ground charcoal or alumina. This phenomenon is utilized in purifying proteins by *adsorption chromatography*, in which protein molecules selectively adsorbed to an inert material are then eluted (for example, by altering the salt concentration or pH).

adventitious. Designating a structure produced in an uncharacteristic position. For example, roots produced at the nodes of grass stems and buds produced on leaf surfaces are adventitious.

adventive embryo. A nonzygotic plant embryo that develops from the cells of the nucellus. Adventive embryony is a common phenomenon in *Citrus* species, the seeds of which often contain several viable embryos.

aecidium (aecium). A sorus characteristic of fungi of the order Uredinales, including the *rusts. It contains sporogenous hyphae that produce asexual *aecidiospores*, which are the first binucleate spores of the life cycle, the next being teleutospores (*see* teleutosorus).

aerenchyma. A form of parenchymatous tissue with numerous air spaces between the individual cells. It is found mainly in aquatic plants, to which it gives buoyancy.

aerobe. An organism that uses aerobic respiration, i.e. one that requires the presence of free oxygen for life and growth.

aerobic respiration. A type of cellular *respiration in which organic foodstuffs, usually carbohydrates, are completely oxidized to carbon dioxide and water using free oxygen from the atmosphere. The overall equation is usually written: $C_6H_{12}O_6 + 6O_2 = 6CO_2 + 6H_2O$. By this process the maximum chemical energy is extracted from the organic substrate.

The initial stage, in which glucose is degraded to pyruvate (*see* glycolysis), occurs in both aerobic and anaerobic respiration; it takes place in the cell cytoplasm. In aerobic respiration pyruvate is converted to acetyl coenzyme A and subsequent processes occur in the mitochondria of the cell. Acetyl CoA then enters the *Krebs cycle, where it is converted to carbon dioxide and hydrogen atoms (or their electron equivalents). The latter are passed to the *electron transport chain, where they reduce a series of catalytic pigments (*see* cytochrome, flavoprotein) and are passed

to molecular oxygen to form water. This process is coupled to phosphorylation (*see* oxidative phosphorylation), in which the energy released at each stage of the electron transport chain is used to generate ATP. *Compare* anaerobic respiration.

aerotaxis. *See* taxis.

aestivation. 1. (in botany). The way in which young flower parts are folded in the bud before opening. *See also* ptyxis. 2. (in zoology). Dormancy or sluggishness during a dry hot period. Some lungfish, e.g. *Protopterus*, aestivate by burying themselves in swamp mud before it dries out in the hot season and re-emerge when the rains start. *Compare* hibernation.

aethalium. A large spore-producing structure of the Myxomycetes. It may be stalked or sessile and consists of a wall, the *peridium*, within which the spores are produced and a *capillitium* may form. The capillitium is a meshwork of nonliving hygroscopic threads that aid spore liberation.

afferent. 1. Designating a nerve or neurone that transmits ingoing information from the peripheral receptors to the CNS; i.e. any sensory neurone.
2. Designating a blood vessel that breaks up to form a capillary bed, especially any of the arteries of the aortic arches of fish that lead from the dorsal aorta to the gills. *Compare* efferent.

affinity chromatography. A technique for isolating biological molecules that depends on the specific affinity of one molecule for another. For example, to isolate a coenzyme, enzyme molecules may be bound to an inert matrix in a column (column *chromatography). If a solution containing the coenzyme is passed through the matrix, the coenzyme will be specifically retained because of its affinity for the enzyme. Coenzyme molecules may then be retrieved by elution under conditions in which binding affinity is reduced.

aflatoxin. A poisonous metabolite of the fungus *Aspergillus*. It came into prominence in the 1950s when the death of a large number of turkeys was traced to groundnut meal contaminated by *Aspergillus flavus*. Contamination of stored nuts and cereals in warm and humid climates by *Aspergillus* is suspected of being the cause of some liver diseases (especially cancers) in these parts of the world.

afterbirth. *See* placenta.

after-ripening. The period of dormancy of many apparently mature seeds, particularly of the Rosaceae, that cannot be broken by conditions normally favourable for germination. During this period physiological changes, such as degradation of inhibitors, must occur before the seed can become sensitive to external conditions. It ensures that premature germination (for instance, just before winter) does not occur.

agamospermy. Any type of apomixis excluding vegetative propagation.

agar. A complex mucilaginous polysaccharide extracted from seaweeds and used as a gelling agent for solidifying liquid nutrient media. Many types of microorganisms can be grown on the gel surface as only very few bacteria produce enzymes capable of liquifying the gel. Agar gels melt at 100°C but solidify at about 44°C.

agglutination. A process in which cells or bacteria cross-link with or attach to each other when the antigens on the surface of their cells interact with antibodies (*agglutinins*), which form bridges linking the antigen determinant sites of the different cells. Agglutination reactions are used to identify blood groups, bacteria, etc.

aggression (in animal behaviour). Any of various actions involving threatening postures and activities and attacks on other animals. The term is usually restricted to all types of behaviour shown by an animal that serve to dis-

place other animals, usually those of the same species and especially in defence of a *territory.

Agnatha. The class containing the earliest and most primitive vertebrates, characterized by the absence of jaws. Agnathans are aquatic fishlike animals that lack the paired fins typical of true fishes, although some fossil types had a single anterior pair of finlike appendages. There are several fossil orders (known collectively as the Ostracodermi), including the *Osteostraci and *Heterostraci, as well as the modern *Cyclostomata (lampreys and hagfish).

agonistic behaviour. Any or all of various types of animal behaviour associated with aggression, including threatening postures, appeasement, and flight. Some types of agonistic behaviour have evolved into displays, which keep the actual fighting to a minimum.

agranulocyte. One of a group of white blood cells having no distinct cytoplasmic granules, e.g. lymphocytes and monocytes. *Compare* granulocyte.

Agrobacterium. A genus of bacteria. The species *A. tumefaciens* is responsible for the plant disease crown gall, which is known to be caused by a DNA *plasmid within the bacterium. This plasmid, once carried to the plant cells by the bacterium, is capable of independent replication within the cells in the absence of the bacterium. Persistence of the bacterial infection is therefore not necessary for the persistence of the disease. Following the discovery of the *Agrobacterium* plasmid and its ability to replicate in the cells of many plants, it has come to be widely used as a DNA vector for the introduction of new genes into plant cells, i.e. genetic engineering in plants. The new DNA sequence is spliced into the plasmid DNA, the whole DNA circularized, and the chimaeric plasmid introduced into the plant cells in culture. The scheme is particularly effective for plant species in which a complete new plant, capable of sexual reproduction, can be grown from a single transformed cell. *See also* clone.

air bladder. *See* swim bladder.

air sacs. 1. Blind-ending extensions of the bronchi in birds, projecting from the lungs and extending into most regions of the body. The compression and expansion of the air sacs, which is effected by contraction and relaxation of surrounding muscles and by movements of the limbs during flight, ensures a constant flow of air over the respiratory surface. In most flying birds diverticula of the air sacs penetrate the marrow cavity of many bones (the *pneumatic bones*), reducing the body weight.
2. Small bladder-like dilations of the tracheae in many swiftly flying insects. Respiratory movements of the insects bring about the collapse and expansion of these sacs, which increases ventilation of the tracheal system.

alanine (ala). An amino acid, $CH_3CH(NH_2)COOH$, one of the 20 common *amino acids found in proteins.

alata. A winged adult in those insects (such as aphids) in which a wingless form (*aptera*) also occurs.

albinism. 1. The absence of pigmentation in the skin, hair, and eyes, found in some animals and thought to be due to a recessive gene.
2. The absence of chlorophyll in the leaves or stems of plants in the layers in which it usually occurs.

albumen. *See* albumin.

albumin. One of a group of simple proteins that are soluble in water and coagulated by heat. The best-known albumins are those occurring in the blood (*serum albumins*). The water-soluble protein of egg white was formerly known as *albumen*. In fact it consists of a number of proteins, notably *ovalbumin*, which contains a carbohydrate prosthetic group and is thus a conjugated, rather than a simple, protein.

albuminous cell. *See* companion cell.

alburnum (sapwood). *See* wood.

aldose. A *monosaccharide, such as glucose or ribose, that possesses an aldehyde group ($-CHO$).

aldosterone. A potent *mineralocorticoid hormone secreted by the adrenal glands of mammals from the cells of the outer cortex (glomerulosa zone) and by the adrenal tissue of many other vertebrates. It was finally isolated and crystallized from cortico-adrenal extracts in 1953, by Simpson and Tait. Aldosterone secretion can be stimulated by ACTH, but angiotensin is a more important regulator, operating independently of trophic factors from the pituitary gland. Deprivation of sodium and reduced blood volumes also stimulate secretion.

aleurone grain. A storage body of plant tissues, particularly those of seeds. It is surrounded by a single membrane and stores mainly proteins and the enzymes necessary for their mobilization (hence it is sometimes called a *protein body*). It is variously regarded as a special type of vacuole or a type of *aleuroplast. *See* aleurone layer.

aleurone layer. The outermost layer, several cells in thickness, of the endosperm of cereal seeds. The cells contain aleurone grains for food storage and they synthesize the enzyme α-amylase, which catalyses the digestion of starch in the endosperm. The signal for α-amylase synthesis is a gibberellin secreted by the scutellum of the embryo at the onset of germination.

aleuroplast. A plastid that stores protein, often in the form of grains. *See* aleurone grain.

Algae. A large group of thallophytes whose plant bodies vary from microscopic unicells through coenocytes and filamentous forms to the giant kelps. They possess chlorophyll and most are photosynthetic. Sex organs are either unicellular or multicellular; the cells of multicellular sex organs are all gametic (except in the Charophyceae and Rhodophyta). The classification of the algae is constantly changing but there are seven major groups most frequently recognized. These are *Chlorophyta, *Chrysophyta, *Cyanophyta, *Euglenophyta, *Phaeophyta, *Pyrrophyta, and *Rhodophyta. Classification is based on (1) form of the nuclear material, (2) form of the photosynthetic membranes, (3) types of pigment present, (4) storage products formed, (5) nature of the cell wall, (6) methods of reproduction, and (7) structure and number of flagella. The flagellated unicellular algae are regarded by zoologists as animals and placed in the subclass Phytomastigina (*see* Mastigophora).

alimentary canal. The canal in animals through which foodstuffs pass, to be broken down by mechanical and chemical means until they are in a form suitable for absorption and assimilation by the body tissues. The anterior and posterior sections are lined with ectoderm; the midsection, in which digestion and absorption occurs, is lined with endoderm (*see also* intestine). In the Coelenterata and Platyhelminthes the canal has a single opening. In other Metazoa a distal opening, the *anus, is present and food is propelled from the mouth to the anus by the action of cilia and/or muscles. Reverse movements of food may occur (as in ruminant mammals) or food may be temporarily located in diverticula (as in molluscs). The alimentary canal shows a diversity of morphological and biochemical specializations to suit particular diets, e.g. carnivorous, fluid, filter feeders, etc. It becomes adapted for the sequential processing of food, with regions for reception, storage, mechanical breakdown, chemical digestion, absorption, and faeces formation. The terminology of these regions is functional and does not necessarily reflect embryological similarity (*see* foregut, midgut, hindgut). Parts of the canal, e.g. the pharynx and cloaca, may be secondarily utilized for nondigestive functions. A canal is absent

in parasites and other animals whose food is ingested in an absorbable form.

HETEROCYCLIC GROUP	ALKALOID
indole	lysergic acid reserpine strychnine
pyridine	nicotinic acid nicotine
reduced pyridine	coniine cocaine
quinoline	quinine
isoquinoline	morphine papaverine
pyrimidine	barbituric acid
purine	caffeine

Representative alkaloids

alkaloids. A heterogeneous group of basic nitrogen-containing substances that are produced by plants and have potent pharmacological activities. Alkaloids are often of complex structure, typically with heterocyclic rings containing nitrogen; they can be classified according to the type of heterocyclic group present (see table).

Most alkaloids are produced by dicotyledonous plants (ergotamine, obtained from the fungus *Claviceps purpurea*, is a notable exception) and particular alkaloids are usually restricted to certain families or genera. All members of the family Papaveraceae produce alkaloids; in other families, e.g. Ranunculaceae, Apocynaceae, Solanaceae, alkaloids are produced only by certain genera.

Alkaloids show varied pharmacological activites. They can act as analgesics (e.g. morphine), tranquillizers (e.g. reserpine), respiratory stimulants (e.g. nicotine), vasoconstrictors (e.g. scopolamine), local anaesthetics (e.g. cocaine), muscle relaxants (e.g. strychnine), and psychedelic agents (e.g. psilocybin, LSD). Many alkaloids or their synthetic derivatives are used medicinally, e.g. cinchona (to treat malaria), morphine, and reserpine. Some are poisons, notably coniine (from hemlock) and strychnine.

The function of alkaloids in plants is still a matter of conjecture. For example it has been suggested that they are by-products of metabolism; alternatively they may provide protection against insects that feed on the plants.

alkanes. *See* chemical fossils.

alkaptonuria. A hereditary disease, due to a single *recessive gene, that is characterized by the absence of the enzyme homogentisic acid oxidase. Homogentisic acid, normally formed and oxidized during the metabolism of the amino acids tyrosine and phenylalanine, accumulates in the urine, which turns black on exposure to air – the main symptom of the disease. The condition affects about 1 in 1 000 000 individuals.

allantois. *See* extraembryonic membranes.

allele (allelomorph). One of a pair of genes that occupy the same relative position (*locus*) on homologous chromosomes and separate during meiosis. Alleles are responsible for the production of contrasting characteristics, such as normal or vestigial wings in *Drosophila* and round or wrinkled seed coats in peas. Since different alleles of one gene sequence may differ by no more than a

single base, there is a very large number of possible alleles for any one gene. Only a few of these variant alleles give rise to detectable differences in phenotype. When alleles are present in pairs, one is often *dominant to the other, which is known as the *recessive. The wild-type allele is usually dominant; recessives arise by mutation and are usually deleterious. In Mendelian genetics, there are several ways of representing alleles. They are often represented by the initial letter of the characteristic produced by the dominant allele, so that round seeds (dominant) would be denoted *R* and wrinkled seeds (recessive) as *r*. Alternatively the dominant, or wild type, is represented as + and the recessive by the initial letter (or two letters) of its characteristic. Thus in *Drosophila*, normal wings is represented as + and vestigial as *vg*.

The term *allelomorph* is also used for the characteristic produced by an allele. *See also* pseudoallele, multiple allele.

allelic exclusion. Failure of one of the two allelic forms of a gene to be expressed in a diploid cell. It differs from simple genetic dominance in that the repressed allele may be preferentially expressed in other cells. The best-known examples involve the genes coding for antibody; within any one antibody-producing cell only one type of antibody molecule is elaborated, even if the organism is heterozygous for the relevant gene.

allelomorph. *See* allele.

allelopathy. A chemical interaction between organisms in which one organism suppresses the germination, growth, or reproduction of the other by releasing toxins into the environment. It occurs particularly between freshwater animals, flowering plants, bacteria, and fungi. Barley, for instance, releases an alkaloid from its roots that can suppress weed growth.

alloantigen. *See* isoantigen.

allogamy. Cross-fertilization in plants.

allograft. *See* homograft.

allopatry. The occurrence of populations in geographically different places. *See* (allopatric) speciation. *Compare* sympatry.

allopolyploidy. *See* polyploidy.

all-or-none. Designating a response that takes one of two discrete levels, either no response or maximal response, whatever the stimulus intensity. A stimulus characteristically elicits no response unless it is above a threshold value, when it initiates an explosive chain reaction. The initiation of a nervous impulse is a typical all-or-none event.

allostery. A property displayed by many proteins with two or more receptor sites, in which occupation of one site alters the specificity of the other available sites. Allostery is believed to depend on changes in the shape of the protein in response to its association with the first molecule, which involves some readjustment in the entire tertiary structure of the polypeptide chain. The regulatory protein that controls the activity of the *lac* operon in *Escherichia coli* is believed to be an allosteric protein; association with inducer molecule affects its affinity for the operator sequence and so permits derepression of the operon.

allotetraploid (amphidiploid). A tetraploid produced by allopolyploidy. *See* polyploidy.

alpha-helix. A regular right-handed helical structure that is the stable configuration of many polypeptide chains and contributes to the secondary and tertiary structure of the protein. The peptide bond and α-amino acid carbon form the backbone of the helix, which is stabilized by hydrogen bonds between amino acids in successive turns of the helix (see illustration). The hydrogen bonds are formed between the peptide nitrogen of one amino acid and the carbonyl oxygen of the amino acid four residues

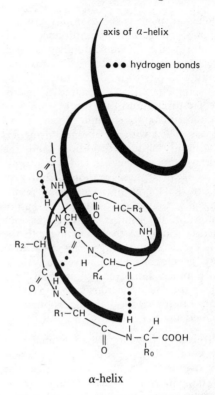

axis of α-helix

●●● hydrogen bonds

α-helix

along, giving a periodicity of 3.6 amino acid residues per turn of the helix. *Compare* beta-pleated sheet.

ALS. *See* antilymphocyte serum.

alternation of generations. The condition of having more than one type of individual to complete the *life cycle, occurring very commonly in both animals (especially parasites) and plants. The generations usually differ from each other in appearance and reproduction. The most usual type of alternation is between sexual and asexual generations. For example, in many hydrozoan coelenerates a sexual medusoid phase alternates with an asexual polypoid phase. In bryophytes the dominant generation (i.e. the most conspicuous plant in the life cycle) is the sexual (gametophyte) phase. The zygote develops into the asexual (sporophyte) phase, the capsule, which produces spores that give rise to the sexual plants. In pteridophytes the dominant plant is the sporophyte, whose spores, on germination, produce small prothalli (the gametophyte phase), which bear the sex organs. In seed plants, too, the sporophyte is dominant but the gametophyte phase is reduced to microscopic proportions (*see* seed).

In most plants alternation of generations is associated with an alternation in diploid and haploid conditions and the intervention of meiosis and karyogamy. The asexual phase is diploid and produces the spores by meiosis; the resulting gametophyte is haploid and karyogamy (of the gametes) restores the diploid condition of the sporophyte. In the life cycles of some organisms more than two generations alternate regularly with each other. For example, in many red algae the life cycle runs gametophyte – carposporophyte – tetrasporophyte – gametophyte.

altruism. Behaviour by an animal that appears to help others of its species at its own expense. But natural selection favours individuals that maximize their genetic contribution to future generations, and such behaviour usually obscures the fact that the animal is actually increasing the likelihood that its genes will be passed on. Parents that put themselves at risk in protecting their offspring are an example, but group behaviour in which more distant relatives are protected will also favour gene survival. The selective process resulting from such behaviour has been termed by Hamilton *kin selection*.

alveolus. **1.** A blind-ending sac that occurs at the terminus of a bronchiole of the lung of reptiles and mammals and forms the respiratory surface. Exchange of gases between the air and the blood takes place across the moist thin vascular epithelium lining the alveoli.
2. The cavity in the jaw bone that encloses the root of a tooth.
3. A sac of secretory cells at the ending of a duct in some glands, especially the mammary gland.

amanitin. A drug obtained from the poisonous fungus *Amanita phalloides* (death cap). α-amanitin is a cyclic octapeptide that owes its toxicity to its potent suppression of RNA polymerase II in eukaryotic cells, and thus of messenger RNA synthesis. Its strong specificity for this polymerase has led to its frequent use in cell biology for studies of RNA synthesis and RNA polymerase activity, especially since another drug, *actinomycin D, has a complementary specificity for ribosomal RNA synthesis.

amino acids. Organic compounds bearing both a free carboxyl group and an amino group. There are several hundred naturally occurring amino acids and their derivatives but only 20 are commonly found in proteins: they are listed as follows.
Hydrophobic amino acids
alanine
valine
leucine
isoleucine
proline (also 4-hydroxyproline)
phenylalanine
tryptophan
methionine
Polar amino acids
glycine
serine
threonine
cysteine
tyrosine
asparagine
glutamine
Acidic amino acids (bearing a net negative charge at neutral pH)
aspartic acid
glutamic acid
Basic amino acids (bearing a net positive charge at neutral pH)
lysine
arginine
histidine
(See also individual entries for these amino acids).

These are α-amino acids bearing the L configuration (*see* optical activity), with the general formula:

$$R \overset{\displaystyle COO^-}{\underset{\displaystyle NH_3^+}{-\overset{|}{\underset{|}{C}}-H}}$$

where R = H or an organic group.

The exceptions are glycine, which is not optically active, and proline, which is a substituted amino acid (imino acid). Although distinguished by their presence in proteins, these 20 amino acids have important physiological roles in their free state, participating in major anabolic and catabolic processes of the cell. Other biologically important amino acids are citrulline and *ornithine (α-amino acids taking part in the urea cycle), β-alanine (the precursor of pantothenic acid), γ-aminobutyric acid (*GABA) (a neurotransmitter), and D-glutamate (a constituent of bacterial cell walls). Amino acids can be synthesized by green plants and other autotrophs; many amino acids can be synthesized by heterotrophic organisms from the materials of their food but some, the *essential amino acids, form part of their food. Amino acids exist as zwitterions (dipolar ions). This physical state is responsible for a number of their properties, e.g. high melting points due to attraction between oppositely charged groups in the crystalline state. Complex mixtures of amino acids are fractionated by *chromatography and *electrophoresis.

Amino acids can be oxidized to form Krebs cycle intermediates or their precursors with the production of energy (*see* transamination, deamination). In mammals this occurs mainly in the liver and kidney.

amitosis. An unusual process of nuclear division, not involving mitosis, in which the nucleus is pinched into two by a constriction. The details of how it occurs are uncertain, but the two nuclei formed from the parent nucleus are probably not identical. Amitosis occurs in some protozoans (including the macronucleus of the Ciliata), in the endosperm of flowering plants, and in the embryonic membranes and cartilage of mammals.

ammocoete. The larva of the lamprey (*see* Cyclostomata). On hatching it is tiny and transparent and lives buried in mud. The ammocoete feeds by separating food particles from a water current passing through the pharynx with the aid of mucus secreted by the *endostyle, a food-trapping device also found in amphioxus. After three or four years it undergoes metamorphosis into the adult form.

Ammonoidea. An extinct subclass of cephalopod molluscs, in existence from Silurian to Cretaceous times. Ammonites were characterized by an external many-chambered shell marked with intricate suture lines.

amniocentesis. A minor operation performed on some pregnant women to provide information about the genetic constitution of the foetus. A needle is passed through the abdominal wall and uterus into the amniotic cavity and a sample of the amniotic fluid is withdrawn. This sample is then centrifuged and stray foetal cells in the fluid are sedimented. These cells are then examined for any biochemical and chromosomal abnormalities, such as *Down's syndrome.

amnion. *See* extraembryonic membranes.

amniote. One of a group of vertebrates that are characterized by four *extraembryonic membranes (yolk sac, amnion, allantois, and chorion), i.e. the reptiles, birds, and mammals (the Amniota). Evolution of the amniote egg, an adaptation to terrestrial life, ensures that the embryo develops within a fluid-filled cavity and dispenses with the need for laying the egg in water. *Compare* anamniote.

Amoeba. A genus of Protozoa belonging to the class *Sarcodina. The cells are simple in organization and very plastic in shape, moving by means of pseudopodia. Almost all species are aquatic, though some are internal parasites of vertebrates; the freshwater species *A. proteus* is one of the best known organisms in biology. Cells of other types that resemble true amoebae in appearance and movement are described as *amoeboid*; for example, the amoeboid cells of slime moulds.

amoebocyte. An amoeba-like cell found in the body fluids of coelomates. It is frequently phagocytic and has digestive and excretory functions.

AMP (adenosine monophosphate, adenylic acid). A mononucleotide consisting of D-ribose phosphate and adenine. One or two additional phosphoric acid groups can be esterified onto the initial phosphate to yield ADP and ATP, respectively. *See also* cyclic AMP.

Amphibia. The class of the Vertebrata that contains the first tetrapods. Amphibians typically have the tetrapod characteristics of four pentadactyl limbs, a pelvic girdle articulating with the sacrum, a tail for balancing, and a middle ear apparatus for detecting air-borne sounds. Adult amphibians live on land, in damp places, but they must return to water to breed as they lack the amniote egg of reptiles and birds. The aquatic larvae have gills for respiration and undergo metamorphosis to the lung-breathing adult. Amphibians first appeared in the Devonian and early types resembled the crossopterygian fishes (*see* Rhipidistia) from which they evolved. Modern amphibians show many modifications of these early forms. There are three subclasses: the extinct *Labyrinthodontia and *Lepospondyli and the modern *Lissamphibia (salamanders, frogs, etc.).

amphicribal. *See* amphiphloic.

amphidiploid. *See* allotetraploid.

amphigastria (under-leaves). The leaves of leafy liverworts that lie in the midventral line and are reduced in size compared with the two dorsal rows.

amphimixis. The union of male and female gametes, resulting in fertilization and the formation of a zygote; true sexual reproduction. *Compare* apomixis.

Amphineura. A class of the Mollusca in which the body is elongated, with mouth and anus at opposite ends. In the subclass Polyplacophora, e.g. *Chiton*, the mantle secretes a shell of eight overlapping plates that cover the dorsal surface and the gills are arranged in two rows, one on each side of the body. In the Aplacophora, e.g. *Neomenia*, the mantle contains calcified spicules and there are no gills; gaseous exchange takes place through the skin.

amphioxus. *See* Cephalochordata.

amphipathic. Designating compounds, such as fatty acids and phospholipids, that have both a hydrophobic portion and a polar portion. In aqueous solution these molecules orientate with the hydrophobic groups together at the centre of a sphere and the polar groups on the surface, forming a *lipid micelle.

amphiphloic (periphloic, amphicribral). Designating plant vascular tissue in which the phloem surrounds the xylem. *Compare* amphixylic.

Amphipoda. An order of malacostracan crustaceans whose members typically have a laterally compressed body. Amphipods include marine and freshwater forms (e.g. the shrimp *Gammarus*) and the terrestrial sandhoppers (e.g. *Orchestia*), which usually remain near the high-tide mark. As in the Isopoda, the body lacks a carapace and has a brood pouch in the female. Some of the thoracic appendages are used in feeding; the abdominal appendages function in swimming and respiration and (in some species) the last three pairs are specialized for jumping.

amphistylic jaw suspension. An arrangement in which the jaws are suspended from the cranium both by ligaments between the neurocranium and the upper jaw and by the hyomandibular. It occurs in many fossil fish, e.g. the Cladoselachii. *Compare* autostylic jaw suspension, hyostylic jaw suspension.

amphitropous (orthoamphitropous). *See* ovule.

amphivasal. *See* amphixylic.

amphixylic (perixylic, amphivasal). Designating plant vascular tissue in which the xylem surrounds the phloem. *Compare* amphiphloic.

amylase (diastase). One of a class of widely occurring enzymes that hydrolyse *starch or glycogen into disaccharides and glucose.

amylopectin. *See* starch.

amyloplast. A plastid that can store starch, usually as grains; it is found mainly in the endosperm of storage organs, e.g. roots, tubers, and seeds. The term is usually restricted to those leucoplasts whose main function is the storage of starch but it may be applied to all plastids that store and synthesize starch, such as chloroplasts, carrot chromoplasts, etc.

amylose. *See* starch.

anabolism. The sum of the processes involved in the synthesis of the constituents of a cell (*see* biosynthesis). ATP, produced during catabolism, provides the energy for these processes. Anabolism includes the synthesis of proteins, lipids, monosaccharides, and nucleic acids from their constituents or simple precursors. *See also* metabolism.

anacampylotropous. *See* ovule.

anaerobe. An organism that uses *anaerobic respiration, i.e. one that lives and grows in the absence of free oxygen.

anaerobic respiration. Cellular *respiration in which chemical energy is produced by a series of reactions in which molecular oxygen is not involved, and therefore the organic substrate, usually carbohydrate, is never completely oxidized. Organisms may be *obligatory anaerobes*, i.e. they never use free oxygen for respiration, or *facultative anaerobes*, i.e. they are able to switch the metabolism of foodstuffs from an aero-bic to an anaerobic pathway to survive temporary periods of oxygen deficiency. All fermentations are types of anaerobic respiration. In obligatory anaerobes, and in some facultative anaerobes, the incompletely oxidized product is excreted, e.g. in alcoholic *fermentation. In animal and plant cells and in most microorganisms glucose is broken down to lactic acid by *glycolysis, with the production of ATP. In animal cells, when oxygen becomes available, lactic acid may be completely oxidized (*see* oxygen debt).

analogous organs. Organs or parts of the body of different species of animals or plants that have different evolutionary origins but have become adapted to serve the same purpose. For example, the wings of a bat and the wings of an insect are analogous organs. *Compare* homologous organs.

anamniote. One of a group of vertebrates whose embryos do not produce an amnion, allantois, and chorion, i.e. the fishes and amphibians. *Compare* amniote.

anamphitropous. *See* ovule.

anaphase. The third stage of *mitosis and *meiosis.

anaphylaxis. A severe reaction occurring in an individual pre-exposed to an antigen following re-exposure to the same antigen. The reaction results from the local action of histamine, serotonin, and bradykinin, whose release from the mast cells is apparently mediated by antibodies at the cell surface.

anapsid. Designating the primitive condition of the amniote skull, in which the roofing of membrane bones remains intact. This condition is found in early fossil reptiles and in modern chelonians (*see* Anapsida). *Compare* diapsid, synapsid.

Anapsida. The subclass of the Reptilia that contains the modern tortoises and turtles and the earliest reptiles, which were ancestral to many later groups.

They evolved from the Amphibia (*see* Labyrinthodontia) in the Carboniferous and are characterized by a solidly roofed (*anapsid) skull. There are two orders, the extinct *Cotylosauria and the modern *Chelonia.

anatomy. *See* morphology.

anatropous. *See* ovule.

androcyte. The cell produced in the penultimate stage of antherozoid formation: an undifferentiated cell that develops into the antherozoid.

androdioecious. Designating a plant species in which bisexual and male flowers are produced on separate plants.

androecium. The male reproductive organs of a flower, i.e. the stamens collectively.

androgen. Any of a group of 19-C (carbon) steroid hormones with masculinizing properties, produced from acetate and cholesterol by the testis in all vertebrates, but also, in smaller amounts, by the ovaries and adrenal cortex in mammals. The growth and function of the male sexual organs and the development of male secondary sexual characteristics are dependent on androgens released from cells of the testis interstitial tissue, which is under the regulation of pituitary luteinizing hormone. Androgens released from cells of the seminiferous tubules promote spermatogenesis, and this release is regulated by pituitary follicle-stimulating hormone.
The predominant natural androgens are *testosterone and *androsterone. Following their isolation in the 1930s, however, many other weakly androgenic steroids (e.g. *androstenedione*) have been found. Most of these are thought to be metabolic products of testosterone, but the metabolite *dihydrotestosterone*, found in many androgen-responsive tissues, is more potent than testosterone and has been proposed as the active form of the hormone. The general metabolic action of androgens is in nitrogen retention and protein anabolism; synthetic anabolic steroids are used to promote the growth of muscle and bone for therapeutic and athletic purposes. There is evidence that androgens, like oestrogens, can regulate the expression of particular genes and show feedback effects on the central nervous system.

andromonoecious. Designating a plant species in which male and bisexual flowers are produced on the same plant.

Androsterone

androsterone. The first androgen to be isolated (in 1931) from male human urine (see formula). This and similar 17-keto steroids are excretory metabolites of androgens formed by the testis and adrenal cortex but can be measured clinically as a diagnostic indication of male sex hormone.

anemophily. Pollination with wind as the vector carrying pollen from the anther to the stigma. Anemophilous flowers, such as grasses, have petals that are inconspicuous or absent, no scent or nectar, large quantities of light dusty pollen, long feathery stigmas, and anthers projecting from the flower.

anergized culture. *See* habituated culture.

aneuploidy. A condition in which the chromosome number of a nucleus, cell, or organism is not an exact multiple of the haploid number. One or more chromosomes may be present more than twice (*see* polysomy, trisomy) or as only a single chromosome (*see* monosomy). When both members of a homologous pair are missing the condition of *nullisomy results. Aneuploidy may be a normal or abnormal condition and is typically brought about by the *nondisjunction of one or more pairs of homologous chromosomes. *Compare* euploidy.

Angiospermae   (Angiospermophyta, Anthophyta). A huge and diverse group of vascular plants (a subdivision of the Spermatophyta) characterized by seeds borne in an ovary. They are divided into two major subgroups: the *Monocotyledonae and *Dicotyledonae.

angiotensin. Either of two polypeptides released from a liver globulin protein in the blood. *Angiotensin I* is a decapeptide released under the influence of *renin*, an enzyme secreted by the kidney. Another enzyme removes the two terminal amino acids of angiotensin I to form an octapeptide, *angiotensin II*. The amino acid sequences were determined, and angiotensin synthesized, in 1956 (see formula). Angiotensin I is apparently an inactive storage form in the blood, but angiotensin II is a potent vasopressor (i.e. it raises blood pressure), causes contraction of the uterus, and stimulates the secretion of aldosterone from the adrenal cortex. It is found only in the blood of people with high blood pressure.

angstrom. Symbol: °A. A unit of submicroscopic distance equal to one tenth of a nanometre (one ten thousandth of a micrometre). It is used by biologists for very small distances that can be measured only under the electron microscope; e.g. the width of the double cell membrane is 75°A.

aniline stains. *See* staining.

animal behaviour. The study of all the processes by which an animal responds to changes in its environment, both internal and external. Animal behaviour can be approached from a psychological or a physiological basis. The psychologists are concerned primarily with the observation of the behaviour itself, studied under natural conditions (*ethology*) or in the laboratory (*experimental psychology*). The physiologists relate behaviour to the functioning of the nervous system of the animal.

animal pole. The point on the surface of an animal ovum that is nearest to the nucleus. In eggs with unevenly distributed yolk, it is the region in which there is least yolk. *Compare* vegetal pole.

anisogamy. The sexual fusion of dissimilar gametes, the extreme form being *oogamy.

annealing. *See* denaturation.

Annelida. A phylum of metamerically segmented invertebrates, the segmented worms. They have a soft cylindrical body covered by a thin cuticle and often bearing chaetae; the body wall contains layers of circular and longitudinal muscles and the body cavity is a coelom, features that, together with the metamerism, provide an efficient means of locomotion. The alimentary canal runs from the mouth at the front to the posterior anus. There are well-developed blood vascular and nervous systems and excretion is by metanephridia (*see* nephridium). The larvae, if present, are *trochophores. The phylum contains the classes *Polychaeta (bristle worms), *Oligochaeta (earthworms), *Hirudinea (leeches), and *Archiannelida.

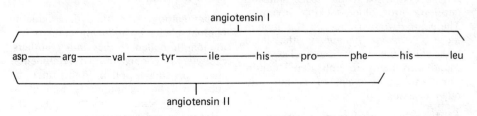

Human angiotensin

annual. A plant that completes its life cycle – from germination to flowering, fruiting, seed production, and death – in one season. *Compare* biennial, ephemeral, perennial.

annual ring. *See* growth ring.

annular thickening. A pattern of secondary wall formation in primary xylem vessels and tracheids in which the wall material is laid down in circular bands at right angles to the long axis of the cell. It is usually the first type of thickening to appear and occurs in the earliest protoxylem elements. *Compare* spiral, reticulate, scalariform, and pitted thickenings.

annulus. 1. An area in the walls of some fern sporangia in which the cells are thickened on their anticlinal and inner periclinal walls. On drying, considerable tension is set up in the outer unthickened periclinal walls of these cells, which causes the sporangium to split open at the *stomium at dehiscence.
2. A ring of tissue remaining on the stipe of the fruiting body of some fungi, e.g. certain mushrooms, after the pileus has expanded.
3. Any ring-shaped structure in animals, such as one of the segments of an annelid worm or one of the rings into which the external surface of a leech is divided.

Anoplura (Siphunculata). An order of wingless eyeless exopterygote insects, the sucking lice, which are ectoparasites of mammals. The flattened transparent body bears piercing and sucking mouthparts for feeding on the host's blood and the prehensile legs have sharp claws for attachment to the host. The eggs (nits) are attached to the host's hair and develop into blood-sucking nymphs. There are two varieties of the human louse (*Pediculus humanus*): the head louse and the body louse. They are found universally in unhygienic conditions and are carriers of typhus and other diseases.

ANS. *See* autonomic nervous system.

antagonism. 1. The interaction of two substances, e.g. drugs or hormones, acting in the same system in such a way that one partially or completely inhibits the effect of the other.
2. The interaction of two types of organism existing in close association in such a way that the growth of one is inhibited by the other.

anteaters. *See* Edentata, Pholidota (scaly anteater), Monotremata (spiny anteater).

antenna. One of a pair of jointed threadlike appendages on the head of many arthropods. Crustacea have two pairs, the first smaller pair being known as *antennules*, while in the Insecta, Chilopoda, and Diplopoda there is only one pair. Antennae are typically sensory in function, usually being concerned with smell and touch, but in some Crustacea they are used for swimming or for attachment.

antennule. One of the first pair of jointed threadlike sensory appendages on the head of Crustacea. *See* antenna.

anterior. 1. Designating the front part of an animal, i.e. the part that precedes when the animal is moving. In many bilaterally symmetrical animals cephalization has occurred at the anterior end. In bipedal animals, including man, the anterior surface corresponds with the *ventral surface.
2. Designating the part of a lateral bud or flower that is furthest away from the main axis.
Compare posterior.

anther. The part of the angiosperm microsporophyll formed by the pollen sacs. Together with the filament it comprises the stamen.

anther culture. A method of producing haploid plants by inducing embryo formation in pollen. Either intact anthers, excised at a particular developmental stage, or single pollen grains may be cultured. The technique is limited to certain genera, notably in the Solanaceae and Gramineae.

antheridium. The male gametangium of the fungi, algae, bryophytes, and pteridophytes, usually consisting of a short stalk bearing a more-or-less globular head containing the gametes. The head may consist of a single cell (fungi and algae) or one to several layers of discrete cells (bryophytes and pteridophytes).

antherozoid (spermatozoid). A motile male gamete with one to many flagella, characteristic of the fungi, algae, bryophytes, and pteridophytes but also produced in a few gymnosperms, e.g. *Cycas, Ginkgo.*

anthocarp. A composite fruit, such as a syconus, that is formed from several flowers.

Anthocerotae. *See* Hepaticae.

anthocyans. Water-soluble pigments of higher plant vacuoles, comprising the *anthocyanidin* *flavonoid pigments and their glycosides, the *anthocyanins*. They are largely responsible for the red, purple, and blue colours of flowers, fruits, leaves (contributing to autumn shades), and buds. Many change colour with acidity, commonly from red to blue as acidity decreases.

Anthophyta. *See* Angiospermae.

Anthozoa (Actinozoa). The class of the Cnidaria containing the corals and sea anemones, in which medusae are absent and the polyps are more complex in structure than those of the Hydrozoa. The mostly colonial subclass Alcyonaria (Octocorallia), characterized by eight tentacles, contains the soft corals (e.g. *Alcyonium*), which secrete a gelatinous matrix, and the horny corals (e.g. *Gorgonia*), with a horny axial skeleton. The Zoantharia includes the solitary sea anemones (e.g. *Actinia*) and the colonial stony (or true) corals (e.g. *Astrangia*), which secrete a calcareous skeleton. This subclass typically has more than eight tentacles.

Antiarchi. *See* Placodermi.

antibiotics. Organic compounds, of variable structure and low molecular weight, that are synthesized and excreted by certain microorganisms and inhibit or kill the growth of other microorganisms. The toxicity is selective, usually because the antibiotics act against certain specific metabolic compounds of the microorganisms. For example, the *penicillins and vancomycin block specific steps in the cell wall synthesis of bacteria and many antibiotics, including *streptomycin, *neomycin, kanamycin, and the *tetracyclines, selectively interfere with protein synthesis in bacteria. Nystatin selectively interferes with the cell wall synthesis of eukaryotes. *See also* actinomycin D.

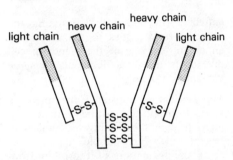

Structure of an antibody molecule

antibody. A protein synthesized in a vertebrate in response to an antigen or to a hapten associated with a carrier, with either of which it specifically reacts. Antibody and antigen will combine only at specific sites on the surface of their molecules. There are usually two (for antibody) or more (for antigen) sites on each molecule, known as the *combining sites* of the antibody and the *determinant sites* of the antigen. There are two different types of antibody. *Humoral antibody* is a free molecule, released into the blood and body fluids, that either directly combines with and neutralizes bacterial toxins or coats bacteria to enhance their phagocytosis. *Cell-bound antibody* is formed on the surface of sensitized lymphocytes. It is responsible for the cell-mediated immune response in such reactions as the rejection of skin transplants, the delayed hypersensitivity to tuberculin in subjects immune to tuberculosis infection, etc. Animals also possess some natural antibody without known antigenic stimulation.

Antibodies belong to the globulin class of proteins and there are five major structural types (*see* immunoglobulin). The accepted structure for antibody postulates two heavy and two light polypeptide chains linked by disulphide bonds (see illustration). The shaded areas of the chains represent the antigen-binding sites: the so-called variable regions of one light chain and one heavy chain both contribute to the specificity of each of the two antigen-binding sites.

anticlinal (in botany). Designating the plane at right angles to the surface of an organ, e.g. one of the planes of cell division in meristematic tissue. *Compare* periclinal.

anticoagulant. A substance that prevents blood from clotting. Anticoagulants can interfere with the clotting mechanism in several ways; for example, heparin prevents the formation of thrombin from prothrombin.

anticodon. *See* codon.

antidiuretic hormone (ADH). *See* vasopressin.

antigen. A substance that stimulates an animal to form a specific *antibody. There are three types of antigen: *extrinsic* (not a constituent of the cell), *intrinsic* (a constituent of the cell), and *occult* (a self-antigen that does not reach antibody-forming tissues). The antigenicity of a substance usually depends on the size of the antigen molecule and its chemical configuration; proteins having a molecular weight of less than 10 000 are less effective in producing antibody. Antigen introduced into a animal that is immune to it is rapidly eliminated as a result of complexing with antibody, a process termed *immune clearance. See also* hapten.

antilymphocyte serum (ALS). Serum containing antibodies produced by one species of animal against lymphocytes from a different species. *Antihuman lymphocyte serum*, usually prepared by immunizing horses with thoracic duct lymphocytes, has been used to reduce or suppress the rejection of organ and tissue transplants.

antipodal nuclei. Nuclei produced at the chalazal end of certain *embryo sacs.

antiserum. A serum containing high levels of antibody to a particular antigen. Antisera may be injected to give passive *immunity against specific diseases.

Anura. The order of the Amphibia (subclass *Lissamphibia) that contains the frogs and toads. The adults are highly specialized for jumping, having a short backbone, no tail, very long powerful hind legs, and a strengthened pectoral girdle to absorb the shock of landing. The aquatic larvae (tadpoles) undergo a rapid and extensive metamorphosis in which the tail is absorbed and the gill slits are replaced by lungs. Most frogs, e.g. *Rana*, live in damp places or are aquatic but some, e.g. *Hyla* (tree frog), are arboreal. Toads, e.g. *Bufo*, are better adapted to drier habitats, having a dry warty skin.

anus. The distal opening of the alimentary canal, present in all groups except the Coelenterata and Platyhelminthes, through which unabsorbed food and waste products are voided as faeces. It arises at or near the blastopore of the embryonic archenteron and, in some groups, opens into a cloaca. It is often controlled by a sphincter.

aorta. The large blood vessel of adult tetrapods that carries oxygenated blood from the ventricle of the heart to the body. *See also* dorsal aorta, ventral aorta.

aortic arches. Six paired arteries of vertebrate embryos, each running from the *ventral aorta through the visceral arches to the *dorsal aorta. The arches are numbered I to VI antero-posteriorly. In fish, arches III to VI break up into capillaries in the gills for oxygenation of the blood. I and II pass down gill-less arches between the mouth and spiracle and spiracle and first gill, respectively. In adult tetrapods I and II are lost, III gives rise to the carotid arteries supplying the head, IV (one side of which is lost in birds and mammals) to the *systemic arch supplying the body, V is lost, and VI gives rise to the *pulmonary arch* supplying the lungs (*see* pulmonary artery).

apical dominance. The phenomenon, widespread in the plant kingdom, whereby growth of apical buds inhibits growth of lateral buds. In higher plants it may be partially controlled by auxins produced in the apical buds; recently, abscisic acid has also been shown to inhibit lateral bud growth. Gradual loss of apical dominance with age is typical of trees, resulting in greater lateral branching.

apical meristem. A meristem that occurs at the apex of a shoot or root and consists of one or more *initials together with their recent derivatives, which are themselves meristematic for some distance proximal to the apex. The length of this meristematic tissue that is regarded as apical meristem varies according to different authorities: in shoots the term is often restricted to the part above the youngest leaf buttress. The term *promeristem* is applied solely to the initial cells at the very tip while the term *protomeristem* (or *metrameristem*) is sometimes used for the more extensive meristematic region. Lower plants, such as many algae, bryophytes, and pteridophytes, usually possess a single initial, the *apical cell.* Higher vascular plants (gymnosperms and angiosperms) possess a group of initial cells and the arrangement of the tissues in their apical meristems has proved very complex and variable (*see* histogen theory, tunica-corpus theory).

These tissues include the *protoderm, *procambium, *ground meristem, and in the root apex the *calyptrogen. *See also* quiescent centre.

aplanospore. An asexual nonmotile spore.

apocarpy. The state of an angiosperm gynoecium of having free (unjoined) carpels, as in the buttercup. *Compare* syncarpy.

apocrine secretion. *See* secretion.

Apoda. An order of limbless wormlike tropical amphibians (subclass *Lissamphibia), e.g. *Gymnopis.* They are specialized for burrowing, having a pointed head with a solidly built skull; the eyes are reduced or absent (there is a sensory tentacle on the head). They lack a middle ear and in some species calcified scales are buried in the skin. The eggs are laid on land but the larvae are washed into pools, where they undergo a slight metamorphosis to the adult form.

apoenzyme. *See* cofactor.

apogamy. A type of apomixis in which the unfertilized female gamete or associated cell of a plant gives rise to an embryo. In pteridophytes and angiosperms there are two types of apogamy: *vegetative* and *parthenogenetic.*
In pteridophytes vegetative apogamy involves the development of the sporophyte from cells in the prothallus or from a cell in the archegonial wall. In parthenogenetic apogamy the sporophyte arises from an unfertilized oosphere. These sporophytes are haploid but produce normal spores.
In angiosperms vegetative apogamy occurs when a cell of the nucellus or one of the synergidae or antipodal cells develops into the embryo. In parthenogenetic apogamy the unfertilized oosphere gives rise to the embryo. The oosphere may be haploid, in which case the resultant plant is usually sterile and smaller than the normal diploid plant, e.g. *Solanum* species; or diploid (formed

from a megaspore that has not undergone meiosis), when a normal diploid plant is produced, e.g. *Taraxacum* species.

apomixis. A type of reproduction in which fusion of male and female gametes does not take place. In angiosperm plants a diploid cell of the ovule (either a cell of the nucellus or a megaspore that has not undergone meiosis) may develop into the embryo and the rest of the ovule develops into the seed (*see* apogamy). The process therefore mimics sexual reproduction. In some cases a pollen grain is necessary to trigger apomixis, and in these cases it is very difficult to distinguish apomixis from normal sexual reproduction (*amphimixis*). *See also* apospory, agamospermy, parthenogenesis.

apoplast. The complex of adjoining cell walls continuous throughout a plant. It may represent one of the main pathways of water movement outside the xylem, since up to 50 per cent of the cell wall can be free space containing water.

aposematic coloration. *See* warning coloration.

apospory. A type of apomixis in which a cell of the sporophyte of pteridophytes, angiosperms, and some mosses gives rise to a gametophyte without the production of spores: as meiosis has not taken place the resulting gametophyte is diploid. In pteridophytes the gametophyte may develop from cells of the sporangium, the placenta, or any cells of the leaf; in mosses protonemata may arise directly from the sporogonium. In angiosperms a cell of the integument may give rise to the embryo, i.e. the true megaspore has been replaced.

apostatic selection. A mechanism that tends to maintain *polymorphism in populations that are genetically polymorphic (e.g. some snail species) and in which some morphs are more abundant than others. It occurs when predation favours the survival of the morph that is visually distinct from the norm (the *apostate*) by killing a greater proportion of the common one than of the rare. This is likely to result in a balanced polymorphism.

apothecium. An *ascocarp in which the hymenium is borne on the upper surface of a flat or cup-shaped pileus, which may be sessile or borne on a stipe. The characteristic fruit body of the order Tuberales (truffles) is regarded as a sessile closed apothecium in which the hymenium has become very convoluted and forms the bulk of the flesh. *Compare* cleistothecium, perithecium.

appeasement. Any type of agonistic animal behaviour, other than flight, that prevents an attack or stops a fight between members of the same species. The animal losing the fight signals to the winner, by a ritual appeasement gesture, that it is ready to submit.

appendix (vermiform appendix). The narrow blind-ending terminal portion of the caecum of the alimentary canal of some mammals. In man and apes it is of doubtful and possibly vestigial function.

appetitive behaviour. Any pattern of animal behaviour that leads to the satisfaction of a specific need. Examples of appetitive behaviour are the searching by a animal for food or a mate. Such goal-directed activities are ended by a stereotyped *consummatory act, e.g. feeding, copulation. *Compare* exploratory behaviour.

apposition (in botany). The addition of successive layers of cellulose to the inner part of the cell wall of a plant cell: a type of growth that increases the thickness of the wall. *Compare* intussusception.

aptera. *See* alata.

Apterygota. A subclass of small wingless insects, derived from wingless ancestors, in which metamorphosis is slight or absent. There are four orders, which are not closely related: the *Thysanura and *Diplura (bristletails), *Collembola (springtails), and *Protura. *Compare* Pterygota.

aqueous humour. The clear watery fluid filling the space in front of the lens in the vertebrate eye. It is secreted by the ciliary body and is the medium through which the lens and cornea receive nutrients.

arachidonic acid. *See* essential fatty acids.

Arachnida. A class of the Arthropoda in which the body is divided into an anterior cephalothorax (*prosoma*) and a posterior abdomen (*opisthosoma*). The cephalothorax bears prehensile *chelicerae, *pedipalps, and four pairs of walking legs; there are no antennae and the eyes are simple. The sexes are separate and development is direct. Respiration is carried out by *lung books or *gill books and/or tracheae, and excretion is by *coxal glands and *Malpighian tubules. Arachnids are mostly terrestrial and carnivorous. There are several orders, including the *Scorpiones (scorpions), *Pseudoscorpiones, *Araneae (spiders), *Opiliones (harvestmen), and *Acari (ticks and mites). *See also* Merostomata.

arachnoid mater. The soft middle layer of tissue that invests the tetrapod brain and spinal cord. It is connected to the inner layer by delicate strands of tissue that cross the fluid-filled *subarachnoid space, which separates the two layers. *See also* meninges.

Araneae. The largest and most successful order of the class Arachnida, containing the spiders. They have pointed chelicerae for capturing and poisoning the prey and sensory pedipalps with crushing bases; digestion is external. In the males the pedipalps are modified as accessory sex organs. The abdomen, which is unsegmented, is joined to the cephalothorax by a narrow waist and bears the *spinnerets.

arbovirus. *See* virus.

Archaeornithes. An extinct subclass of the Aves containing only the genus *Archaeopteryx* of the Upper Jurassic, the most primitive bird. *Archaeopteryx* was very similar to the small arboreal thecodonts from which it evolved, retaining the reptilian features of a long tail, teeth, and a largely reptilian skeleton. However the body had a covering of feathers (indicating that *Archaeopteryx* was homoiothermic) and the clawed digits were specialized for grasping. The bones were not pneumatic and the sternum lacked a keel: features suggesting that *Archaeopteryx* had weak flying muscles and a gliding flight. *Compare* Neornithes.

Archegoniatae (in older plant classification schemes). A group of plants whose female reproductive organ is an archegonium, i.e. the bryophytes, pteridophytes, and most of the gymnosperms.

archegonium. The female sex organ of bryophytes, pteridophytes, and many gymnosperms. It comprises a tubular *neck*, consisting of tiered cells surrounding central *canal cells*, and a swollen basal *venter* containing the oosphere. The canal cells, which represent abortive female gametes, break down at maturity to provide a liquid medium through which the antherozoids can pass.

archenteron. The embryological gut cavity, which is formed by the infolding of the germ layers at gastrulation and opens to the exterior by the *blastopore. It is lined with endoderm.

archesporium. The tissue, group of cells, or individual cell from which the spores arise in a sporangium.

Archiannelida. A class of small marine annelid worms, most of which are scavengers and have a protrusible tongue. They are thought to have evolved from the Polychaeta, and are sometimes included in this class, but have become simplified and modified for their way of life.

Archimycetes. *See* Myxomycophyta.

Archosauria. The subclass of reptiles that contains the dinosaurs and ptero-saurs – the dominant terrestrial and aerial vertebrates of the late Mesozoic – and the modern crocodiles. They are characterized by a diapsid skull without a pineal opening, long strong teeth in deep sockets (*thecodont teeth*), and pow-erful jaws with a wide gape. The sub-class contains the orders *Thecodontia, *Crocodilia, *Saurischia and *Ornithis-chia (dinosaurs), and *Pterosauria.

Arctogea. A zoogeographical region con-sisting of the northern continents (Europe, Asia, and North America), Africa, and Indochina. It can be subdi-vided into four regions: the Palaearctic and Nearctic (sometimes together called the Holarctic as their faunas are very similar), the Ethiopian, and the Oriental. *See* zoogeography.

arginine (arg). An amino acid, $H_2NC(:NH)NH(CH_2)_3CH(NH_2)COOH$, one of the 20 common *amino acids occurring in proteins. Arginine is an intermediate in the *urea cycle.

aril. A fleshy outgrowth of some seeds that is derived from the funicle. The aril of the nutmeg produces the spice mace (the seed itself being the nutmeg).

armadillos. *See* Edentata.

aromatic ring. A cyclic structure of six carbon atoms that is an integral part of the structure of benzene and many other hydrocarbons. Benzene has a very sim-ple structure in which each carbon atom is also bonded to a hydrogen atom: many other more complex hydrocarbons possess other molecules or groups in place of the hydrogen atoms, but retain the carbon ring structure. *See also* purine, pyrimidine.

arousal. A certain level of responsivenss in an animal resulting from the activa-tion of the brain by nerve impulses transmitted from the *reticular activat-ing system to the higher centres. The strength of the behavioural response, e.g. attack, flight (*behavioural arousal*), is related to the secretion of adrenaline, which produces increased heart beat, blood flow, etc. (*physiological arousal*).

arrow worms. *See* Chaetognatha.

arteriole. A small artery that supplies blood directly to the capillary bed. It resembles the large arteries except that the tunica media, in all but the pulmo-nary arterioles, is composed entirely of smooth muscle cells, 15–20 µm in length.

arterio-venous anastomosis. A small blood vessel that short-circuits blood from the arterioles directly to the ven-ules, thus bypassing the capillary bed. It has thick muscular walls that contract in response to stimulation of the sympa-thetic nerves that supply them.

artery. A blood vessel that conveys blood from the heart to the capillary bed. It is lined with an endothelial coat (*tunica intima*) resting on a thin elastic membrane (*lamina elastica interna*), the whole being encased in a thick fibromuscular coat. This coat is further divided into two layers, a thick inner layer (*tunica media*), composed of smooth muscle or elastic tissue, and a thin outer layer (*tunica externa*), com-posed chiefly of collagen fibres.

Arthrodira. *See* Placodermi.

Arthrophyta. *See* Sphenopsida.

Arthropoda. The largest phylum in the animal kingdom. Arthropods are bilater-ally symmetrical segmented invertebrates with a characteristic tough chitinous exoskeleton, which necessitates growth by *ecdysis. Each segment bears a pair of jointed appendages, which are modi-fied for feeding (*see* mouthparts), walk-ing, swimming, etc. The coelom is reduced to cavities around the gonads and excretory organs and the body cav-ity is a *haemocoel. There is a ventral nerve cord with a pair of cerebral gan-glia and paired segmental ganglia. Simi-larities with the Annelida indicate that the two groups probably arose from the same stock. The Arthropoda, the only invertebrate phylum with aquatic, terrestrial, and aerial members, contains the classes *Crustacea, *Insecta, *Chilopoda and *Diplopoda (Myriapoda), *Arachnida, *Pycnogonida, *Merostomata, and *Trilobita (extinct).

arthrospore. See oidium.

articular. A bone of the lower jaw of all bony vertebrates except mammals that is derived from *Meckel's cartilage and hinges with the quadrate. In mammals it is represented by the malleus (see ear ossicles).

Articulatae. See Sphenopsida.

articulation. A surface of apposition of two parts of a skeleton, typically forming a joint. It is designed to allow movement of one part with respect to the other.

artificial insemination. A method of artificially introducing semen into the reproductive tract of the female. It is used extensively in animal breeding, especially of cattle, sheep, etc., as it enables a male with desirable characteristics to fertilize a large number of females without transporting the mating animals. Under correct conditions semen can be stored for relatively long periods. The method is also applied in human reproduction.

Artiodactyla. The order of the Eutheria that contains the even-toed ungulates: large herbivorous hoofed mammals in which the weight of the body is supported on the third and fourth digits. The order includes the pigs and hippopotamuses as well as the cud-chewing cloven-hoofed camels and ruminants (see Ruminantia). Compare Perissodactyla.

Aschelminthes. A group (or phylum) of wormlike unsegmented usually aquatic pseudocoelomate invertebrates that have a complete alimentary canal and (in many types) a pharynx but lack respiratory and blood systems. The group contains six phyla (sometimes regarded as classes), including the *Rotifera, *Gas-

trotricha, *Nematoda, and *Nematomorpha.

Ascidiacea. See Urochordata.

ascocarp. A fruit body of the fungal group Euascomycetidae, producing asci and possessing a wall that is distinct from the stroma (in which it may be embedded). The asci are produced either in loculi (see cleistothecium) or on a hymenium (see apothecium, perithecium), but a gradation exists between the different types. See also ascostroma.

ascogonium. A female reproductive structure of some ascomycetes in which plasmogamy occurs prior to ascus formation. It is a globular uninucleate or multinucleate body, often with a *trichogyne. Compatible nuclei from antheridia or spermatia are emptied into the ascogonium (via the trichogyne if one is present); the nuclei within the ascogonium then form into pairs, one male and one female. In some ascomycetes these pairs of nuclei then take part in the formation of a dikaryotic mycelium, which eventually produces asci; in others short ascogenous hyphae are produced directly from the ascogonium. See also ascus.

Ascomycetes. A group of mycelial fungi (Eumycophyta) whose sexual reproduction results in the formation of asci (see ascus). The ascomycetes are divided into three subgroups according to the way in which the asci are borne. In the Hemiascomycetidae (which includes the yeast family, Saccharomycetaceae) the asci are naked, i.e. there are no ascogenous hyphae or ascocarps; in the Loculoascomycetidae the asci are borne in an *ascostroma; and in the Euascomycetidae they develop in an *ascocarp. The last group includes most of the common ascomycetes. The dikaryotic hyphae of ascomycetes do not possess clamp connections (compare Basidiomycetes).

ascorbic acid (vitamin C). A water-soluble vitamin (see formula), present in cit-

Ascorbic acid

rus fruits and some vegetables. It is required in the diets of primates, guinea pigs, and the Indian fruit bat as these animals are unable to synthesize it. A lack of this vitamin leads to scurvy in man. Its precise role is not known but it acts as a cofactor in the oxidation of tyrosine and the synthesis of cartilage, bone, and dentine and it may take part in oxidation-reduction reactions as it readily undergoes oxidation. More general therapeutic and prophylactic properties have been claimed for it but these have not been satisfactorily established.

ascostroma. An ascus-producing structure of the fungal group Loculoascomycetidae, in which the stroma forms the wall of one or more loculi within which the asci are produced. *See also* ascocarp.

ascus. The characteristic structure producing sexual spores in the Ascomycetes. In the higher members the asci are borne on a hymenium in an *ascocarp. Some lower ascomycetes produce individual asci on hyphae, and in the unicellular Saccharomycetaceae (yeasts) a single zygotic cell is transformed into an ascus.
Asci develop from dikaryotic cells. In the Saccharomycetaceae and Taphrinales these are formed by sexual fusion of similar gametangia. Alternatively sexual fusion occurs between an *ascogonium and either an antheridium or a *spermatium, and in some ascomycetes between mycelia of compatible strains. The dikaryotic cells divide by *crozier formation to form *ascus mother cells*, each of which divides by meiosis and mitosis to form eight haploid *ascospores*.

asexual reproduction. Any form of reproduction in which new individuals are derived from a single parent without the production of gametes or special reproductive structures. It is common in plants, in which it usually involves *vegetative propagation or the production of spores or gemmae, and in lower animals and microorganisms that reproduce by *fission, *budding, etc. *Compare* sexual reproduction.

asparagine (asn). An amino acid, $NH_2COCH_2CH(NH_2)COOH$, one of the 20 common *amino acids occurring in proteins.

aspartic acid (aspartate, asp). An amino acid, $HOOCCH_2CH_2CH(NH_2)COOH$, one of the 20 common *amino acids found in proteins. Aspartic acid serves as a precursor of pyrimidines, necessary for nucleotide synthesis, and is an intermediate in the *urea cycle. Aspartate is also physiologically active, causing depolarization of neurones in the mammalian central nervous system and in invertebrates.

Aspergillus. A genus of filamentous ascomycete fungi. *A. nidulans* has been extensively used in genetic research and *A. fumigatus* causes the disease aspergillosis. Other *Aspergillus* species (e.g. *A. flavus*) are spoilers of stored grains and nuts and produce *aflatoxins.

aspirin. A widely used analgesic drug that also reduces inflammation and fever. Its analgesic and anti-inflammatory action are thought to be due to its effect of inhibiting synthesis of *prostaglandin at damaged tissue.

assembly rules (in island biogeography). Rules (devised by Diamond) that explain why only certain combinations of species exist on a given island. In some cases this may be due to *competition and exploitation of resources, which minimize the amount of unused resources available to potential new invaders.

assimilation. The process of incorporation of simple molecules, produced from food by digestion and absorbed into the body, into the complex compounds forming the constituents of the organism.

association. A large plant community or group of communities characterized by a particular type of vegetation, e.g. forest, grassland, growing in a region in which the abiotic factors are uniform. Associations usually consist of climax communities, but the term is sometimes used for communities that are in a successional development. Associations that are made up of several communities have more than one dominant species, known as the *co-dominant species*. The communities themselves are known as *consociations*. For example, a deciduous forest association may consist of oak woods, ash woods, and beech woods (the consociations); oak, ash, and beech are the co-dominant species.

assortative mating. A type of mating in which males and females do not choose their mates at random.

aster. A collection of short microtubules sometimes seen radiating from a centriole, originally named from its appearance when viewed with the light microscope.

Asteroidea. The class of the Echinodermata that contains the starfish, e.g. *Asterias*. The star-shaped body, in which the laterally projecting arms are not sharply delimited from the central disc, is covered with a skeletal test. The mouth is situated on the ventral surface. Suckered tube feet on the undersurface of the arms function in feeding and locomotion.

atactostele. *See* stele.

atavism. The phenomenon in which a characteristic of an organism does not occur in its immediate descendants but does appear in subsequent, usually distant, generations. The word is not in modern scientific usage as this phenomenon can now be explained in terms of recessive genes.

ataxia telangiectasia. A rare inherited disease of man. Affected individuals develop tumours following X-irradiation, apparently due to a defect in certain of the DNA polymerase enzymes responsible for *DNA repair.

atlas. The ring-shaped first vertebra of tetrapods, much modified in amniotes to permit free movement of the head on the body. Its articulation with the occipital condyle of the skull allows nodding of the head and its articulation with the *axis allows rotatory movement of the head. *See also* vertebral column.

ATP

ATP (adenosine triphosphate). A nucleotide consisting of adenine and D-ribose to which three phosphate groups are attached. Two of these groups are attached by *pyrophosphate* bonds (see formula); hydrolysis of these bonds is accompanied by a large change in free energy. This energy is used very widely in biological systems to drive energy-requiring processes by coupling the two types of reaction. An example of such a reaction is:

ATP is synthesized from *ADP during photosynthesis (using energy derived from sunlight) and during oxidative phosphorylation (in which energy is derived from the catabolism of carbohydrates, fatty acids, etc.).

atrium. 1. The second chamber of the primitive vertebrate heart, whose thin muscular walls pump blood from the *sinus venosus into the *ventricle. The evolution of lungs in tetrapods has led to subdivision of the atrium, the left side receiving oxygenated blood from the lungs and the right side receiving deoxygenated blood from the body tissues. The atria open into a single ventricle in amphibians and into paired ventricles in amniotes. *See also* auricle.
2. The chamber surrounding the gill slits of invertebrate chordates, connecting with the exterior by a small pore (*atriopore*).
3. Any similar chamber communicating with the exterior, e.g. the *genital atrium* of the Cestoda.

atropous (orthotropous). *See* ovule.

attachment constriction. *See* centromere.

attenuation. The loss of virulence of a pathogenic microorganism, induced by making successive subcultures under controlled conditions of medium and temperature. The phenomenon was first observed by Louis Pasteur (1822–95), who used it as the basis of *vaccination. Attenuated suspensions of certain pathogenic microorganisms introduced into a patient induce immunity to the disease caused by the virulent form.

auditory capsule (otic capsule). The cartilaginous or bony part of the vertebrate chondrocranium that encloses the inner ear. *See also* mastoid process.

auditory nerve (vestibulocochlear nerve). *See* cranial nerves.

auricle. A sac in the wall of the *atrium of the vertebrate heart. The word is commonly used as a synonym for atrium.

auricularia. A larva of the Holothuroidea, having a sinuous ciliated band for locomotion. *See* dipleurula.

Australasian. (Designating) the region made up of Australia, New Guinea, Tasmania, New Zealand, and the islands south and east of Wallace's line, which together form the zoogeographical region of Notogea. *See* zoogeography.

Australopithecus. A genus of *fossil hominids of the Lower Pleistocene. This genus, together with related similar ones, are known as *australopithecines*. The first *Australopithecus* skull was found in 1924 by Professor Raymond Dart at Taung, Botswana, named *A. africanus*, and dated about 3 million years old. In 1938 skulls of a larger and more robust hominid were discovered at Kromdraai and Swartkrans, in southern Africa; about 2 million years old, they were thought to belong to a related genus, *Paranthropus*, and were named *P. robustus*. Excavations from 1959 onwards in Tanzania by Dr. L. S. B. Leakey (1903–73) and his family produced more australopithecine fossils, including *Zinjanthropus boisei* (now renamed *A. boisei*), 1.75 million years old, and *A. afarensis*, 3.5 million years old.
Australopithecines have a hominid dentition but a very small brain capacity (500 cc, compared with 1300 cc for modern man and 390 cc for chimpanzees). They exhibit primitive bipedalism and were tool-users. They cannot be regarded as human and are best considered to represent a prehuman phase of hominid evolution. In the early 1960s, Leakey found some skeletons more advanced than *Australopithecus* and assigned them to an early species of man, which he named *Homo habilis* (*see also* Homo). The brain of *H. habilis* is larger than that of *Australopithecus* (670 cc), the bipedalism is more advanced, and these hominids were capable of a manlike grip. The artefacts found with the fossils suggest that *H. habilis* was a tool maker, with a definite cultural style, as well as a tool user. There is still con-

siderable controversy as to whether *H. habilis* is distinctive enough to be placed in a separate genus or whether it should be regarded as a species of *Australopithecus*; it is certainly clear, however, that in east Africa, 1.5–2 million years ago, there lived bipedal hominids capable of making stone tools.

autecology. The ecology of single individuals or species. *Compare* synecology.

autodiastylic jaw suspension. A modification of *autostylic jaw suspension in which the upper jaw is fused to the neurocranium. It occurs in the Holocephali and Dipnoi.

autoecious. 1. Designating rust fungi that require only one host species to complete their life cycle. For example, the rust *Puccinia antirrhini*, which completes its life cycle on antirrhinums, is autoecious.
2. (or **monoecious**) Designating insect species (such as aphids) that do not show an annual alternation between primary (woody) and secondary (herbaceous) host plants, remaining on one host species throughout the year. *Compare* heteroecious.

autogamy. 1. (in zoology). A type of reproduction in certain Protozoa, notably *Paramecium*, that resembles conjugation but occurs within a single cell. In *P. aurelia* division of the two micronuclei results in the formation of two gametic nuclei, which fuse to form a zygote. This then divides to form two macronuclei and four micronuclei and the cell divides to produce two daughter cells.
2. (in botany). Self-fertilization.

autograft. A *graft derived from the tissues of the recipient.

autoimmunity. An abnormal state in which an immune response occurs between an individual's antibodies and certain constituents of its own cells or tissues. The diseases in which autoimmunity has been shown to be one of the contributory factors are known as

autoimmune diseases; they are either organ-specific, e.g. Addison's disease, or nonorgan-specific, e.g. rheumatoid arthritis.

autolysis. Self-destruction of a tissue, cell, or part of a cell. It occurs either within a lysosome (*autophagy) or when lysosomes release their enzymes into the cytoplasm, causing digestion of cellular or extracellular materials. It occurs just prior to and after the death of a cell, in damaged tissues, or as part of a developmental process such as metamorphosis, as in the resorption of a tadpole tail. It is also common in cells with a high turnover of contents.

autonomic movements (autogenic or spontaneous movements). Movements of plants induced by internal stimuli. They include growth itself, *nutation, protoplasmic streaming, chromosome movement during nuclear division, locomotion of motile algae, fungi, spores, and gametes, and some movements mediated by pulvini. *Compare* paratonic movements.

autonomic nervous system (ANS). The part of the vertebrate peripheral nervous system that supplies smooth and cardiac muscle and glands in a regulative but generally not a triggering capacity. For example, the ANS can modify but not initiate the heart beat, which is triggered by the pacemaker. The ANS is entirely efferent. It controls activities that under normal circumstances are involuntary (autonomic), but it does not mediate reflexes involving skeletal muscle. Its activity is controlled from higher centres located principally in the medulla oblongata and hypothalamus of the brain, which receive and integrate appropriate sensory information and coordinate autonomic activities with the activities of the other parts of the nervous system. Autonomic innervation, except to the adrenal medulla, involves a two-neurone pathway. The first neurone, which is myelinated and preganglionic, leaves the central nervous system in the ventral root of the segmental nerve. It synapses in a ganglion with many unmyelinated postganglionic neurones, which terminate at the effectors.

The system is anatomically divided into two parts. The *sympathetic nervous system* emerges from the cranial, thoracic, and lumbar regions of the central nervous system. It is characterized by short preganglionic fibres, with ganglia close to the spinal cord, and numerous far-reaching postganglionic fibres with *adrenergic nerve endings. The *parasympathetic nervous system* emerges from the cranial and sacral regions of the central nervous system and is characterized by long preganglionic fibres and ganglia close to the target organ. The postganglionic fibres, which are *cholinergic, are shorter and fewer in number than those of the sympathetic system. Each preganglionic fibre therefore innervates a more restricted region. Most autonomic effectors receive a dual innervation; some, e.g. the blood vessels of the skin and limbs, receive only sympathetic fibres. The primary function of the sympathetic nervous system is homeostatic: it regulates heat loss by controlling blood vessel tone, the activity of the sweat glands, the erection of hair, etc. It is also capable of a widespread discharge that prepares the animal for an emergency. For example, it increases the heart rate, constricts the blood vessels (except those to the heart and skeletal muscles), mobilizes glucose from the liver, and stimulates the release of adrenaline from the adrenal medulla, which in turn elicits a more general 'flight and fight' response. The parasympathetic nervous system, by virtue of its anatomy, has a more restricted effect; it promotes vegetative functions in individual organs (e.g. digestive activity of the gut), including glandular secretion and muscular contraction. In organs with a dual innervation, parasympathetic stimulation tends to antagonize emergency functions promoted by sympathetic stimulation. For example, the heart rate is reduced by parasympathetic stimulation through the *vagus nerve and increased by sympathetic stimulation.

The visceral nervous system of arthropods has structural and functional analogies with the vertebrate autonomic system.

autophagy. The process by which a cell degrades portions of its own cytoplasm, particularly individual organelles, by enclosing them within specially formed vacuoles (*autophagic vacuoles*), usually derived from membranes of smooth endoplasmic reticulum, i.e. self-phagocytosis. Autophagic vacuoles are a type of secondary *lysosome. Autophagy probably occurs in the normal turnover of cell constituents but is most active during certain phases of development, such as embryonic development and senescence, when gross modifications or degradations are effected. *See* autolysis.

autopolyploidy. *See* polyploidy.

autoradiography. The technique of producing an image of a radioactive specimen by the effect of the ionizing particles emitted by the specimen on a radiation-sensitive medium, such as a photographic emulsion. Autoradiography is used in histology to show the distribution of particular substances in tissues and organs. A radioactive isotope of the substance (commonly called a *tracer*) is introduced into the organism or cell. After enough time for the tracer to be incorporated into a larger molecule or transported to a particular site, the specimen is killed, fixed, and sectioned. When sections have been mounted on slides they are overlaid by photographic emulsion, which – on development after a suitable exposure – will reveal in the grain pattern the location of isotope decay in the specimen.

autosome. Any chromosome other than a sex chromosome, occurring in diploid cells as *homologous chromosomes.

autostylic jaw suspension. An arrangement in which the jaws are suspended from the cranium by ligaments between the neurocranium and the palatoquadrate bar or quadrate bone of the upper jaw. It is found in the earliest fossil fish and in all tetrapods except mammals. A modified form of autostyly occurs in the Holocephali and Dipnoi (*see* autodiastylic jaw suspension) and in mammals. In modern groups it is probably secondarily acquired. *Compare* hyostylic jaw suspension, amphistylic jaw suspension.

autotetraploid. A tetraploid produced by autopolyploidy. *See* polyploidy.

autotomy. The voluntary breaking off of a part of its body by an animal, usually to escape from a predator that has taken hold of the part. Autotomy is common in arthropods and lizards. A lizard can break off its tail by strong muscular contraction, which severs the vertebral column through a weak zone between two vertebrae behind the pelvic girdle.

autotrophic (lithotrophic). Designating organisms (*autotrophs*) that synthesize their organic requirements from inorganic precursors, utilizing carbon dioxide and nitrates or ammonium salts as sources of carbon and nitrogen respectively. The source of energy for these syntheses is either light via photosynthesis (*photoautotrophic* organisms) or inorganic chemical reactions independent of light via chemosynthesis (*chemoautotrophic* or *chemosynthetic* organisms). The classification of organisms according to their sources of carbon and energy is shown in the diagram. Some microorganisms may be assigned to more than one category, depending on growth conditions.

All photoautotrophs contain chlorophyll; they include green and some purple bacteria and all green plants. Chemoautotrophs comprise certain bacteria that derive energy for biosynthesis (including carbon dioxide assimilation) from oxidation of reduced inorganic compounds, e.g. oxidation of ammonia to nitrite or nitrite to nitrate (nitrifying bacteria), hydrogen sulphide to sulphur (colourless sulphur bacteria), and ferrous to ferric compounds (iron bacteria). Autotrophic organisms are important as primary producers, their activities ultimately supply-

	AUTOTROPHIC (Lithotrophic)	HETEROTROPHIC (Organotrophic)
	Principal carbon source inorganic (carbon dioxide)	Principal carbon source organic
PHOTOTROPHIC (Photosynthetic) Use light energy	PHOTOAUTOTROPHIC (Photolithotrophic) Includes all green plants (plants with chlorophyll); green and purple sulphur bacteria	PHOTOHETEROTROPHIC (Photoorganotrophic) Includes very few organisms, e.g. purple nonsulphur bacteria, some algal flagellates
CHEMOTROPHIC Use energy from chemical processes	CHEMOAUTOTROPHIC or CHEMOSYNTHETIC (Chemolithotrophic) A few bacteria	CHEMOHETEROTROPHIC (Chemoorganotrophic) Includes the great bulk of nonphotosynthetic organisms: all animals and fungi; most bacteria; some parasitic flowering plants

Classification of cellular organisms according to their principal source of carbon and source of energy

ing the energy and carbon requirements of heterotrophic organisms.

auxiliary cell. *See* carpogonium.

IAA

auxin. One of a class of plant growth substances produced in growing shoot and root apices and having diverse effects. The two most common auxins are *indoleacetic acid* (*IAA*) (see formula) and *indoleacetonitrile* (*IAN*).

Movement is polar, always away from the apex. Auxins stimulate cell elongation in a zone just behind the apex (though high concentrations can inhibit growth) and mediate certain tropic movements, for example phototropism and geotropism. They also promote cell division (with kinins), as in renewal of cambial activity of trees in spring and initiation of lateral and adventitious roots; apical dominance (usually with abscisic acid); pollen tube growth; and fruit set and growth. They retard abscission, working antagonistically to abscisic acid. Synthetic auxins, such as *α-naphthaleneacetic acid* (*NAA*), *indolebutyric acid* (*IBA*), and *2,4-dichlorophenoxyacetic acid* (*2,4-D*), are used widely in horticulture, agriculture, and experimental work (being cheaper and more stable than IAA). 2,4-D, very toxic to broad-leaved species, is used as a weedkiller among grass crops (narrow-leaved), including cereals and lawns. The others are used in potato storage to inhibit lateral bud sprouting, in sprays for fruit trees to prevent premature fruit drop, and to induce flowering in pineapples and parthenocarpy in tomatoes. Natural sources of IAA include bacteria, yeast, mould fungi, and human urine.

auxospore. The liberated protoplast of the Bacillariophyceae (diatoms), which increases in size before forming a new frustule. Due to the method of cell division, the frustule gradually diminishes in size; auxospore formation occurs when the minimum size is reached.

auxotrophic. Designating microorganisms that require one or more specific factors (e.g. particular amino acids) for healthy growth. Auxotrophs are mutant strains of microorganisms that do not have these special requirements. *Compare* prototrophic.

Aves. The class of vertebrates that contains the birds, most of whose characteristics are adaptations to flight. The skeleton is composed of light but strong pneumatic bones (*see* air sacs); the forelimbs are modified as wings with three digits (the third digit is greatly elongated); and in most forms the sternum bears a keel for the attachment of flight muscles. The short deep body is covered with *feathers, which form the flight structures and protect against heat loss, and oxygenated and deoxygenated blood are separated in the four-chambered heart. Birds are homoiothermic and oviparous. Their jaws are elongated into a horny beak and the teeth are reduced or absent.

The class evolved from arboreal reptiles of the order *Thecodontia in the Jurassic and retains many reptilian characteristics, including scaly feet and a diapsid skull. There are two subclasses: the extinct *Archaeornithes and the *Neornithes.

avidin. A component of raw egg white that induces deficiency of the vitamin *biotin.

axenic culture (pure culture). A culture containing only one type or species of microorganism. A culture containing more than one type of microorganism is known as a *mixed culture.*

axil. The angle formed by the adaxial surface of a branch or leaf and the shoot that bears it. The axil of a leaf may produce one to several axillary buds and is regarded as the only normal site for lateral bud development. The formation of all other buds (except apical buds) is termed *adventitious*.

axis. The second vertebra of tetrapods, modified in amniotes to permit rotation of the head on the body. In amniotes the axis bears the *odontoid peg*, which projects into and rotates within the atlas and is embryologically derived from the centrum of the atlas. *See also* vertebral column.

axon. The long unbranched process that arises from the cell body of a *neurone and is specialized for the transmission of impulses over long distances.

axoneme. The characteristic central strand (*axial filament*) of cilia and eukaryotic flagella, comprising a ring (cylinder) of nine pairs of microtubules surrounding a core of two microtubules. Exceptionally, the central pair may be absent, as in the male gametes of some diatoms.

Azotobacter. A genus of flagellated rod-shaped Gram-negative bacteria that are strictly aerobic and are characterized by their ability to use molecular nitrogen as their nitrogen source. *See* nitrogen fixation.

B

Bacillariophyceae. A group of mainly unicellular chrysophyte algae, the diatoms, forming a principal constituent of marine and freshwater plankton. They are characterized by cell walls in the form of a *frustule and by *auxospore formation.

bacillus. Any rod-shaped bacterium. *See* bacteria.

backbone. *See* vertebral column.

back cross. The mating of an F₁ hybrid with one of its homozygous parents. When the parent is a double recessive, this cross is known as a *test cross* and is used to determine whether an individual is homozygous or heterozygous for a particular gene. For example, if the parents of the F₁ were *AA* and *aa*, the offspring of the F₁ would be 25% *AA*, 50% *Aa*, and 25% *aa*. To distinguish between the phenotypically identical *AA* and *Aa*, each may be back-crossed to the double recessive parent. The cross between the homozygous *AA* and its *aa* parent produces progeny all of which are *Aa* (phenotypically *A*). When the heterozygous *Aa* is crossed with *aa*, 50% of the progeny are *Aa* and 50% are *aa* (phenotypically *a*).

bacteria. A heterogeneous group of microorganisms classified with the blue-green algae as prokaryotes (*see* cell) and characterized by a *cell wall that contains the polymer *mucopeptide.

Bacteria can be subdivided into broad groups based mainly on the rigidity and shape of the cell wall and type of locomotion. The *eubacteria* (or true bacteria) comprise the vast majority. They all have a rigid cell wall whose shape and chemical structure is responsible for such features as the Gram reaction (*see* Gram's stain) and antigenic properties, which are used for further subdivision of the group. The cell wall of some eubacteria is surrounded by a *capsule. Eubacteria typically possess flagella, whiplike structures used in locomotion (*see* flagellum). Two major orders of eubacteria can be distinguished by the distribution of the flagella: the Eubacteriales (e.g. *Escherichia, Bacillus, Staphylococcus, Streptococcus*) have *peritrichous flagella; the Pseudomonadales (e.g. *Vibrio, Pseudomonas*, Nitrosomonas) have terminal (*polar*) flagella. Some eubacteria also bear shorter appendages called *pili. The other groups of bacteria all have flexible cell walls and (in motile forms) different types of locomotion (*see* myxobacteria, spirochaetes, mycoplasmas).

Bacteria can also be classified by such features as cell shape, form of colony, and type and products of metabolism. There are two basic types of bacterial cell: the spherical *coccus* and the rodlike *bacillus* (the latter includes spiral and filamentous forms and vibrios). They occur as single cells, chains, or clusters. Bacteria show a variety of nutritional and physical requirements. A few are *autotrophic, including the green and purple sulphur bacteria, which are photosynthetic and can grow on a simple medium of sulphur or sulphides and other inorganic salts. Most bacteria are heterotrophic and many live as saprophytes. *Escherichia coli* can grow on a medium similar to that required for the sulphur bacteria with the addition of a carbon source (such as glucose); *Lactobacillus* requires a much more complex medium containing amino acids, vitamins, etc., and some parasites, e.g. *Treponema pallidum* (the syphilis bacterium), will grow only on the medium of living animal tissues. Some bacteria are aerobes (they require oxygen for metabolism); others are anaerobes (they do not require, or are inhibited by, oxygen). Most anaerobic bacteria have a fermentative metabolism (*see* fermentation). Some bacteria, e.g. the *lactic acid bacteria, are characterized by a particular end product of carbohydrate metabolism.

Reproduction in many bacteria is by binary *fission. However, some eubacteria (e.g. *Bacillus*) form *endospores and the *actinomycetes reproduce in a way similar to some fungi. Sexual reproduction occurs only very rarely and is restricted to a few groups (*see* conjugation). Exchange of genetic material can also occur by *transduction and *transformation.

Bacteria are widely distributed throughout the environment. Many bacteria, including the *coliform bacteria, occur within the bodies of other animals and do not usually harm their hosts. Some bacteria, the pathogens, cause disease in

their hosts (animal or plant) when they invade certain tissues or secrete toxins. For example, *Staphylococcus* in the skin causes boils; *Diplococcus* in the lungs causes pneumonia. Other diseases for which bacteria are responsible include scarlet fever, diphtheria, tuberculosis, cholera, and brucellosis (in man and animals); blights, wilts, rots, etc. (in plants). Bacteria in the soil are essential for recycling the elements (*see* carbon cycle, nitrogen cycle) and fixing them into organic matter (*see* nitrogen fixation). The activities of many bacteria are of economic importance to man; for example in the treatment of sewage, in industrial fermentations, and in the production of *antibiotics, vitamins, etc.

bacterial conjugation. *See* conjugation.

bacteriochlorophyll. The principal *photosynthetic pigment of most photosynthetic bacteria. It is related to chlorophyll a.

bacteriocidal. Designating toxic chemicals that destroy bacteria. Bacteriocides, which include phenol and its derivatives, hypochlorite (OCl^-), mercuric chloride, and organic mercury compounds, are often called *disinfectants*. *Compare* bacteriostatic.

bacteriocin. Any of a group of antibacterial proteins produced by bacteria. Different bacteriocins are produced by different groups of bacteria and are often designated by the name of the producing organism, e.g. *colicins* are derived from *E. coli* and *staphylococcins* from some *Staphylococcus* species. These proteins are coded by genes carried on distinct plasmids (rather than in the main bacterial genome). Certain bacteriocins tend to aggregate into large complexes, some of which show a striking similarity in the electron microscope to the tails of bacteriophages.

bacteriolysis. The destruction of bacteria by any agent. *See* lysis.

bacteriophage (phage). A *virus whose host is a bacterium. Bacteriophages

phage	size (daltons × 10⁶)	chromosome	host
Qβ, R17	4	single-stranded RNA, 3 genes	*Escherichia coli*
OX 174	11	single-stranded DNA, 9 genes	*Escherichia coli*
T2, T4, T6	220	double-stranded DNA, 60 genes	*Escherichia coli*
λ	66	double-stranded DNA	*Escherichia coli*
P1, P2		double-stranded DNA	*Salmonella*

Representative bacteriophages

range in size and complexity from Qβ, a tiny icosahedral particle with a molecular weight of 4×10^6 daltons, to the T-even phages (T2, T4, T6), with a complex head and tail structure and 50 times the molecular weight of Qβ (see table). Qβ contains a single-stranded RNA chromosome that carries only three genes, whose products are involved in replication of the phage RNA and capsid production. T4 contains a double-stranded DNA chromosome coding for about 60 genes whose products are either structural components of the phage particle or are needed for synthesis of phage nucleic acid. T4 has a complex structure (see illustration). The DNA is wound inside the head, and after the phage becomes attached to the bacterial surface, the tail core is forced through the cell wall by contraction of the sheath, so that the infecting DNA can pass through it into the bacterium. After injection of the DNA a lytic cycle follows: the host cell switches its metabolism entirely to the production of new bacteriophages, leading ultimately to lysis of the host cell and the release of new viral particles. Some phages do not induce an immediate lytic cycle. Instead their DNA becomes inserted into the host chromosome and remains dormant, only occasionally leaving the host DNA and initiating a lytic cycle (*see also* lysogeny).

Unlike viruses that infect eukaryotes, almost no bacteriophage enters its host cell as a whole particle. Most insert only their RNA or DNA into the host cell. Like other viruses, bacteriophages are parasitic in the RNA, DNA, and protein-synthesizing machinery of their hosts.

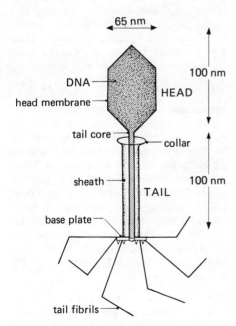

Structure of a bacteriophage

Phages have a high host specificity and this property is utilized in *phage typing*, a method of identifying bacterial isolates by observing their susceptibility to lysis by different bacteriophage types. *See also* transduction.

bacteriostatic. Designating chemicals that inhibit the growth of bacteria without destroying them. *Compare* bacteriocidal.

Balbiani ring. *See* puff.

baleen (whalebone). Parallel horny plates hanging down from the roof of the mouth in the Mysticeti (whalebone whales; *see* Cetacea). Water taken into the mouth is driven out through gaps between the plates while plankton, on which the animals feed, is retained on the plates.

banding. 1. The banded pattern of the giant *polytene chromosomes in salivary gland tissues of *Drosophila* and elsewhere. Banding of the polytene chromosomes is visible within the nucleus of the living cell and may also be visualized by phase contrast or orcein staining of squashed preparations. The bands of these chromosomes are often referred to as *chromomeres*, and when the genes within a band are active the band is seen to acquire a puffed appearance.
2. A pattern induced by various staining techniques in metaphase chromosomes from many organisms. Different patterns of bands may be produced by the use of such agents as trypsin, heat, or alkali dyes, alone or in combination. Chromosome banding techniques permit unequivocal identification of separate chromosomes within a set and thus more accurate assignment of genes to particular chromosomes.

BAP. *See* 6-benzylaminopurine.

barb. 1. (in zoology). One of the hairlike structures borne on the shafts of *feathers.
2. (in botany). A stiff hooked hair.

barbule. 1. (in zoology). One of the processes of the barbs of *feathers.

2. (in botany). One of the teeth forming the inner row of teeth in the peristome of some mosses.

Barfoed's test. A biochemical test for monosaccharide. Barfoed's reagent, an aqueous solution of copper acetate and acetic acid, is added to a solution or suspension of the suspected monosaccharide. The positive result is a red precipitate; the negative result is the absence of any precipitate. This test is based on the reduction of cupric acetate to red insoluble cuprous oxide.

bark. All the tissues outside the vascular cambium region of the stems and roots of plants, either in a primary or secondary state of growth. The term is also used more specifically for the tissues resulting from phellogen activity, together with any primary or secondary tissues that may be separated from the outside of the phellem as a result of phellogen activity. When the term bark refers to all the tissues outside the vascular cambium, the periderm and tissues of the axis isolated by it are refered to as the *outer bark* (or *rhytidome*). The bark (broad definition) of certain plants yields important substances, e.g. quinine from *Cinchona* species, cinnamon from *Cinnamomum zeylanicum*, and *cork from *Quercus suber*. *See also* periderm.

barnacles. *See* Cirripedia.

baroreceptor (baroceptor). A receptor, found in the walls of many parts of the cardiovascular system, that is sensitive to the distension of the structure in which it lies caused by a rise in blood pressure. Stimulation of the afferent fibres from baroreceptors brings about reflex vasodilatation, slowing of heart rate and output, and depression of respiration. The most important baroreceptors are situated in the systemic arch, *carotid sinus, and left atrium.

Barr body (sex chromatin). A small structure, staining deeply for heterochromatin, seen in the interphase nucleus of the homogametic (usually female) sex of some animals and typically found in women. Barr bodies are thought to be condensed X chromosomes and the number present in the nucleus is always one less than the number of X chromosomes. They are used in sex determination tests of athletes and in the identification of abnormal genetic conditions characterized by multiple or deficient sex chromosomes. For example, an abnormal female (superfemale) containing three X chromosomes has two Barr bodies, while a woman suffering from *Turner's syndrome, and therefore having only one X chromosome, has no Barr body.

bars of Sanio. See crassulae.

basal body (kinetosome, blepharoplast). A body identical in structure to a *centriole, found always at the base of a cilium or eukaryote flagellum. Basal bodies may arise from centrioles, as in ciliated epithelia of vertebrates; from other basal bodies, as in *Paramecium*; or independently, as in the flagellate stage of the protozoan *Naegleria*. They are essential for the formation of cilia and flagella, possibly acting as centres for the initiation of microtubule assembly in these organelles.

basal metabolic rate. The rate of metabolism of an animal in a resting state as measured by its consumption of oxygen. It is a measure of the oxidative catabolism necessary to maintain the fundamental processes of an organism, e.g. circulation of blood, muscular contraction accompanying respiration. Basal metabolic rate varies with the age and sex of an individual and is also affected by hormones and environmental temperature.

basement membrane. The thin layer of mucopolysaccharide and fibrous material that lies at the base of epithelial cells and acts as a barrier between the surface epithelium and underlying tissues. It is composed of two layers. The *basal lamina*, 50–100 nanometres thick, lies adjacent to the bases of the epithelial cells and is composed of mucopolysaccharide and fine filamentous material. The *reticular lamina* lies at the periphery of the basal lamina and consists of a meshwork of reticular and collagen fibres. As well as acting as a supporting structure for the epithelium, the basement membrane is thought to provide a barrier controlling the exchange of molecules between the epithelium and underlying tissues.

base pairing. The linking of the complementary pair of polynucleotide chains of DNA by means of hydrogen bonds between the opposite purine and pyrimidine bases. Watson and Crick realized that stable base pairs were formed only between adenine and thymine (A–T) and guanine and cytosine (G–C). The specificity of the base pairing enables the exact *replication of DNA and also determines its correct *transcription into RNA and the *translation of RNA into protein.

base ratio. The ratio of the number of adenine and thymine bases (A + T) to the number of guanine and cytosine bases (G + C) in the DNA of a particular species. For any one species the amount of adenine is equal to the amount of thymine, similarly the amount of guanine is equal to the amount of cytosine: furthermore the ratio of A + T to G + C is constant. The base ratio varies widely between different species; for example among bacteria it ranges from 0.35 to 2.7.

basic stains. See staining.

basidiocarp. A fruiting body of the higher basidiomycete fungi. Basidiocarps are the most obvious manifestations of these fungi and include mushrooms, toadstools, and similar bodies. In some basidiocarps the hymenium is exposed from the beginning; other basidiocarps are closed at first with the hymenium becoming exposed at maturity; some remain closed so that the spores are released when the peridium rots or is broken.

Basidiomycetes. A group of mycelial fungi (Eumycophyta) whose sexual reproduction results in the formation of basidia, which (except in the *rusts and *smuts) are borne on basidiocarps (*see* basidium). The dikaryotic hyphae of these fungi possess *clamp connections (*compare* Ascomycetes). Basidiomycetes are divided into two groups on basidium structure. In the Heterobasidiomycetes (which includes the rusts and smuts) the basidium is either septate or deeply divided or consists of a promycelium formed from a teleutospore; in the Homobasidiomycetes (which includes most of the common basidiomycetes) it is club-shaped.

basidium. The characteristic structure producing sexual spores in the Basidiomycetes. In the higher members basidia are produced in a hymenium on a *basidiocarp but in many lower basidiomycetes they are borne individually on a hypha. Basidia are produced on the dikaryotic mycelium resulting from the plasmogamy of monokaryotic mycelia of different strains. Formed from the terminal cell of a hypha, a basidium is typically club-shaped and produces a single haploid *basidiospore* at the tips of four sterigmata. Its violent discharge from the sterigma seems to be associated with a droplet of water exuded at the base of the basidiospore a few seconds before its release.

basifixed. Designating an anther that is fixed by its base to the top of the filament. *Compare* dorsifixed, versatile.

basipetal (in botany). Undergoing development from apex to base, i.e. with the oldest structure at the apex, as of leaves and inflorescences. *Compare* acropetal, centripetal, centrifugal.

basophil. A polymorph whose cytoplasmic granules stain intensely with basic dyes, e.g. methylene blue. Basophils comprise 0.5_1 per cent of the white cells of human blood. Although their precise function is not known, basophils are rich in histamine and their granules, like those of mast cells, contain heparin.

bast. *See* fibre.

Batoidea. The order of the Elasmobranchii that contains the skates and the smaller rays, which are specialized for living on the sea bottom. They have a dorso-ventrally flattened body with dorsal eyes and ventral gill openings. The pectoral fins, which are greatly expanded and fused to the head, are the principal locomotory organs and the small pointed tail is used as a rudder. The Batoidea are sometimes included in the order *Selachii.

bats. *See* Chiroptera.

B chromosomes (accessory chromosomes). Supernumerary chromosomes found in maize, rye, grasshoppers, and many other animal and plant species. B chromosomes appear to be dispensable genetically and they are normally composed of highly condensed chromatin. *Compare* A chromosomes.

beetles. *See* Coleoptera.

Benedict's test. A biochemical test for sugars, used in the same way and to test the same substances as *Fehling's test. However, Benedict's solution, an alkaline copper sulphate solution and sodium citrate, is a single solution and so mixing is not necessary. The positive result for relatively large quantities of sugar and the negative result are the same as those of Fehling's test (i.e. a brick red precipitate and a blue solution, respectively). But small quantities of sugar, which would not be detected with Fehling's solution, give a green precipitate with Benedict's solution; slightly larger quantities give a yellow precipitate. It is therefore possible to produce quantitative results by comparing the colour of the test solution with a series of known standards.

Bennettitales. *See* Cycadopsida.

Benson-Calvin-Bassham cycle. *See* photosynthesis.

benthos. The organisms living on the bottom of a sea or lake, including the littoral and sublittoral organisms and those of the deep water. *Compare* nekton, plankton.

6-benzylaminopurine   (6-benzyladenine, BAP). A synthetic cytokinin (*see* kinin), one of the most active of a number of substituted adenines that show cytokinin activity.

berry. A succulent *fruit lacking a stony endocarp.

beta decay. A radioactive transformation in which a radioactive isotope emits an electron or a positron. The emitted particles (sometimes called *beta particles*) are widely used in such biochemical techniques as scintillation counting and autoradiography, in which the radioactive isotope is used as a marker molecule.

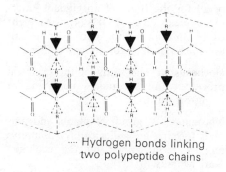

···· Hydrogen bonds linking two polypeptide chains

β-pleated sheet

beta-pleated sheet. A regular folding of polypeptide chains that constitutes the secondary and tertiary structure of some proteins. The polypeptide chains are linked to each other by hydrogen bonds between the carbonyl ($-C=O$) and imino ($-NH$) groups (see illustration). *Compare* alpha-helix.

bicollateral bundle. A vascular bundle having two strands of phloem, one in a centripetal and the other in a centrifugal position relative to the xylem. *Compare* centric bundle, collateral bundle.

bicuspid valve. *See* mitral valve.

biennial. A plant that completes its life cycle – from germination to flowering, fruiting, seed production, and death – in two years. In the first year it makes food that is stored in an underground storage organ during the first winter. In the second year the food is used when the plant produces flowers, fruits, and seeds. Carrot and parsnip are biennials. *Compare* annual, ephemeral, perennial.

bilateral symmetry. The symmetrical arrangement of the body organs of an animal so that only one plane, usually passing longitudinally through the midline at right angles to the dorsal and ventral surfaces, divides the animal into right and left halves that are approximately mirror images of each other. Bilateral symmetry is associated with movement in which one end of the animal constantly leads; it is characteristic of all free-moving animals.
Plants or plant organs (particularly flowers) showing this type of symmetry are termed *zygomorphic*. *Compare* radial symmetry.

bile. An alkaline secretion of the vertebrate liver, discharged into the small intestine through the bile duct. It is composed of cholesterol and the *bile pigments, which are excretory products, and lecithin and *bile salts, which assist in the emulsification of fats.

bile duct. The duct in vertebrates that drains bile from the bile tubules of the liver and discharges it into the small intestine. *See also* gall bladder.

bile pigments. Coloured compounds excreted in the bile. They are the degradation products of haemoglobin, which are formed in the vertebrate liver by removal of iron and protein moieties. The oxidized form is *biliverdin,* which is often reduced to *bilirubin.*

bile salts. Alkaline compounds formed in the liver and discharged into the small intestine as part of the bile. They consist of the sodium salts of cholic acid combined with taurine (*taurocholate*) or with glycine (*glycocholate*) and assist in the emulsification of fats by lowering the surface tension of fat droplets.

bilirubin. *See* bile pigments.

biliverdin. *See* bile pigments.

binocular vision. Overlap of the visual fields of the eyes so that the fovea of both eyes can focus on the same object, thus permitting perception of depth and distance. It is found in primates and many predaceous vertebrates, e.g. birds of prey, and is associated with incomplete cross-over of the *optic nerve.

binomial nomenclature. The method of naming plants and animals devised by the Swedish botanist Linnaeus (1707–78) and still used today. Each species is given a two-part name made up of a generic name and a specific epithet (trivial name). For example, in the species *Homo sapiens*, *Homo* is the generic name and *sapiens* is the specific epithet. When a new plant or animal is discovered it is named in Latin by its discoverer, a description of it is published in Latin, and a *holotype is preserved. The name of the discoverer is written in an abbreviated form after the species; for example, the wolf is *Canis lupus* Linn. (or L.), named by Linnaeus, and the primrose is *Primula vulgaris* Huds., named by Hudson. There are strict rules governing the naming and publication of new species and these are laid down in the International Codes of Nomenclature, of which several forms exist. For wild plants there is the International Code of Botanical Nomenclature (ICBN); cultivated plants are governed by a separate code, the International Code of Nomenclature for Cultivated Plants (ICNCP). The naming of animals is governed by the International Code of Zoological Nomenclature (ICZN). *See also* species, subspecies, variety.

bioassay. The identification or quantitative estimation of a substance by measuring its effect in a biological system under controlled conditions. For example, the amount of auxin in a solution is proportional to the curvature induced when it is applied to one side of a growing coleoptile. Microorganisms are often used in bioassays; vitamins and amino acids can be assayed by measuring the amount of growth (e.g. dry weight of biomass) they will support, and antibiotics can be assayed by measuring the inhibition of growth they produce.

Biochemical Oxygen Demand (BOD). A measure of the organic pollution of water. It is the amount of oxygen (expressed in mg O_2 per litre of water) that is taken up when a sample containing a known amount of oxygen in solution is kept at 20°C for (usually) five days (BOD_5). The oxygen is used up by microorganisms that feed on the organic matter in the sample. The 1911 Royal Commission recommended a maximum of 20 for the BOD of an effluent entering a clean river (BOD<4) with eight times dilution; this has become an accepted standard for sewage effluent.

biochemistry. The study of the chemical processes and substances occurring in living organisms.

biocoenosis. A group of plants and animals forming an ecological *community: an old term coined by the ecologist Karl Möbius in 1877.

biodegradable. Capable of being decomposed by bacteria and other microorganisms. Sewage constituents and some packaging materials are biodegradable.

bioengineering. The manufacture and use of artificial replacements for body organs that have been lost or are malfunctioning, such as artificial limbs, heart pacemakers, etc.

biofeedback. An experimental technique by which an individual can learn to control physiological functions (such as heart rate) that are normally under the control of the autonomic nervous system. Information about these functions is fed back to the subject via such devices as electrocardiograms and he learns to control them consciously. The method has been used in the experimental treatment of such conditions as hypertension.

biogenesis. The doctrine that living organisms arise only from other living organisms and never from nonliving matter. It also states that organisms can only arise from others like themselves, i.e. of the same species, and not from very different unrelated ones. *Compare* spontaneous generation.

biological clock. The mechanism thought to be responsible for the operation of the *circadian rhythm and other *biorhythms. Biological clocks continue to operate even when environmental conditions are kept artificially constant, but eventually break down in the absence of the environmental stimuli that normally keep them synchronized.

biological control. The control of pests by exploiting their natural enemies or by interfering with their life cycle. Examples of biological control are the use of the cactus moth *Cactoblastis* to combat the spread of the prickly pear cactus (*Opuntia*) in Australia and the sterilization of the males of certain insect pests, notably the screw worm.

biology. The study of living things.

bioluminescence. The production of light by living organisms. Bioluminescence occurs in many species, including bacteria, fungi, deep-sea coelenterates and crustaceans, and some insects, notably fireflies and glow-worms. The light is emitted by a compound, known as *luciferin*, when it undergoes oxidation catalysed by an enzyme, *luciferase*. The luciferin of the firefly forms a complex with ATP, luciferyl adenylate, which is bound to luciferase. During oxidation, this activated luciferin emits light as it returns to the ground state.

biomass. The total weight of living matter in a population. Biomass is usually expressed in terms of living or dry weight per unit area. *See also* pyramid of biomass, standing crop.

biome. A particular region or set of regions that has characteristic climatic or other physical conditions and supports flora and fauna that show adaptations to these conditions. Grassland, desert, tropical and temperate forests, and tundra are all biomes. The sea may be considered as a single biome; all its organisms are adapted to life in salt water although not all are adapted in the same way.

biopoiesis. The creation of living material from nonliving replicating molecules, which occurred at the beginning of the origin and evolution of life. *See* origin of life.

biorhythm. Any of the regularly recurring physiological or behavioural events that are assumed to be at least partly under the control of a *biological clock. Examples include *circadian rhythms and the annual rhythms of hibernation and migration seen in animals.

biosphere. The part of the earth and the atmosphere that is inhabited by living organisms.

biosynthesis. The synthesis of biological molecules by a cell (*see* anabolism). Biosynthesis involves a sequence of reactions starting from simple precursors and utilizing the ATP and reduced coenzyme, e.g. NADPH, produced during catabolism.

biosystematics. The branch of *systematics that deals with the variation and evolution of a taxon, often using experimental methods. *See also* taxonomy.

biotechnology. The industrial use of biological processes. Classical examples are the use of fermenting yeasts to produce beer, wine, and industrial alcohol, *Lactobacillus* species in yoghurt production, and such microorganisms as *Penicillium* and *Streptomyces* to produce antibiotics. *Genetic engineering has dramatically increased the scope of biotechnology, enabling the use of yeasts and bacteria to produce, cheaply and on a large scale, such proteins as insulin, interferon, blood serum proteins, and many others for medical and commercial use.

biotic environment. The array of living organisms whose activities may affect the ecology of an individual or a species, such as predators and parasites. The physical and chemical factors affecting an organism are its *abiotic environment*.

Biotin

biotin. A vitamin of the B complex (see formula) that functions as a coenzyme in processes involving the fixing of carbon dioxide, as in fatty acid synthesis and formation of Krebs cycle intermediates. Biotin is particularly abundant in egg yolk, liver, and yeast; deficiency of the vitamin causes dermatitis and loss of hair. A biotin deficiency can be induced in rats by including raw egg white in the diet. This contains *avidin*, which forms a complex with biotin that is not split by enzymes of the digestive tract.

Biotin is bound covalently to a lysine residue of the enzyme involved in fixing carbon dioxide, four molecules of the vitamin being bound per molecule of enzyme. Carbon dioxide is bound to this complex, forming an N-carboxy-enzyme-biotin complex, which then transfers CO_2 to the substrate.

biotype. 1. A group of organisms of a genotypically identical population.
2. A physiological *form, i.e. one produced by physiological specialization.

bipinnaria. A planktonic larva of the Asteroidea that has two ciliated lateral projections. *See* dipleurula.

biramous appendage. The forked appendage typical of the Crustacea. It consists of two branches, the *endopodite* and *exopodite* (which may or may not be similar), arising from a basal portion, the *protopodite*, composed of two segments: the *coxopodite* attached to the body and the *basipodite*. There are two types of biramous appendage, the flattened lobed *phyllopodium* and the narrow *stenopodium*.

birds. *See* Aves.

bisexual. *See* hermaphrodite.

Bismarck brown. *See* staining.

Biuret test. A biochemical test for protein. Sodium hydroxide and a few drops of 1% copper sulphate are added to the suspected protein. The positive result is the appearance of a violet colour; the negative result is that the solution remains blue.

bivalent. Any pair of homologous chromosomes at the stage of pairing during *meiosis.

Bivalvia (Lamellibranchia, Pelecypoda). A class of marine or freshwater molluscs in which the body is laterally compressed and the shell consists of two dorsally hinged valves. The head is poorly developed and the large paired gills are used for respiration and (in many forms) for filter feeding. Some bivalves, e.g. *Mytilus* (mussel), are anchored to a substratum by a tough mass of filaments (*byssus*). Others burrow into sand, e.g. *Cardium* (cockle); in rock, e.g. *Pholas* (piddock); or in wood, e.g. *Teredo* (shipworm). Some bivalves, e.g. *Pecten* (scallop), swim to escape predators by clapping the shell valves together.

bladder. 1. A sac, lined with smooth muscle, in which urine from the kidneys is stored before being discharged. It is present in some fishes, e.g. teleosts, as a dorsal dilation of the Wolffian duct, and in many tetrapods (excluding birds and some reptiles), in which it develops as a diverticulum of the cloaca. In mammals it is drained by the ureters and opens via a sphincter into the urethra. Also called: **urinary bladder.**
2. Any other fluid- or gas-filled sac in animals. *See* gall bladder, swim bladder.
3. A hollow inflated structure in certain plants. For example, the leaves of *Utricularia* (bladderwort) bear bladders with trap-door entrances in which small invertebrates are caught.

bladderworm. *See* cysticercus.

blastema. *See* regeneration.

blastocoel. The cavity that appears within the ball of blastomere cells of many animals at the end of cleavage and forms the central cavity of the *blastula.

blastocyst. The blastula of mammals, which consists of a hollow sphere of cells (*see* trophoblast) with an inner mass of cells at one side from which the embryo develops.

blastoderm. The type of blastula formed by cleavage of a yolky egg. Because cleavage occurs only at the animal pole, the blastoderm of vertebrates such as birds consists of a flat disc of cells on the top of the yolk.

blastomere. One of several small cells formed from an animal zygote during *cleavage.

blastopore. The temporary opening into the interior cavity (*archenteron) of a gastrula, which forms in most animals by an invagination of superficial cells and usually becomes the anus of the adult.

blastula. The stage of the early animal embryo that succeeds *cleavage and precedes *gastrulation. A blastula is usually made up of a hollow ball of cells (*blastomeres*), with a wall one to several cells thick; the central cavity is the *blastocoel*. *See also* blastocyst, blastoderm.

blepharoplast. The *basal body of a flagellum.

blind spot. The area of the vertebrate retina where the optic nerve leaves the eye; it is devoid of visual cells.

blood. The fluid tissue that fills the *blood vascular system. It consists of a liquid (*see* blood plasma) containing blood cells (*see* red blood cell, white blood cell), *platelets, dissolved respiratory gases, digestive and excretory products, proteins, hormones, salts, etc. It often contains *respiratory pigment, either free in the plasma (many invertebrates) or in cells (vertebrates and some invertebrates).

blood capillary. *See* capillary.

blood cell (blood corpuscle). *See* white blood cell, red blood cell.

blood clotting (blood coagulation). The conversion of whole blood or plasma into a gel, which occurs when blood is released from the circulation, usually as a result of injury to the blood vessels. The process proceeds by the sequential activation of several soluble proteins (*clotting factors*) in blood plasma (*see* thrombin, thromboplastin) and results in the production of the fibrous protein *fibrin from the soluble precursor fibrinogen, which gives rise to the gel matrix. Calcium ions and *platelets are essential cofactors for clotting. *Compare* fibrinolysis.

blood corpuscle (blood cell). *See* white blood cell, red blood cell.

blood groups. Types of blood classified on the basis of the different antigens present on the surface of the red blood cells, which are genetically determined. The antigens are distinguished by means of specific serum antibodies that combine with them. The first human blood group system to be discovered (by

Landsteiner in 1900) was the ABO system. There are four groups within this system, A, B, AB, and O, characterized by the presence of antigen A, antigen B, both antigens A and B, or no antigen, respectively, on the red blood cells. The serum of a person of blood group A contains antibody to antigen B and group B serum contains antibody to antigen A; group AB contains no antibody and group O contains antibodies to both antigens A and B. Knowledge of this system enabled the first successful blood transfusions to be made. For example, if blood containing anti-A antibody (i.e. blood of groups B or O) is mixed with blood containing antigen A (i.e. from groups A or AB) agglutination (clumping) will occur due to the antigen-antibody reaction. A person of blood group A can receive a blood transfusion only from other people of group A or from group AB.

There are about 20 other blood group systems, including the rhesus (Rh), Hh, Lewis, and Sese systems. The MN and P systems do not generate corresponding antibodies in man (except on rare occasions) and are therefore clinically less important.

Blood group antigens are also found in secretions of the body, especially saliva and gastric juice, and these secretions have proved useful sources of the specific antigenic material used to study the blood groups.

blood plasma. The clear colourless fluid of vertebrate blood in which blood cells are immersed. It consists basically of water in which all the soluble components of blood, e.g. plasma proteins, inorganic ions, sugars, and hormones, are dissolved. Blood cells can be separated from the plasma by centrifuging uncoagulated blood.

blood platelet. *See* platelet.

blood pressure. The pressure of blood in the main arteries of mammals. In resting humans, blood pressure normally oscillates between about 120 mmHg at *systole and about 80 mmHg at *diastole.

Blood pressure varies in response to climatic conditions, exercise, and posture.

blood serum. The fluid that remains when coagulated blood is centrifuged. It consists essentially of blood plasma without those factors involved in clotting.

blood vascular system. A continuous series of vessels and/or spaces through which blood is pumped around the body. The system effects the transport of respiratory gases, digestive and excretory products, etc., and is found in all animals except those invertebrates small enough for exchange to occur by diffusion across the body. Most invertebrates have an *open blood vascular system*, in which blood flows partly or wholly through tissue spaces and thus bathes the cells directly. In a *closed blood vascular system*, found in vertebrates and some invertebrates, all the blood is contained in blood vessels and so can be pumped at a higher pressure. *See also* haemocoel, heart.

blood vessel. Any of various tubular structures that convey blood throughout the tissues of vertebrates. *See* artery, arteriole, vein, venule, capillary, sinusoid.

blubber. A thick layer of fat deposited in the dermis of some marine mammals, especially the Cetacea (whales).

blue-green algae. *See* Cyanophyta.

BOD. *See* Biochemical Oxygen Demand.

body cavity. The internal cavity of most Metazoa in which many organs are suspended, including the heart, lungs, gastrointestinal tract, liver, kidneys, etc. The body cavity often contains fluid and is bounded by the *body wall*; in mammals it is partitioned by the diaphragm or a similar structure into an anterior *thorax and a posterior *abdomen. *See* coelom, haemocoel.

Bohr effect. The influence of carbon dioxide on the oxygen-carrying capacity of the respiratory pigment of the blood.

Most pigments exhibit a negative Bohr effect, i.e. the volume of oxygen that the blood can hold is reduced when dissolved carbon dioxide renders the blood acid. This adaptation facilitates the maximum exchange of oxygen between the gills or lungs and the tissues, as blood carbon dioxide is low at the respiratory surface, where oxygen is taken up, and high in the tissues, where oxygen is released.

bone. The calcified connective tissue that forms the skeleton of higher vertebrates, having supportive, protective, and metabolic functions. There are two histologically distinct types: (1) *compact bone*, typified by cylinders made up of concentric lamellae of bony tissue, each surrounding a central *Haversian canal and interspersed with lacunae containing bone cells (*see* osteocyte, osteoblast, osteoclast, ossification) linked by fine channels (*canaliculi*), and (2) *spongy bone*, chemically identical to the compact type but consisting of a meshwork of thin bars of bony tissue (*trabeculae*) containing many large intercommunicating spaces. The matrix of bony tissue (dry and fat-free) contains 30–35% organic material, chiefly collagen fibres (96%), which are responsible for the tensile strength of bone. The inorganic constituents of the matrix, the bone salts, comprise 65–70% of its dry weight and confer hardness and rigidity on the bone. The chief constituent of bone salts is hydroxyapatite ($Ca_{10}(PO_4)_6(OH)_2$), but sodium, magnesium, potassium, chloride, fluoride, bicarbonate, and citrate ions are also present. Bone also represents a mobilizable store of calcium and phosphate ions, controlled by *parathyroid hormone and *calcitonin. *See also* cartilage bone, membrane bone.

borax-carmine. *See* staining.

botany. The study of plants.

Bowman's capsule. The part of a nephron consisting of the cup-shaped end of a uriniferous tubule. It surrounds a knot of capillaries, the *glomerulus*. *See* kidney.

Brachiopoda. A small phylum of bivalved marine invertebrates, the lamp shells, living in shallow waters attached to a firm substratum. The shell differs from that of bivalve molluscs in consisting of dorsal and ventral (as opposed to lateral) valves, and brachiopods are further distinguished by the possession of a *lophophore, which protrudes from the shell. The phylum was far more numerous and widely distributed in Palaeozoic times; living brachiopods include *Terebratella*, with an articulated shell; and *Lingula*, in which the shell valves are held together by muscles only.

bract. A small leaflike structure that subtends a flower or inflorescence or (in bryophytes) that surrounds an archegonium, antheridium, or sporangium.

bracteole. A small bract, typically borne on a flower stalk.

bract scale. One of several scales on the female cone of the Coniferales that each subtends, and shows varying degrees of fusion with, a single *ovuliferous scale.

bradykinin. *See* kinin.

brain. 1. The anterior end of the neural tube of the vertebrate central nervous system, which is enlarged and elaborated to coordinate and control the activities of the whole nervous system. The evolution of the brain is characterized by the multiplication of interconnecting tracts between its different parts and the development of dorsal outgrowths of laminated *grey matter, which receive all the sensory input to the nervous system, exercise extensive control over motor output, and are the seat of the higher mental faculties.
2. The cerebral *ganglia of the invertebrate nervous system, which are the dominant integrative centres and are thus functionally analogous to the vertebrate brain.

brain stem. The part of the vertebrate brain comprising the whole of the midbrain and the medulla oblongata of the hindbrain; it structurally resembles and is continuous with the spinal cord. The brain stem, which retains a ventrally thickened central core of grey matter around the ventricles with an outer layer of white matter, gives rise to some *cranial nerves, although the segmental origins of these are obscured. It modifies and integrates reflex commands from higher centres.

branchial arch. One of a series of *visceral arches in fish that support the gills.

Branchiopoda. The most primitive living Crustacea. Most branchiopods inhabit fresh water (*Artemia* (brine shrimp) is an exception) and have flat fringed appendages (phyllopodia) for filter feeding, respiration, and locomotion. Parthenogenesis is common. The subclass includes the Anostraca, e.g. *Chirocephalus* (fairy shrimp), which lack a carapace; the Notostraca, e.g. *Apus* (tadpole shrimp), in which the body is largely enclosed in a carapace; and the Cladocera, e.g. *Daphnia* (water flea), which have enlarged forked and feathered second antennae for swimming.

brand spore. A uredospore of the Uredinales (*rusts) or a teleutospore of the Ustilaginales (*smuts).

bristletails. *See* Diplura, Thysanura.

brittle stars. *See* Ophiuroidea.

bronchiole. A fine air tubule of the tetrapod lung, leading off from a bronchus and terminating (in reptiles and mammals) in numerous alveoli. Smooth muscle in the walls of the bronchioles controls the size of the lumen. Bronchioles lack the cartilage and mucus glands of the bronchi.

bronchus. One of the two main air tubes of the vertebrate lung. Each bronchus, formed by branching of the trachea, supplies one lung and itself branches numerous times to form progressively smaller bronchi and finally bronchioles. The bronchi are supported by incomplete rings of cartilage and are lined by a glandular epithelium that secretes

mucus, which traps dust and is propelled by cilia to the mouth.

brown algae. *See* Phaeophyta.

brown fat. *See* fat.

Brownian motion. The random motion of particles in a solution caused by collision with surrounding molecules, which are themselves thermally agitated. Brownian motion can be observed, using a microscope, in the particles of colloidal solutions and it also occurs in the protoplasm of dead cells. The original description was by the British botanist Robert Brown (1773–1858), who observed the random movements of pollen grains in liquids.

brush border. A region of surface epithelium whose cells have many *microvilli.

Bryophyta. One of the two groups of *Embryophyta, in which the plant body is differentiated into stems and leaves (or sometimes has a flattened thallus) but lacks true vascular tissues and roots. The sporophyte formed from the embryo is wholly or partly parasitic on the gametophyte. The group contains the *Hepaticae (liverworts) and *Musci (mosses).

Bryozoa (Polyzoa). *See* Ectoprocta, Entoprocta.

buccal cavity. The cavity of the mouth: an inturned area of ectoderm derived from the stomodaeum and specialized for the reception of food. It leads to the pharynx.

bud. 1. A short axis bearing a densely packed series of leaf or flower primordia that is produced by an apical meristem. In active buds the axis elongates with the progressive unfurling of the primordia. Dormant buds, produced (for example) during winter or if growth is inhibited by an apical meristem higher up the plant, usually have one or more whorls of outer protective scale leaves, which are shed when growth is resumed. Buds normally occur at the apex of shoots and in the axils of leaves but

they may be produced adventitiously anywhere on the plant. They are sometimes a means of vegetative propagation, dropping from the parent plant and taking root.
2. An outgrowth of an organism that becomes detached from the parent and develops into a new individual. *See* budding.

budding. 1. Asexual reproduction in which a new individual is produced as an outgrowth (*bud*) of the parent. Among animals (in which it is also termed *gemmation*) it is common in coelenterates (e.g. *Hydra*), sponges, bryozoans, and urochordates. Internal buds are produced by some groups, notably freshwater ectoprocts (*see* statoblast) and freshwater sponges (*see* gemmule). In plants budding occurs in the unicellular fungi, including the yeasts.
2. A method of grafting the buds of plants (*see* graft). Also called: **bud grafting**.

buffer. A solution that resists a drastic change in pH on the addition of alkali or acid. A buffer solution commonly consists of a mixture of a weak acid and its conjugate base (e.g. acetic acid and sodium acetate) or a weak base and its conjugate acid (e.g. ammonium hydroxide and ammonium chloride). The buffering capacity derives from the small degree of dissociation of the acid or base (e.g. $CH_3COOH = CH_3COO^- + H^+$). Added acid ($H^+$) is mopped up by acetate anions (CH_3COO^-) from the conjugate base and added alkali (OH^-) is combined with protons furnished by dissociation of the acid. Buffers are essential in maintaining the physiological pH of cytoplasm and extracellular fluids. The phosphate buffer system ($H_2PO_4^-/HPO_4^{2-}$) is the main intracellular buffer and bicarbonate (H_2CO_3/HCO_3^-) is the main extracellular one. Organic phosphates and proteins also serve as buffers in nature.

bugs. *See* Hemiptera.

bulb. An organ of perennation and usually also of vegetative propagation in plants that consists of a modified shoot whose stem is very short and is surmounted by fleshy scale leaves or thickened leaf bases, which store food. The following season, growth occurs by one or more buds inside the bulb, using food stored in the bulb. If only one bud grows, the bulb is acting only as an organ of perennation. If two buds grow, two new shoots arise, and at the end of the season two new bulbs are made; in this case vegetative propagation has occurred. Examples of bulbs are onion, daffodil, and tulip. *Compare* corm.

bulbil. A small bulblike organ of vegetative propagation, in size and weight similar to a large seed, that drops off the parent plant. It may be dispersed in water, such as rain splash, then roots and grows independently. In some plants, e.g. in some *Allium* species, bulbils grow in places normally occupied by flowers; in others they grow as axillary buds on the lower part of the stem or directly from the foliage leaves. *Compare* turion.

bulla. The projection of the skull that encases the middle ear in mammals.

bundle sheath. A layer one to several cells thick, endodermal in origin, surrounding the vascular bundles of angiosperm leaves. In dicotyledons it is also called *border parenchyma*. The sheath may be extended abaxially and adaxially to contact the epidermis in the form of *bundle sheath extensions*. The cells of the sheath are usually parenchymatous but in some dicotyledons they may be sclerenchymatous; they sometimes contain chloroplasts and may form a *starch sheath.

buoyant density. The density at which a molecule 'floats' in an equilibrium density gradient of such a medium as caesium chloride (*see* density gradient centrifugation). The buoyant density of DNA molecules can be used to calculate the *base ratio: the higher the guanine

+ cytosine content of the DNA, the higher the buoyant density.

butterflies. *See* Lepidoptera.

C

cadaverine. *See* polyamines.

caddis flies. *See* Trichoptera.

caducous (in botany). Short-lived and falling early. The stipules of many plants and the transient leaves that appear on cladode-producing plants, such as *Ruscus aculeatus* (butcher's broom), are caducous.

caecum. A blind-ending diverticulum, especially of the gut. In amniotes a caecum occurs at the junction of the small and large intestines and contains bacteria for the digestion of cellulose. In insects it is one of a number of diverticula of the midgut with secretory and absorptive functions.

Cainozoic. *See* Cenozoic.

calciferol (vitamin D2). *See* vitamin D.

calcitonin. A polypeptide hormone secreted by the C-cells of the thyroid and/or parathyroid glands of mammals and by the ultimobranchial bodies of lower vertebrates that lowers plasma calcium levels, thus antagonizing the effects of parathyroid hormone. It was first recognized in 1961, by Copp and Cameron, as a factor in commercial parathyroid extracts. In 1963, Hirsch, Gautier, and Munson discovered that a similar substance was produced by rat thyroid glands. This was termed *thyrocalcitonin* and subsequently identified as a straight-chain polypeptide consisting of 32 amino acids.

callose. A polysaccharide (a β-1,3-linked polymer of glucose closely resembling laminarin) found particularly in the sieve-plate walls of sieve tubes. Heavy callose deposits sometimes seal off sieve tubes, as in normal inactivation processes (seasonal or permanent) or after injury (response being within minutes).

callus. A proliferation of parenchymatous cells produced in vascular plants to cover wounds and in regeneration. It can also be induced to form in *in vitro* cultures from individual cells, in some cases giving rise to new plants, and has been used to study the processes of differentiation. *See* suspension culture.

calorie. A unit of energy equal to the amount of heat needed to raise the temperature of 1 gram of water by 1°C. For most purposes the calorie has now been replaced by the *joule* (1 calorie = 4.1868 joules), but the *Calorie* (or *kilogram calorie*), equal to 1000 calories, is often still used to express the energy value of foods.

Calvin cycle. *See* photosynthesis.

calyptra. A cap formed from the venter of the archegonium of bryophytes and pteridophytes that surrounds the growing sporophyte. In mosses it is frequently carried up as the seta elongates. The calyptra is probably at least partially a protective device, but in some mosses its presence has also been shown to be necessary for the normal development of the sporophyte.

calyptrogen. The separate meristem at the root apex of vascular plants that gives rise to the root cap. In some plants the root cap and the epidermis of the root have a common meristem, which is known as the *dermatocalyptrogen*. *See also* apical meristem.

calyx. The sepals of a flower, collectively.

CAM. *See* crassulacean acid metabolism.

cambium (lateral meristem). A *meristem that occurs parallel with the long axis of an organ and is responsible for secondary growth in that organ. The two major cambia are the *vascular cambium*, giving rise to secondary *vascular tissue, and the *phellogen* (or *cork cambium*), giving rise to the *periderm.

Cambrian. The first period of the Palaeozoic era, extending from 600 to 500 million years ago. It was named after Cambria, the medieval name for Wales. This is the first period in which structural fossils are found. The animal fossils include brachiopods, trilobites, and the burrows of worms; the plant fossils are mainly algae and fungi. *See also* geological time scale.

campylotropous (orthocampylotropous). *See* ovule.

Canada balsam. The material widely used in mounting tissues and specimens in the making of permanent preparations on microscope slides. It is a gum dissolved in xylene, which is totally immiscible in water; this is why the processes of *dehydration and *clearing are necessary before mounting. A thin layer of balsam is sandwiched between the slide and coverslip and enables details of the preparation to be clearly seen under a light microscope.

cancer. Any of a broad range of diseases produced by malignant tumours, which are not only capable of invasive growth into surrounding tissue but also of spread (*metastasis*) via the bloodstream and the lymphatic system to parts of the body distant from their site of origin. (The term is also applied to the malignant tumour itself.) Cancers are often subdivided into *carcinomas, *sarcomas, *lymphomas, and so on, depending on the tissue in which they arise.

canine tooth (eye tooth, dog tooth). A conical pointed tooth of mammals situated between the incisors and premolars, usually one on each side of the upper and lower jaws. They are particularly well developed in carnivorous mammals, in which they are used for seizing prey and fighting, whereas they are absent in virtually all rodents. In some mammals,

such as the wild boar, they are modified as tusks.

CAP (catabolite activator protein). A molecule that, together with cyclic AMP, binds to the CAP site of the *lac* operon in *E. coli*. The presence of CAP protein plus cyclic AMP facilitates the binding of RNA polymerase to the *promoter sequence and thus greatly increases the efficiency of transcription of the *lac* operon.

capillary. One of numerous fine blood vessels, approximately 5–20 μm in diameter, that form an intercommunicating network (*capillary bed*) in almost all vertebrate tissues and are supplied with and drained of blood by arterioles and venules respectively. They are minute tubes of endothelium composed of flattened pavement cells, which are separated from the surrounding tissue cells by a layer of connective tissue. The capillary bed is the principal site at which dissolved gases, inorganic ions, water, and proteins are exchanged between the blood and intercellular fluid under the influence of osmotic and hydrostatic pressures.

capillitium. *See* aethalium.

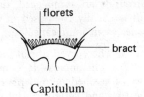

Capitulum

capitulum. A type of racemose inflorescence in which the axis is enlarged and flattened or curved and many small flowers (*florets*) are borne on or in it, often surrounded by an involucre of bracts (see illustration). The flowers are sessile and crowded together, with the oldest flowers to the outside and the youngest to the inside of the inflorescence. The whole capitulum typically has a superficial resemblance to a single flower, as in the daisy, thistle, and fig.

capping. 1. The modification of most eukaryotic messenger RNA molecules after transcription by the addition of a methylated guanosine residue to the 5′ ends. *See also* tailing.
2. An energy-dependent concentration of a specific protein at a localized region of the cell surface. When measured by the use of fluorescent antibodies, the antibody often binds initially to all parts of the surface, but is eventually swept to one end of the cell along with the specific antigen.

capsid. The protein coat of a virion, which encloses the viral DNA or RNA and is made up of protein subunits called *capsomeres. See* virus.

capsule. 1. A dry dehiscent polycarpellary *fruit.
2. The part of a bryophyte sporophyte in which the spores are produced.
3. A gelatinous or slimy substance secreted by some bacteria and forming a protective coat on the outer surface of the cell wall. Most eubacteria have capsules of polysaccharide, but some Gram-positive bacteria, e.g. *Bacillus* species, secrete capsules of poly-D-glutamic acid, and *Acetobacter xylinum* is unique in producing a capsule of cellulose fibrils.
4. A protective or supportive structure that surrounds an animal cell, tissue, or organ. It is usually composed of connective tissue, as in joint capsules.

carapace. 1. The curved dorsal section of the shell of chelonians. It consists of five rows of ossified dermal plates fused with the ribs and vertebrae and overlaid with epidermal horn. *Compare* plastron.
2. The dorsal section of the exoskeleton of some crustaceans, enlarged to shield several segments of the body.

carbohydrates. An important group of compounds consisting of carbon, hydrogen, and oxygen, with the general formula $C_x(H_2O)_y$. Carbohydrates can be subdivided into three main groups: the *monosaccharides and *disaccharides (the sugars) and the *polysaccharides (e.g. starch, glycogen, cellulose).

carbol-fuchsin. *See* staining.

carbon cycle. The circulation of carbon atoms in nature, brought about mainly by the metabolic processes of living organisms. Carbon dioxide in the atmosphere is used by green plants when they carry out photosynthesis to build up the complex organic compounds that form their tissues. When the plants are eaten by herbivores, the organic compounds are incorporated into their own metabolism, and a similar incorporation occurs when carnivores feed on the herbivores. Carbon dioxide is released by all plants and animals during respiration; it is also liberated when organisms die and their tissues are broken down by bacteria in the processes of decay. Carbon dioxide is also released into the atmosphere when fuels such as coal, which are of plant origin, are burnt.

Carboniferous. The fifth period of the Palaeozoic era, extending from 350 to 270 million years ago. It was named after the extensive coal measures formed during this time. Coal consists of the fossilized remains of swamp plants, which included lycopsids such as *Lepidodendron*, tree ferns, horsetails, pteridosperms (seed ferns), and gymnosperms such as the Cordaitales. The animal fossils include corals, brachiopods, bryozoans, bivalve molluscs, and land animals such as insects and the first amphibians. *See also* geological time scale.

carboxylase. An enzyme that catalyses the transfer of carbon dioxide.

carcerulus. A schizocarpic *fruit formed from a superior ovary in which the mericarps adhere to a central axis.

carcinogen. Any agent that causes cancer. Chemical carcinogens include benzpyrene, aflatoxin B_1 (produced by certain moulds growing on foodstuffs), and mustard gas (sulphur mustard) used in World War I to gas troops. Ultraviolet light and other ionizing radiation (such as X-rays) are also carcinogens. The former can cause skin cancer while high doses of X-rays can cause leukae-mia and other cancers. Most, possibly all, carcinogens are also *mutagens (i.e. they cause genetic mutations).

carcinoma. Any malignant tumour that arises in epithelial tissue. *See also* cancer, carcinogen. *Compare* sarcoma.

cardiac muscle. The muscle of vertebrate hearts. It consists of a network of branching multinucleate cells cemented together by adhesions between the membranes, so that the structure can withstand the rhythmic contractions that maintain the heart beat. *See also* pacemaker.

cardinal vein. Either of two paired longitudinal veins of fish and embryo tetrapods, the *anterior cardinal vein*, conveying blood from the head, and the *posterior cardinal vein*, carrying blood from the rest of the body. They unite to form the *common cardinal vein* (*Cuvierian duct), which drains into the sinus venosus of the heart. In adult tetrapods the anterior cardinal vein is replaced by the jugular vein and anterior vena cava, and the posterior cardinal vein by the posterior vena cava.

carina. *See* keel.

carinal canal. A canal formed by the breakdown of the protoxylem elements in some sphenopsid pteridophytes, such as *Equisetum* (horsetails).

carnassial teeth. The modified last upper premolar and first lower molar of many Carnivora (e.g. dogs and cats), which have cusps with very sharp cutting edges for shearing tendons, cracking bones, etc.

carnitine. A vitamin-like substance, $(CH_3)_3NCH_2CH(OH)CH_2COOH$, that occurs in muscle and functions in the transport of fatty acids across the mitochondrial membrane in *fatty-acid oxidation. It can be synthesized by higher animals but is required in the diet of several insects, including mealworms (*Tenebrio* species). *See also* vitamin.

Carnivora. An order of the Eutheria containing mammals characterized by powerful jaws and teeth specialized for biting and tearing flesh, including long pointed stabbing canines, two pairs of shearing carnassials (modified cheek teeth), and sharp crushing premolars and molars. The well-developed claws, sometimes retractile, often assist in killing prey. Carnivores include running forms, e.g. *Canis* (wolf, dog); stalking and springing forms, e.g. *Felis* (cat); burrowers, e.g. *Meles* (badger); and semiaquatic forms, e.g. *Lutra* (otter). Most carnivores are flesh eaters; exceptions include the Ursidae (bears), which are omnivorous, and *Ailurus* (panda), a herbivore. *See also* Creodonta.

carnivore. A flesh-eating animal. *See also* food chain. *Compare* herbivore, omnivore.

carotene. *See* photosynthetic pigments.

carotenoid. *See* photosynthetic pigments.

carotid artery. A paired vertebrate blood vessel that originates from the third aortic arch and supplies oxygenated blood to the head. Two *common carotid arteries* arise from the aorta and each branches into an *internal* and an *external carotid artery* in the neck region. In birds and mammals the origin of the carotid arteries from the aorta varies in different species. *See also* innominate artery, subclavian artery.

carotid body. A chemoreceptor that is situated at the bifurcation of the carotid artery of tetrapods and responds to changes in the oxygen and carbon dioxide pressure and pH of the blood. It consists of a mass of sensitive receptor cells (*glomus cells*), rich in blood capillaries, from which afferent nerve fibres synapse with the nerve endings of the carotid sinus. A reduction in blood-oxygen pressure stimulates the cells of the carotid body and leads to a reflex slowing of the heart.

carotid sinus. A dilated portion of the internal carotid artery, situated close to its origin in the neck, that contains receptors responding to alterations in blood pressure (*see* baroreceptor). Nerve fibres from the carotid sinus travel to the medulla oblongata; stimulation of the fibres results in reflex vasodilatation and slowing of the heart rate and output.

carpal bones. The bones of the proximal part of the tetrapod hand. The primitive arrangement of twelve bones in three rows has been modified in many species by reduction, fusion, and repositioning of the bones. *See also* pentadactyl limb.

carpel. The basic unit of the angiosperm gynoecium, corresponding to a single megasporophyll plus its associated ovules. In most angiosperms the carpel is differentiated into *stigma, *style, and *ovary. The primitive carpel, from which this type is thought to have evolved, is envisaged as a longitudinally folded leaflike structure whose free margins acted as stigmatic surfaces. The margins became progressively fused so that the stigmatic surfaces shifted to the apex of the carpel and finally to the end of a prolongation, the style. The carpels of a flower may be free (*apocarpous*) or united to form a single structure (*syncarpous*). *See also* pistil.

carpogonium. The female sexual organ of the Rhodophyta (red algae), which is produced on plants of the haploid gametophyte generation and comprises a basal portion containing the female nucleus and a *trichogyne. After fertilization by means of a *spermatium the carpogonium gives rise to *carpospores* enclosed in a *cystocarp* (or *gonimocarp*). On liberation the carpospores give rise to the next generation in the life cycle: either the *tetrasporophyte or a new gametophyte generation (usually with the intervention of a *Chantransia stage).

carpospore. The spore produced from a fertilized *carpogonium.

carpus. The complex of carpal bones, forming the wrist in man.

carrier (in genetics). An individual who is *heterozygous for a *recessive gene. For example, a woman may have one normal X chromosome and one carrying a recessive colour-blindness mutation. She will be phenotypically normal but those of her sons who inherit the mutant X chromosome will be colourblind. She is therefore a carrier of the disorder.

cartilage. Hard but flexible tissue that has supportive functions and is present in all vertebrates to a greater or lesser extent. It consists of a firm resilient matrix deposited intercellularly by cells called *chondroblasts*, which become enclosed by the matrix as *chondrocytes*. There are at least three different forms of cartilage: *hyaline cartilage* (the most common), *fibrocartilage*, and *elastic cartilage* (the last two differ only in the nature of their matrices). The matrix of hyaline cartilage consists of *chondroitin sulphate in which is embedded fine collagen fibrils; that of fibrocartilage is mainly white fibrous (collagenous) tissue; elastic cartilage is permeated with a network of elastic fibres. The entire adult skeleton of some lower vertebrates, notably the Chondrichthyes, consists of cartilage and most of the skeleton of mammals is initially laid down as cartilage. In adult mammals hyaline cartilage persists in the larynx, trachea, bronchi, and at the ends of the bones of movable joints. Fibrocartilage persists in the tendons, and elastic cartilage in the external ear and epiglottis.

cartilage bone (replacing bone). A bone formed by the *ossification of an embryonic cartilage precursor (*endochondral ossification*). All the limb and girdle bones (except the clavicle) and the bones of the trunk and the base of the skull are cartilage bones. *Compare* membrane bone.

caruncle. A fleshy integumentary outgrowth of some seeds, e.g. *Ricinus* (castor-oil), arising close to the micropyle.

caryopsis. A dry indehiscent *fruit with fused testa and endocarp, characteristic of the Gramineae (grasses).

casein. A phosphoprotein that is the principal protein of milk. It can be precipitated from milk by the action of rennin and forms the basis of cheese.

Casparian strip (Casparian band). A belt of thickening on the radial and transverse walls of endodermal cells (*see* endodermis); it may be narrow or as wide as the cell. It is probably initiated in the middle lamella by the deposition of phenolic and unsaturated fatty substances, followed by the laying down of suberin and lignin in the primary wall. It cements the protoplast to the cell wall, so that even under plasmolysis any soil solution reaching the stele passes through a selective barrier of cytoplasm. A Casparian strip is also laid down in the cells of the exodermis when this tissue is developed.

caste. One of the several types of morphologically and physiologically specialized individual occurring in populations of some social insects, notably the Hymenoptera (ants, bees, wasps) and *Isoptera (termites). For example, colonies of honeybees consist of workers (sterile females), a queen (a fertile female), and drones (males). *See also* polymorphism.

catabolism. The sum of the processes involved in the breakdown of molecules in order to provide energy in the form of ATP for the anabolic processes of the cell (*see* anabolism). Catabolism involves the oxidation of nutrients (e.g. carbohydrates, lipids, proteins) taken in by the organism and the organism's own food reserves (e.g. starch, glycogen) by such processes as *glycolysis, *proteolysis, *glycogenolysis, and *fatty-acid oxidation.

catabolite repression (glucose effect). A phenomenon in microbial metabolism in which glucose (or metabolites produced from glucose) inhibits pathways of enzyme synthesis. The role of this con-

trol system is to permit preferential catabolism of glucose whenever it becomes available, glucose being the preferred carbon source for growth. There is some evidence to suggest that, at least in bacteria, catabolite repression depends on reduction by glucose of cellular levels of cyclic AMP, and thus on the effective operation of *CAP protein.

catalase. An enzyme that catalyses the decomposition of hydrogen peroxide to oxygen and water. It occurs widely in mammalian tissues (e.g. the liver) and prevents accumulation of (and tissue damage by) hydrogen peroxide that is produced during metabolism.

catalyst. A substance that is responsible for accelerating a chemical or physical reaction, the quantity of the substance remaining unchanged as a result of the reaction. The catalysts of biological reactions are the enzymes.

catecholamines. Amine derivatives of catechol (2-hydroxyphenol), which act as hormones or neurotransmitters. The three most important physiologically active catecholamines are *noradrenaline, *adrenaline, and *dopamine.

cathepsin. A proteolytic enzyme located in the lysosomes, responsible for autolysis after death of the cell. *See* proteolysis.

catkin. A type of raceme in which the inflorescence is usually pendulous and the individual flowers are unisexual, small, reduced, and sessile, as in birch. Catkins usually have either all male or all female flowers on one inflorescence. *Compare* spike.

caudal vertebrae. The bones of the tail region of the *vertebral column.

cauliflory. The condition of having flowering shoots produced on an axis with marked secondary thickening (such shoots probably arise from the pericycle). It occurs, for example, in *Theobroma cacao* (cocoa tree).

cauline (in botany). Pertaining to the stem. For example, the cauline constituent of vascular tissue occurs in the stem; its foliar constituent in the leaves.

C-cells (parafollicular cells). A line of cells, present in all vertebrates, that are derived from the last pair of gill pouches. They secrete calcitonin. In mammals, they are incorporated into the thyroid and parathyroid glands and in lower vertebrates they form the ultimobranchial bodies.

C$_4$-dicarboxylic acid pathway (Hatch-Slack pathway). *See* photosynthesis.

cDNA. *See* complementary DNA.

cell. The basic structural and functional unit of all living organisms (except viruses). The *cell theory was first propounded in 1838–39, the climax of almost two centuries of observation beginning with drawings by Robert Hooke in 1665 of the cellular structure of cork.

All cells contain protoplasm and are delimited by a *membrane, the *plasmalemma* (*plasma membrane* or *cell membrane*), through which controlled exchange between the cell and its environment occurs. Cells also contain genetic material (DNA), which controls inheritance, and the machinery (including *ribosomes) needed to transcribe and translate the *genetic code into proteins. All cells are derived from pre-existing cells, usually by division but sometimes by fusion (e.g. zygotes). Cells

Major Differences Between Prokaryote and Eukaryote Cells

	prokaryote	eukaryote
SIZE	av. diam. 0·5–3 μm	up to 40 μm diam. common; commonly 1000 to 10 000 times volume of prokaryote cells
GENETIC MATERIAL	single molecule of circular DNA; no true chromosomes; no true nucleus; no nucleolus	DNA associated with proteins, forming chomosomes; contained in nucleus, with nucleolus
ORGANELLES	few organelles; no double-membrane-bound organelles	double-membrane-bound organelles present, e.g. mitochondria, plastids, nucleus; great diversity of single-membrane-bound organelles, e.g. lysosomes, microbodies, spherosomes, endoplasmic reticulum, Golgi apparatus
PROTEIN SYNTHESIS	70S ribosomes (many other details of protein synthesis differ, including susceptibility to different antibiotics)	80S ribosomes (larger than 70S)
CELL WALLS	cell walls contain poly-saccharides and amino acids	plant cell walls usually polysaccharide; animal cells lack rigid walls
FLAGELLA	flagella simple, lacking microtubules; not membrane-bounded; 20 nm diameter	flagella complex, with microtubules, and membrane-bounded; 200 nm diameter
RESPIRATION	mesosomes	mitochondria

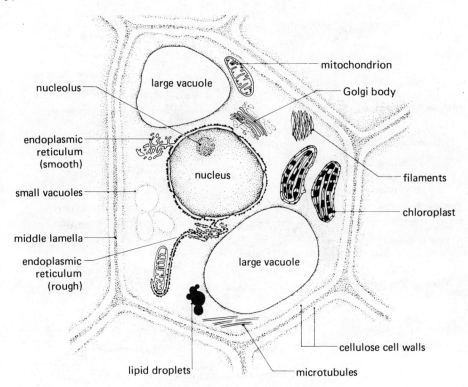

nucleolus

large vacuole

mitochondrion

Golgi body

endoplasmic
reticulum
(smooth)

nucleus

filaments

small vacuoles

chloroplast

middle lamella

endoplasmic
reticulum
(rough)

large vacuole

cellulose cell walls

lipid droplets

microtubules

Fig. 1: Generalized plant cell

vary greatly in size and form. The smallest known free-living cells are the mycoplasmas, with a diameter of about 0.1 μm; the largest are the egg cells, notably the eggs of birds (e.g. ostrich) and reptiles, which contain a high proportion of stored foods. The average cell is about 0.5–20 μm in diameter. Cells are characterized by a high degree of internal organization, involving division of labour between various *organelles. Organisms may be unicellular or multicellular; in the latter, cells become specialized for particular functions, building tissues, organs, etc., and can be of very diverse types.

Early in evolution two fundamentally different cell types emerged: the *prokaryote* and *eukaryote* types. Prokaryotic cells lack true nuclei, their genetic material lying free in the cytoplasm. Eukaryotic cells, which probably evolved from prokaryotes, have their genetic material contained within a *nucleus, separated from the cytoplasm by the membranes of the nuclear envelope. Prokaryotes are unicellular and include bacteria, blue-green algae, and some other organisms. Eukaryotes can be unicellular or multicellular and comprise plants and animals. Eukaryote cells are on average much larger than prokaryote cells and more complex, with greater scope for diversity, particularly in multicellular organisms. Some of the major differences between the two types of cell organization are listed in the table. The *cell wall, present in plants and prokaryotes, is usually included as part of the cell, which then comprises the cell wall plus *protoplast*. In eukaryotes, plant cells differ most conspicuously from animal cells in the usual presence of cell walls and *plastids. Plant cells also often have large *vacuoles and, except for lower plants, lack centrioles. Otherwise eukaryotic cells share many common features (see Figs. 1 and 2). Some

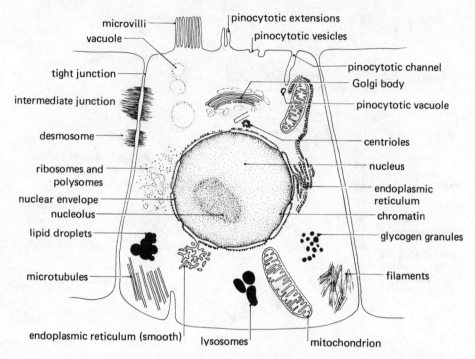

microvilli ⎯ pinocytotic extensions
vacuole ⎯ pinocytotic vesicles
pinocytotic channel
tight junction ⎯ Golgi body
intermediate junction ⎯ pinocytotic vacuole
desmosome ⎯ centrioles
ribosomes and polysomes ⎯ nucleus
nuclear envelope ⎯ endoplasmic reticulum
nucleolus ⎯ chromatin
lipid droplets ⎯ glycogen granules
microtubules ⎯ filaments
endoplasmic reticulum (smooth) lysosomes mitochondrion

Fig. 2: Generalized animal cell

eukaryotes are not strictly cellular, possessing much larger units of protoplasm containing many nuclei (*see* syncytium, plasmodium, coenocyte).

cell body (perikaryon). The part of a *neurone that comprises the nucleus and surrounding cytoplasm, excluding the dendrites and axons.

cell cycle. The complete series of events that occurs in a dividing cell from one mitosis to the next. It is divided into various phases. In the *G₁ phase*, following mitosis, only one half of each chromosome (one chromatid), and hence only half the normal amount of DNA, is present. This is followed by the *S phase*, in which each chromatid duplicates itself, and the *G₂ phase*, in which duplication is complete but mitosis has not yet occurred. Mitosis itself occurs in the *M phase*. The time taken for the cycle varies, the minimum being about 10 hours.

cell division. The process by which a cell divides into two. Division of the nucleus by *mitosis, *meiosis, or more rarely by *amitosis is followed by division of the cytoplasm into two by constriction. New cell membranes are formed, and in plants a middle lamella and cell wall are laid down.

cell fusion. *See* somatic hybridization.

cell lineage. The history of the development of each of the cells produced by cleavage of a zygote.

cell membrane. *See* membrane.

cell plate. The plate formed in dividing plant cells at the position where the new cell wall is being laid down. It appears in the *phragmoplast between the daughter nuclei at telophase of nuclear division and spreads gradually across the cell in the plane of the equator of the disappearing spindle. It consists initially of a series of small membrane-bound vesicles. These fuse, and their contents form first the middle lamella and then the primary cell walls (which will separate the daughter cells), new vesicles being added to the plate from closely associated Golgi bodies. The channels left between the fusing vesicles become plasmodesmata. The vesicle membranes line the two sides of the plate and become the plasmalemmae of the daughter cells. The spreading plate finally unites with the plasmalemma and walls of the mother cell, thus completing cell division.

cell theory. The theory that animal and plant bodies are made up of cells and that the development of the organism is due to division and differentiation of the cells. It was first proposed by Schleiden (for plants) and Schwann (for animals) in 1840.

cellulose. A polysaccharide consisting of long straight unbranching chains of β-D-glucose residues joined by 1,4 links. Cellulose microfibrils form the framework of the cell wall of most green plants and some fungi. Within each microfibril cellulose chains form crystalline lattices known as *micelles*, which are separated by groups of more randomized cellulose chains. The great tensile strength of cellulose is obvious in such products as cotton, which is almost pure (98%) cellulose.

cell wall. The wall surrounding the protoplasts of most prokaryotes and most plant cells (animal cells lack highly organized walls but are often invested with a diffuse polysaccharide layer called the *glycocalyx*; mucopolysaccharides and proteins are also often present).

In higher plants cell wall formation starts in telophase of nuclear division, with the laying down of a thin primary wall on each side of the middle lamella of the *cell plate. The primary wall consists of cellulose microfibrils running through a matrix of complex polysaccharides (hemicelluloses and pectic substances), some protein (including enzymes), and free spaces filled with

water. Pores called *plasmodesmata*, sometimes concentrated in primary pit fields (*see* pits), perforate the wall at intervals, allowing cytoplasmic contact between neighbouring cells. In some cells, e.g. leaf mesophyll cells, the primary wall remains the only wall. In others a secondary wall of one or more layers is laid down inside the primary wall, the microfibrils running in different well-defined directions in the different layers. The secondary wall lacks pectic substances. Lignification, especially in the secondary layers, greatly strengthens some cell walls, as in xylem vessels, tracheids, and sclerenchyma cells. Areas of the wall in which little or no secondary thickening occurs form pits.

Cell wall synthesis involves cytoplasmic activity. Sugars for the polysaccharides of the matrix material pass through a membrane system as follows:

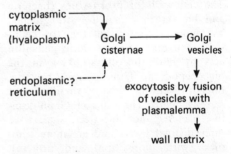

Cellulose is woven from the outside surface of the plasmalemma. The system of cell walls contributes greatly to the mechanical strength and support of the plant. The tensile strength of cellulose fibrils can approach that of steel; the elastic but relatively inextensible nature of the walls allows large turgor pressures to develop in tissues, which aids in the support of large structures. Water may move through cell walls (*see* apoplast) as well as in the lignified xylem vessels. Other modifications include the secretion of protective substances, e.g. cutin by epidermal cells and suberin in cork cell walls, and increased surface area for absorption in *transfer cells.

The cell walls of algae are more variable in structure and composition. For example, the cell walls of the Rhodophyta, Chlorophyta, Phaeophyta, and Xanthophyceae contain a greater variety of fibrous and matrix carbohydrate, although cellulose is usually present. The unicellular and colonial phytoflagellates and their derivatives have many other types of surface coating or supporting structures, e.g. external scales, spines, or plates of such materials as silica, chitin, or lime; diatoms are enclosed by silica boxes (see frustule). Other algae, e.g. Euglenophyta, Dinophyceae, and Cryptophyceae, are supported mainly or exclusively by internal bands or plates covered superficially by the plasmalemma, forming a pellicle rather than an external wall.

Cell walls of fungi differ from those of other plants in containing chitin in varying proportions, although some types have cellulose.

The cell walls of prokaryotes (bacteria and blue-green algae) are strengthened by *mucopeptide rather than by cellulose or lignin. The antibiotic penicillin acts by inhibiting cross-linking in the mucopeptide in Gram-positive bacteria, thus preventing wall formation and causing death. The walls of Gram-negative bacteria and blue-green algae have three distinct layers and are more complex (with more lipid and protein), though thinner, than those of Gram-positive bacteria. The walls of many bacteria and blue-green algae are surrounded by a thin or voluminous sheath or *capsule, which may be firm, mucilaginous, or slimy.

cement (cementum). The layer of calcified tissue that covers the submerged roots of teeth. Although similar in chemical composition and structure to bone, it normally lacks Haversian systems and canaliculi although these may develop as it increases in thickness with age.

Cenozoic (Cainozoic). The third and most recent era of the *geological time scale, extending from 70 million years ago to the present day. It is divided into two periods, the *Tertiary and *Quaternary, regarded by some British and continental authorities as separate eras.

centipedes. See Chilopoda.

Central Dogma. The basic hypothesis of molecular genetics, postulated by Crick in 1958, that genetic information is transferred only one way: from DNA to RNA to protein. Some RNA viruses, however, have been shown to be able to direct the synthesis of DNA from their RNA genome in the cells they invade; a reverse transcriptase has been proposed as catalysing the reaction. See also transcription, translation.

central nervous system (CNS). The part of the nervous system that has a high concentration of cell bodies and synapses and is therefore the principal site of integration of nervous activities. In invertebrates, except those possessing only a *nerve net, the CNS consists of a collection of paired segmental ganglia connected by commissures and a paired ventral nerve cord. In vertebrates it is developed from the embryonic *neural tube, which gives rise to the *brain, lying within the skull, and the dorsal *spinal cord, lying in the vertebral column. In all species the central nervous system gives off peripheral nerves that relay information from the receptors and to the effectors. These may be linked in *reflex arcs, which mediate simple stereotyped behaviour patterns. In both vertebrates and invertebrates increasing complexity of behaviour is associated with decreasing autonomy of individual regions of the central nervous system and increasing dominance of one section. Because of its close association with primary sense organs (the olfactory, optic, and auditory receptors), the cerebral region of the CNS (the cerebral ganglia of invertebrates and the brain of vertebrates) becomes elaborated to integrate and coordinate activity of the whole nervous system. It may also develop the faculty for advanced forms of nervous function, such as memory.

61 centromere

Localization of the integrative centre has necessitated the development of rapid through-conducting pathways within the central nervous system, e.g. *giant fibres, to mediate efficient communication with the end organs. *Compare* peripheral nervous system.

centrarch. Designating a protostelic stele in which the protoxylem is central to the axis. *Compare* endarch, exarch, mesarch.

centre. A region of the central nervous system that has a specific physiological function. For example, the respiratory centre of the vertebrate medulla oblongata controls respiratory movements. Functional centres may or may not be anatomically distinct.

centric bundle. A vascular bundle in which one vascular tissue completely surrounds the other, i.e. it is either *amphiphloic or *amphixylic. *Compare* bicollateral bundle, collateral bundle.

centrifugal (in botany). Undergoing development from inside outwards, i.e. with the oldest structure innermost, as of xylem. *Compare* centripetal, acropetal, basipetal.

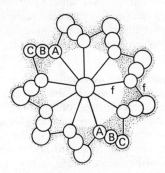

ABC – triplet of microtubules
f – connecting fibrils
– electron-dense material

Centriole (transverse section), viewed from proximal end

centriole. An organelle located close to the nucleus in most animal and lower plant cells but absent from prokaryotes and higher plants. Centrioles usually occur in pairs and, in interphase cells, are arranged at right angles to one another. They can be observed in a distinctly staining region of the cytoplasm, the *centrosome* (or *centrosphere*). Each centriole consists of a hollow cylinder, about 200 nm in diameter and 300–700 nm long, composed of nine triplets of microtubules connected by fibrils at the proximal end (see illustration); the cylinder is closed at its distal end.

During nuclear division in most organisms, the centrioles migrate to opposite poles of the newly formed spindle, where they remain in close association with the microtubules of the spindle (and of the asters when present). Just before, or during, nuclear division the centrioles replicate so that each daughter cell contains two. In many Protozoa and algae the centrioles function as *basal bodies.

centripetal (in botany). Undergoing development from outside inwards, i.e. with the oldest structure outermost, as of xylem. *Compare* centrifugal, acropetal, basipetal.

centromere (**attachment constriction, kinetochore, kinomere, spindle attachment**). The small area of a chromosome that does not stain with basic dyes during mitosis and meiosis; at interphase it is single while the rest of the chromosome is made up of two chromatids. The centromere is the part of the chromosome that becomes attached to the equator of the spindle during mitosis and causes homologous chromosomes to orient equidistant from the spindle in meiosis. Chromosomes often have centromeres that are more or less centrally placed (*metacentric* chromosomes), but some have the centromere located off centre (*acrocentric* chromosomes) or even terminally (*telocentric* chromosomes). Centromeres are composed of *heterochromatin and the DNA found in and around the centromere consists of short highly *repetitious sequences, the so-called *centromeric DNA*.

centrosome (centrosphere). *See* centriole.

centrum. The spool-shaped main part of a vertebra, situated ventrally to the spinal cord. Adjacent centra are joined by a symphysis to provide a firm flexible rod that functionally replaces the primitive notochord. *See also* vertebral column.

Cephalaspida. *See* Osteostraci.

cephalin. *See* phospholipids.

cephalization. The concentration of sense organs, nervous tissue (brain), and food-catching organs at the anterior end of the body, forming a head.

Cephalochordata (Acrania). A marine subphylum of the Chordata in which the chordate characteristics of metameric segmentation, notochord, dorsal nerve cord, and gill slits are retained throughout life (*compare* Urochordata). Excretion is by nephridia. The subphylum is typified by *Branchiostoma* (amphioxus), a small burrowing fish-shaped animal with pharynx and gill slits modified for food collecting (*see* endostyle) as well as for respiration.

cephalodium. A small outgrowth in a lichen thallus containing a secondary alga, usually a species of *Nostoc*.

Cephalopoda. The most advanced class of the Mollusca, characterized by a ring of prehensile tentacles around the mouth and well-developed sensory organs, e.g. eyes, and nervous system (some cephalopods can learn to distinguish shapes). Part of the foot is modified as a *siphon*, through which water is forced by contraction of the muscular mantle during locomotion. Some cephalopods, e.g. *Nautilus* (pearly nautilus), have a many-chambered external shell acting as a buoyancy chamber; in others the shell is internal, as in *Sepia* (cuttlefish), or absent, as in *Octopus*. The females of the genus *Argonauta* (paper nautilus) secrete a papery 'shell' containing the eggs. The class includes the extinct group *Ammonoidea (ammonites).

cephalothorax. *See* thorax.

cercaria. The last larval stage of endoparasitic flukes (order Digenea; *see* Trematoda), which is produced asexually by the *redia larva in the secondary host, a snail, and resembles the adult, differing only in the possession of a tail. The cercaria leaves the snail and encysts until it infects the primary host (either by being eaten (*Fasciola*) or by penetrating the skin (*Schistosoma*)), in which it becomes sexually mature. *See also* miracidium, sporocyst.

cerci (*sing.* **cercus**). A pair of appendages at the posterior end of the abdomen of some arthropods, particularly insects. They may be long and filamentous, as in the mayflies, or short and curved, as in the earwigs.

cerebellum. Paired dorsal elaborations of the anterior auditory region of the vertebrate hindbrain, consisting of a core of white matter with, in mammals, an outer layer of grey matter. Because of its primitive association with the *acoustico-lateralis system, the cerebellum acts as a reflex centre for the maintenance of body equilibrium and orientation. In mammals it receives and integrates all sensory information relevant to locomotion, effecting coordinating modifications to body movements initiated by the higher centres, e.g. the cerebral cortex.

cerebral cortex (pallium). A superficial layer of *grey matter that invests the cerebral hemispheres of amniotes and forms the principal region of integration for the whole nervous system. In mammals it is highly folded to accommodate the extensive development of the *neopallium*. This takes over the integrative functions of the brain stem, tectum, and corpus striatum, receiving sensory information and sending motor instructions directly, without relay, through the specially developed pyramidal tracts. Distinct areas of the neopallium are identified with different sensory and motor functions (the sensory cortex and motor cortex). In the so-called 'blank' areas

$$CH_3(CH_2)_{12} = CH - CH - CH - CH_2 - O -$$

with attached groups: OH, NH below the chain, $C=O$ and $CH_3(CH_2)_{22}$; and a sugar ring bearing CH_2OH, OH, H, HO, OH, H.

Cerebroside

reside the highest mental faculties, e.g. intellect and personality.

cerebral hemispheres (cerebrum). Paired dorsal outpushings of the olfactory region of the vertebrate forebrain. They have become increasingly enlarged and elaborated by the development of a superficial layer of grey matter, the *cerebral cortex. In amniotes their functions are extended beyond the correlation of olfactory information to include the other senses; in mammals they are the dominant region of the brain and the seat of the highest mental faculties.

cerebroside. One of a group of glycolipids occurring abundantly in the myelin sheaths of nerves. The molecule consists of sphingosine, substituted with a fatty acid, and a sugar molecule, usually D-galactose or D-glucose (see formula). One group of cerebrosides, the *sulphatides*, contains a sulphate group esterified to the C3 atom of the galactose molecule; they are abundant in the white matter of the brain.

cerebrospinal fluid (CSF). The fluid that bathes the vertebrate central nervous system, filling the spaces inside and outside the brain and spinal cord. It is secreted into the ventricles by the *choroid plexus and passes through the hindbrain foramina into the *subarachnoid space, where it is reabsorbed into the veins. Slow and selective secretion by the choroid plexus ensures that the CSF contains few cells or large molecules; its function is to protect the nervous tissue from harmful chemicals and from mechanical damage.

cerebrum. See cerebral hemispheres.

cervical vertebrae. The bones of the neck region of the *vertebral column.

cervix. The neck of the uterus: a narrow passage at the lower end of the uterus that opens into the vagina. Viscosity of the mucus within the cervix varies according to changes in the menstrual cycle.

Cestoda. The most specialized class of the Platyhelminthes, comprising the tapeworms. They are endoparasites in the gut of vertebrates, absorbing the host's food through their body wall (they lack a gut) and having a complex life cycle involving one or more intermediate hosts. *Taenia* is a typical tapeworm, in which the primary host is man and the intermediate host a pig. The body is long and ribbon-like, with an outer cuticle and a small head (*scolex*) bearing hooks and suckers for attachment to the host. It is divided into segments (*see* proglottis), each containing hermaphrodite reproductive systems. The eggs develop into six-hooked embryos (*see* onchosphere), which are excreted by man and develop into *cysticercus larvae in the pig.

Cetacea. An order of the Eutheria containing the whales: marine mammals with a hairless streamlined body, no hind limbs, forelimbs modified as stabilizing flippers, and a tail with horizontal flukes providing the propulsive force for locomotion. Cetaceans have an insulating blubber layer beneath the skin and the respiratory outlet is a dorsal blowhole. The Odontoceti (toothed whales), such as *Delphinus* (dolphin) and *Orcinus* (killer whale), feed on fish and have numerous peglike teeth; the Mysticeti (whalebone whales), including *Balaenoptera musculus* (blue whale), feed on plankton filtered from the sea in *baleen plates in the mouth, which replace the teeth.

chaeta. A chitinous bristle characteristic of oligochaete and polychaete worms. Chaetae are arranged in groups of a few (oligochaetes) or many (polychaetes) on each side of each body segment. The chaetae of polychaetes are borne on the parapodia. *See also* seta.

Chaetognatha. A phylum of small marine coelomate invertebrates, the arrow worms, forming a constituent of plankton. Their semitransparent torpedo-shaped bodies are divided into head, trunk, and tail regions and bear lateral and tail fins. The rounded head bears eyes and grasping food-catching spines. Chaetognaths are hermaphrodite.

chalaza. 1. (in botany). The region of an *ovule at which the nucellus, integuments, and funicle merge with each other.
2. (in zoology). One of two twisted cordlike supporting structures attaching the yolk to the membranes in a bird's egg. It is formed from part of the dense albumen.

chalazogamy. *See* pollen tube.

chalcone. *See* flavonoid.

chalones. Substances found in mammalian tissue homogenates that, when applied to intact tissue cells, inhibit mitosis, particularly in the presence of adrenaline and corticosteroids. The action of chalones suggests a role in cancer and the ageing processes. They were first described in epithelial tissue, in the early 1960s, by Bullough and Laurence, and epithelial chalone is thought to be a glycoprotein of high molecular weight.

chamaephyte (in *Raunkiaer's classification). A plant whose perennating buds are situated close to the ground but are still exposed to the air. Many herbaceous and woody plants are chamaephytes.

Chantransia stage. A simple filamentous stage produced by some red algae, developing from the carpospores (*see* carpogonium) and resembling plants of the algal genus *Chantransia*. Terminal cells of the filaments act as apical cells and give rise to the sexual plants. Plants of the Chantransia stage also produce *monospores, from which new Chantransia-stage plants arise. *See also* tetrasporophyte.

Charophyceae. An unusual group of plants, the stoneworts, usually classified as *Chlorophyta (green algae) but sometimes put into a separate division, the Charophyta, on such features as the unique female apparatus, which consists of an oosphere invested in spirally arranged enveloping filaments.

chasmogamy. The formation of large conspicuous flowers that are adapted to cross-pollination, usually by insects or wind. *Compare* cleistogamy.

chela. An arthropod appendage modified as a pincer. For example, the chelae of the Decapoda (crabs, lobsters, etc.) are modified from the first and second thoracic limbs.

chelicera. One of a pair of pincer- or clawlike appendages on the head of the Arachnida that are used for capturing or tearing the prey. Some arachnids have a poison gland at the bases of the chelicerae.

Chelonia. The order of anapsid reptiles that contains the turtles and tortoises. The short flattened body is encased in a bony carapace, usually overlain by large horny epidermal plates (tortoiseshell) and fused to the trunk vertebrae and ribs so that the limb girdles are, uniquely, within the rib cage. The head, neck, tail, and limbs can be withdrawn into the shell for protection. Teeth are absent, being functionally replaced by horny beaklike jaws. Some chelonians, e.g. *Testudo* (tortoise), are terrestrial herbivores but most are aquatic or amphibious carnivores, including the freshwater *Chrysemys* (terrapin) and the marine *Dermochelys* (leathery turtle). The limbs of these aquatic forms are modified as paddles.

chemical fossils. Organic molecules of presumed biogenic origin, which may have survived unchanged but are usually breakdown products of larger molecules. A few constituents of living cells are resistant to hydrolysis and tend to break up into characteristic recognizable fragments. The presence of these fragments in geological strata (especially of Pre-Cambrian age) is used as evidence for living (biogenic) systems having existed at the time of formation of the rocks in which they are found. The two groups of molecules regarded as the most reliable indicators of biogenic origin are the *alkanes* (saturated hydrocarbons, including phytane, pristane, and the isoprenoids) and the *porphyrins. See also* origin of life.

chemoautotrophic (chemosynthetic). *See* autotrophic, chemotrophic.

chemoheterotrophic. *See* heterotrophic, chemotrophic.

chemoreceptor. A *receptor that responds to alterations in the chemical composition of the medium that surrounds it. Chemoreceptors include the *taste buds and the *carotid body.

chemostat. A vessel for the culture of bacteria and other microorganisms in which steady-state growth is maintained by a constant inflow of nutrients and outflow of microorganisms and their products. In a normal culture bacterial growth rate declines as limiting nutrients are used up, but in a chemostat growth remains exponential.

chemosynthetic (chemoautotrophic). *See* autotrophic, chemotrophic.

chemotaxis. *See* taxis.

chemotrophic. Designating organisms (*chemotrophs*) that use energy from chemical reactions independent of light to synthesize their organic requirements. The reactions involve inorganic or organic molecules obtained from the environment; the former are characteristic of *chemoautotrophs*, the latter of *chemoheterotrophs*. *See also* autotrophic (for classification).

chemotropism. Tropic movement in response to a chemical (*see* tropism). The hyphae of some fungi grow towards certain substrates; pollen tubes grow down through the stigma and style towards the ovary in response to substances such as sugars.

chiasma (*pl.* **chiasmata**). The cross connection formed by homologous chromosomes at the diakinesis stage of meiosis. Chiasmata result from the *crossing over of DNA at an earlier stage in the meiotic cycle, and for any one pair of homologous chromosomes there may be one or more chiasmata.

chiasma-type theory. A theoretical interpretation of the relationship between DNA recombination and the formation of chiasmata in chromosomes during meiosis. The theory, which was initially advanced by such geneticists as Janssens and Darlington, suggests that DNA recombination is the initial event and leads to the visible cytological phenomenon of *crossing over and *chiasmata, which characterizes the diplotene stage of meiosis. *See also* Holliday model.

chilling. The exposure of plants to low temperatures, either naturally or artificially, to bring about various physiological changes. Some plants need chilling to break the dormancy of their seeds or buds, while others require it at the seedling stage to induce flowering. *See also* vernalization.

Chilopoda. The class of the phylum Arthropoda that contains the centipedes, e.g. *Lithobius*. The flattened body is divided into numerous segments, the first segment bearing poison claws and each of the rest having one pair of legs. Centipedes are terrestrial, breathing air through tracheae; excretion is by *Malpighian tubules. *See also* Myriapoda.

chimaera. 1. A plant or animal whose tissues are of two different genotypes, produced either by mutation or by grafting. A plant chimaera produced by grafting is known as a *graft hybrid. A *periclinal chimaera* is a plant in which tissues of one genotype form a 'skin' over those of the other type. The 'skin' may be produced by grafting, giving a graft hybrid, or by mutation in the growing point of a plant, resulting in either the tunica or corpus layers of the apical meristem lacking chlorophyll. This mutation produces a layer of yellow tissue around the edge of the leaf or a yellow centre with green edging; it is probably the way in which many variegated plants with yellow edges or centres are produced. Chimaeric rats and mice, which are used experimentally during development, are readily produced by mixing together cells of very early embryos.
2. *See* Holocephali.

Chiroptera. The order of the Eutheria that contains the bats, the only mammals capable of true flight. They are mainly nocturnal and are characterized by a hairless flight membrane (*patagium*) extending from the elongated forearm and the four elongated fingers to the hind limbs and, usually, the tail. The first finger and the toes are smaller, free, and clawed. Bats have specialized ears with large pinnae and use *echolocation to avoid objects and to catch food. The order includes the insectivorous bats, e.g. *Rhinolophus* (horseshoe bat); the vampire bats of South America, e.g. *Desmodus*; and the large fruit-eating bats, e.g. *Pteropus* (flying fox).

chi square test. A statistical test, frequently used in the life sciences, which reveals the probability that a set of experimental values will be equalled or exceeded by chance alone for a given theoretical expectation.

chitin. A linear mainly unbranched nitrogen-containing polysaccharide. It is the main component of the hyphal wall of most fungi, forming microfibrils like cellulose. It forms the main constituent of the exoskeleton of arthropods and the scales of some unicellular algae, its strength and resistance making it suitable as a protective covering.

Chlamydospermae. *See* Gnetopsida.

chlamydospore. A thick-walled resting spore. The term is usually applied to a spore formed from a portion of a fungal hypha, but brand spores and the spores of some protozoans are also known as chlamydospores.

chloramphenicol. An antibiotic originally obtained from *Streptomyces* bacteria but now produced synthetically. In addition to its worldwide use in medicine (although it has been less favoured in recent years because of the correlation of aplastic anaemia with high doses of this drug), the compound is widely used experimentally as a potent inhibitor of bacterial protein synthesis both *in vitro* and *in vivo*, because of its specific interaction with bacterial ribosomes.

chlorenchyma. Parenchymatous tissue containing numerous chloroplasts, as in the mesophyll of a leaf.

chlorocruorin. A red/green *respiratory pigment closely resembling haemoglobin, found in the plasma of four families of tube-living Polychaeta.

chlorophyll. *See* photosynthetic pigments.

Chlorophyta. Green algae (*see* Contophora): colonial, coenobial, filamentous, thalloid, or siphonaceous plants whose principal pigments are chlorophylls a and b and β-carotene. They possess pyrenoids and form starch as a storage product; the cell walls are cellulose; and flagellate cells have two or four similar flagella. Included in this group are *Chlamydomonas* and *Ulva* (sea lettuce). The *Charophyceae are sometimes grouped with the Chlorophyta and sometimes classified as a separate group, Charophyta.

chloroplast. A plastid in which *photosynthesis is carried out. Chloroplasts occur in all photosynthetic organisms except photosynthetic bacteria and blue-green algae. In land plants there may be a hundred or more chloroplasts in a single cell. Each is typically shaped like a biconvex lens, with a diameter of 3–10 μm, and is surrounded by two membranes (the envelope). Inside is a *lamellar system* (stationary phase) and a gel-like *stroma* (mobile phase). The lamellae consist of a series of membranes (*see* lamella) that form fluid-filled sacs called *thylakoids*. At intervals, stacks of circular thylakoids called *grana are formed, linked by inter-grana lamellae. The lamellar system is the site of the light reactions of photosynthesis: its membranes contain chlorophylls and carotenoids (*see* photosynthetic pigments, photosynthetic unit, quantasome). Chloroplasts contain ribosomes, either bound to the lamellar membranes or free in the stroma; the stroma also contains fibrils of DNA and lipid droplets (*see* plastoglobuli) as well as the soluble components of the chloroplast, including the enzymes of the dark reactions of photosynthesis.

The chloroplasts of algae are more variable than those of higher plants in features such as shape, storage products, types of photosynthetic pigments, structure of lamellae, and in the frequent presence of pyrenoids.

The protein-synthesizing machinery of chloroplasts resembles that of prokaryotes, with 70S ribosomes (smaller than cytoplasmic ribosomes) and DNA not contained within a nuclear envelope. It has been suggested that chloroplasts are descendants of prokaryotic organisms that invaded heterotrophic eukaryotic cells early in evolution and have since coexisted with them in a symbiotic relationship. Chloroplasts have been shown, however, to be only partially autonomous, their DNA coding for some but not all of their own proteins. *See also* etioplast.

chlorosis. The loss of chlorophyll in a plant, resulting in the leaves and other normally green parts becoming yellow (*chlorotic*). Chlorosis can be induced by disease, by deficiencies of iron, magnesium, sulphur, nitrogen, etc., by senescence, or by other conditions that prevent chlorophyll synthesis, such as lack of, or sometimes excessive, light.

choanae (internal nares). The paired openings by which the *nasal cavity communicates with the mouth: present in tetrapods and the Choanichthyes (crossopterygians and lungfish). The choanae are situated in the roof of the mouth, anteriorly except in crocodiles and mammals; in these animals development of a false *palate necessitates a posterior opening.

Choanichthyes. A subclass of the Osteichthyes containing the orders *Crossopterygii (lobe-finned fishes) and *Dipnoi (lungfishes). Typical features include a functional lung and internal and external nares (*see* choanae), which allow air breathing at the surface of the water without opening the mouth. The paired fins, which have a very narrow base and a prominent fleshy lobe, are freely movable as only one of their skeletal elements articulates with the girdle. In early forms the body was covered with *cosmoid scales and the tail was heterocercal.

choanocyte (collar cell). A cell bearing a single flagellum encircled at its base by a delicate protoplasmic collar or funnel-shaped rim. Choanocytes line the body of sponges (*see* Porifera) and the action of their flagella causes water currents to flow through the central cavity. Food particles in the water adhere to the collar and pass into the cytoplasm. Choanocytes resemble certain Protozoa (the choanoflagellates) of the class Mastigophora.

cholecystokinin-pancreozymin. A gastrointestinal hormone, released from the mucosal cells of the duodenum, consisting of *cholecystokinin*, which stimulates contraction and evacuation of the gall bladder, and *pancreozymin*, which stimulates secretion of digestive enzymes by the pancreas. Its discovery followed Haper's findings, in 1940, that denervated and transplanted gall bladders still contracted when fat, fatty acids, dilute acids, and peptones entered the duodenum. These substances are now known to stimulate cholecystokinin secretion. Extraction and purification of pig mucosal fractions have failed to separate the two hormone activities and partial determination of structure has revealed a single hormone of about 30 amino acid residues.

Cholesterol

cholesterol. A major animal sterol (see formula), being an important constituent of plasma membranes and occurring in bile, plasma, blood cells, egg yolk, etc. It is the parent compound of many other steroids and its presence in excess in human blood is suspected as being a contributory factor in cardiovascular disease.

choline. A basic compound, $OHC_2H_4N(CH_3)_3OH$, that is a constituent of a number of phospholipids, notably lecithin (phosphatidyl choline), and of the neurotransmitter acetylcholine. Choline can be synthesized by man in adequate amounts but is an essential nutrient for some animals and microorganisms. *See also* vitamin.

cholinergic. Designating a nerve fibre or nerve ending that releases *acetylcholine as a neurotransmitter from the presynaptic membrane of its synapses. Vertebrate voluntary motor neurones, parasympathetic and preganglionic sympathetic neurones, and some invertebrate neurones are cholinergic. *Compare* adrenergic.

Chondrichthyes. The vertebrate class containing the cartilaginous fishes, which first appeared in the late Devonian. They are predominantly marine predators, characterized by a cartilaginous endoskeleton, a skin covering of *placoid scales (which are modified in the mouth as rows of teeth), pectoral and pelvic fins, and the absence of lungs and swim bladder. In the male of many types the pelvic fins are partly modified as *claspers, for internal fertilization. The class is divided into the subclasses *Elasmobranchii (sharks, skates, and rays) and *Holocephali (chimaeras). *Compare* Osteichthyes.

chondriosome. An obsolete term for *mitochondrion.

chondroblasts and chondrocytes. See cartilage.

chondrocranium. The fused series of cartilaginous structures formed in the vertebrate embryo to protect and support the brain, internal ear, eye, and nasal regions. It is usually ossified in adults. *See also* neurocranium.

chondroitin. A mucopolysaccharide consisting of a repeating unit of D-glucuronic acid and N-acetyl-D-galactosamine. Chondroitin sulphates are major components of cartilage, bone, and other connective tissues.

Chondrostei. A group of bony fishes of the subclass Actinopterygii that contains *Acipenser* (sturgeon) and *Polypterus* (bichir), as well as numerous extinct forms (e.g. *Palaeoniscus*), common from Devonian to Cretaceous times. The internal skeleton is partly cartilaginous. *Polypterus* has many primitive features, being covered with thick bony scales and possessing functional lungs, but the dorsal fin is subdivided and the tail is symmetrical. In *Acipenser* the fins are unspecialized and the tail is heterocercal, but most of the bony scales have been lost and a swim bladder is present. *Compare* Holostei, Teleostei.

Chordata. A major phylum of metamerically segmented coelomate animals characterized by a *notochord (present at some or all stages of the life history), a dorsal tubular nerve cord lying immediately above the notochord, and a number of pharyngeal *gill slits. There is a post-anal tail, which is the main propulsive organ in aquatic chordates. The phylum is divided into three subphyla, the *Urochordata and *Cephalochordata (grouped together as the Protochordata) and the *Vertebrata. All invertebrate chordates are marine.

chorion. 1. *See* extraembryonic membranes.
2. A hardened *egg membrane that surrounds and protects the eggs of insects. It lies external to the vitelline membrane.

choroid. The middle layer of the wall of the vertebrate eye, external to the retina, containing nutritive blood vessels and a dark pigment that absorbs light and thus prevents internal reflection. The rim of the choroid forms the *ciliary body and the *iris. There is an analogous layer in the eyes of cephalopods. *See also* tapetum.

choroid plexus. A highly vascular folded area of the epithelium of the roof of the ventricles of the vertebrate brain. It secretes *cerebrospinal fluid and is the medium through which exchange of materials between blood and cerebrospinal fluid occurs.

chromaffin tissue. A tissue composed of groups of modified neural cells that synthesize and secrete catecholamines. It was named in 1865, when the ability of such cells to stain brown with dichromate solutions (the *chromaffin reaction*) was first demonstrated. Improved staining techniques and electron microscopy have shown that the catecholamines are complexed with protein, ATP, and calcium and magnesium ions in large gran-

ules within the cells; these granules release their contents by exocytosis when the cells are stimulated. Chromaffin tissue occurs in all vertebrates, particularly in the *adrenal glands but also in the lungs, skin, and various other parts of the body. It is also found in certain invertebrate groups, e.g. annelids. Catecholamines are synthesized in chromaffin tissue from the aromatic amino acids phenylalanine and tyrosine in a process analogous to the synthesis of noradrenaline in noradrenergic neurones. But in chromaffin tissue, most noradrenaline is then converted to adrenaline by a methyl transferase enzyme, which in mammals is activated by corticosteroids. This may explain the close association between chromaffin and steroid-producing tissues in the mammalian adrenal gland.

chromatid. One of the two threadlike structures joined together by a *centromere that result from chromosome duplication during interphase. Mitotic chromatids are identical but meiotic chromatids may be dissimilar as a result of *crossing over. Chromatids of the same chromosome separate from one another at anaphase of mitosis and at anaphase II of meiosis. When chromatids fail to separate, *polytene chromosomes are formed.

chromatin. The material of which the chromosomes are composed. DNA and protein are the main constituents of chromatin, most of the protein being *histone. The DNA and histone are organized into basic units called *nucleosomes, which are arranged in solenoidal arrays within the chromosome. Chromatin is subdivided into *euchromatin and *heterochromatin, depending on its staining properties, degree of condensation, and state of compaction during the cell cycle.

chromatography. Any of several techniques for separating or analysing mixtures of liquids or gases by selective absorption. In its simplest and original

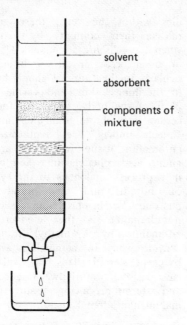

solvent

absorbent

components of
mixture

Column chromatography

form, *column chromatography*, the mixture is poured into the top of a vertical glass column containing a powdered inactive absorbent, such as aluminium oxide or kieselguhr (see illustration). The mixture is washed through the column by a solvent. Different compounds absorb on the solid (called the *stationary phase*) to different extents and thus move down the column at different rates, the more strongly absorbed components travelling more slowly. If the column is long enough the mixture separates and if the components are coloured, as in the pioneering work on plant pigments, coloured bands develop down the tube. Usually they are washed through the column (*eluted*) and collected. *Paper chromatography* is an analytical technique in which the stationary phase is a sheet of filter paper. A spot of the sample is placed near one edge and eluted by allowing the solvent to soak along the paper, thus carrying the components along and separating them. Colourless compounds are observed by viewing in ultraviolet light or by chemical staining. The technique is particu-

larly useful for analysing mixtures of amino acids (as from the hydrolysis of proteins). The acid is characterized by the distance it moves relative to the distance moved by the solvent under standard conditions. A similar technique is *thin-layer chromatography*, in which the stationary phase is a thin layer of aluminium oxide or other absorbent produced by coating a glass plate with a slurry and allowing it to dry. Chromatographic techniques can also be applied to mixtures of gases, although these are used less often in biology. *See also* affinity chromatography.

chromatophore. 1. (in animals). A pigment-containing cell, especially one that causes integumentary colour changes in many crustaceans and lower vertebrates. Three types of chromatophore have been described. *Melanophores,* the most common and best-studied chromatophores, contain melanin that becomes dispersed into the cell periphery causing darkening of the skin. Dermal melanophores, responsible for the rapid colour changes of many vertebrates, are under hormonal regulation in most species but are directly innervated by nerve fibres in some fishes and reptiles (e.g. chameleon). Epidermal melanophores, which are more widely distributed, produce slower adaptive changes and are regulated by *melanocyte-stimulating hormone. These cells also deposit melanin into surrounding epidermal cells and cause the pigmentation of mammalian hair (melanophores are often called *melanocytes* in mammals). *Iridophores* are iridescent pigment cells that contain reflecting platelets or crystalline deposits of purines. *Xanthophores* are yellow pigment cells, containing carotenoids and pteridines.
All vertebrate chromatophores are regulated by melanocyte-stimulating hormone and *melatonin; crustacean chromatophores are controlled by homologous substances.
2. (in plants). A chromoplast: a type of *plastid.

3. (in prokaryotes). A membrane-bound vesicle containing pigment, such as a *thylakoid.

chromocentre. *See* heterochromatin.

chromomere. One of many small bead-like granules that occur along the length of a chromosome, staining most deeply at prophase of mitosis and meiosis. When chromosomes pair during zygotene of meiosis, chromomeres of homologous chromosomes are specifically aligned, chromomere to chromomere. Chromomeres probably represent regions of tightest coiling of *euchromatin during mitosis and meiosis. They can be readily visualized at meiotic prophase and are also apparent at the bases of the loops of *lampbrush chromosomes; they are also probably homologous to the condensed bands of the giant *polytene chromosomes found in some insect tissues.

chromonema. Any of the coiled thread-like strands that make up a chromosome. Each chromonema consists of a DNA double helix conjugated with histone.

Chromophyta. Contophoran algae (i.e. eukaryotic algae with flagella) that contain chlorophylls a and c (and often additional pigments, such as fucoxanthin). The group includes the *Chrysophyta, *Phaeophyta, and *Pyrrophyta. *Compare* Chlorophyta.

chromoplast. *See* plastid.

chromosome. One of a number of threadlike structures that occur within the nucleus of a eukaryotic cell and constitute the genetic material of the cell, consisting of *DNA associated with RNA and protein (mainly histones). The term chromosome has also been applied to the genetic material of prokaryotes (bacteria and blue-green algae) and viruses, although in these organisms the 'chromosome' consists solely of DNA (or RNA for certain viruses) without associated protein and is never visible as the threadlike structure of eukaryotes.

The *chromatin of which a chromosome is composed is made up of basic structures called *nucleosomes, which are organized in the chromosome in a closely packed ordered arrangement. The DNA of the chromosomes consists of a linear sequence of nucleotides, and certain sections of this sequence constitute the hereditary units, the *genes.

Chromatin can be stained with basic dyes. Typically, chromosomes become visible as basophilic threads with a non-staining region, the *centromere, only when the cell is undergoing *mitosis or *meiosis. It is thought that at these times the chromatin becomes more tightly coiled into a spiral, a process known as *spirilization*, and long threads observed in the interphase nucleus may be uncoiled chromosomes. In early prophase of mitosis and later prophase of meiosis each chromosome differentiates into two identical strands, the *chromatids, formed by duplication of the chromosome during the S phase of the cell cycle. The exact division of the chromosome during mitosis ensures that no portion of the genetic material is lost from the cell.

The number of chromosomes in the nucleus is always constant for any one species, although chromosomes may be present in the haploid, diploid, or polyploid state, depending on the type of cell or organism. Chromosomes differ from each other in length, shape, and position of the centromere; pairs of *homologous chromosomes in diploid cells are identical in these respects. The chromosomes determining sex are known as *sex chromosomes; the others are called *autosomes*. *See also* lampbrush chromosome, polytene.

chromosome map. *See* genetic map.

chrysalis. The *pupa of the Lepidoptera (butterflies and moths).

chrysolaminarin (leucosin). An insoluble white polysaccharide food reserve of the algal group Chrysophyta.

Chrysophyceae. A group of chrysophyte algae possessing fucoxanthin in addition to their other pigments (*see* Chrysophyta). *See also* Haptophyceae.

Chrysophyta. A heterogeneous group of chromophyte algae whose members are mostly unicellular (a few are filamentous or coenocytic). Their principal pigments are chlorophylls a and c and β-carotene and their main storage products are chrysolaminarin and oils (never starch). Motile cells (when formed) generally have two dissimilar *flagella (one whiplash, one tinsel). The group includes the *Chrysophyceae, *Xanthophyceae, *Bacillariophyceae, and *Haptophyceae.

chyle. The contents of the lacteals and thoracic duct of vertebrates following a period of absorption. It consists of a fine milky suspension of fat droplets in lymph.

chylomicrons. Minute particles of lipoprotein in the blood and lymph that are the form in which lipids are transported from the intestine.

chyme. Food as it leaves the vertebrate stomach, in the form of a milky semidigested pulp.

chymotrypsin. A proteolytic enzyme that acts as an exopeptidase in vertebrates (*see* proteolysis). It is secreted by the pancreas in the form of an inactive precursor, *chymotrypsinogen*, which is activated by trypsin.

ciliary body. The muscular rim of the fused choroid and retinal layers of the eyes of vertebrates and cephalopods, from which the lens is often suspended by ligaments. It secretes the aqueous humour and in amniotes is responsible for *accommodation.

ciliary feeding. A method of feeding, found in many protochordates and other aquatic invertebrates, in which food particles are filtered from water that is drawn into the mouth by the action of cilia.

Ciliata. The class containing the most highly organized Protozoa. All have locomotory cilia (*see* cilium) at some stage of the life cycle and most have a meganucleus and micronucleus (*see* nucleus) and a mouth. The class includes the Holotricha, e.g. *Paramecium,* which are uniformly covered with cilia; the Peritricha, e.g. *Vorticella,* which have cilia only around the mouth; and the Spirotricha, e.g. *Stentor,* in which the cilia around the mouth are fused or otherwise specialized for feeding.

ciliated epithelium. A region of surface epithelium composed of ciliated columnar cells, i.e. tall cells having cilia on their exposed surfaces. It is responsible for the transport of fluid and particles along the surface of the epithelium, which is accomplished by the rhythmic beating of the cilia, and is therefore found lining the nasal cavity, respiratory tract, oviducts, and uterus. It is often found in association with *goblet cells and mucus-secreting glands.

cilium. A motile organelle identical in structure to a eukaryotic *flagellum but shorter (5–10 μm) and usually arranged in groups. Cilia are common in all animal phyla (except the Nematoda and Arthropoda) but are rare in plants (they occur in the male gametes of cycads and *Ginkgo*). They are characteristic of ciliate protozoans, free-swimming larvae of many marine animals, and certain epithelial cells of higher animals, e.g. epithelia lining the trachea of mammals. Although there is no absolute distinction between cilia and flagella in eukaryotic cells, cilia are commonly characterized by beating together to move water over a surface, whereas flagella exist singly or in small groups and propel water along their axes. Groups of cilia commonly beat with a *metachronal rhythm. Cilia may be grouped in rows called *membranelles*; cilia within one row beat simultaneously and each row beats in metachronal rhythm with other rows, as in the peristome of *Stentor*.

circadian rhythm (diurnal rhythm). A periodic endogenous change occurring in all living organisms, operating independently of daily rhythmical changes in the environment but normally synchronized to the 24-hour light/dark cycle. Such rhythms occur in the leaf, flower, and growth movements of plants and in the changes in body temperature and fluctuations in hormone secretion in animals. Their presence indicates the existence of a *biological clock* in animals and plants but the site and mode of action of this mechanism are largely unknown. Experiments with moths suggest that a circadian rhythm associated with pupation is modulated by a secretion from the brain. Evidence suggests that the response of animals to drugs and environmental changes varies according to the phase in the circadian rhythm.

circulatory system. Any series of vessels or spaces in animals through which fluid flows, e.g. the *blood vascular system or the *lymphatic system.

Cirripedia. A subclass of sessile marine Crustacea that contains the barnacles. The adults live attached by the anterior end to rocks, ships, etc., either by means of a stalk, e.g. *Lepas* (goose barnacle), or without one, e.g. *Balanus* (acorn barnacle). Many cirripedes, e.g. *Sacculina,* are parasites. In the free-living forms calcareous plates are embedded in the leathery carapace and the fringed thoracic limbs project upwards for filter feeding. Barnacles are hermaphrodite and develop via free-swimming *nauplius and *cypris* larvae. The cypris eventually becomes attached to the substratum by cement glands in the antennules.

cis **configuration.** The location of two alleles on the same chromosome as defined by the *cis-trans test. Since the test was used by Benzer to define the unit of genetic function, a structural gene sequence came to be known as a *cistron.

cisternae (*sing.* **cisterna).** Flattened sac-like vesicles of the *endoplasmic reticulum and *Golgi apparatus, which are often involved in cell transport and storage processes.

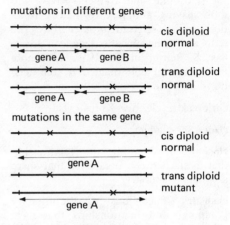

Cis-trans test

cis-trans test. A test to define the unit of genetic function, originally devised by Benzer for bacteriophage genetic studies (see illustration). It determines whether independent mutations of the same phenotype occur within a single gene or in several genes involved in the same function.

Two homologous chromosomes are brought together in the same diploid cell. When two mutations occur in the same chromosome they are said to be in the *cis* position; when they occur in different chromosomes they are in the *trans* position. If each mutation occurs in a different gene the resultant diploid phenotype is normal in both the *cis* and *trans* diploids as the alleles of the nonmutant chromosome make up the deficiences in the mutant chromosome, i.e. *complementation occurs. If both the mutations occur in the same gene, only the *cis* diploid is normal; the *trans* diploid is mutant since the different mutations affect the same function and complementation cannot occur. The latter result constitutes a *negative cis-trans test* and defines a gene purely by function; this functional gene is known as a *cistron*.

cistron. The length of DNA that codes for a particular protein, via the intermediate *messenger RNA. Genes coding for ribosomal and transfer RNA, and those having a purely regulatory function, are not referred to as cistrons. The term was coined by the American geneticist S. Benzer in the 1950s to denote the functional unit defined by the *cis-trans test.

citric acid cycle. *See* Krebs cycle.

clade. *See* cladistics.

cladistic. Designating the relationship that exists between organisms that share a common ancestry.

cladistics. The study of evolutionary groupings and relationships that have arisen from *cladogenesis, including the method of classification based on this type of evolution. In a cladistic classification, organisms are placed into taxonomic groups called *clades* when they share characteristics that are thought to indicate common ancestry. It assumes that two new species are formed suddenly, by splitting from a common ancestor (*see* punctuated equilibrium), and not by gradual evolutionary change. A diagram indicating these relationships (called a *cladogram*) therefore consists of a system of dichotomous branches, each point of branching representing divergence from a common ancestor. The opponents of neo-Darwinism argue that the major branching patterns of cladograms correspond to large-scale evolutionary events that cannot be explained by orthodox neo-Darwinism, which postulates a series of small changes occurring over a long period of time.

cladode. A stem that is modified to resemble and function as a leaf (the true leaves are reduced to scales). It carries out photosynthesis but contains fewer stomata than a leaf of similar size. Cladodes are characteristic of xero-

phytes, e.g. butcher's broom, in which water loss is reduced without a similar reduction in photosynthetic activity. *See also* phylloclade, phyllode.

cladogenesis. The separation of a particular evolutionary sequence into two or more separate lineages. Study of such evolutionary groupings and divisions is termed *cladistics.

cladogram. *See* cladistics.

Cladoselachii. An order of the Elasmobranchii containing extinct sharklike fishes, e.g. *Cladoselache*, that flourished in the Devonian and became extinct in the Carboniferous. They typically had broad-based paired fins, a heterocercal tail, and *amphistylic jaw suspension.

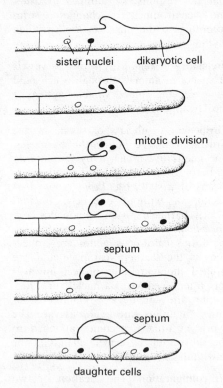

Clamp connection

clamp connection. A mechanism occurring in the division of dikaryotic cells of many basidiomycete fungi to ensure that sister nuclei become separated in daughter cells. The stages are illustrated in the diagram. *Compare* crozier formation.

claspers. 1. The *intromittent organs of elasmobranch fish, consisting of a pair of grooved rodlike appendages – modifications of the inner lobes of the pelvic fins – one on each side of the cloaca. **2.** The intromittent organs of various other animals, especially insects, in which they consist of a pair of tubular outgrowths of one of the rear abdominal segments.

class. A group used in the *classification of living organisms. A class consists of a number of similar or closely related orders or occasionally of only one order. Classes are usually large and easily recognized groups. For example, the subphylum Vertebrata (vertebrates) includes the classes Mammalia (mammals), Aves (birds), Reptilia (reptiles), Amphibia (amphibians), Osteichthyes (bony fish), Chondrichthyes (cartilaginous fish), and Agnatha (jawless fish). Classes are grouped into phyla (or subphyla) in zoology and divisions (or subdivisions) in botany.

classification. Any method of arranging living organisms into systematic groups or a systematic order. There are two types of classification, natural and artificial. An *artificial classification* is based on a few characteristics only and is used for a special purpose; it does not attempt to reflect evolutionary relationships. Examples of artificial classifications are the listing of organisms alphabetically and the arrangement of plants according to their habits (trees, shrubs, and herbs) or according to their uses. A *natural classification* is a hierarchical arrangement of organisms in a series of ranked groups and is based on the similarities and differences between them. The most natural group is the *species, an interbreeding group at the base of the hierarchy whose members have many characteristics in common. Species are grouped into genera (*see* genus), which are grouped into *families, then into *orders, *classes, and finally into

phyla (*see* phylum) for animals or *divisions for plants. At each stage up the hierarchy the number of similarities between members of a group becomes fewer, for example members of the same class have less in common than members of the same species. Precisely what a natural classification represents is open to argument. According to one school of thought natural classifications should be phylogenetic, i.e. they should reflect evolutionary relationships, so that members of the same group at any level of the hierarchy should have a common ancestor. However, such a classification may be difficult to produce and can be misleading if evolution proceeds at different rates in different lineages. The opposite school of thought postulates that natural classifications can only be phenetic, reflecting morphological, cytological, and biochemical similarities. Much of the work in this field has been done by the numerical taxonomists, who are well equipped to deal mathematically with large numbers of characteristics. In practice, classifications in use today are based on phylogeny as far as possible but are modified for groups that have obviously evolved at different rates. *See also* binomial nomenclature, cladistics, taxonomy.

clavicle. A ventral membrane bone of the *pectoral girdle of some vertebrates, articulating with the scapula and the sternum and functioning as a brace for the former. It forms the collar bone in man.

clearing. A process used in the preparation of permanent microscope slides of organisms or tissues. It consists of immersing the material in a clearing agent after *dehydration and prior to *embedding in paraffin wax or mounting in *Canada balsam. The purpose of clearing is to remove the dehydrating agent and to make the tissues transparent. One of the best clearing agents is oil of cloves, which is very expensive and usually used only before mounting. Xylene is widely used prior to embedding but tends to cause shrinkage of tissues.

cleavage (segmentation). The mitotic division of the zygote that occurs immediately after fertilization and produces a ball of smaller cells (*blastomeres*) without an overall increase in size (*see* blastula, blastocyst). Animal zygotes have several different types of cleavage. In *holoblastic cleavage*, seen in ova with little or no yolk (e.g. mammals), the whole cell divides into blastomeres; in *meroblastic cleavage*, characteristic of yolky animal ova (e.g. birds), only the non-yolky part of the cell undergoes cleavage. *Bilateral cleavage*, occurring in the vertebrates, results in a bilaterally symmetrical arrangement of blastomeres; in *spiral cleavage*, seen in annelids and many molluscs and turbellarians, alternating asymmetric divisions occur, resulting in a spiral arrangement of blastomeres. *See* morula.

cleidoic egg. The egg of an oviparous terrestrial animal, such as an insect, reptile, or bird, which is enclosed within a tough shell that protects the embryo and limits water loss.

cleistocarp. A moss capsule that lacks a peristome or operculum and releases the spores by the irregular disintegration of its wall. *See also* cleistothecium.

cleistogamy. The formation of flowers that do not open and in which self-pollination occurs. Cleistogamous flowers are often small and inconspicuous and are produced at the end of the flowering season, after the normal flowers, if cross-pollination has not occurred. *Compare* chasmogamy.

cleistothecium. A type of *ascocarp that is completely closed so that the asci develop in chambers (*loculi*) in the ascocarp tissue. The ascospores are released by decay of the cleistothecium wall. The term *cleistocarp* is sometimes used synonymously with cleistothecium.

climacteric (in botany). The period during, or just prior to, ripening of many fruits when respiration markedly increases, reaching a peak or plateau of activity before declining again as the fruit senesces. It is associated with *ethylene production and usually with hydrolysis of food reserves. It may be rapid (e.g. avocado) or moderate (e.g. apple); in some fruits (e.g. orange) it is absent. Picking the fruit generally hastens the process. Chemical control of the climacteric (and hence ripening) can be commercially employed in the storage of fruits; it can be regulated (as for banana storage) or suppressed by high carbon dioxide or low oxygen concentrations or by nitrogen atmospheres (for long storage).

climax (in ecology). The final steady state of a community that has developed in a formerly uninhabited area. Colonization results in successions of plants and animals (*see* sere), which eventually end in a stable *climax community*. Because of the widespread effects of man on the natural environment, true climax communities, such as the Caledonian forest in Scotland, are confined to very small areas of relatively unspoiled habitat. A climax community is only relatively permanent, since in the long term it is subject to further changes as a result of such factors as climate changes, which bring about organic evolution.

cline. A smooth gradation of characteristics from one end of the range of a species to the other, usually brought about by gradients of climate, soil, or other environmental variables. It is difficult to place members of a cline in suitable taxa. Although the individuals at each end of the cline differ from each other sufficiently to be given subspecies status, the variation within the cline is too gradual to establish discontinuities by means of which each subspecies could be separated from the next.

clisere. A succession of climax communities in a particular region, each formed as a result of changes in climate in that region.

clitellum. A highly glandular and vascular saddle-like region of the epidermis of the Oligochaeta (earthworms) and Hirudinea (leeches), functioning in reproduction. It assists in binding two copulating worms together and, after copulation, secretes a cocoon into which the eggs are deposited. The cocoon then passes forward over the worm, receiving, as it passes the spermatheca, spermatozoa that fertilize the eggs.

clitoris. A small erectile body of female amniotes, anterior to the vagina and urethra, that is homologous with the male penis.

cloaca. The single posterior chamber of all vertebrates except placental mammals, agnathans, and actinopterygian fishes into which the terminal parts of the alimentary canal and the kidney and reproductive ducts open. A cloaca is present in the embryo of placental mammals; in adults there are two (or in the females of some mammals three) separate openings.

clonal selection theory. An important theory in immunology, originally proposed by Sir Macfarlane Burnet, proposing that each antibody variant is within the cellular capability of an organism at or soon after birth. When an organism encounters a new antigen, the cell or cells capable of elaborating antibody against this antigen are stimulated to divide, thus forming a specific cell clone. Further stimulation with antigen will lead to further proliferation of the clone and thus to enhanced antibody production. Retention of the cell clone explains the relative permanence of acquired *immunity. The theory also suggests that self-tolerance (*see* immunological tolerance) results from destruction of certain antibody-determining cells specific for 'self' antigens during a crucial period of self-recognition during foetal or very early adult life.
Clonal selection theory of antibody formation is now widely accepted in preference to opposing theories that antibody is 'custom-built' in response to specific instructions from any new antigen encountered.

clone. 1. A group of organisms that are genetically identical because they have been produced by some sort of nonsexual reproduction or by sexual reproduction involving inbreeding a pure line. Typical asexual methods are vegetative propagation in plants and parthenogenesis in animals. Modern techniques of nuclear transfer also permit the injection of a number of somatic cell nuclei, of identical genetic constitution, into enucleated eggs. Such eggs, following introduction into a receptive female animal, then develop to yield a clone of identical organisms at birth.
2. A population of cells descended from a single parent cell. DNA sequences are said to be cloned when they are inserted into *plasmids and introduced into host bacteria in the techniques of *genetic engineering.

clotting factors. A group of protein factors (at least twelve) that are enzymically inactive in normal plasma but become activated when blood is removed from the circulation (usually by injury) and cause *blood clotting. The term also includes nonprotein factors, such as calcium ions, platelets, and phosphoglycerides, that are involved in clotting.

club moss. *See* Lycopsida.

Cnidaria. A subphylum of the Coelenterata, sometimes regarded as a distinct phylum, consisting of mostly marine animals whose saclike bodies contain muscle cells for locomotion and stinging cells (*cnidoblasts) for defence and food capture. A ring of tentacles surrounds the mouth. Two structural types, the *polyp and *medusa, often occur during the life cycle. There are various larval stages, including the *planula. The subphylum is divided into the classes *Hydrozoa, *Scyphozoa, and *Anthozoa. *Compare* Ctenophora.

cnidoblast (thread cell). A specialized stinging cell in the ectoderm of the

Cnidaria, used for capturing prey and for defence. Each cnidoblast contains a *nematocyst*, a fluid-filled capsule with a lid (*operculum*) enclosing a coiled hollow thread. The thread is everted when the *cnidocil*, a small sensory bristle beside the operculum, is stimulated. There are several types of nematocyst. The largest has barbs at the base of the thread and injects the prey with a paralysing poison contained in the capsule; some types coil around the prey and others are adhesive. A nematocyst can be discharged only once and is discarded and replaced after use.

cnidocil. The sensory bristle of a nematocyst. *See* cnidoblast.

CNS. *See* central nervous system.

CoA. *See* coenzyme A.

coarctate. *See* pupa.

cobalamin. *See* cyanocobalamin.

cocarcinogen. Any compound that increases the potency of a *carcinogen.

coccus. Any spherical bacterium. *See* bacteria.

coccyx. The fused caudal vertebrae of tailless primates. *See also* vertebral column.

cochlea. A diverticulum of the sacculus of the inner ear of crocodiles, birds, and mammals that contains sense cells for the appreciation of sound. The cells lie on a membrane that vibrates when sound waves are transmitted to the perilymph in the cochlea by the movement of the stapes on the fenestra ovalis. Cells at different positions in the cochlea are activated by different pitches of sound.

cockroaches. *See* Dictyoptera.

cocoon (in zoology). A protective envelope produced by many invertebrates as a covering for their eggs and/or developing larvae. For example, a cocoon is formed by earthworms, as a secretion of the *clitellum, and by some spiders, as a product of the *spinnerets.

co-dominant. *See* association, dominant.

codon. The basic coding unit of *messenger RNA, consisting of a triplet of nucleotides that determines the incorporation of a particular amino acid into a polypeptide chain. The complementary triplet of nucleotides on *transfer RNA is called the *anticodon*. Codon-anticodon pairing provides the specificity for translating genetic information – transcribed from DNA into messenger RNA – into protein. *See also* genetic code, transcription, translation.

Coelacanthini. A specialized suborder of the Crossopterygii in which choanae are absent and the tail is symmetrical. These fishes first appeared in the Devonian and early fossils were of freshwater origin; by Triassic times, however, coelacanths were predominantly marine. They were formerly thought to have become extinct in the Cretaceous, but in 1938 the first living coelacanth of recent times, *Latimeria*, was caught off the east coast of South Africa. *Latimeria* is a large deep-sea fish with blue cosmoid scales and long strong lobed fins. The lung is reduced to a swim bladder.

Coelenterata. A large successful phylum of acoelomate aquatic (mostly marine) invertebrates characterized by a diploblastic typically radially symmetrical body. The body wall consists of two cellular layers separated by noncellular jelly (*mesoglea) and encloses a body cavity (*coelenteron) with a single opening (mouth) to the exterior. The phylum includes the *Cnidaria (hydra, jellyfish, sea anemones, and corals) and *Ctenophora (comb jellies).

coelenteron. The body cavity of the Coelenterata, which functions as the digestive cavity and has a single opening, the mouth. It may be subdivided by mesenteries, as in sea anemones (class Anthozoa), or elaborated into a canal system, as in the subphylum Ctenophora and the jellyfish (class Scyphozoa). In some coelenterates, e.g. jellyfish, the gametes are discharged into it.

coelom. The main body cavity of many triploblastic animals. Situated in the mesoderm and therefore lined with mesothelium, it is filled with fluid (*coelomic fluid*) and contains the viscera. Ciliated tubes (*coelomoducts) connect the coelom to the exterior and allow the exit of gametes and excretory products. In many higher animals the coelom is divided into separate cavities, e.g. in man the coelom is the pericardial cavity (enclosing the heart), the peritoneal cavity (enclosing the gut), and the pleural cavity (containing the lungs). In the Arthropoda however, it is restricted to the cavity of the gonads and excretory organs, the main body cavity being a *haemocoel. The main advantages of a coelom are that the body wall muscles are separated from the gut and can move independently, which confers greater locomotory powers and allows differentiation of the gut for various functions. As the coelom does not contain blood, its presence necessitates the development of a *blood vascular system, providing more efficient transport of essential substances.

coelomoduct. A ciliated tube that is formed as an outpushing of the coelom to the exterior and provides an exit for gametes and excretory products from the coelom. In many animals the coelomoducts develop into specialized structures for the transport of gametes or waste products (*see* oviduct). *Compare* nephridium.

coenobium. A colony of motile cells formed by some green algae of the orders Volvocales and Chlorococcales. The form of the colony is characteristic of the species; for example, *Gonium pectorale* is a plate of 16 cells, *Eudorina elegans* is a sphere of 32 cells. The colony consists of biflagellate cells embedded in a gelatinous matrix, with protoplasmic connections between the cells providing some degree of coordination. In some species a degree of differentia-

tion may be evident as a polarity in the colony, with reproductive cells restricted to one end.

coenocyte. A vegetative structure consisting of a multinucleate cytoplasmic mass bounded by a cell wall, such as occurs in some algae and fungi. It is formed by cytoplasmic growth and nuclear division without cell wall formation. The whole plant body may be a single coenocyte, as in the green alga *Vaucheria*, or it may consist of many coenocytes, as in the green alga *Cladophora* and many fungi. In the algae a coenocyte with any septa is sometimes termed a *siphon* (the algae are described as *siphonaceous*). *Compare* cell, plasmodium, syncytium.

coenosorus. *See* sorus.

coenospecies. One of a group of species that can intercross to form hybrids that are sometimes fertile.

coenzyme. An organic molecule acting as an enzyme *cofactor. Examples of coenzymes are *coenzyme A, *NAD, *FAD, and *pyridoxal phosphate.

Coenzyme A

coenzyme A (CoA). A coenzyme mononucleotide synthesized from pantothenic acid (see formula). It functions in the transfer of acetyl groups (with which it combines to form *acetyl CoA*) and fatty acyl groups, which are bound to the thiol group of the molecule, and it therefore has an important role in the Krebs cycle and in fatty acid synthesis and oxidation.

quinone form

CH_3O

CH_3O

CH_3

CH_3

$(CH_2-CH=C-CH_2)_nH$

reduced (quinol) form

CH_3O

CH_3O

OH

OH

CH_3

CH_3

$(CH_2-CH=C-CH_2)_nH$

Coenzyme Q

coenzyme Q (ubiquinone). A coenzyme in the *electron transport chain that consists of a substituted benzoquinone. When it receives hydrogen or electrons from a flavoprotein it is reduced to the quinol (see formula) and can then reduce the next member of the chain.

coevolution. A type of evolution that occurs when an organism, such as a plant, changes genetically through a selection pressure imposed by another organism, such as a grazing insect, and this leads to the insect's changing as a result of the plant's change.

cofactor. A nonprotein substance essential for the activity of certain enzymes. An enzyme-cofactor complex is known as a *holoenzyme*; an enzyme without its cofactor and hence inactive is an *apoenzyme*. Cofactors may be metal ions (e.g. Na^+, K^+, Mg^{2+}) or organic molecules called *coenzymes*, such as coenzyme A, NAD, and pyridoxal phosphate. Some coenzymes are tightly bound to the enzymes as *prosthetic groups (e.g. NAD and NADP); cofactors other than

prosthetic groups can be removed easily, e.g. by dialysis.

The cofactor confers activity either by forming a bridge between the substrate and the enzyme or by actually taking part in the reaction, e.g. by donating hydrogen in electron transport. Coenzymes and vitamins are closely related, many vitamins being essential for the synthesis of coenzymes. For example, NAD is synthesized from nicotinic acid.

cohesion theory. The currently accepted theory for explaining the ascent of sap in plants, especially tall trees. It relies on the fact that water molecules show both strong mutual attraction and a strong attraction to the walls of any containing vessel. A column of water can thus withstand considerable tension before breaking. It is possible, therefore, for the tension caused by transpiration from the leaves to be transmitted through the column of water in the xylem to the roots, so causing water movement through the plant. *See also* water potential.

colchicine. An alkaloid obtained from the roots of the autumn crocus (*Colchicum autumnale*). Colchicine inhibits spindle formation in tissues undergoing mitosis, which results in the cells becoming polyploid. This property is utilized in agriculture and horticulture to produce new polyploid varieties or species.

Coleoptera. The order of endopterygote insects, possibly the largest order in the animal kingdom, that contains the beetles and weevils. The forewings are modified as hard leathery *elytra*, which protect the membranous hind wings and soft abdomen at rest, and the head, projected into a snout in the weevils, bears biting mouthparts. Beetles are found universally in a great variety of habitats, both on land and in fresh water, and are variously adapted for their ways of life. The larvae, too, show great variation: some are predators, some caterpillar-like, and others grublike. Many larvae and adults are serious pests, e.g. the flour beetle (*Tribolium*), the larva (wood-worm) of the furniture beetle (*Anobium*), and the larva (wireworm) of the click beetle (*Elater*). Others, e.g. the aphid-eating ladybirds (*Coccinella*), are benefi-cial.

coleoptile. A protective sheath over the plumule of the embryo of the Gramin-eae (grasses). It is usually conical, with a pore at the apex through which the foliage leaves emerge, but in some prim-itive grasses it is an open leaf. The cole-optile is variously interpreted as repre-senting part of the cotyledon (together with the *scutellum), a modified foliage leaf, or a structure without homology in other embryos.

coleorhiza. A protective sheath covering the radicle of the embryo of the Gra-mineae (grasses), possibly representing part of the suspensor, part of the hypo-cotyl, or a suppressed primary root with the radicle as an adventitious root.

colicin. *See* bacteriocin.

coliform bacteria. A group of Gram-neg-ative peritrichous rod-shaped eubacteria that obtain their energy by fermentation or aerobic respiration. They can be divided into two main groups on the basis of their products of fermentation: one group, which includes *Escherichia*, produces various organic acids while the other group, which contains *Klebsiella*, produces butylene glycol as well as cer-tain organic acids. Coliform bacteria can be further subdivided according to their ability to utilize lactose (*Salmonella*, *Proteus*, and *Shigella* are unable to) and to produce gas when fermenting other sugars (only *Salmonella* and *Proteus* can do this).

collagen. The principal structural protein of the white fibres of metazoan connec-tive tissue. It is synthesized by fibroblasts and, when boiled, yields gela-tin. The fundamental unit of collagen fibres, *tropocollagen*, is a helix of three polypeptide chains about 280 nanome-tres (2800 $\overset{\circ}{A}$) long. Collagen has a high content of the amino acids glycine, ala-nine, proline, and hydroxyproline, the latter being found in few other proteins. Collagen is virtually inert metabolically, having a half-life of many years; it has a high tensile strength but is relatively inelastic. *Compare* elastin.

collar cell. *See* choanocyte.

collateral bundle. A vascular bundle composed of a single strand each of xylem and phloem. *Compare* bicollateral bundle, centric bundle.

Collembola. An order of small wingless insects of the subclass Apterygota, the springtails. They are characterized by a forked springing organ at the end of the body, used for jumping when disturbed, and a sucker-like ventral tube projecting downwards from the first abdominal segment. Springtails are very abundant and are universally distributed, occur-ring in soil, under bark, on the surface of ponds, and on sandy beaches. In some parts of the world, e.g. Australia, they are serious plant pests.

collenchyma. A supporting tissue of young plant stems, leaves, and flowers, usually situated beneath the epidermis. The cells are usually elongated parallel to the longitudinal axis of the plant and their cell walls are thickened with cellu-lose and pectins in various ways. Col-lenchyma remains as a supporting tissue in mature herbaceous plants but is usu-ally replaced in trees and shrubs by sclerenchyma.

colon (large intestine). The distal region of the intestine in vertebrates, highly developed in mammals for the absorp-tion of water and formation of faeces. Bacteria within the colon synthesize vitamins and digest cellulose; they also putrefy various constituents of the fae-ces.

colony. **1.** A group of individual animals or plants living together and dependent on one another to a varying degree. In some colonies the individuals are struc-turally connected and function as a sin-gle unit; this type of colonial organiza-

tion occurs in the Porifera (sponges), Hydrozoa, Ectoprocta, and many algae. In other colonies the individuals are not structurally connected but often, notably in insect colonies, show a high degree of social organization.
2. A group of bacterial or yeast cells arising from a single parent cell on an agar culture medium.

colostrum. Fluid produced by the mammary glands immediately after the birth of the young before the production of mature milk. It is an important source of nutrients, fluid, and antibodies for newborn mammals and also contains enzymes that clear mucus from the digestive tract.

colour blindness. Any of several genetic defects causing imperfect perception of colours. For example red-green colour blindness is an X-linked recessive characteristic (*see* sex linkage) in which hemizygous males and homozygous females cannot distinguish red from green. The molecular defects in colour blindness involve absence of or defects in one of the three visual pigments that absorb green, red, and blue light respectively.

columella. 1. A small column of sterile tissue within a sporangium, usually representing a continuation of the stalk. A columella is present, for example, in the sporangia of some myxomycetes and most bryophytes.
2. A small core of cells in the root cap of some vascular plants that contains large starch granules, which function as statoliths, and is thought to be gravity-sensitive.

columella auris. The sole *ear ossicle of amphibians, reptiles, and birds. It is homologous with the hyomandibular bone of fish and the stapes of mammals.

commensalism. An association between two organisms in which one of them, the *commensal,* derives benefit from the other, the *host,* which neither benefits nor suffers from the association. For example, the colonial hydrozoan *Hydrac-*

tinia echinata lives on whelk shells occupied by a species of hermit crab. The coelenterate obtains food particles from the crab, which is unaffected by the association. *See also* symbiosis.

commissure. A transverse tract of nerve fibres that connects symmetrical parts of the central nervous system on the two sides of an animal. Commissures in annelids and arthropods connect ganglia of the double nerve cord and a commissure in vertebrates unites the two sides of the brain (*see* corpus callosum).

community (in ecology). A collection of *populations of animals and plants that occur naturally together in a defined area or *habitat. The individuals and populations within the community interact with one another and with the abiotic (nonliving) surroundings, the community and abiotic surroundings together constituting an *ecosystem. Communities have attributes not shared by the populations that comprise them: species richness or number, *diversity, growth form and structure, dominance (*see* dominant), relative abundance, and trophic structure (*see* food chain). *See also* association.

companion cell. A specialized parenchymatous cell associated with a sieve element in the phloem of angiosperms. It arises from the same meristematic cell as the associated element but further cell divisions may produce more than one companion cell per element. Companion cells retain their nucleus and probably play a role in regulating the activities of the enucleated phloem element (there are conspicuous sieve areas between companion cells and the associated element and the companion cells die when the sieve element disorganizes). Companion cells are absent from pteridophytes and gymnosperms, but certain cells with dense proteinaceous contents in gymnosperms are often associated with the phloem elements; they are called *albuminous cells* and may be comparable with companion cells.

compass plant. A plant whose leaf edges have a permanent north-south orientation.

compensation point. The light intensity at which the rate of uptake of carbon dioxide (or evolution of oxygen) during *photosynthesis of a green plant is exactly balanced by its rate of carbon dioxide evolution (or oxygen uptake) during respiration, i.e. net gas exchange is zero. Strictly, this is the *light compensation point* since the compensation point can also be defined in terms of carbon dioxide (CO_2) concentration. The *CO_2 compensation point* is the CO_2 concentration at which the rate of uptake of CO_2 during photosynthesis is exactly balanced by the rate of CO_2 output by respiration. Most plants have high CO_2 compensation points (about 50 ppm CO_2) owing to the occurrence of *photorespiration (which releases CO_2 in the light); these are C_3 *plants*. Some plants have low CO_2 compensation points (about 5 ppm CO_2), including certain algae, e.g. *Chlorella*, and C_4 *plants*, e.g. maize, in which photorespiration is negligible.

compensatory hypertrophy. *See* regeneration.

competent. Designating embryonic cells at an early stage of development, when they have the ability to differentiate into any of various types of cell. *Compare* determined, presumptive.

competition. The demand of organisms within a *community for the same substance when this is in short supply or when access to it is limited. *Interspecific competition* occurs between individuals of different species. Plant species may compete for light, nutrients, water, etc., and animals for food, shelter, mates, etc. The result may be competitive displacement of one organism by another or, in a stable community, competing organisms may become separated spatially, temporally, or ecologically (*see* niche). *Intraspecific competition* occurs within the species. It may lead to increased

rates of mortality and emigration or to decreased size and fecundity. *Scramble intraspecific competition*, e.g. between caterpillars on a leaf, leads to a more-or-less equal sharing of resources until they run out; at this point, proportional mortality increases rapidly. *Contest competition* leaves a fixed number of survivors as population density increases, with a *density-dependent increase in mortality. It occurs, for example, among the nestlings of many birds of prey, in which the eggs are incubated as they are laid; the resulting unequally sized nestlings compete unequally: if food is in short supply, only the largest survive.

complement. A group of proteins, some with enzymic activity, that is present in the blood and combines with antibody to cause lysis of bacteria and other cells. It consists of nine components (C_1–C_9) and the activation of the C_1 molecule leads to the sequential activation of the other components. The intermediate stages in the complement sequence are responsible for other biological activities, including the action of *opsonin, chemotaxis of polymorphs, and the lysis of red blood cells (*see* haemolysis).

complemental males. The small and often degenerate males of certain animals, which live on or within the body of the female. The existence of dwarf complemental males in some species of barnacle may be a means to ensure cross-fertilization, as most barnacles are hermaphrodite. The dwarf males typically have suppressed female organs and live semiparasitically within the mantle cavity of a hermaphrodite partner.

complementary bases. Bases that normally pair in opposite strands of double-stranded DNA or RNA, i.e. guanine–cytosine, adenine–thymine, and adenine–uracil (*see* base pairing). Complementary DNA or RNA strands are those with complementary base sequences.

complementary DNA (cDNA). DNA synthesized *in vitro* from a messenger

RNA template and used in cloning. *See* genetic engineering.

complementation. The phenomenon in which two homologous mutant chromosomes brought together in a diploid cell or fungal heterokaryon produce a wildtype phenotype. The mutations are assumed to be in different cistrons, the deficiency of one being supplied by its wild-type allele in the homologous chromosome. *See* cis-trans test.

complement fixation. The ability of certain antigen-antibody complexes to bind (fix) the components of complement. This property is utilized in the *complement fixation test*, which enables antibodies to be detected in the presence of known antigens, and vice versa. The test is used in the diagnosis of syphilis and certain viral infections.

composite fruit. A type of *fruit that is formed from an inflorescence. *See also* pseudocarp.

compound eye. A type of image-forming eye found in insects and crustaceans, consisting of numerous columnar units called *ommatidia*. Each ommatidium contains a cuticular lens underlaid by a crystalline cone and bordered by pigment cells. Below the cone lies the *retinula*, a group of six to eight light-sensitive cells that synapse with the optic nerve and secrete a central rod of closely packed microtubules, the *rhabdome*. In *apposition eyes*, characteristic of diurnal insects, the cone is in close contact with the rhabdome and is surrounded by the pigment cells so that each ommatidium is isolated and can focus a separate section of the visual field. Such eyes give a detailed mosaic image. In *superposition eyes*, common in nocturnal insects, there is a space between the cone and the rhabdome and the pigment is concentrated around the lens. Light entering an ommatidium obliquely may pass through it to another, thus increasing visual sensitivity at the expense of acuity.

concanavalin A (ConA). A protein, isolated from Jack beans (*Canavalia ensiformis*), that is able to bind specifically to and agglutinate transformed (tumour) cells. ConA is a *lectin that binds to glucose and mannose residues in the cell surface.

conceptacle. One of a number of small flask-shaped depressions in the lamina of certain thallose algae (such as the Fucales), which are lined with paraphyses, open to the surface by means of an ostiole, and in which the gametangia are produced. Sterile depressions, similar to conceptacles and known as *cryptostomata*, occur over the whole thallus and may function in mucilage production.

conditioned reflex. A simple form of learning in which a reflex action is modified by experience. If two stimuli are given repeatedly together, an animal transfers the reflex response normally associated with one stimulus to the other, so that eventually the second stimulus, if given alone, will evoke the response. The innate reflex, which is retained, is the *unconditioned reflex*; the reflex that is acquired as a result of learning is the conditioned reflex. It is not permanent and requires periodic reinforcement by the simultaneous administration of both unconditioned and conditioned stimuli.

conditioning. One of several *learning processes brought about in animals under experimental conditions. *Classical conditioning*, based on the work of the Russian physiologist I. P. Pavlov (1849–1936), involves the induction of a *conditioned reflex, by which an animal learns to respond to a stimulus in a way not normally associated with that stimulus. In *operant conditioning*, an animal is given reinforcement (usually reward) when it spontaneously responds to a stimulus. It then learns to respond more frequently or more intensely to that stimulus.

Condylarthra. An extinct order of the Eutheria containing ancestral ungulates (hoofed herbivorous mammals), in existence in the Palaeocene and Eocene, from which the modern Artiodactyla and Perissodactyla evolved.

condyle. The curved convex articular surface of the type of joint that allows free movement in one or two planes but only limited rotation, e.g. the condyles of the femur and tibia at the human knee joint. *See also* occipital condyle.

cone. 1. (in botany). *See* strobilus.
2. (in zoology). A light-sensitive cell of the retina of most vertebrates. Cones differ from *rods in details of the shape and visual pigment of their outer segment. In addition, each cone is connected to the brain by a single fibre of the optic nerve; hence the cones are responsible for visual acuity, i.e. appreciation of detail. Sensitivity to colour is conferred by three populations of cones with maximum absorptions in the red, blue, and green regions of the spectrum. *See also* fovea, macula.

congenital. Present from the time of birth. Congenital disorders include hereditary diseases, such as *phenylketonuria; disorders arising from errors of foetal development; and conditions due to an abnormal chromosome complement, such as *Down's syndrome.

Congo red. *See* staining.

conidium (conidiospore). An asexual spore of certain fungi that is abstricted from the tip or the side of special hyphae called *conidiophores.* Conidia may consist of one cell or of several cells; in the latter case the septa may be longitudinal, transverse, or mixed.

Coniferopsida (Coniferophyta). A group of gymnosperms with *pycnoxylic wood, needle-shaped, paddle-shaped, or fan-shaped leaves (basically dichotomous in form or venation), and seeds with bilateral symmetry. There is only one entirely fossil group, Cordaitales; the rest contain fossil and extant members and include most of the common gymnosperms. The Ginkgoales contains a single living species, *Ginkgo biloba* (maidenhair tree); the Taxales includes the yews; and the Coniferales includes the pines, firs, cypresses, larches, cedars, spruces, and hemlocks.

conjugated protein. A compound consisting of a sequence of amino acids (simple protein) to which a nonprotein (*prosthetic*) group is attached. The nonprotein portion may be a nucleic acid (*see* nucleoprotein), lipid (*see* lipoprotein), polysaccharide (*see* glycoprotein), flavin nucleotide (*see* flavoprotein), etc.

conjugation. 1. The union of gametes, particularly isogametes, in sexual reproduction.
2. The union of two individuals for the exchange of genetic material. In this sense the term is usually applied to the type of sexual reproduction occurring in most Ciliata and certain algae (order Conjugales) and to a method of transfer of genetic material in certain bacteria.
In *Paramecium* and other ciliate Protozoa two individuals unite and a protoplasmic bridge forms between them. In each cell the macronucleus disintegrates and the micronucleus divides meiotically to produce two gametic *pronuclei*, one of which migrates to the other cell and fuses with the remaining pronucleus to form a zygote. The cells then separate and the zygotes divide to form new micro- and macronuclei, with the eventual production of four daughter cells from each parent.
Conjugation in such algae as *Spirogyra* involves the aligning of the cells of two filaments and the formation of a *conjugation tube* between them. Two cells each produce one gamete. The male gamete from one cell moves through the tube by amoeboid action to fuse with a female gamete in the other cell.
Conjugation occurs in a few Gram-negative bacteria (*Escherichia, Shigella,* and *Salmonella*) and in *Pseudomonas aeruginosa* and *Streptomyces coelicolor*; it is

determined by the *F factor. Genetic material, usually in the form of the F factor, is transferred from a donor (or male) bacterial cell to a recipient (or female). The donor and recipient come into close contact and in many bacteria gene transfer occurs by means of cell-to-cell bridges. In *Escherichia*, the F factor directs the synthesis of special *pili, termed the F, or sex, pili, which are believed to be involved in gene transfer.

conjunctiva. A transparent layer of epidermis and connective tissue covering the cornea and inner eyelid of the vertebrate eye.

conjunctive tissues. *See* ground tissues.

connective tissue. The matrix of cellular and fibrous material in vertebrates in which more highly organized structures, e.g. nerves, blood vessels, etc., are embedded. The fibrous material usually consists of bundles of *collagen (white fibrous tissue) with smaller amounts of *elastin (yellow fibrous tissue) and *reticular fibres, which are embedded in a semifluid gelatinous ground substance of mucopolysaccharides and scleroproteins. The two most common cellular elements of connective tissue are *fibroblasts and *histiocytes. Also present are mesenchyme cells, plasma cells, mast cells, pigment cells, and fat cells. The principal mucopolysaccharides of the ground substance are hyaluronic acid, chondroitin, chondroitin sulphate, and keratin sulphate, which are thought to be synthesized by the fibroblasts. Besides having supportive and packing functions in the form of loose tissue (*areolar tissue*), connective tissue is often present as an integral component of more highly organized tissues and organs, such as tendons and ligaments.

consociation. One of the smaller communities in an *association, such as an oak wood in a deciduous forest.

constitutive enzyme. An enzyme that is synthesized continuously, in the absence of its substrate and regardless of the cell's requirements. For example, the bacterium *Escherichia coli* always synthesizes an enzyme that breaks down glucose. *Compare* inducible enzyme.

consumer. A heterotrophic organism in an *ecosystem that ingests other organisms or organic matter. Consumers may be carnivores, herbivores, omnivores, parasites, or scavengers. *See also* food chain.

consummatory act. An instinctive and stereotyped action in animal behaviour that ends a pattern of *appetitive behaviour. For example, feeding and drinking are the consummatory acts following the appetitive searching for food and water.

contact insecticide. A substance that poisons insects by penetrating the body surface or entering the tracheal system and does not need to be ingested. Examples of contact insecticides are DDT and dieldrin.

continental drift. The gradual and continuous change in the geographic position, size, and number of the continents, which, according to current geological theory, are believed to be drifting across the surface of the earth. It is thought that the drift has been continuing for a least 700 million years. In Palaeozoic times there was a single supercontinent called *Pangaea*, which was composed of the present continents fitted together like a jigsaw puzzle, the east coast of South America united to the west coast of Africa, and so on. The break-up of Pangaea can be dated from the end of the Palaeozoic (200 million years ago). The southern arm, *Gondwanaland, and the northern arm, *Laurasia, drifted apart to become two separate supercontinents, which subsequently underwent further fragmentation to produce the present-day configuration of the continents.

Continental drift can explain much of the distribution of present-day and fossil flora and fauna without postulating unlikely land bridges connecting fixed continents. *See also* zoogeography.

Contophora. Eukaryotic algae possessing flagella, i.e. all the eukaryotic algae except the Rhodophyta. They are divided into two main groups: *Chromophyta and *Chlorophyta. *Compare* Aconta.

contour feathers. *See* feathers.

contractile vacuole. A cavity in a cell, functioning in *osmoregulation, that periodically fills with clear fluid (usually water) and then collapses, discharging its contents to the exterior. It is characteristic of all freshwater Protozoa and all members of the class Ciliata and is found in the cells of freshwater sponges. Some protozoans, e.g. *Amoeba*, have a single vacuole but in some of the more complex forms, e.g. *Paramecium*, the vacuole may be refilled by smaller accessory vacuoles and connected to the exterior by a reservoir.

conus arteriosus. The small thick-walled fourth chamber of the primitive vertebrate heart, passing blood from the ventricle to the aorta. In lungfish and amphibians it contains the spiral valve, which aids separation of oxygenated and deoxygenated blood. The conus arteriosus forms the root of the aorta and pulmonary arteries in adult amniotes.

convergence (convergent evolution). The evolutionary process in which certain organs or whole organisms become modified in the same way to perform the same function. It is caused by similarities in the habits of the organism or in the environment. Convergence results in a resemblance between initially dissimilar parts or organisms.

Copepoda. A large subclass of Crustacea whose members lack a carapace and compound eyes. Many copepods form an important constituent of plankton, e.g. *Calanus* in marine waters and *Cyclops* in fresh waters. In these free-living forms the first thoracic appendages are modified for feeding and the remaining ones are used in rapid swimming. Some copepods, e.g. *Salmincola*, are parasites of animals, especially fish.

coracoid. A cartilage bone of the ventral part of the *pectoral girdle in teleosts and tetrapods. The coracoid forms part of the glenoid cavity except in placental mammals, in which it is reduced to a peg on the scapula. It is an important wing brace in birds.

corals. *See* Anthozoa.

Cordaitales. *See* Coniferopsida.

corium. *See* dermis.

cork (phellem). The outer layer of *periderm, consisting of air-filled dead cells with impervious suberized walls. *Quercus suber* (cork oak) produces a very thick cork that can be peeled off and used commercially; its lightness, elasticity, and imperviousness make it ideal for bottle corks, fishing floats, shock-absorbers, etc.

cork cambium. *See* phellogen.

corm. An organ of perennation and usually also of vegetative propagation in plants that consists of the swollen base of the stem, which stores food and is surrounded by protective scale leaves. The following season growth occurs by one or more buds at the base of the scale leaves, using food stored in the corm. If only one bud grows, the corm is acting only as an organ of perennation. If two buds grow, two new shoots arise, and at the end of the season two new corms are made; in this case, vegetative reproduction has occurred. Examples of corms are crocus and gladiolus. *Compare* bulb.

cornea. The transparent exposed portion of the sclerotic layer of the eye of vertebrates and cephalopods. In terrestrial vertebrates the curvature of the cornea refracts incoming light rays and thus effects the gross focusing of the image on the retina.

cornification (keratinization). The process by which a cell accumulates the fibrous protein keratin, which eventually replaces the entire cytoplasm, leaving a dead horny (*cornified*) cell. It occurs mainly in vertebrate *epidermis and related structures, e.g. hairs, nails, etc. In epidermis, the cells become increasingly cornified as they approach the exposed surface, the outermost layer (*see* stratum corneum) consisting entirely of dead cornified squamous cells.

corolla. The petals of a flower, collectively.

coronary vessels. Paired blood vessels in vertebrates that supply the heart muscle. The *coronary arteries* arise from the aorta, and the *coronary veins* return blood to the sinus venosus (in fish and amphibians) or left atrium (in amniotes).

corpora allata and corpora cardiaca. Paired endocrine glands associated dorsally with the insect brain. The posterior corpora allata are ectodermal in origin and secrete *juvenile hormone. The corpora cardiaca, of neural origin, form a neurosecretory storage and release centre for a hormone from the brain that stimulates peripheral glands, e.g. the prothoracic glands, concerned with growth and moulting. It also contains intrinsic secretory cells, which release substances implicated in neural and carbohydrate metabolism.

corpus callosum. A massive tract of nerve fibres that connects the neopallial regions of the two *cerebral hemispheres of mammals.

corpus luteum. A temporary endocrine gland formed within the Graafian follicle of the mammalian ovary after ovulation. It develops from certain cells of the follicle that enlarge to become *luteal cells*, containing lipid droplets and yellow pigments. The corpus luteum secretes progesterone. This hormone was first isolated from the corpus luteum in 1934, but the association of the gland with the preparation of the uterus for implantation has been known since the early 1900s. The development of the corpus luteum is initiated by a rise in secretion of luteinizing hormone, but prolactin is also required to maintain progesterone secretion. If ovulation is not followed by fertilization and pregnancy, the corpus luteum degenerates (*see* oestrous cycle). During most of pregnancy in a number of mammals, e.g. rabbit, the gland continues to be an important source of progesterone, but in others, including man, the placenta becomes the main source of this hormone after the first months of gestation.

corpus meristem. *See* tunica-corpus theory.

corpus striatum (basal ganglia, basal nuclei). Part of the cerebral hemispheres of vertebrates consisting of neurones having motor functions. It forms the chief part of the cerebrum in fishes and is an important centre for integration in birds; in mammals it is overlaid by the cerebral cortex, by which it is controlled.

cortex. 1. A composite tissue situated beneath the epidermis and above the endodermis of the roots and stems of vascular plants. It contains mainly parenchyma, but collenchyma, sclerenchyma, and vascular bundles may also be present. The cortex is derived from the corpus meristem and is most prominent in young stems and roots. It may also be found in some lower terrestrial plants, such as bryophytes, and also in some algae, fungi, and lichens.
2. The outer layer or part of an animal organ, notably of the cerebral hemispheres (*see* cerebral cortex), *adrenal glands (*adrenal cortex*), or *kidney (*renal cortex*).
3. The outer cytoplasm of a cell (*see* ectoplasm).

corticosteroid. Any of a large group of steroids synthesized in the mammalian adrenal cortex from cholesterol. A few of these are secreted in significant amounts and demonstrate hormone activity. Corticosteroid hormones possess 21 carbon atoms, with a double bond at C4 and ketonic groups $(C=O)$ at C3 and C20. They can be subdivided depending on whether their principal action is on carbohydrate metabolism (*see* glucocorticoid) or on electrolyte metabolism (*see* mineralocorticoid). They all facilitate adaptive responses in mammals in order to maintain homeostasis and survival under conditions of stress. Their mechanism of action has been shown in some instances to involve the mediation of RNA and protein synthesis.

CH₂OH
C=O
HO

O

Corticosterone

corticosterone. A *glucocorticoid hormone secreted by most mammals in lesser amounts than cortisol. In some small mammals, e.g. rodents, however, it is the main glucocorticoid secreted. It was first isolated in 1937 from extracts of bovine tissue (see formula).

corticotrophin. *See* ACTH.

CH₂OH
C=O
HO--OH

O

Cortisol

cortisol (hydrocortisone). The principal *glucocorticoid hormone secreted by the adrenal cortex of many mammals, including man. It was first isolated in 1937, from extracts of bovine tissue (see formula).

CH₂OH
C=O
O ---OH

O

Cortisone

cortisone. The first biologically active *glucocorticoid to be isolated from the adrenal cortex (in the early 1930s) and the first corticosteroid to be used successfully to treat rheumatoid arthritis (see formula).

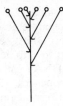

Corymb

corymb. A type of racemose inflorescence in which the flowers occur in flat-topped clusters due to the lower pedicels being long and the upper ones short (see illustration). An example is candytuft.

cosmoid scale. A bony scale, characteristic of primitive fishes of the subclass Choanichthyes, composed of a basal layer of dense laminated bone (*isopedin*), a middle layer of spongy vascular bone, and an outer layer of hard *cosmine*, which consists of dentine with numerous pulp cavities, coated with modified enamel (*ganoine*). In the modern Dipnoi the scales have been reduced to large thin plates. *Compare* ganoid scale, placoid scale.

Cot value. A measure of DNA complexity based on hybridization (annealing) of single-stranded DNA (*see* denaturation).

'Co' refers to DNA concentration; 't' to the time of hybridization in seconds. Cot values are derived from *Cot curves*, which are obtained by heating a sample of purified DNA until the double helices have come apart and the molecules are single-stranded. When the sample is placed in renaturing conditions, the rate of annealing for any particular sequence present is dependent on its complexity or its frequency in the DNA sample. Short, simple, and highly repeated sequences will renature very quickly, while long, complex, and scarce sequences (the so-called *unique sequences*) will renature very slowly, if at all. Thus DNA fractions with low Cot values are likely to contain abundant and simple short sequences, whereas those with high Cot values are likely to be scarce and relatively complex. A Cot curve of mammalian DNA will reveal four or more separate fractions, each a distinct type of DNA sequence. They are, going from low to high Cot value, (1) *foldback DNA, usually indicating *palindromic sequences; (2) highly *repetitious DNA; (3) moderately repetitious DNA; and (4) unique-sequence DNA.

cotyledon (seed leaf). The embryonic or first leaf of angiosperms and gymnosperms, which is very often markedly different in form from subsequent leaves; for example, it may be much simpler or modified as a storage organ. In plants with epigeal germination the cotyledons develop chloroplasts and become the first photosynthesizing leaves. The number of cotyledons varies according to the plant group. Gymnosperms have up to a dozen, the number varying in each plant. The English botanist John Ray (1627–1705) first realized the significance of the number of cotyledons in angiosperms and named those with a single cotyledon the *Monocotyledonae and those with two, the *Dicotyledonae.

Cotylosauria. An extinct order of the Anapsida that contains the earliest reptiles. They evolved from labyrinthodont Amphibia in the Upper Carboniferous and became extinct in the Upper Triassic. The suborder Captorhinomorpha, carnivores with a sprawling gait, flattened skulls, and pointed teeth, were the true stem reptiles, giving rise to later reptiles and therefore, indirectly, to mammals and birds. Examples of this group are *Limnoscelis* and *Captorhinus*.

counterstaining. *See* staining.

coupling factors. *See* oxidative phosphorylation.

courtship. The type of animal behaviour shown by one sex (usually the male) to the other prior to copulation, often in the form of *display behaviour. It serves to ensure that mating takes place between members of the same species, of different sexes, and with a female who is receptive to the male.

coxa. The basal segment of the leg of an insect, between the trochanter and the thorax.

coxal gland. One of a pair (or two pairs) of excretory organs in arachnids. They are situated in the floor of the cephalothorax and are connected to ducts that open near the base of the legs of the fifth segment.

coxopodite. *See* biramous appendage.

C$_3$ and C$_4$ plants. *See* photosynthesis.

cranial nerves. A series of ten (in anamniotes) or twelve (in amniotes) paired nerves that arise from the brain of vertebrates and supply the head, neck, and viscera with sensory and/or motor innervation. The nerves are numbered according to the anterior to posterior order in which they arise from the human brain. Nerves I and II (*olfactory* and *optic nerves*) are predominantly sensory. Nerves III, IV, and VI, the *oculomotor*, *trochlear*, and *abducens*, are motor nerves that supply the muscles of the eyeball. Nerve V, the *trigeminal*, is a mixed nerve in fishes and amphibians but mainly motor in terrestrial vertebrates; it supplies the superficial muscles of the face and arises in close association with nerve VII (*facial*). Nerve VIII, the *vestibulocochlear* (formerly the *auditory*), is sensory and innervates the inner ear. The mixed *glossopharyngeal* nerve (IX) serves the tongue, pharynx, and (in fishes) the first gill slit. Nerve X, the *vagus nerve, is a mixed nerve. Nerves XI and XII, the *accessory* and *hypoglossal*, are both motor; the accessory supplies the neck, larynx, and pharynx and the hypoglossal innervates the muscles of the tongue.

The two nerves arising from the forebrain are nonsegmental: the olfactory is derived from sensory epithelium and the optic nerve is a tract of the brain. The nerves arising from the brain stem are homologous with the spinal nerves, although their segmental origin is obscured and their dorsal and ventral roots do not fuse.

Craniata. *See* Vertebrata.

cranium. The vertebrate skull. *See* splanchnocranium, neurocranium.

crassulacean acid metabolism (CAM). An adaptation shown by various succulent plants (originally observed in the Crassulaceae) that enables them to continue to photosynthesize when the stomata are closed. CAM plants fix large quantities of carbon dioxide during the night by incorporating it into a 3-carbon compound to form the 4-carbon malic acid, one of the Krebs cycle acids. In the morning, when photosynthesis begins to compete with this dark fixation, the malic acid is broken down to release the carbon dioxide, which is then reduced to carbohydrate in the usual way.

crassulae (bars of Sanio). Narrow bands of thickening occurring in certain gymnosperms in the intercellular substance and primary cell walls above and below the pit pairs in the tracheids.

C_{12}/C_{13} ratio. Used to indicate whether the constituents of a geological deposit are biogenic in origin or not. Living systems take up C_{12} in preference to the heavier isotope, thus low C_{12} counts (indicated by low radioactivity) in the deposit indicate that it is of biogenic origin. *See also* origin of life.

creatine. A weakly basic nitrogenous organic compound present in muscle. Its phosphate, *phosphocreatine* (or *phosphagen*), is an important energy reserve, undergoing a large change in free energy on hydrolysis. The end product of creatine catabolism, *creatinine*, is a major nitrogenous constituent of urine.

creatinine. *See* creatine.

cremocarp. A schizocarpic *fruit characteristic of the Umbelliferae.

Creodonta. An extinct suborder of the Carnivora in existence from the Palaeocene to the early Pliocene. The group showed great diversity of size, form, and habits. Early creodonts, e.g. *Tricentes*, were small predatory mammals with unspecialized teeth; later forms included *Arctocyon*, a large omnivore with blunt teeth, and *Mesonyx*, a large hoofed scavenger with blunt-cusped molars, indicating that creodonts may have been related to the Condylarthra. Others, e.g. *Hyaenodon*, were more typical carnivores with shearing carnassial teeth.

Cretaceous. The third and last period of the Mesozoic era, extending from 135 to 70 million years ago. It takes its name from the chalk that makes up much of the rock of this period. Chalk itself is a fossil, being composed of planktonic flagellates known as *coccoliths*, which secreted calcareous shells. The most important plants of this period were the angiosperms (flowering plants), which had replaced the gymnosperms as the dominant land flora by the Upper Cretaceous. The Age of Reptiles reached its peak with the adaptive radiation and increase in size of the dinosaurs (*see* Saurischia, Ornithischia). At the end of the Cretaceous the dinosaurs, aquatic reptiles, and marine ammonites became extinct, which allowed the mammals, which had been evolving during the Cretaceous, to replace the reptiles as the dominant land fauna. *See also* geological time scale.

crickets. *See* Orthoptera.

Crinoidea. The most primitive class of the phylum Echinodermata. The larvae are always sessile, being attached to the substratum by a stalk, while the adults are either sessile or free-living. The oral surface of the body is uppermost, with the mouth surrounded by feathery arms, which bear tube feet and ciliary grooves and are used in feeding. The class contains the stalked sea lilies (e.g. *Metacrinus*), a remnant of a formerly numerous and widely distributed group, and the free-living feather stars, e.g. *Antedon.*

crista. 1. A spot of sensory epithelium in the ampullae of the vertebrate *semicircular canals that resembles the *macula but lacks an otolith. The structure of the ampulla is such that the crista responds only to a change in the rate of movement of the head.
2. *See* mitochondrion.

critical group. A group consisting of a number of organisms that cannot easily be placed in smaller taxonomic groups, although they are clearly related and variations exist between them. This problem arises in apomictic species of plants that sometimes have true sexual reproduction and is found in the genus *Rubus* (brambles, etc.), in which some 400 species have been recognized.

Crocodilia. The only extant order of the Archosauria, which contains the crocodiles, e.g. *Crocodilus* of tropical regions; the wider-snouted alligators, e.g. *Alligator*, of America; and various related forms. Crocodilians are semiaquatic aggressive carnivores with numerous strong teeth. They are found in fresh waters and estuaries and use their powerful crested tail in swimming. The external nares, which can be closed, are at the tip of the long snout with the internal nares (choanae) opening far back in the mouth. As in mammals, there is a bony false palate, which, with

the fleshy flaps at the back of the mouth, ensures that no water enters the respiratory passages. They can thus swim practically submerged and the mouth can be kept open under water. The body is protected by horn-covered bony plates and the heart is four-chambered, which is unique among living reptiles.

Cro-Magnon man. *See Homo.*

crop. A distensible expanded section of the gut in some animals, specialized for the storage of food. The crop of birds is a ventral dilation of the oesophagus; in female pigeons, glands of the crop are stimulated by prolactin to secrete *crop milk,* used to feed the nestlings. In invertebrates the crop arises from the foregut and is frequently a site of digestion by enzymes from the saliva.

cro protein. A protein found in bacterial cells infected with bacteriophage and responsible for determining the choice of the lytic cycle of viral replication instead of lysogeny. The *cro* protein has the effect of blocking synthesis of a repressor molecule that would normally prevent commitment to the lytic cycle (the name is an acronym for *c*ontrol of *r*epressor and *o*ther things).

cross. An organism produced from cross-fertilization, or the act of producing such an organism.

crossing over. The process of DNA exchange between homologous portions of chromatids in meiosis. The probable mechanism of crossing over is that described in the *Holliday model, and it is this reciprocal exchange that produces genetic *recombination. Crossing over is also responsible for the *chiasmata often visible in meiotic chromosomes, although according to present thinking the location of the primary DNA cross over is not necessarily the same as that of the visible chiasmata. The recombination that results from crossing over generates new genetic variation by the breakdown of existing *linkage groups.

Crossopterygii. The order of the Choanichthyes that contains the lobe-finned fishes. These mostly freshwater fishes first appeared in the Devonian and became all but extinct by the end of the Mesozoic. There are two suborders, the *Rhipidistia, from which all land vertebrates evolved, and the *Coelacanthini, a specialized side-branch containing the only surviving crossopterygian, *Latimeria*. The Crossopterygii are sometimes regarded as a subclass of the Osteichthyes.

cross-over value. The percentage of recombinants (the products of recombination) in the total number of offspring from a given cross. This figure indicates the amount of crossing over between two genes and thus the degree of linkage between them. Cross-over values are used in making *genetic (*or* linkage) maps, which show the relative positions of the genes on the chromosomes, as the values are roughly proportional to the distance between the genes. If two genes are far apart on a chromosome crossing over is very likely to occur between them, and a high cross-over value is obtained. There is much less chance of crossing over occurring between two genes that are close together on a chromosome, and a lower cross-over value is obtained. Cross-over values are not precisely proportional to the distance apart of genes because of interference (the fact that crossing over does not occur in certain regions of the chromosome) and because the formation of chiasmata is affected by environmental conditions.

crown gall. *See Agrobacterium.*

crozier formation (hook formation). A method of cell division occurring in dikaryotic ascogenous hyphae of many ascomycetes as a means of ensuring that sister nuclei become separated in daughter cells. The stages of the process are illustrated in the diagram. *Compare* clamp connection.
The term *crozier* is sometimes used for a young circinately folded fern frond.

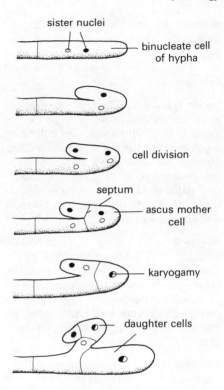

Crozier formation

Crustacea. A class of arthropods whose members are mostly aquatic, breathing by gills. The head bears *compound eyes, two pairs of antennae, and *mouthparts made up of mandibles, two pairs of maxillae, and three pairs of maxillipedes. The body is divided into a thorax, often covered with a dorsal carapace, and an abdomen, and its appendages are typically forked and specialized for different functions (*see* biramous appendage). The sexes are usually separate and development is indirect, via a *nauplius larva. The class includes the subclasses *Branchiopoda, *Ostracoda, *Copepoda, *Cirripedia (barnacles), and *Malacostraca (woodlice, crabs, shrimps, etc.).

cryobiology. The study of the effects of very low temperatures on living organisms. Applications of this study include *cryopreservation*, in which cells and tissues can be frozen and stored for long periods. In this way sperm can be stored for artificial insemination and blood for transfusion. *Cryosurgery* is the use of extreme cold to destroy unwanted tissues.

cryptic coloration. The type of colouring in an animal that causes it to be camouflaged in its environment. The coloration may resemble that of the surroundings, causing the animal to merge with its background, or it may contain disruptive patches of colour, which obscure the outline of the animal. *Compare* warning coloration.

cryptogam (in former classification schemes). Any plant of the Thallophyta, Bryophyta, or Pteridophyta, so called because their sexual reproductive organs remained unknown for a long time. The pteridophytes were sometimes called the *vascular cryptogams. Compare* phanerogam.

Cryptophyceae. A group of unicellular algae usually classified as *Pyrrophyta but sometimes raised to a group of equivalent rank, Cryptophyta. These algae vary in form: some lack cell walls, some are colourless heterotrophs, and some form symbiotic associations with coelenterates and sponges. They are not known to undergo any form of sexual reproduction.

cryptostoma (*pl.* **cryptostomata**). A depression in certain thallose algae that is similar to a *conceptacle but sterile; it is thought to function in mucilage production.

CSF. *See* cerebrospinal fluid.

Ctenophora. A subphylum of Coelenterata, sometimes regarded as a distinct phylum, containing *Pleurobrachia* (comb jelly), *Cestum* (Venus' girdle), etc. Their saclike often globular bodies bear eight longitudinal rows of fused cilia (*combs* or *ctenes),* used for locomotion. Most species have tentacles armed with adhesive cells (*lasso cells* or *colloblasts*) for the capture of food. *Compare* Cnidaria.

cultivar. A cultivated *variety of a plant produced in horticulture or agriculture: a taxon below the subspecies level.

culture. A population of microorganisms, especially bacteria or fungi, grown on a solid or liquid nutrient *culture medium* for study in the laboratory. *Agar is commonly used for solidifying liquid culture media. *See also* tissue culture.

cupule. A small protective cup-shaped structure in many plants, such as occurs around the base of an acorn, the seed of the yew (in which it is bright red and fleshy), or surrounding the gemmae in some liverworts. The cupule of the extinct pteridosperms (seed ferns) contained one to several ovules and is not homologous with any structure in other seed-bearing plants. It may have functioned as an additional integument, as an ovary, or as a perianth; some pteridosperm cupules were glandular and probably produced nectar-like substances.

cusp. A pointed projection on the biting surfaces of mammalian molar and premolar teeth. The number of cusps on the molars may vary from three to six, depending on the species.

cuticle. A layer covering, and secreted by, the epidermis of plants and many invertebrates.
In plants the cuticle consists of a fatty substance called *cutin. It is particularly conspicuous on the aerial organs of higher plants, where it is interrupted only by stomata and lenticels. Its thickness varies, depending partly on the environment. The cuticle restricts water loss through transpiration and may also impart some mechanical strength and resistance to disease. Young roots characteristically have very thin cuticles. Various structures in seeds, e.g. ovules, integuments, nucellus, are often surrounded by a cuticle.
In invertebrates the cuticle functions principally as a protection against mechanical or (in endoparasites) chemi-

cal damage. It is usually strengthened with elastic fibres (in nematodes), deposition of calcium carbonate (in molluscs and crustaceans), or cross-linking of chitin (in insects). In nematodes and arthropods the cuticle provides a rigid skeleton and in insects it protects the animal against water loss. It is periodically moulted to permit growth (*see* ecdysis).

cuticularization. The formation of a cuticle.

cutin. A fatty substance formed from a mixture of complex derivatives of fatty acids. It impregnates the outer wall of the epidermis of plants and forms a separate layer, the *cuticle, outside this wall. Cutin is relatively impermeable to water and gases, restricting water loss (transpiration).

cutinization. The process of impregnation of a plant cell wall with cutin.

cutis. *See* skin.

cutting. Part of a plant, e.g. a stem, root, or leaf, that is detached from the parent and, when planted, grows into a new plant. It therefore serves as a means of vegetative propagation.

Cuvierian duct (common cardinal vein). A paired vein of fish and embryo tetrapods that returns all venous blood to the heart from the cardinal veins. It becomes the terminal part of the anterior vena cava in adult tetrapods. *See* cardinal vein.

C value paradox. The paradox presented by comparisons of *C value* among eukaryotic organisms. C value is the amount of DNA present in the haploid genome of an organism, usually expressed in picograms per cell (1 picogram $= 10^{-12}$ g). Generally, the C value increases with the complexity of the organism, but in some cases the C value is very variable in closely related organisms and certain genera, such as *Protopterus* (lungfish) and *Lilium*, have very much larger genomes than man. A further aspect of the paradox is that the

higher eukaryotes appear to have much higher C values than they can utilize for strictly genetic purposes: the human genome, for example, theoretically has enough DNA in the haploid state for about 3 million genes but it is unlikely that more than 50 000 different genes are actually utilized. The following is a selection of C values (in picograms) for different species:

E. coli 0.0044
Neurospora 0.017
Drosophila 0.18
chicken 1.25
Xenopus 3.15
maize 3.9
Protopterus 142.0
Lilium 32.8
man 3.4

$R_1 = CH_3$ $R_2 = CH_2\overset{\displaystyle O}{\underset{\displaystyle NH_2}{C}}$ $R_3 = CH_2CH_2\overset{\displaystyle O}{\underset{\displaystyle NH_2}{C}}$

Cyanocobalamin

cyanocobalamin (vitamin B$_{12}$). A vitamin of the B complex (known as the *liver factor*) that can be absorbed from the intestine only in the presence of *intrinsic factor*, a secretion of the gastric mucosa. Defective secretion of intrinsic factor (and therefore absence of cyanocobalamin from the tissues) results in pernicious anaemia. Cyanocobalamin contains a nucleus of four pyrrole rings (a *corrin* nucleus) to which cobalt is chelated, with cyanide and a nucleotide coordinated to the cobalt (see formula). The form of the vitamin with coenzyme activity (*cobalamin*) has a 5-deoxyadenosyl group in place of the cyanide. Cobalamin is required for methionine synthesis, nucleotide synthesis, and for the conversion shown below, which occurs in fatty-acid oxidation:

$$\text{methylmalonyl CoA} \underset{\substack{\text{methylmalonyl} \\ \text{mutase}}}{\overset{\text{cobalamin}}{\rightleftharpoons}} \text{succinyl CoA}$$

Cyanophyta (Myxophyta). Blue-green algae: a group of primitive nonmotile organisms with a fossil history stretching back to the Pre-Cambrian (*see* origin of life). Blue-green algae are unicellular, colonial, or filamentous; their cells lack both an organized nucleus (there is no nuclear membrane or nucleolus) and chloroplasts (the pigment-containing membranes are distributed in single thylakoids throughout the cell). The principal pigments are chlorophyll a, β-carotene, c-phycocyanin, and c-phycoerythrin; storage products are glycogen, oil, and protein. No sexual reproduction occurs and flagellate cells are never produced.

Because of their primitive structure, particularly the lack of a nucleus, the blue-green algae are grouped with the bacteria as prokaryotes (*see* cell).

Blue-green algae are abundant in plankton and contribute to blooms; some forms can also tolerate extreme conditions and are found in hot or very saline springs.

Cycadopsida (Cycadophyta). A group of gymnosperms with *manoxylic wood, large frondlike leaves (basically pinnate in form or venation), and seeds with radial symmetry. There is one living group, the Cycadales (cycads), and a large and heterogeneous collection of fossil forms, including the Bennettitales

and the Pteridospermales (or Cycadofilicales) – the seed ferns, plants morphologically indistinguishable from ferns but possessing seeds. Pteridosperms are sometimes separated from the Cycadopsida and placed in a group, the Pteridospermae, equivalent in rank to the Gymnospermae and Angiospermae.

cyclic AMP (adenosine-3′,5′-monophosphate). A cyclic form of the nucleotide adenosine monophosphate (*see* AMP), which functions as an important regulator of metabolic processes in animals and bacteria. Cyclic AMP acts as a mediator in the action of many hormones, including vasopressin, the catecholamines (adrenaline and noradrenaline), many pituitary hormones (e.g. ACTH), and the prostaglandins. The hormones act by stimulating the formation of cyclic AMP from ATP by the enzyme adenyl cyclase in the target region specific to the hormone. The subsequent activity stimulated by cyclic AMP varies in different organs; for example it stimulates glycogenolysis in liver and skeletal muscle, lipolysis in adipose tissue.

cyclosis. 1. A type of cytoplasmic streaming in which the cytoplasm rotates continuously around the cell periphery. It is typical of many plant cells, including immature phloem sieve cells.
2. The circulation of organelles within the cell cytoplasm, as in the passage of food vacuoles through the cell of *Paramecium*.

Cyclosporae. See Phaeophyta.

Cyclostomata. The order of the Agnatha containing the most primitive living vertebrates: the lampreys, e.g. *Petromyzon* (sea lamprey), and hagfish, e.g. *Myxine*. These fishlike, vertebrates are characterized by the absence of paired fins, a secondarily cartilaginous skeleton, a single nasal opening, and a row of spherical gill pouches (*see* gill slit). Jaws are functionally replaced by a round suctorial mouth with horny 'teeth' and a protrusible 'tongue' used to rasp the flesh of fish. Lampreys live attached to fish by means of their mouth, feeding on their blood and flesh. The adults are found in seas or rivers and spawn in fresh water, the eggs hatching into *ammocoete larvae. Hagfishes are scavengers on the sea bottom and have no larval stage.

cyme. *See* cymose inflorescence.

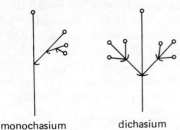

monochasium   dichasium

Cymose inflorescences

cymose inflorescence. A type of inflorescence in which growth is *sympodial* (or *definite*), i.e. the main axis does not continue to grow but forms a flower. Growth continues by a lateral bud, which in turn forms a flower, with growth continuing by a bud on its axis. This results in the oldest flowers of the inflorescence being at the top and the youngest at the bottom. Any cymose inflorescence is known as a *cyme*. A *monochasial cyme* (or *monochasium*) is a cymose inflorescence in which the growth of each branch is continued by only one lateral bud, as in *Geum*. In a *dichasial cyme* (or *dichasium*) the growth of each branch is continued by two opposite lateral buds, as in *Lychnis*. See illustrations. *See also* verticillaster. *Compare* racemose inflorescence.

cypsela. A small achene-like *fruit, characteristic of the Compositae.

cysteine (cys). An amino acid, $HSCH_2CH(NH_2)COOH$, one of the 20 common *amino acids occurring in proteins. Cysteine is a precursor of coenzyme A and of *cystine*, which consists of two cysteine molecules joined by a disulphide bond. In polypeptide chains

cysteine forms disulphide bridges with cysteine molecules in the same or adjacent polypeptide chains, so contributing to the secondary and tertiary structure of proteins.

cysticercus (bladderworm). A larva of some tapeworms (*see* Cestoda). It consists of a fluid-filled bladder with an inverted scolex and develops from an *onchosphere in the muscle of the secondary host. When the secondary host is eaten by the primary host, the cysticercus develops into a sexually mature tapeworm; for example, *Taenia* bladderworms in pork develop into tapeworms in the human body.

cystine. *See* cysteine.

cystocarp (gonimocarp). *See* carpogonium.

cystolith. A crystalline aggregate of calcium carbonate that is deposited on a cellulose peg in certain plant cells known as *idioblasts* and fills the lumen of the cell.

cytidine. A *nucleoside consisting of D-ribose and cytosine linked with a β-glycoside bond.

cytochromes. Conjugated proteins that contain *haem as the prosthetic group and form part of the *electron transport chain, transferring electrons from flavoproteins to molecular oxygen. During electron transfer the iron of the cytochrome passes reversibly between FeII and FeIII valencies. There are at least five cytochromes in the mitochondria of higher animals and plants: *cytochromes b*, *c*, c_1, *a*, and a_3. The terminal two cytochromes in the chain (*a* and a_3) form a copper-containing complex, *cytochrome oxidase*, which is the only component of the chain capable of reducing molecular oxygen. The copper of cytochrome oxidase undergoes a transition between CuI and CuII during electron transfer to oxygen. The complex is inhibited by carbon monoxide, cyanide, and hydrogen sulphide.

cytogenetics. The branch of biology that links the study of cell structure (cytology) with that of inheritance (genetics). Such studies relate the structure and behaviour of chromosomes during mitosis and meiosis to data derived from observations of Mendelian ratios and phenotypic expression. Human cytogenetics is widely used for the diagnosis of inherited disease and forms a basis for genetic counselling of prospective parents.

cytokinesis. The division of cytoplasm that follows nuclear division during cell division. In plants it begins in early telophase with *cell plate formation and is controlled by the *phragmoplast.

cytokinin (phytokinin). A naturally occurring plant *kinin.

cytology. The study of cells, especially by means of light or electron microscopy.

cytolysis. The disruption of a cell, usually by destruction of the plasmalemma.

cytomegalovirus. *See* virus.

cytoplasm. The living contents of a cell bounded externally by the plasmalemma, including an aqueous ground substance (*hyaloplasm*, *cell sap*, or *cell matrix*) containing *organelles and various inclusions but excluding the nucleus and visible vacuoles. The term is often restricted to the ground substance alone, excluding all organelles except ribosomes. The hyaloplasm is an apparently structureless colloidal solution of macromolecules (lipids, phospholipids, proteins, nucleic acids, etc.) and a true solution of small molecules (sugars, amino acids, nucleotides, etc.) and ions (potassium, magnesium, calcium, etc.). It provides the necessary physical and metabolic continuum between the cell components, acting as a reservoir for many essential metabolites and containing materials in transit as well as the enzymes of certain metabolic pathways, including glycolysis. Cytoplasm is the site of protein synthesis, which takes place on ribosomes lying free in the hyaloplasm or bound to the endoplasmic reticulum.

In amoeboid cells, the colloidal state of the cytoplasm varies from viscous (*plasmagel*) to fluid (*plasmasol*), the outer regions (*ectoplasm* or *cortex*) often being more viscous than those inside (*endoplasm*). In some cells streaming of the cytoplasm is also observed, either in fixed channels through gel-like neighbouring cytoplasm, as in the plasmodium phase of slime moulds, or en masse around the cell (*cyclosis), as in immature phloem cells or in leaf cells of freshwater plants (such as *Elodea*).

cytoplasmic inheritance. The transmission of hereditary characters via the DNA of plasmids or extranuclear organelles, such as mitochondria and chloroplasts. Unlike the genes of the chromosomes, mutations in mitochondrial and chloroplast DNA segregate in a non-Mendelian way, as the phenotype of the progeny is determined by the number and phenotype of these organelles in the cytoplasm of the zygote. *See also* plasmagene, plastogene.

Cytosine

cytosine. A pyrimidine base (see formula) that is an essential constituent of the nucleic acids (*see* DNA, RNA). *See also* nucleotide, nucleoside.

cytosol. The soluble part of *cytoplasm remaining after the particles (organelles, etc.) have been separated, e.g. by centrifugation.

cytotaxonomy. *See* taxonomy.

D

2,4,-D. 2,4-dichlorophenoxyacetic acid, a synthetic *auxin.

dalton. A unit of mass used to express molecular weight, based on 1/12 of the mass of the isotope carbon 12 and equal to $1.660\,33 \times 10^{-27}$ kg. It is also known as the *atomic mass unit (amu)*.

dance of the bees. The movements performed by worker honeybees when they return to the hive after finding food. These movements indicate the location of the food to the other workers. The dance was first analysed by von Frisch, who distinguished two main types of movement: the *round dance* and the *waggle dance.* The round dance indicates that food is about l00 yards or less away. The waggle dance indicates the direction of food that is further away; the bee transposes into a vertical plane the angle between the sun and the line of the path from the hive to the food source. If the source of the food is directly towards the sun, the dance is performed directly upwards on the vertical comb of the hive.

dark reaction. *See* photosynthesis.

dark repair. *DNA repair carried out by a special type of DNA polymerase in the absence of visible light. The repair involves the enzymatic removal of dimers from the DNA molecule (thymidine dimer formation is a common result of exposure of DNA to radiation) and synthesis of normal segments to replace those excised. *See also* photoreactivation.

Darwinism. The theory of evolution proposed by Charles Darwin in 1859, in *The Origin of Species*. His argument runs as follows. All organisms produce more offspring than actually survive; these offspring differ from each other,

i.e. they show variations, some of which are heritable. Certain variations enable the individual to survive when the population is acted upon by the forces of *natural selection. Individuals showing these variations are able to combat the environment more successfully and therefore have a better chance of breeding and passing on their variations to their progeny. In a slowly but continuously changing environment this process results in a gradual change in the whole population and, ultimately, in the evolution of new species. Darwin also suggested the importance of *sexual selection in evolution.

He based his theory on findings acquired during his voyage around the world in the *Beagle* (1831–36), compiling evidence from comparative anatomy, palaeontology, geographical distribution, and embryology. A. R. Wallace (1823–1913), working independently of Darwin, arrived at the same theory using evidence from the distribution of related groups of organisms and their natural classification.

Darwin knew nothing of the patterns of Mendelian heredity (*see* Mendelism) and the source of the variation on which his theory is based. The modern version of Darwinism, *neo-Darwinism*, incorporates subsequent discoveries in genetics and cytogenetics. It elucidates the source of *variation and stresses the nature and importance of *isolating mechanisms and *genetic drift in the formation of new species. *Compare* Lamarckism.

dating techniques. Any of various methods of dating palaeontological finds, either by dating the specimens themselves or the sites from which they were obtained. *Relative dating methods* date finds in relation to one another, so that it is possible to say that one fossil is the same age as or older than another but not to give an age in millions of years. Such techniques are based on the comparison of geological strata and on chemical analyses. *Absolute (chronometric) methods* date fossils in terms of their age in years before the present. There are several different methods, the most important of which is *radioactive dating; *dendrochronology (tree-ring dating) and *varve dating are useful for more limited periods of time. The dates given by these methods may vary, as wrong assumptions made in each method compound errors. The techniques are usually performed on material at the site, rather than on the fossils themselves, as they may damage the fossils; it is therefore important to ensure that the fossil is of the same age as the strata in which it is found.

day-neutral plant. *See* photoperiodism.

deamination. The enzymic removal of an amino group ($-NH_2$) from an amino acid or other amine. The enzyme glutamate dehydrogenase couples *transamination with the oxidative deamination of glutamic acid:
glutamic acid + NAD = α-ketoglutaric acid + NADH + NH_3
The ammonia produced by the reaction is converted in the liver to *urea, which is excreted.

Decapoda. 1. The order of the Malacostraca containing the most specialized crustaceans. These include the prawns (e.g. *Palaemon*), shrimps (e.g. *Crangon*), lobsters (e.g. *Homarus*), and crayfishes (e.g. *Astacus*), all of which have a long abdomen ending in a tail for backward swimming, as well as the hermit and true crabs (e.g. *Pagurus, Cancer*), which have a much reduced abdomen. The head and thorax are fused and covered with a carapace. The last five thoracic segments each bear a pair of walking legs, the first and second pairs often having pincers (*chelae*), used in feeding and defence.
2. An order of the class Cephalopoda whose members have ten tentacles around the mouth. It includes *Sepia* (cuttlefish) and *Loligo* (squid).

decidua. The thick and highly modified *endometrium that lines the uterus of most mammals during pregnancy. It is thrown off and removed, together with the placenta, after parturition.

deciduous. Designating vascular plants that show seasonal shedding of leaves, each leaf lasting only one season (the leaves shed in this way are also termed deciduous). The condition of being deciduous is not an indicator of taxonomic status. *Compare* evergreen.

deciduous teeth (primary teeth, milk teeth). The first of the two successions of teeth occurring in most mammals, which are eventually replaced by the *permanent teeth. While being similar to the permanent teeth in structure, they are less highly developed and often fewer in number. Of the grinding teeth (*see* premolar, molar), only the premolars are represented in the deciduous dentition.

decomposer. A heterotrophic organism in an *ecosystem that breaks down dead organic matter into its constituent parts, utilizing some and releasing others to be used by the producers. *See also* food chain.

deficiency. A chromosomal aberration resulting in loss of a gene or series of genes by *deletion. (The word is also often used as a synonym for deletion.) Deficiencies are often lethal to the affected organisms, but may alternatively be apparent as a mutant phenotype. Cytogenetics can reveal structural evidence of chromosomal deficiency, as in the polytene chromosomes of certain Diptera. Some *aneuploid tissues or organisms are deficient in one or more chromosomes of the normal complement.

deficiency disease. Any disease resulting from the absence of an essential nutrient, particularly a vitamin, trace element, or essential amino acid, from the diet. For example, scurvy is a disease caused by a vitamin C deficiency.

degeneration. 1. The reduction or loss of an organ in the course of evolution so that it becomes a *vestigial organ.

2. The death and disorganization of cells.

3. The death and disorganization of nerve fibres.

deglutition. The action of swallowing. Voluntary movement of the tongue forces the food backwards to the pharynx. This initiates reflex closure of the larynx by the epiglottis and of the nasal passages by the soft palate, so that food is prevented from entering the trachea as it passes through the pharynx to the oesophagus.

dehiscence. The bursting open of certain plant structures, especially reproductive organs, at maturity to release their contents. The pattern of dehiscence is characteristic for the particular organ. The wall of the organ may be modified (*see* stomium, annulus) or the dehiscence may be in particular directions (as, for example, in *introrse and *extrorse anthers). Types of dehiscence include *operculate* (by an *operculum), *poricidal* (by means of pores, as in poppy capsules), *loculicidal* (opening into the loculi of certain fruits), and *septicidal* (splitting along the septa between the loculi in certain fruits).

dehydration. A process used in the preparation of permanent microscope slides of organisms or tissues. It consists of gradually removing the water from the material by immersing it successively in more concentrated solutions of ethanol (ethyl alcohol) and finally in absolute alcohol. If the material is placed directly from water into absolute alcohol it loses water so quickly that the cells shrink or change shape. The material must be dehydrated before clearing because the oil or xylene used for clearing and the solvent used in mounting are not miscible with water and the mount becomes cloudy if it contains any water.

dehydrogenase. One of a group of enzymes that catalyse oxidation-reduction reactions by transferring hydrogen from the substrate to another substance.

Many of the respiratory enzymes are dehydrogenases.

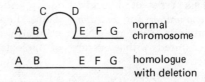

Deletion observed during pairing of homologous chromosomes

deletion. A type of chromosome mutation in which a section of a chromosome is lost during mitosis or meiosis. For example, if a chromosome contains the genes ABCDEFGH, the deletion of section CD results in the gene sequence ABEFGH. Some deletions can be recognized when chromosomes pair at prophase of meiosis. A loop is formed to allow normal pairing on either side of the deleted portion (see illustration). *See also* deficiency.

deme. A unit in experimental *taxonomy consisting of a group of individuals with measurable common characteristics, implying a closeness of relationship. These characteristics are usually genetic (in a *genodeme*) or cytological (in a *cytodeme*). A population unit in which breeding is likely to occur is called a *gamodeme*; this unit is, of course, much smaller than the whole species.

denaturation. Changes occurring in a protein or nucleic acid molecule when it is exposed in solution to extremes of heat or pH or to agents such as urea and detergents. Some such changes are reversible. A change in conformation is produced by loss of noncovalent bonds and an unfolding of the polypeptide chain (in proteins) or of double helical regions (in nucleic acids), with the loss of some or most secondary and tertiary structure. The changes may be indicated by an alteration of physical properties (such as the hardening of the white of an egg on boiling) or a loss of biological activity. Nucleic acid denaturation is often termed *melting*. It is commonly reversible and forms the basis for techniques of *nucleic acid hybridization and the determination of *Cot values. This type of hybridization is called *renaturation* (or *annealing*). Some simple proteins, such as RNase, can also be renatured with a return of biological activity.

dendrite. One of many short branching cytoplasmic processes arising from the cell body of most *neurones. Dendrites make synaptic contacts with other neurones and thus form the input region for excitation from these neurones.

dendrochronology. A technique used to date archaeological sites and to correct datings of fossils obtained by the radiocarbon method (*see* radioactive dating). It involves counting the annual rings of wood laid down by trees and relies on the fact that each annual ring is unique and therefore identifiable. Dendrochronology can be applied when the lifespans of a living tree and a fossil tree on the same site overlap. An annual ring of the same year can be recognized in both trees within the period of overlap, and therefore the dead tree can be dated. This technique can be extended back from the dead tree to older wood on the site that was used for buildings, etc. Bristlecone pines, which live to an age of 5000 years, have been used to correct radiocarbon datings. By dating a fossil bristlecone using the dendrochronology method – 8000-year-old fossils have been dated in this way – and by measuring the amount of radioactivity in such a fossil, it is possible to correct the age of other fossils on which only radiocarbon methods have been used.

dendrogram. A diagram, in the form of a family tree, showing the relationships between organisms or groups of organisms.

denitrification. The process by which facultative aerobic soil bacteria (*denitrifying bacteria*) reduce nitrates to nitrites, nitrous oxide, or nitrogen in anaerobic conditions. *See also* nitrogen cycle.

density dependence. A proportional increase in mortality (or reduction in fecundity) of a population as its density increases. Regulation of populations (i.e. the imposition of upper and lower limits through a negative feedback process) cannot occur without density dependence.

density gradient centrifugation. The use of artificial concentration gradients of such solutions as caesium chloride or sucrose to enhance the separation of components of different density by centrifugation. In the case of sucrose gradients the mixture of components is normally layered on top of the gradient and after a suitable time and speed of centrifugation separate fractions of the gradient are isolated and the distinct components recovered from them. Caesium chloride gradients, however, are often run to equilibrium, so that the distinct biological components finally take up a position in the gradient where the density of the caesium chloride matches their own density (*see also* buoyant density). In this situation, the resolution improves with the time of centrifugation.

dental formula. A formula for expressing the numbers of incisors, canines, premolars, and molars in the upper and lower jaws of a mammal (see illustration). It consists of a series of fractions of which the digit above the line indicates the number of teeth in one half of the upper jaw and the digit below the line, those in one half of the lower jaw. Each fraction is prefixed by the initial letter of the tooth type referred to.

man $\quad$ i$\frac{2}{2}$. c$\frac{1}{1}$. p (pm)$\frac{2}{2}$. m$\frac{3}{3}$.

rabbit $\quad$ i$\frac{2}{1}$. c$\frac{0}{0}$. p$\frac{3}{2}$. m$\frac{3}{3}$.

cat $\quad$ i$\frac{3}{3}$. c$\frac{1}{1}$. p$\frac{3}{2}$. m$\frac{1}{1}$.

Dental formulae

dentary. A tooth-bearing membrane bone of the margin of the vertebrate jaw. In lower vertebrates it is one of several lower-jaw bones, but in birds it forms the sole skeletal element of the lower beak and in mammals it is the only bone of the lower jaw and articulates with the squamosal.

denticle. *See* placoid scale.

dentine. The yellow calcified tissue that covers the pulp cavity of a tooth both above and below the gum and is sensitive to touch, cold, etc. Its chemical composition is similar to bone, consisting of about 75% inorganic and 25% organic material. Within the dentine matrix run many minute canals (*dentinal tubules*), 2–4 µm in diameter, in which lie processes of the *odontoblasts and occasionally nerve fibres and blood vessels.

dentition. The number, type, and physiology of the teeth of an animal. Animals whose teeth are all of the same type, i.e. most nonmammalian vertebrates, are said to have *homodont* dentition whereas those whose teeth are not of the same form, e.g. most mammals, are said to have *heterodont* dentition. The dentition of animals having two successions of teeth (*see* deciduous teeth, permanent teeth) is known as *diphyodont*; that of animals with only one set of teeth throughout life is *monophyodont*. Animals in which the teeth are continuously discarded and replaced throughout life have a *polyphyodont* dentition. *See also* dental formula.

deoxyribonuclease. *See* DNase.

deoxyribonucleic acid. *See* DNA.

depolarization. A reduction in the potential difference across a membrane.

dermal bone. *See* membrane bone.

Dermaptera. An order of nocturnal exopterygote insects, the earwigs (e.g. *Labia*). They are characterized by a long body, delicate semicircular hind wings protected at rest by small leathery forewings, and forceps-like cerci at the tip of the abdomen, which are used in defence and aid the folding of the hind wings. Earwigs have biting mouthparts and are omnivorous; some species do not fly.

dermatogen. The part of the apical meristem that gives rise to the epidermis. *See* histogen theory.

dermatome. *See* mesoderm.

dermis (corium). The inner living layer of vertebrate *skin. The thick matrix contains connective tissue, which provides strength and flexibility; fat, providing insulation; blood vessels, for temperature control and, in amphibians and fishes, respiration; sensory nerve endings; and *chromatophores. The armour of bones derived from the dermis in primitive vertebrates is represented in modern forms by the *dermal bones* of the skull and by fish scales (*see* membrane bone).

Dermoptera. An order of the Eutheria that contains a single genus, *Cynocephalus* (*Galeopithecus*) (flying lemur), a nocturnal arboreal herbivorous mammal of southeast Asia. It glides by means of a hairy membrane extending from the forelimbs to the hind limbs and tail. The dentition is unique.

desmosome. *See* junctional complex.

determined. Designating embryonic cells following the stage of competence, when the fate or direction of differentiation of the cell has become irreversibly established, irrespective of any subsequent environmental influences. *Compare* competent, presumptive.

detritus. Fragments of decomposing organisms.

Deuteromycetes. *See* Fungi Imperfecti.

deutoplasm. Nutritive substances within an ovum, especially yolk.

Devonian. The fourth period of the Palaeozoic era, extending from 400 to 350 million years ago. It was named after Devon, where rocks of the period were first recognized. The Devonian is the first period during which fossils of vertebrates and vascular plants are abundant. The vertebrate fossils are fish, including jawless ostracoderms, primitive jawed placoderms, and the earliest representatives of the Chondrichthyes and Osteichthyes. The vascular-plant fossils are pteridophytes, including the famous Rhynie Chert flora of the Middle Devonian, which consists of very well-preserved psilophytes. *See also* geological time scale.

dextran. A storage polysaccharide of bacteria and yeasts that consists of branched chains of D-glucose residues.

dextrin. *See* starch.

dextrose. *See* glucose.

diabetes (diabetes mellitus). A disorder of sugar metabolism caused by a lack of the pancreatic hormone *insulin. Unutilized glucose accumulates in large quantities in the blood (hyperglycaemia) and is excreted in the urine (glycosuria). The use of alternative energy sources leads to loss of weight and disturbances in the *acid-base balance. There appears to be a hereditary tendency to the disorder, which may be triggered by various factors.

diageotropism. *See* geotropism.

diakinesis. A stage of the prophase of the first division of *meiosis.

dialysis. A technique for the separation of substances of high molecular weight, such as proteins and polysaccharides, from low-molecular-weight solutes, such as salts. The mixed solution is placed in a *dialysis tube*, which is made of a semipermeable membrane, e.g. cellophane, and is surrounded by distilled water. The solutes, e.g. sodium chloride and glucose, pass out through the membrane while the proteins, etc., are retained within the tube. The procedure is also widely used to alter the concentrations of various dissolved salts in a solution

in which large molecules or cell extracts are dissolved or suspended.

diapause. A form of hibernation that can occur at any specific stage in the life cycle of certain insects and involves a period of suspended metabolism and complete cessation of growth and development. The diapause is a seasonal adaptation (usually a photoperiod response) that, through changes in brain neurosecretion, enables the species to survive hazardous environmental conditions and produce offspring in favourable conditions.

diaphragm. A domed sheet of tendon and muscle separating the thoracic and abdominal coelomic cavities of mammals. Depression of the diaphragm, accompanied by expansion of the rib cage, causes air to be sucked into the lungs.

diaphysis. The shaft of a mammalian long bone, which contains an ossification centre. *See* epiphysis.

diapsid. Designating a condition of the amniote skull in which the roofing of membrane bones is pierced by two openings in the cheek and temple, allowing greater room for the jaw musculature and resulting in improved jaw function. This condition is found in many reptiles (*see* Archosauria, Lepidosauria) and in birds. *Compare* anapsid, synapsid.

diaspore (disseminule). Any structure produced by a plant, either sexually or asexually, that serves to disseminate the species. Diaspores include seeds, spores, gemmae, etc.

diastase. *See* amylase.

diastole. The phase in the beating of the heart when all parts (i.e. atria and ventricles) are relaxed. It occurs immediately after ventricular *systole and in man lasts for about 0.4 seconds. *Atrial* and *ventricular diastole* are the phases during which the atria and ventricles, respectively, are relaxed and refill with blood; these phases must not be confused with *true diastole*, when all chambers are relaxed.

diatoms. *See* Bacillariophyceae.

dicaryosis and dicaryon. *See* dikaryosis, dikaryon.

dichasium. *See* cymose inflorescence.

dichogamy. The maturation of anthers and stigmas in a flower at different times: a mechanism that encourages cross-pollination. The condition in which the anthers mature first, known as *protandry*, is most common and occurs in rosebay willowherb and many composites. When the stigmas mature first the condition is known as *protogyny* and is much rarer, although more effective. Complete dichogamy rarely occurs; there is usually an overlapping period when both anthers and stigmas are ripe, which allows self-pollination to occur if cross pollination has failed.

dichotomy. Bifurcation of an organ or structure into two equal portions. *Unequal dichotomy* is growth by bifurcation in which one side of the fork is somewhat larger or more vigorous than the other, without being truly dominant. *Compare* monopodium, sympodium.

Dicotyledonae. The larger of the two subgroups of angiosperms (*compare* Monocotyledonae). Dicotyledons are characterized by the possession of two cotyledons in the embryo. The vascular bundles of the axes usually form a ring around the pith and there is usually some evidence of a vascular cambium (*see* vascular tissue). The leaves are typically pinnately or palmately veined; the floral parts, if not numerous, are usually in fives (or multiples of five), occasionally in fours, rarely in threes; and the pollen grains are *tricolpate* (i.e. with three germ pores) or derived from a tricolpate type. The group includes hardwood trees, shrubs, and many herbaceous plants.

Dictyoptera. The order of exopterygote insects that contains the cockroaches and mantids. They have leathery fore-wings, which protect the larger delicate hind wings, and the females lay their eggs in capsules (*oothecae*). Cockroaches (suborder Blattodea) are cosmopolitan nocturnal omnivorous insects and a pest of dirty places; they seldom fly but can run quickly. Mantids (suborder Mantodea), which are mostly tropical or subtropical, are distinguished by their spiny forelegs, which are used to capture prey and are held together below the head when resting (hence: praying mantis).

dictyosome. The stack of cisternae that, together with associated vesicles, forms the *Golgi apparatus.

dictyostele. *See* stele.

Dictyostelium. *See* slime fungus.

difference equation (in ecology). An equation that models changes in an organism's population in a stepwise way, often showing generation-by-generation changes. A basic form is: $N_{t+1} = F(N_t)$, where N_t is the number of individuals in the population at time t and N_{t+1} is the number at the next stage. F is a function such as a fecundity or mortality parameter. Difference equations are used in population models for organisms with distinct generations, such as some insects. For this reason, they are not appropriate for populations of mammals, birds, fish, etc., in which individuals from several generations exist at the same time.

differentiation. 1. A phase of growth during which unspecialized cells become specialized for particular functions. The young unspecialized cells of organisms, particularly embryonic or regenerating cells of animals and meristematic cells of plants, adopt specialized functions and structures during growth depending partly on their position in relation to other cells. In this way the tissues and organs of the mature organism are built up. The mechanisms of differentiation are poorly understood; factors such as physical constraints and chemical gradients are probably involved. The fact that a mature differentiated cell can, under suitable conditions, revert to an embryonic undifferentiated state when isolated from its neighbours indicates that differentiation involves no actual loss of information (in the form of DNA) but rather a masking of irrelevant information.

2. A process used in the preparation of microscope slides of organisms or tissues. It consists of the removal of excessive stain after the staining process and is done by placing the overstained section in acid alcohol.

diffuse-porous. Designating wood with the vessels evenly distributed in the *growth ring.

Digenea. An order of the *Trematoda (flukes), sometimes regarded as a separate class of the Platyhelminthes.

digestion. The process of breakdown, by physical and chemical means, of complex foodstuffs into simple molecules that can be absorbed and assimilated by the body tissues. Digestion may be *intracellular*, in which food particles are taken into the cells of the alimentary canal by phagocytosis (as in the Coelenterata), or *extracellular*, in which enzymes are released from the glands of the gut wall onto food that is either in the gut cavity (as in mammals) or outside it (as in the Diptera). Many groups utilize bacteria in the gut to digest complex plant polysaccharides such as cellulose. *See also* intestine.

digit. A finger or toe (or corresponding part) of the vertebrate *pentadactyl limb. The digits may bear claws, hooves, or nails distally.

digitigrade. Designating a gait of mammals in which the weight of the body is borne on the digits, the metacarpals (or metatarsals) being raised from the ground. The digitigrade gait is characteristic of cats, dogs, rodents, etc. *Compare* plantigrade, unguligrade.

dihybrid. An organism considered as heterozygous for two pairs of alleles, such as *AaBb*. *Compare* monohybrid.

dikaryon (dicaryon). A heterokaryon with two nuclei per cell. *See* heterokaryosis.

dikaryosis (dicaryosis). *Heterokaryosis with two nuclei per cell.

dimorphism. A type of heteromorphism in which two forms of individuals are produced in a single species. For example, it occurs in animals in which the two sexes differ in appearance (*sexual dimorphism*) and in the life cycle of the Cnidaria and Pteridophyta (*dimorphism of generations*).

Dinophyceae. A group of planktonic unicellular algae, the dinoflagellates, forming part of the *Pyrrophyta. Most dinoflagellates are biflagellate, with one flagellum encircling the cell, the other trailing backwards (sometimes both are apical). The cells often contain fucoxanthin. Marine forms are typically naked protoplasts but freshwater forms normally possess a cell wall, which may have spiny processes or thickened plates (as flotation devices). Sexual reproduction is rare and usually oogamous.

dinosaurs. *See* Ornithischia, Saurischia.

dinucleotide. *See* nucleotide.

dioecious. Designating a plant species in which separate male and female flowers are produced on separate plants. *Compare* monoecious.

dioestrus. *See* oestrous cycle.

diphycercal. Designating the type of tail characteristic of lungfish and certain other fishes, in which the vertebral column extends horizontally to the tip of the caudal fin, which is composed of two equal lobes. *Compare* heterocercal, homocercal.

diphyodont. *See* dentition.

diplanetism. A condition occurring in some phycomycete fungi (the

Oomycetes) that possess two types of zoospores (and hence two swarming stages in the life cycle). The first type, which has two apical flagella, forms a resting spore after swarming; this later germinates to release the second type of zoospore, which has laterally inserted flagella.

dipleurula. The planktonic bilaterally symmetrical larva of the Echinodermata, which has a ciliated band forming a closed loop for locomotion and an adoral ciliated band around the mouth for feeding. The dipleurula becomes variously modified in the different echinoderm classes to support the increased larval weight (*see* auricularia, bipinnaria, doliolaria, pluteus). Similarities to the *tornaria larva in development and structure indicate affinities between the Echinodermata and Chordata.

diplobiont (diplohaplont). An organism having both diploid and haploid somatic states. *See also* life cycle.

diploblastic. Designating animals whose body walls are composed of only two layers of cells, ectoderm and endoderm, separated by a layer of gelatinous material (mesoglea). The Coelenterata are diploblastic; all other Metazoa are triploblastic.

diploid. (Designating) any nucleus, cell, or organism that possesses twice the haploid number of chromosomes. All chromosomes except the sex chromosomes occur in homologous pairs, which resemble each other in size, shape and the position of the centromere. When a diploid nucleus undergoes meiosis, the homologous pairs separate and haploid nuclei are formed. If the haploid number is *n*, the diploid number is 2*n*; for example in man 2*n* = 46. In animals, diploidy occurs in most cells except those of the gametes, which are haploid. It is found in the sporophyte generation of plants with alternation of generations and also in some stages of the life history of many algae and fungi. *Compare* haploid.

diplont. An organism having a diploid somatic state. *See also* life cycle.

Diplopoda. The class of the Arthropoda that contains the millipedes, e.g. *Julus*. The cylindrical body is covered with a calcareous cuticle and is divided into numerous segments, each of which is the product of the fusion of two embryonic segments and therefore bears two pairs of legs. Millipedes are herbivorous and terrestrial, breathing through tracheae. Excretion is by *Malpighian tubules. *See also* Myriapoda.

diplotene. A stage of the prophase of the first division of *meiosis.

Diplura. An order of wingless insects of the subclass Apterygota, the two-pronged bristletails. They are small eyeless mostly unpigmented insects with biting mouthparts and two long tail bristles. They are found in soil, under stones etc., where they feed on decaying organic matter.

Dipnoi. The order of the Choanichthyes containing the lungfishes, which first appeared in the Devonian. In modern lungfishes the endoskeleton is reduced, the scales are large and thin, the paired fins are modified, and the tail is symmetrical. Lungfishes live in fresh water, in areas subject to seasonal drought. *Neoceratodus* of Queensland is the most primitive and cannot live out of water. *Protopterus* of the Nile and *Lepidosiren* of South America survive droughts by burrowing in the mud, leaving a small opening for breathing (*see* aestivation). The heart and blood system are adapted for pulmonary respiration and resemble those of the Amphibia.

Diptera. A large order of endopterygote insects, the true (or two-winged) flies, characterized by only one pair of wings; balancing organs (*see* haltere) replace the hind wings. The mouthparts are suctorial, and in some species piercing, for feeding on plant juices, decaying organic matter, or blood. The pupae are often protected in a barrel-shaped *puparium.* The order includes the fragile craneflies (e.g. *Tipula*) and mosquitoes (e.g. *Culex*) as well as the more compact houseflies (e.g. *Musca*), blowflies (e.g. *Calliphora*), tsetse-flies, fruit flies (e.g. **Drosophila*), etc.

disaccharides. A group of carbohydrates consisting of two monosaccharides united by a glycosidic linkage (*see* glycoside). The three most common disaccharides are *maltose, *sucrose, and *lactose.

disjunction. The normal separation of pairs of homologous chromosomes and their movement to opposite poles during anaphase I of meiosis. *Compare* nondisjunction.

displacement activity. An action performed by an animal that is apparently trivial and irrelevant to the situation with which it is faced. Displacement activities occur when the drive for the normal pattern of behaviour is blocked. The blocking of a drive may be caused by the presence of two conflicting drives; for example, one of a pair of herring gulls may start nest-building activities when torn between the urge to fight or flee. It may also result when a single drive does not receive the correct *releaser; a stickleback engaged in courtship behaviour may start nest-fanning movements if it does not receive the correct response from the female.

display behaviour. Activities performed by an animal that act as specific signals, particularly to members of the same species. The activities may be movements, sounds, the sudden revealing of bright plumage, etc.; they are most frequently seen in *courtship and *aggression.

disseminule. *See* diaspore.

distal. Designating the part of a tissue, organ, limb, etc., that is furthest away from the point of attachment or origin. For example, the fingers are at the distal end of the forelimb. *Compare* proximal.

diurnal rhythm. *See* circadian rhythm.

diversity. An attribute of ecological communities. Diversity can be measured crudely by the number of species present but this takes no account of their relative rarity or abundance. One type of diversity measure records the number of individuals and the number of species (e.g. the α-index of Williams). Others quantify the apportioning of individuals between species (e.g. the *Shannon-Wiener index*).

diverticulum. A blind-ending pouch or tube formed from the outpushing of a canal or cavity. Diverticula occur normally in parts of the alimentary canal (*see* caecum) but they sometimes arise as abnormal structures, e.g. tracheal diverticula.

division. A unit used in the *classification of plants. A division consists of a number of classes, or occasionally of only one class, with certain important characteristics in common. For example, the division Spermatophyta consists of all plants that bear seeds. Large divisions are divided into subdivisions; the Spermatophyta is subdivided into the Angiospermae and Gymnospermae. The subdivisions are divided into classes. The corresponding unit in animal classification is the phylum; the term phylum, however, is used in some plant classification schemes as a synonym for division.

dizygotic twins. *See* fraternal twins.

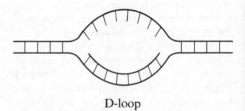

D-loop

D-loop (displacement loop). A structure occurring in DNA at the beginning of replication in which a short length of DNA is displaced from its complementary strand by a length of newly synthesized DNA. The structure is visible in the electron microscope as a 'bubble', single-stranded on one side and double-stranded on the other (see illustration).

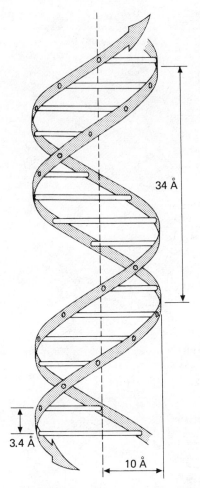

34 Å

3.4 Å

10 Å

Fig. 1: Three-dimensional double helical structure of a DNA molecule

DNA (deoxyribonucleic acid). A nucleic acid that is the major constituent of the chromosomes and is the hereditary material of the majority of living organisms (in some viruses the hereditary material is RNA). In eukaryotic organisms it is associated with proteins (notably histones) and RNA; in prokaryotes it is probably the sole constituent of the chromosomes (*see also* gene).

The three-dimensional structure of DNA was elucidated by Watson and Crick. A DNA molecule consists of a *double helix* of two polynucleotide chains linked by hydrogen bonds and hydrophobic interactions between complementary base pairs (see Figs. 1 and 2). The two chains are of opposite polarity, i.e. they run in opposite directions: the terminal nucleotide at one end of one chain is attached to the 3' carbon atom of its sugar while that at the other end is linked to its sugar at the 5' carbon atom; the opposite arrangement occurs in the complementary chain. Unlike RNA, DNA is stable to alkaline hydrolysis and is stable in its helical configuration. Each nucleotide consists of the sugar deoxyribose and phosphoric acid combined by an ester linkage at the 5' carbon atom of the sugar, with one of four nitrogenous bases linked to the 1' carbon of the sugar and facing into the centre of the helix. Adjacent nucleotides are linked by phosphodiester bonds between the phosphate of one and the 3' carbon of the next. The four bases are the purines adenine and guanine and the pyrimidines cytosine and thymine. The sequence of nucleotide base pairs constitutes the genetic information of the cell (*see* genetic code); a great number of base sequences is possible, reflecting the diversity of organisms, and the sequence and number of pairs is constant for any one species (*see* base ratio). For example, the bacterium *Escherichia coli* contains approximately 4×10^6 base pairs; the DNA of man contains approximately 10^9.

The sum of the purine bases is equal to the sum of the pyrimidine bases. Hydrogen bonding between the bases is highly specific: adenine will pair only with thymine and guanine only with cytosine (*see* base pairing), giving this equality of bases. This specificity enables DNA to undergo semiconservative *replication, and new histone molecules associate with each new daughter strand of DNA to give new copies of the chromosomes. DNA functions as the genetic code by the synthesis of RNA (*see* transcription).

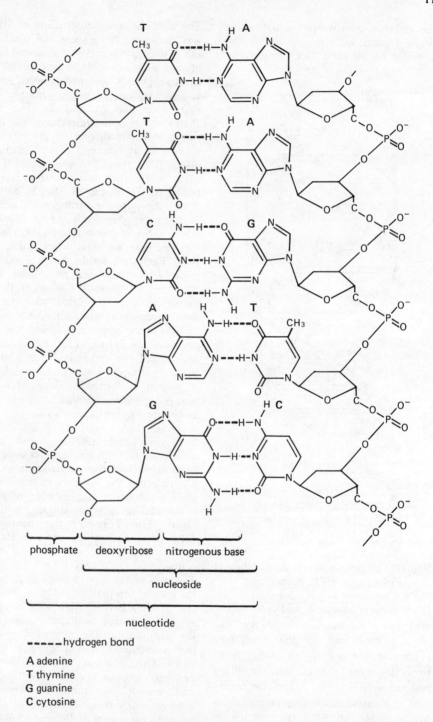

Fig. 2: Part of a DNA molecule showing hydrogen bonding between complementary base pairs

*Messenger RNA is then used for the determination of the amino acid sequence in protein synthesis. In higher eukaryotes there is probably much more DNA than is required to code for protein (*see* C value paradox), some being regulatory and much perhaps redundant.

DNA ligase. An enzyme responsible for bonding the newly inserted nucleotides together during cellular DNA synthesis, so yielding a long polymer of nucleotides. The enzyme is now widely used in genetic engineering to join together reassociated DNA with overlapping ends.

DNA modification. Alteration of DNA in which particular bases have additional side groups added to them by the action of specific enzymes. The best-known modification to DNA is methylation, which is used to protect genomic DNA from attack by restriction endonuclease enzymes in bacteria. In eukaryotes, methylation of certain bases is involved in the synthesis of transfer RNA and there is also evidence that rarely transcribed sequences are frequently rich in methylated bases.

DNA polymerase. *See* polymerase.

DNA repair. A process carried out by specific enzymes (including DNA polymerases and ligases) that reduces the damage to a DNA base sequence inflicted by radiation and other mutagenic agents. The fact of DNA repair implies that the genetically effective mutation rate is much lower than the initial rate of mutation. DNA repair is a rather complex process involving different mechanisms, some being enhanced by light (*see* photoreactivation) and others occurring in the absence of light (*see* dark repair).

DNase (deoxyribonuclease). Any of various enzymes that degrade DNA. They hydrolyse phosphodiester bonds in the sugar-phosphate backbone and are of two types: *exonucleases and *endonucleases (see illustration). There is a great variety of DNases, some sin-

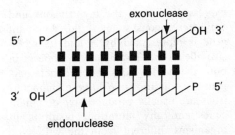

Sites of action of DNases

gle-strand-specific, some double-strand-specific, and some sequence-specific (e.g. *restriction endonucleases).

DNA sequencing. The determination of the sequence of bases along a length of DNA. The first complete nucleotide sequence of a naturally occurring nucleic acid, alanine transfer RNA, was published in 1965, since when the technical difficulties of DNA sequencing have been greatly reduced. Cloning of DNA in bacteria has provided an easy and reliable method of purification. *Restriction endonucleases are used not only to remove the sequence from the cloning plasmid but also to dissect it into a number of fragments of manageable size. DNA fragments are then isolated by *gel electrophoresis and the order of bases in each short fragment determined directly by the selective parallel use of ^{32}P-labelled nucleoside triphosphates.

Docodonta. An extinct order of late Triassic and Jurassic mammals, probably small insectivores, such as the shrewlike *Morganucodon*. The pectoral girdle was composed of the same bones as that of the Monotremata, which suggests that docodonts may be close to monotreme ancestors.

doliolaria. A larva of the Holothuroidea and Crinoidea, having several ciliated rings around the body. *See* dipleurula.

dominance hierarchy. *See* peck order.

dominant. 1. (Designating) the member of a pair of alleles that shows its effect in the phenotype whatever other allele is present. A dominant gene is therefore expressed in both the homozygous and the heterozygous state: if the dominant gene is represented by *A* and its recessive allele by *a*, its phenotype appears in both the homozygous *AA* and heterozygous *Aa* conditions. Wild-type characteristics are usually produced by dominant genes and any mutations resulting in organisms different from the wild type are usually recessive. *See also* incomplete dominance. *Compare* recessive.

2. (Designating) the most prevalent species of plant in an ecological community, such as the oak tree in an oak wood. The dominant species determines the appearance of a community and affects the incidence of the other species in it. Two or more dominant species in the same region are known as *co-dominants* (*see* association).

3. (in animal behaviour). Designating the individual at the top of the social hierarchy (*see* peck order). The dominant animal may behave aggressively to all other members of the social group and leads aggressive activities against attackers if the group is threatened.

donor. A person or animal from whom organs, tissues, or blood are transferred to another individual of the same species or to one of a different species. *See* graft.

DOPA. *See* L-DOPA.

dopamine. A catecholamine intermediate in the synthesis of noradrenaline and adrenaline. In mammals, dopamine is found concentrated in the corpus striatum region of the brain. From the evidence of fluorescent histochemistry, which shows dopamine localized in nerve terminals of the corpus striatum, and from electrophysiology, which shows that neurones in this region are sensitive to local application of dopamine, it is apparent that dopamine is an inhibitory neurotransmitter in the corpus striatum.

Dopamine is also an inhibitory transmitter in other animals, e.g. the snail.

dormancy. A biological state of minimal metabolic activity when growth ceases, primarily enabling organisms to survive periods of adverse conditions.

Most plants or certain of their parts (excluding a few tropical species) undergo dormant periods, often for overwintering though sometimes during drought or other adverse conditions. Seeds often have a dormancy requirement, sometimes with a period of *after-ripening, ensuring delayed growth. Environmental factors, such as temperature and photoperiod (*see* vernalization, photoperiodism), are commonly involved in controlling dormancy of both seeds and buds, ensuring that growth occurs only in suitable conditions or, for seeds, habitats. Biennial and perennial plants often lose their foliage and form dormant buds. These may be parts of underground organs of vegetative reproduction, such as bulbs, corms, and tubers, or aerial parts, such as the buds of woody species. Bacteria and non-seed-bearing plants often form resting spores (*see* endospore). Some seeds and spores can remain dormant for centuries.

Many animals undergo periods of dormancy (*see* aestivation, diapause, hibernation); many invertebrates produce resting buds or spores, such as the *statoblasts of certain freshwater ectoprocts and the *gemmules of freshwater sponges, which also serve for dispersal.

dormin. *See* abscisic acid.

dorsal. 1. Designating the surface of prostrate organisms or structures, such as flatworms and fern prothalli, that is furthest from the substrate (the *upper* surface).

2. (in botany). *See* abaxial.

3. Designating the surface of a chordate that is nearest to the notochord. *Compare* ventral.

dorsal aorta. The vertebrate artery that passes oxygenated blood to the trunk and hind limbs. It is formed by fusion of the six embryonic *aortic arches after they have passed through the visceral arches and in adult tetrapods it arises from the systemic arch.

dorsifixed. Designating an anther that is fused along its back to the filament, which renders it immovable. *Compare* basifixed, versatile.

dosage compensation. The phenomenon displayed by genes on the X chromosome such that, no matter how many X chromosomes are present in the cell, the effective *gene dosage for X-linked loci is the same as that for a cell with only one X chromosome. Thus human individuals with two, three, or four X chromosomes in the set express a gene dosage for that chromosome of only one.

double fertilization (in certain angiosperms). The fertilization of both the egg cell and a polar nucleus by generative nuclei from the *pollen tube.

double helix. *See* DNA.

double recessive. An organism that is homozygous for a recessive gene and therefore phenotypically shows the effect of this gene. It is only in double recessives that the effect of a recessive gene appears in the phenotype. Double recessives are important in back-cross breeding experiments.

down feathers. *See* feathers.

Down's syndrome (mongolism). A congenital condition caused by the presence of an extra copy of chromosome 21, either as a separate chromosome or translocated onto another chromosome (such as chromosome 14). Characterized by mental retardation, typical mongoloid facial features, and a reduced life expectancy, it occurs at a rate of about one per 700 live births.

DPN (diphosphopyridine nucleotide). The former name of *NAD.

dragonflies. *See* Odonata.

drive. The motivation of an animal that provokes behaviour enabling it to satisfy a specific need or to achieve a specific goal.

drop mechanisms. *See* pollen droplet.

Drosophila. A genus comprising the fruit flies: dipteran insects used in genetic research because they are easy to keep in laboratory conditions, have a short life cycle, and produce many offspring.

drupe (pyrenocarp). A typically succulent *fruit with a stony endocarp.

Dryopithecus. A genus of fossil apes from the Miocene and early Pliocene periods, 30–40 million years ago, found in the Punjab of India and in parts of Africa. A very similar genus from Africa is known as *Proconsul*; the two genera together are sometimes called *dryopithecines*. *See also* fossil hominid.

ductless gland. *See* endocrine gland.

ductus arteriosus. A continuation of the sixth aortic arch in the mammalian foetus, connecting the pulmonary arch with the dorsal aorta. It enables blood to be shunted from the right ventricle into the systemic circulation, thus bypassing the lungs. It closes at birth.

dugong. *See* Sirenia.

duodenum. The most anterior region of the intestine of mammals, into which the bile duct and pancreatic duct open. In the duodenum food is digested by bile, pancreatic enzymes, and the enzymes of the succus entericus, which is secreted by glands in the duodenal wall.

duplex. A double helix of *DNA.

duplication. 1. A type of chromosome mutation in which a section of chromosome is doubled during mitosis or meiosis. For example, if a chromosome contains the genes ABCDEFGH, the section CD may be duplicated, resulting in ABCDCDEFGH. Sometimes the duplicated region may be attached to another chromosome. Duplications are known to be the cause of certain mutations, such as the condition known as *Bar eye* in *Drosophila*.
2. The formation of a new chromatid during the interphase following mitosis.

dura mater. The tough outer layer of connective tissue surrounding the tetrapod brain and spinal cord. *See also* meninges.

duramen (heartwood). *See* wood.

dynein. A group of at least four distinct proteins found in the flagella and microtubules of eukaryotic cells and possessing ATPase activity. Dynein occurs in the form of short arms projecting from the microtubule walls (*see* flagellum); its enzymatic activity is believed to be responsible for flagellar movement and microtubule contraction.

E

ear. The vertebrate organ of equilibrium, secondarily adapted for hearing. The receptors for both senses lie in the membranous labyrinth of the *inner ear. Various accessory structures are developed to collect and transmit sound waves to the inner ear: in fish the *swim bladder and *Weberian ossicles; in tetrapods the *outer ear and *middle ear.

ear ossicles. The small bones of the tetrapod *middle ear, which transmit vibrations of the tympanum to the fenestra ovalis of the inner ear and thus activate the sensory cells of the cochlea. The ossicles are homologous with those jaw bones of lower vertebrates that have been made redundant by changes in jaw articulation. The sole ossicle of amphibians, reptiles, and birds is the *columella auris*, which represents the hyomandibular of fish. The three ossicles of mammals, the *incus, *malleus, and *stapes, represent the quadrate, articular, and hyomandibular bones, respectively, and form a lever system that increases the force of the sound waves on the fenestra ovalis.

earwigs. *See* Dermaptera.

ecad. A *form within a species produced as a result of adaptation to its habitat. The characteristics of an ecad are not inheritable.

eccrine secretion. *See* secretion.

ecdysis (moulting). 1. The periodic shedding of the exoskeleton of arthropods to enable growth to occur. In insects and crustaceans the process is controlled by the hormone *ecdysone. *See* instar. **2.** The periodic shedding of the outer epidermal layer (stratum corneum) of reptiles. In snakes the skin is shed in a single piece; in lizards it is moulted in patches.

α-ecdysone

ecdysone (moulting hormone). A steroid hormone of insects and crustaceans that stimulates growth and moulting (ecdysis). The existence of such hormones was demonstrated in the 1920s, by Kopec's studies on moth larvae, but the first ecdysone (*α-ecdysone*) was not isolated until 1954 and the hormones were finally characterized and synthesized in the early 1960s (see formula). Ecdysones were the first hormones shown to act by stimulating the synthesis of messenger RNA by specific gene loci, initially observed by the formation of *puffs on the salivary gland giant chromosomes of certain insect larvae. Several ecdysones are synthesized from cholesterol in the blood of insects and crustaceans, the necessary enzymes being supplied by the *prothoracic glands and *Y-organs, respectively. Similar ecdysone molecules have been isolated from the leaves and roots of plants.

ecesis. The establishment of an invading plant in a community, consisting of its germination, growth, and reproduction.

echidna. *See* Monotremata.

Echinodermata. A phylum of marine invertebrates typically exhibiting radial symmetry in the adults, with the body constructed on a five-part plan. The dermis contains calcareous plates and many groups have external spines. Part of the coelom is modified as the *water vascular system, extensions of which project from the body as hydraulic *tube feet. The water vascular system opens to the exterior by a pore or cluster of pores, the *madreporite*. The larvae (*see* dipleurula) are bilaterally symmetrical and their development reveals affinities with the Chordata. The phylum includes the classes *Crinoidea (sea lilies), *Asteroidea (starfish), *Ophiuroidea (brittle stars), *Echinoidea (sea urchins), and *Holothuroidea (sea cucumbers).

Echinoidea. The class of the Echinodermata that contains the sea urchins (e.g. *Echinus*) and heart urchins (e.g. *Echinocardium*). The body is spherical, heart-shaped, or flattened, with the mouth on the ventral surface, and is covered with a rigid *test* of calcareous plates bearing movable spines, which are used in locomotion and defence.

echolocation. A method used by some animals, especially bats and dolphins, for locating objects in the dark. The animal produces high-pitched sounds that are reflected by the object so that the echo can be detected by the ear or some other sensory receptor of the animal.

ecological niche. *See* niche.

ecology. The study of living organisms in relation to their environment. It embraces all aspects of biology, with emphasis on the ways in which communities of plants and animals interact with one another and with their physical environment.

ecospecies. A group of ecotypes within a species that can cross with one another to produce fertile offspring. *Compare* coenospecies.

ecosystem. A natural unit consisting of living and nonliving parts interacting to produce a stable system. Examples are a lake or a grassland. Four components of an ecosystem can be recognized: (1) the *abiotic* (nonliving) component; (2) the *producers* (autotrophs, mostly green plants); (3) the *consumers* (heterotrophs, chiefly animals feeding on plants or other animals); (4) *decomposers* (heterotrophs, chiefly bacteria, that bring about decay of dead organic matter). The living component of an ecosystem constitutes the *community. The nature of the abiotic component determines the types of organisms found there; the organisms in their turn may gradually alter the nonliving surroundings. For example bare rock can be colonized only by lichens and mosses. They will eventually transform it to humus, so that it will later support grasses, shrubs, and trees. In this way continual change takes place within an ecosystem, with the exchange of materials between the living and nonliving parts.

ecotype. A group of organisms within a species that have morphological or physiological characteristics adapting them to their environment. Different ecotypes of the same species can cross with one another, despite the fact that some of their individual characteristics are inheritable. *See* ecospecies.

ectoderm. The outermost of the *germ layers of metazoan embryos. It develops mainly into epidermal tissue, the nervous system, sense organs, and (in lower forms) the nephridia.

ectoparasite. *See* parasite.

ectoplasm (cell cortex). A thin outer layer of *cytoplasm typical of many animal cells, particularly amoeboid cells (e.g. amoeboid Protozoa and most leuco-cytes). Ectoplasm is usually gel-like (*plasmagel*) and tends to be homogene-ous and lacking in organelles. A similar zone of gel-like cytoplasm is found in many plant cells, where it typically con-tains microtubules.

Ectoprocta (Bryozoa, Polyzoa). A phy-lum of aquatic sessile invertebrates, the moss animals and sea mats, living in colonies within self-secreted calcareous, horny, or gelatinous cases. The individu-als (*polypides*) superficially resemble coe-lenterate polyps but are in fact more advanced, having a coelom, a lophophore, and a U-shaped gut. Each polypide together with its protective case is known as a *zooid*. The Ectoprocta were formerly classified with the *Entoprocta, as part of the phylum Bryozoa, but are now usually regarded as a separate phylum.

ectotrophic mycorrhiza. *See* mycorrhiza.

edaphic factor. One of the characteristics of soil that affects the plants growing there. Edaphic factors may be physical, chemical, or biological and include pH, mineral and humus content, etc.

Edentata. An order of the Eutheria con-taining primitive mammals of the New World, characterized by a reduction and simplification of the teeth, extra articula-tions between the lumbar vertebrae for strength, strongly clawed feet often used for digging, and a typically long snout. The order includes the nocturnal insec-tivorous armadillos (e.g. *Dasypus*), which have protective bony plates encircling the body; the slow-moving herbivorous sloths (e.g. *Bradypus*); and the toothless anteaters (e.g. *Myrmecophaga*).

EEG. *See* electroencephalogram.

effector. A cell or organ that is special-ized to perform an action relative to the environment in response to a stimulus from the nervous system. Effectors include muscles, cilia and other motile systems, glands, etc. An *independent effector* is a cell, such as a cnidoblast,

that contains both receptor and effector units.

effector molecule. A substance that binds to a regulatory molecule to create a complex capable of activating or inac-tivating a gene. For example, allolactose acts as an effector molecule in the acti-vation of the *lac* operon, binding to the repressor molecule and so permitting activation of the operon.

efferent. 1. Designating a nerve or neu-rone that transmits outgoing information from the CNS to the peripheral effector organs (*see* motor neurone).
2. Designating a blood vessel that col-lects blood from a capillary bed, espe-cially any of the arteries of the aortic arches of fish that lead from the gills to the ventral aorta.

egg apparatus. The structure containing the egg cell (ovum) in an *embryo sac.

egg cell. *See* ovum.

egg membrane. A protective (and some-times nutritive) membrane that sur-rounds the fertilized ovum of animals. Most ova are surrounded by a thin *vitel-line membrane* (*primary* or *fertilization membrane*), which is secreted by the ovum itself and prevents entry of fur-ther sperm. Many ova are enclosed by one or two additional membranes. The *secondary membrane* is secreted by folli-cle cells of the ovary; an example is the *chorion of an insect's egg (*see also* zona pellucida). A *tertiary membrane* is sometimes deposited around the egg as it passes down the oviduct and is most common in eggs laid on dry land. The albumen and shell of a bird's egg, the jelly around a frog's egg, and the horny shell of a reptile's egg are tertiary mem-branes.

elaioplast (oleoplast, lipidoplast). A *plastid that stores lipids, either as oils or fats. The chloroplasts of some algae (e.g. diatoms, brown algae) may also be described as elaioplasts since they store oil.

Elasmobranchii. A subclass of the Chondrichthyes whose members are characterized by five to seven pairs of gills opening directly to the exterior; a spiracle; a heterocercal tail; and numerous rows of deciduous teeth that develop in succession. The jaw suspension is usually hyostylic. The subclass includes the orders *Cladoselachii (extinct sharks), *Selachii (sharks), and *Batoidea (skates and rays). *Compare* Holocephali.

elastin. The principal structural protein of the yellow fibres of metazoan connective tissue. Because of its property of extensibility, elastin is found predominantly in elastic structures, e.g. in the walls of large blood vessels and the alveoli of the lungs. *Compare* collagen.

elater. One of a number of hygroscopic structures produced within some sporangia to aid spore dispersal. Elaters are formed from the sporangium wall of many bryophytes; they form a tangled mass (the *elatiophore*) in some myxomycete sporangia; and they are produced from the spore wall in the horsetail *Equisetum arvense*.

electric organ. An effector of some fish that produces an electric current in the surrounding water. In most species it is developed from modified noncontractile muscle cells called *electroplaques*. Nervous stimulation elicits a small potential difference across each electroplaque and, as the electroplaques are arranged in series, an overall voltage of up to 600 V may be produced. In some fish high-voltage pulses are used to paralyse prey or predators; other species maintain a weak electric field to obtain information about the environment that can be used in navigation. The electric field is monitored by electrosensory receptors derived from modified neuromasts.

electrocardiogram (ECG). A record of the alterations in electrical potential that accompany each cycle of cardiac activity. Such alterations are measured at the surface of the body, usually by electrodes attached to the arms and legs, and are recorded as a series of waves through an oscilloscope or similar device.

electroencephalogram (EEG). A recording of the rhythmical changes in electrical potential in the vertebrate brain, which are produced mainly in the cerebral cortex. It is obtained by placing recording electrodes on the scalp. Variations in the standard pattern can be correlated with different normal and abnormal mental states.

electron microscope. *See* microscope.

electron transport chain. An assembly of enzymes and proteins in a biological system that is capable of accepting elec-

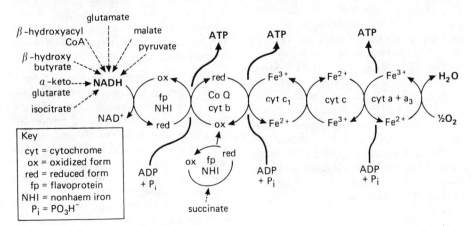

Electron transport chain in mitochondria with probable sites of phosphorylation

trons or hydrogen atoms, which are transferred in an ordered sequence from one component of the chain to the next (via a series of oxidation-reduction reactions involving various substrates) and finally to molecular oxygen. The predominant electron transport chain is that functioning in *aerobic respiration. Also known as the *respiratory chain*, it is present in the inner mitochondrial membranes of eukaryote cells and in the cell membranes of prokaryotes and receives electrons or hydrogen atoms derived from reactions of the *Krebs cycle. Much of the energy released during electron transfer is conserved in the form of ATP by *oxidative phosphorylation. The enzymes of the chain are dehydrogenases, some of which are *flavoproteins, with FAD or FMN as prosthetic groups; other coenzymes involved are *NAD (and NADP) and *coenzyme Q. The protein components of the chain include the *cytochromes (see illustration).

Other electron transport chains occur in the microsomes; these are not coupled to phosphorylation.

electrophoresis. A technique used for the separation of charged molecules, particularly proteins, developed by Tiselius in 1937. Charged molecules in solution will migrate in the presence of an electric field according to their charge; the size and shape of the molecule also affect the rate of migration. Different pHs can be used to obtain different charged species. The technique is commonly performed by using an inert porous medium, such as starch, silica gel, *polyacrylamide gel, or wetted filter paper. The sample is placed in a slot or well at one end of the supporting gel and the electric field is produced by application of direct current. Nonpigmented molecules are detected in the gel by staining procedures or by differential optical absorption. *See also* gel electrophoresis.

elephants. *See* Proboscidea.

elytra (*sing.* **elytron**). The hard leathery forewings of the *Coleoptera (beetles), which form a protective covering for the membranous hind wings at rest.

emasculation. The removal of the anthers of a flower (usually an unopened one) so that it cannot self-pollinate, in order that cross-pollination can be artificially performed.

Embden-Meyerhof pathway. *See* glycolysis.

embedding. A process used in the preparation of permanent microscope slides of organisms and tissues. In light microscopy it consists of immersing the material in melted paraffin wax after dehydration and clearing. The wax impregnates the material and is allowed to set; the embedded material is then cut into thin sections using a *microtome. After sectioning, the wax is removed by dissolving it out in xylene, and the xylene is removed with absolute alcohol. The sections are then hydrated, by placing them in alcohols of decreasing concentration for a few minutes, before staining. In electron microscopy tissues are usually embedded in Araldite.

Embioptera. A small order of gregarious exopterygote insects, the foot spinners, found in the warmer parts of the world. They live in small silken tunnels, built with silk from a spinning gland on the front legs. The order shows sexual dimorphism: the females are wingless and the males have two pairs of wings covered with hairs.

embryo. The structure developed from a zygote prior to hatching or birth (in animals) or germination (in plants). Embryo formation provides a period for the laying down of tissues and organs without the rigours of independent existence or contact with the environment. The animal zygote undergoes repeated mitotic divisions into cells that differentiate into the tissues and organs of the embryo (*see* cleavage, blastula, gastrulation).

Among plants, only the bryophytes, pteridophytes, and seed plants consistently produce embryos. In most plants the zygote differentiates into the young sporophyte plus associated structures that aid its development. The most commonly occurring of these structures is the *suspensor*, which consists of a few cells that elongate to push the embryo further into the parent gametophyte tissue. It is usually formed from the products of one of the cells resulting from the first division of the zygote. In addition to the suspensor, some lower vascular plants possess a bulky structure at the root pole termed the *foot*, which serves as a haustorial organ (in bryophytes it persists as part of the adult sporophyte). In most plants the first division of the zygote is at right angles to the long axis of the archegonium or embryo sac. In *exoscopic development*, seen in bryophytes and certain pteridophytes (e.g. the Ophioglossales), the outer cell gives rise to the shoot and the inner cell to the foot and root. In *endoscopic development without suspensor*, seen in primitive ferns (e.g. the Marattiaceae), the inner cell gives rise to the shoot and the outer cell to the foot and root. In *endoscopic development with suspensor*, seen in many pteridophytes and all seed plants, the embryo develops from the inner cell and the outer cell forms the suspensor. In gymnosperms the gametophyte can produce up to five oospheres, each of which may give rise to up to four embryos, a process known as *cleavage polyembryony*. In this way up to 20 embryos may develop in a single ovule, but one of these usually gains superiority and only one seedling is produced at germination.

embryogenesis. The formation and development of an *embryo from a fertilized egg.

embryology. The study of the development of embryos.

Embryophyta (in some classification schemes). One of the two major subkingdoms of plants (*compare* Thal-

lophyta), characterized by the development of a multicellular embryo from the zygote while the latter is still attached to the parent plant. The gametangia and sporangia are multicellular and the outer layer is sterile and forms a wall (in some seed plants the gametangia are greatly reduced). The group comprises the *Bryophyta and *Tracheophyta.

embryo sac. The structure produced from the megaspore mother cell in angiosperm ovules, comparable with the female gametophyte tissue in gymnosperm ovules and usually regarded as homologous with it. However, the behaviour of its nuclei differs from that of the gymnosperm nuclei and this has led to the suggestion that the embryo sac is without homologue in other seed plants. There are ten main types of embryo sacs, based on the number of nuclei formed by meiosis from the spore mother cell that contribute to its formation and on the ultimate number and arrangement of these nuclei. Whatever their origin, the nuclei eventually form two main groups. At the micropylar end is an *egg apparatus*, consisting of an *egg cell* with or without one to two *synergidae* (*synergid cells*). The egg cell produces the embryo after fertilization; the synergidae probably play a role in the process of fertilization. The other nuclei in the embryo sac are not involved in embryo formation except in nutrition. They form two subgroups: at the chalazal end are a variable number of *antipodal nuclei* (absent in one type of embryo sac); in the middle of the embryo sac are one or more *polar nuclei*. The latter are either haploid or polyploid as a result of fusion of embryo sac nuclei and one of them may be fertilized by a male nucleus from the *pollen tube to form a primary endosperm nucleus.

enamel. The white calcified tissue that covers the exposed surface (crown) of a tooth. It is produced by certain cells of the epithelium (*ameloblasts*) and consists of about 97% inorganic and 3% organic material, the inorganic constituents being almost entirely calcium salts in the form of large apatite crystals. *Compare* bone.

enantiomers. *See* optical activity.

enation. A small lateral projection, devoid of a vascular supply, that is produced by certain primitive vascular plants and may represent an early stage in *microphyll evolution.

endarch. Designating a stele in which the metaxylem develops to the outside of the protoxylem, i.e. centrifugal to it. *Compare* centrarch, exarch, mesarch.

endemism. The condition of organisms being restricted to a particular region, such as an island.

endocarp. *See* pericarp.

endocrine gland (ductless gland). One of a number of organs or discrete groups of cells, found in all vertebrates and various invertebrates, that synthesize hormones and secrete them directly into the circulating blood. Vertebrate endocrine glands include the pituitary, pineal, thyroid, parathyroid, and adrenal glands, the gonads, placenta (in mammals), islets of Langerhans (in the pancreas), and parts of the alimentary tract. They function in close association with the nervous system in most regulatory responses of animals (*see* neuroendocrine systems). Endocrine glands (or their parts) derived from mesoderm, i.e. the adrenal cortex and gonads, produce steroid hormones; those from the ectoderm and endoderm secrete modified amino acids, peptides, or proteins. The significance of endocrine secretion was first clearly demonstrated in 1849, by Berthold. *Compare* exocrine gland.

endocrinology. The study of the structure and function of the endocrine glands and the role of their secretions (hormones) in the chemical integration of the organism.

endocytosis. The process by which a cell engulfs bulk quantities of material by the infolding or extension of the plasma membrane to form a vesicle or vacuole. The process is called *phagocytosis* (cell eating) when the material is particulate; specialized cells in which phagocytosis is a major function (usually animal cells) are called *phagocytes. Digestion of the vesicle contents is effected by fusion with primary lysosomes, forming secondary lysosomes containing the requisite enzymes.

When the material ingested is liquid, the process is called *pinocytosis* (cell drinking). The vesicles formed are often extremely small (*micropinocytosis*). Pinocytosis is characteristic of amoeboid protozoans and many other, often amoeboid, cells, e.g. leucocytes, embryo cells, certain kidney (fluid exchange) and liver cells, and many tissue culture cells. It also occurs in plant cells. Pinocytosis may be a means of acquiring and/or transporting macromolecules such as hormones, proteins, lipids, and glycoproteins.

endoderm (entoderm). The innermost of the *germ layers of metazoan embryos. It lines the archenteron of the gastrula and develops into the lining of the alimentary canal between the stomodaeum and proctodaeum. It also forms a component of the derivatives of the alimentary canal and lines the respiratory tract.

endodermis. The layer of cells surrounding the vascular tissue of plants. It is normally regarded as the innermost layer of the cortex, usually being derived from the same meristem, but it may occasionally arise from the same meristem as the stele. It is distinguished from adjacent cells both physiologically and structurally, the most striking feature being the formation of a *Casparian strip in each cell. The walls of older cells may become heavily impregnated with suberin, cellulose, or lignin, so that in parts of the axis the endodermis may form a complete impervious ring; in other parts of the axis, cells with unthickened walls (*passage cells) allow the passage of solutes between the stele and the cortex. The endodermis is most clearly visible in roots but also occurs in stems and leaves, often being distinct (as in the stems of pterido-phytes). It can also form a boundary between the pith and stele. In some plants the endodermis is represented by a *starch sheath. The starch, mestom, and *bundle sheaths found in angio-sperm leaves are all endodermal in ori-gin.

endogamy. The fusion of gametes from parents that are closely related to one another. *See* inbreeding.

endolymph. The viscous fluid filling the structures of the *inner ear of vertebrates.

endomembrane system. A system of cytoplasmic membranes characteristic of eukaryote cells. In the *endomembrane concept* it is postulated that these mem-branes are developmentally and func-tionally related and that the plasma membrane and the *vacuolar apparatus* (tonoplast of vacuoles and lysosomes) are the two end products of differentia-tion of the outer nuclear membrane and rough endoplasmic reticulum (ER) via intermediate stages (*transition* membrane elements), including the smooth ER, Golgi apparatus, and various vesicles. The system excludes the inner mem-branes of double-membrane bounded organelles (mitochondria, plastids, nuclei). It participates in the synthesis, storage, transport, and modification of many products for use within the cell or for export.

endometrium. The glandular mucous membrane that lines the mammalian uterus. Its thickness and structure vary with the phase of the oestrous cycle, under the control of progesterone and oestrogens. Its function is to receive and possibly to nourish the early embryo (*see* implantation), and in the human female its outer cells are sloughed off

and discharged from the vagina during menstruation (*see* menstrual cycle). *See also* decidua.

endomitosis. The process by which the chromosome number in a nucleus is doubled but nuclear division does not occur, resulting in *polyploidy of the cell. In some cases the chromosomes do not separate from each other and giant chromosomes are produced, as in the salivary glands of *Drosophila* (*see* polytene).

endonuclease. An enzyme (*see* DNase) that cuts a nucleic acid sequence inter-nally by hydrolysing internal phosphodi-ester bonds. *See also* restriction endonuclease. *Compare* exonuclease.

endoparasite. *See* parasite.

endoplasm. The inner *cytoplasm of cells, containing the bulk of the cell organelles and sometimes enclosed by ectoplasm. It is usually sol-like (*plasma-sol*).

endoplasmic reticulum (ER). A system (reticulum) of membranes found in the cytoplasm of virtually all eukaryote cells (see illustration at *cell). It is continu-ous with the outer membrane of the nuclear envelope and in plant cells it frequently terminates at (or may pass through) the plasmodesmata, opposite the ER of adjacent cells. The reticulum typically consists of flattened sacs (*cis-ternae*) and vesicles linked by more tubular portions, forming a network of channels through the cytoplasm whose contents are separate from the rest of the cytoplasm. The ER is called *rough* (*rugose, granular*) when covered with ribosomes and *smooth* when ribosomes are absent. During protein synthesis the ribosomes form spiralled polyribosomes (polysomes) over its surface. The pro-teins made are sometimes passed into the cisternae for transport to other parts of the cell or for export, as with zymo-gen proteins in the exocrine (acinar) cells of the pancreas; these are trans-ported via the cisternae to the *Golgi apparatus prior to export. The ER also works in association with the Golgi apparatus in the formation of *lysosomes and in intestinal epithelia, where smooth ER assembles and passes on triglycerides to the Golgi apparatus. Smooth ER, which is typically vesicular, may itself adopt a lysosomal function: in the gonads of certain animals it synthesizes sterols for steroid hormone synthesis; in the liver it is involved in lipid and cholesterol metabolism and in detoxification processes.

The ER may be a dominant organelle, as in pancreatic acinar cells and in muscle cells. In the latter, smooth ER is specialized to form the *sarcoplasmic reticulum*, which stores calcium needed for contraction (*see* striated muscle). ER is often dominant where its cisternae are used for storage of proteins (sometimes as crystals) and other materials. In some cells, e.g. mature leaf mesophyll cells, it is relatively sparse.

The variety of functions associated with the ER indicates that it has contributed greatly to the diversification of cytoplasmic processes possible in eukaryote cells. *See also* endomembrane system.

endopodite. *See* biramous appendage.

Endopterygota (Holometabola). A group of the Pterygota (winged insects) in which metamorphosis is complete, with a pupal stage, and wings develop within the body of the larva, which does not resemble the adult. The Endopterygota contains the orders *Neuroptera (lacewings), *Megaloptera (alder flies), *Mecoptera (scorpion flies), *Lepidoptera (butterflies and moths), *Trichoptera (caddis flies), *Diptera (flies), *Siphonaptera (fleas), *Hymenoptera (ants, bees, and wasps), *Coleoptera (beetles), and *Strepsiptera (stylops).

end organ. The structure at the terminal of a peripheral nerve, e.g. the *receptor of a sensory neurone or the *end plate of a motor neurone.

endoscopic development (in plants). *See* embryo.

endoskeleton. A skeleton lying entirely within the body of an animal, such as the bony or cartilaginous skeleton of vertebrates or the silica spicules of radiolarians. The vertebrate endoskeleton gives form and support to the body, protects and supports the underlying soft organs, and provides a system of levers and attachments for muscles, which is essential in locomotion. *Compare* exoskeleton.

endosperm. A nutritive tissue in the developing seeds of angiosperms. In many seeds (*nonendospermic* seeds) it is absorbed during the development of the embryo but in some angiosperms, such as palms, it increases greatly and forms the storage tissue of the ripe seed (*endospermic* seeds). It represents part of the gametophyte tissue, since it develops from the embryo sac as a result of double fertilization. One male gamete fuses with the egg to produce the embryo; the other fuses with one or more polar nuclei to form the *primary endosperm nucleus* (which is thus diploid or polyploid). This nucleus then divides to produce the endosperm.

The term endosperm is sometimes used for the female prothallus tissue in the seeds of gymnosperms. However, because it is formed before fertilization, it is not homologous with the endosperm of angiosperms.

endospore. A cell formed within the vegetative bacterial cell of eubacteria of the genera *Bacillus* and *Clostridium*. Under favourable conditions the endospore germinates, giving rise to a vegetative cell. Endospores are highly resistant to heat and are viable for several years in the dry state.

endosporic. Designating spore production within a sex organ or sporangium: the most common type of spore production. *Compare* exosporic.

endostyle. A ciliated glandular groove on the midventral surface of the pharynx in cephalochordates, some urochordates, and larval cyclostomes (*see* ammocoete). Water containing food particles is drawn into the mouth by the action of cilia in the endostyle and other parts of the pharynx. Food is trapped in mucus produced by the endostyle and is passed upwards, around the pharynx, and towards the oesophagus by ciliary action. The water passes out via the gill slits.

endothelium. A single layer of cells that is derived from embryonic mesoderm and lines the internal cavities of vertebrate blood and lymphatic vessels. It is morphologically similar to *epithelium, particularly simple squamous epithelium. *Compare* mesothelium.

endotoxin. A complex macromolecular poison that remains within the bacterium producing it after infection (usually as part of the cell wall). Endotoxins are present in *Salmonella*, *Shigella*, and *Vibrio cholerae*, all of which cause dysentery. The isolated toxins produce an inflammatory response if injected under the skin of animals but their effect on the host during bacterial infection is not known. *Compare* exotoxin.

endotrophic mycorrhiza. *See* mycorrhiza.

end plate. The area of muscle cell membrane immediately below the nerve ending in a *neuromuscular junction.

end-plate potential (EPP). The local graded potential change that is elicited in the postsynaptic (i.e. muscle-cell) membrane of a *neuromuscular junction by the release of neurotransmitter from the nerve ending. *See also* synapse.

end-product inhibition. *See* feedback inhibition.

enrichment culture. A method of isolating a particular type of microorganism in a mixed culture by adjusting medium composition, aeration, pH, illumination, temperature, etc., to favour the growth of the chosen organism.

enteropeptidase (enterokinase). A peptidase enzyme secreted by the vertebrate intestinal glands, forming part of the *succus entericus. It converts trypsinogen to the active form, *trypsin.

enterovirus. An obsolete term for a picornavirus, which was originally thought to infect mainly the digestive tract. *See* virus.

enthalpy (heat content). Symbol: H. A thermodynamic property of a system defined by the equation $H = U + pV$, where U is the *internal energy, V is its volume, and p is the external pressure. In biological systems, the pressure, temperature, and volume remain constant and the change in enthalpy (ΔH) is equal to the change in internal energy (ΔU). During a reaction in which there is a change in H, heat may be liberated from the reactant molecules to the surroundings (as in glucose oxidation) or, conversely, heat may be extracted from the surroundings to the reactant system. These are termed *exothermic* and *endothermic* reactions respectively. By convention, when heat is given out ΔH is taken as negative; when heat is absorbed it is positive.

entoderm. *See* endoderm.

entomology. The branch of zoology concerned with the study of insects, including their anatomy, physiology, distribution, economic importance, etc.

entomophily. Pollination with insects as the vectors carrying pollen from the anther to the stigma. Entomophilous flowers have brightly coloured petals and/or scent to attract insects and nectar (or excess pollen) as food to encourage the insect to visit other similar flowers. The pollen is sticky so that it adheres to the insect, and the anthers and stigmas are often positioned so that the insect brushes against both on its visit to a flower.

Entoprocta (Bryozoa, Polyzoa). A phylum of sessile mostly marine pseudocoelomate invertebrates, solitary or colonial, having a polyp-like body. They superficially resemble the *Ectoprocta, and were formerly classi-

fied with them as a division of the Bryozoa, but the body lacks a true coelom
and lophophore.

entropy. Symbol: *S*. A thermodynamic
property of a system. The more random
or disordered the system, the greater is
the value of its entropy. A compound in
an organized crystal structure has a low
entropy but in the liquid or gaseous
state the entropy is greater as the distribution of the constituent molecules is
more random. The entropy of a system
is dependent on its specific conditions
(e.g. temperature, volume). The change
in the entropy of a system (ΔS) is
defined as the ratio of the heat absorbed
by the system (Δq) to the thermodynamic temperature (T) at which the heat
is absorbed, i.e. $\Delta S = \Delta q/T$. The second law of thermodynamics states that
the entropy of the universe is increasing.

environment (in ecology). The external
surroundings in which an organism
lives, which are influenced and determined by the interactions of climate,
water, light, etc., and other living organisms. The environment affects the
growth, development, and behaviour of
the organism.

enzyme. A highly specialized protein
that catalyses biochemical reactions by
converting one molecule (the *substrate*)
to another molecule (the *product*) by
means of an intermediate enzyme-substrate complex. After the reaction the
product separates from the enzyme surface, leaving the enzyme unchanged, and
may then serve as a substrate in a subsequent reaction in a metabolic pathway.
Enzymes are classified according to the
nature of the substrate they react with
and the type of reaction they catalyse.
Each enzyme is given two names: a
short trivial name (which is the name
most commonly used) and a more
detailed systematic name, based on an
internationally accepted system of classification. Most trivial names end in *-ase*,
which is added to the substrate name,

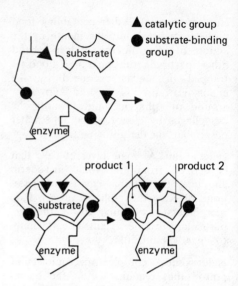

Fig. 1: Binding of substrate to enzyme
by induced fit

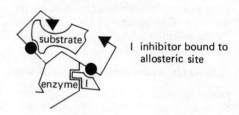

Fig. 2: Noncompetitive inhibition

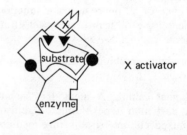

Fig. 3: Enzyme activation

as in *lactase* and *cellulase*, or to the
name of the reaction, as in
dehydrogenase and *carboxylase*. With its

systematic name, each enzyme is given a four-part code number. The first number of the code places the enzyme in one of six general groups indicating the type of reaction involved, i.e. *oxidoreductase (1), *transferase (2), *hydrolase (3), *lyase (4), *isomerase (5), or *ligase (6). The next two numbers indicate reaction subgroups specifying the group involved in the reaction and the fourth number provides the absolute definition of the enzyme. For example, the enzyme alcohol dehydrogenase has the systematic name alcohol: NAD oxidoreductase, code number E.C. (enzyme classification) 1.1.1.1.

Enzymes are present in all cells, the number and composition varying with cell type. They are extremely efficient and some can metabolize as much as 1012 molecules of substrate per second. Maximum efficiency usually occurs within a physiological temperature range and pH; high temperatures or extremes of pH destroy the enzyme. The rate of the reaction is summarized in the Michaelis-Menten equation (*see* enzyme kinetics).

All enzymes can catalyse only one type of chemical reaction and some will operate on one particular substrate only. This specificity derives from their shape. An enzyme consists of one or more chains of amino acids linked together to form a complex structure. Enzymes may also have a nonprotein component, called a *cofactor. The substrate, which is considerably smaller than the enzyme, reacts with a particular area on the enzyme, the *active site*. Most enzymes appear to function according to an *induced-fit* principle whereby the binding of the substrate to the enzyme causes a change in the shape of the latter so that the substrate can fit exactly into the active site. This results in the necessary alignment of catalytic groups (Fig. 1). Attractive forces (electrostatic bonds between oppositely charged groups and *hydrophobic interactions) maintain the substrate in the required position and the reaction can proceed.

The activity, presence, and quantity of an enzyme in a cell can be regulated in various ways. Enzymes can be inhibited both irreversibly and reversibly. Irreversible inhibition is caused by substances reacting with groups at the active site (for example by forming covalent bonds) in such a way as to destroy it or modify it permanently. Reversible inhibition may be competitive or noncompetitive. *Competitive inhibition* occurs when molecules similar to the substrate bind to the active site but cannot induce the correct enzyme shape, so that the reaction cannot proceed. It can be reversed by increasing the concentration of the substrate. *Noncompetitive inhibition*, which is not reversed by increasing the substrate concentration, occurs when a compound is bound to a region of the enzyme other than the active site; this region is known as an *allosteric site*. It does not prevent binding of the substrate to the active site but it alters the shape of the enzyme so that the catalytic groups are not correctly aligned (Fig. 2). This type of allosteric regulation can operate in many ways, for example in *feedback inhibition. It can also serve to activate an enzyme: an activator molecule can affect the active site so as to cause the correct alignment of a substrate molecule (Fig. 3).

The *induction* and *repression* of enzymes is achieved by a coarser type of control. The addition of certain substances (*inducing agents*) to the cell can result in enzyme synthesis (*see* adaptive enzyme). Other molecules (*repressors*) can repress the synthesis of an unneeded enzyme by binding to DNA, so preventing the initial stages of protein synthesis.

enzyme kinetics. The study of the rates of enzyme-controlled reactions. Enzyme kinetics are similar to ordinary chemical reaction kinetics except that they always show the characteristic property of saturation. At low concentrations of the substrate the rate of reaction (v) is proportional to the substrate concentration [S], but at higher substrate concentrations saturation occurs and a maximum rate is achieved (V_{max}).

The rate of reaction is given by the *Michaelis-Menten equation*: $v = V_{max}[S]/(K_M + [S])$. K_M is the *Michaelis-Menten constant*, equal to the substrate concentration at half the maximum velocity. The equation is derived from consideration of an enzyme-catalysed reaction in which an enzyme, E, reacts with a substrate, S, to form an enzyme-substrate complex, ES, which breaks down in a second reaction to form the product, P, and the enzyme, E. The reactions are reversible and have specific rate constants, k_1, k_2, k_3, and k_4.

$$E+S \underset{k_2}{\overset{k_1}{\rightleftharpoons}} ES \underset{k_4}{\overset{k_3}{\rightleftharpoons}} E+P$$

The rate constant k_4 is negligible. The Michaelis-Menten constant is the ratio $(k_2 + k_3)/k_1$.

Eocene. An epoch of the *Tertiary period.

eosinophil. A polymorph having large cytoplasmic granules that stain brilliantly with acid dyes, e.g. eosin. Eosinophils comprise 1–3% of the white cells in human blood. During parasitic infections and some allergic states and skin diseases the number of eosinophils in blood increases – a condition known as *eosinophilia*. Eosinophils may play some role in antibody-antigen reactions, possibly by releasing or absorbing histamine.

eosin Y. *See* staining.

Eosuchia. An extinct order of lizard-like lepidosaurian reptiles, e.g. *Youngina*, that appeared in the Upper Permian and became extinct at the beginning of the Cenozoic. They gave rise to the later lepidosaurs; similarities between the skulls of the Lower Triassic *Prolacerta* and the lizards indicate that *Prolacerta* was probably ancestral to the Squamata.

ephemeral. A plant that completes its life cycle – from germination to seed production and death – more than once in a single year. The life cycle is therefore very short and germination and growth are extremely rapid. Many garden weeds are ephemerals, including groundsel and shepherd's purse. *Compare* annual, biennial, perennial.

Ephemeroptera. The order of exopterygote insects that contains the mayflies (e.g. *Ephemera*), which are found universally, usually near fresh water. The adults rarely live for longer than a day and do not feed (the mouthparts are degenerate). Mayflies have a pair of long tail bristles (*cerci*) and two pairs of transparent wings (the forewings are much the larger), which are held vertically over the body at rest. The long-lived aquatic herbivorous nymphs develop into active winged *subimagos*, a stage unique among insects, which undergo a further moult to produce the adult.

ephyra. A stage in the life cycle of the Scyphozoa. *See* scyphistoma.

epiblast. A small flap of tissue in the embryo of some Gramineae (grasses) that is inserted opposite the scutellum. It is variously interpreted as representing a modified leaf, a rudimentary (and extra) cotyledon, or part of the coleorhiza.

epiboly. A process that occurs during gastrulation of the vertebrate embryo, in which the smaller blastomeres of the animal pole of the blastula grow over and enclose the cells of the vegetal pole.

epicalyx. A whorl of small sepal-like structures found outside and alternating with the sepals in some flowers.

epicarp (exocarp). *See* pericarp.

epicotyl. The shoot axis of the plumule above the cotyledonary node. *Compare* hypocotyl.

epidermis. 1. The outermost layer of cells covering the body of an animal. In invertebrates it consists of a single layer of cells that frequently secretes a protective *cuticle. In most vertebrates the epidermis forms the outer layer of the *skin and consists of several stratified layers in a continual state of renewal; the outermost layer of epidermis in terrestrial vertebrates is composed of dead cornified cells (*see* Malpighian layer, stratum corneum). Epidermal structures include beaks, nails, claws, feathers, and hair; epidermal glands secrete mucus, sweat, and milk.

2. The outer layer of cells in plants. It usually consists of a single layer of rectangular cells that fit closely together to form a covering that protects the plant from attack by bacteria and fungi, mechanical damage, desiccation, etc. The leaves and stems of certain plants have a *multiple epidermis*, consisting of the outer epidermal layer plus the *hypodermis. The epidermis of the aerial parts of many terrestrial plants is covered by a *cuticle, which reinforces its protective function. Epidermal cells are living and parenchymatous in origin. They are derived from the tunica meristem and may be modified to perform various functions, as in *guard cells. The epidermis that bears root hairs is called the *piliferous layer*.

epididymis. A long convoluted tubule in vertebrates that is derived from the anterior part of the embryonic mesonephros and lies close to the testis. Spermatozoa pass from the seminiferous tubules of the testis via the vasa efferentia to the epididymis, where they mature and are stored before passing to the vas deferens or mesonephric duct.

epigamic. Designating an animal characteristic that is attractive to the opposite sex and is therefore concerned in mating or courtship. For example, the colours displayed during courtship by certain animals are epigamic colours.

epigeal (in botany). Developing above ground. Fungal fruiting bodies such as toadstools and mushrooms and seed germination in which the cotyledons are taken above ground by growth of the hypocotyl are termed epigeal. *Compare* hypogeal.

epigenesis. The theory that a fertilized egg develops into an embryo and then into an adult by the gradual production, organization, and increase in complexity of its parts. It was proposed in the 18th century in opposition to the theory of *preformation.

epiglottis. A cartilaginous flap on the ventral wall of the mammalian pharynx. It closes over the glottis during swallowing. *See* larynx.

epigyny. The condition of angiosperm flowers of having the gynoecium below the insertion of the other flower parts, so that the receptacle is fused with it; i.e. having an inferior gynoecium. *Compare* hypogyny, perigyny.

epimers. Two monosaccharides that differ only in their configuration about one carbon atom. For example, D-glucose and D-mannose are epimers with respect to carbon 2.

epinasty. Downward curvature of a plant organ as a result of more rapid growth of its upper side. It is typical of some leaves and petals. *See* nyctinastic movements.

epinephrine. *See* adrenaline.

epiphysis. The end portion of a mammalian long bone, containing an ossification centre distinct from that of the *diaphysis. A plate of cartilage separates the epiphysis from the diaphysis. New cartilage continues to be laid down at the epiphysis side of the plate while ossification takes place at the diaphysis side, until the cartilage is occluded by fusion of the epiphysis and diaphysis at maturity. This arrangement allows the bone to increase in length while it develops a firm ossified articulation.

epiphyte. A plant that grows attached to the surface of another plant to gain a more beneficial position. The epiphyte is nutritionally independent and the supporting plant does not appear to suffer injury. Common epiphytes are orchids growing on the high branches of trees and mosses growing on tree bark.

episomes. Genetic elements sometimes present in a bacterial cell that are able to replicate in either the autonomous state or while integrated into the chromosome. Episomes are able to shift between these two states. *F factors, *bacteriocin factors, and temperate phages are episomes. At one time elements capable of integration were called episomes and those incapable of integration were termed *plasmids, but there is now a tendency to refer to all such elements as plasmids. They are widely used in *genetic engineering.

epistatic. Designating a gene whose presence suppresses the effect of another (nonallelic) gene. This suppressing action is known as *epistasis*. For example, a mutation causing lack of wings in *Drosophila* is epistatic to any mutation causing a change in wing morphology (such as curled or short wings). *See also* hypostatic. *Compare* dominant.

epithelium. Vertebrate tissue that is composed of closely apposed cells separated by very little intercellular substance and is derived from embryonic ectoderm and endoderm. In its simplest form epithelium consists of a continuous layer of cells covering internal and external surfaces, e.g. the skin and the linings of the gastrointestinal, respiratory, and urinogenital tracts. It also forms more specialized structures that either remain in contact with the lining epithelium, e.g. sweat and salivary glands, or completely lose contact, e.g. endocrine glands. Epithelia are classified according to the shape of the cell and the number of cell layers. They may be either *squamous* (flat), *cuboidal*, or *columnar* and are present in one (*simple*) or more (*stratified*) layers, e.g. simple squamous epithelium, stratified columnar epithelium, etc. While morphologically identical to epithelium, the linings of certain cavities that are derived from embryonic mesoderm are known as *mesothelium and *endothelium.

EPP. *See* end-plate potential.

EPSP. *See* excitatory postsynaptic potential.

equatorial plate. The plane of the equator of the *spindle, along which the centromeres of chromosomes come to lie during metaphase of mitosis and meiosis. In mitosis, the centromeres lie exactly on the equatorial plate, while in meiosis the centromeres of homologous chromosomes come to lie on the spindle, on opposite sides of the plate and equidistant from it.

erepsin. A mixture of proteolytic enzymes found in the *succus entericus, secreted by the mammalian intestinal glands.

ergastic substances. An obsolete term for reserve or waste products of metabolism that are stored in, but are not strictly part of, living protoplasm, vacuoles, or cell walls. They include starch grains, tannins, and crystals of calcium oxalate.

ergastoplasm. The term (now obsolete) originally used in classical cytology to designate the cytoplasmic structure now known, since the advent of electron microscopy, as rough *endoplasmic reticulum. Polysomes, associated with this structure, were known as *ergosomes*.

ergosome. *See* ergastoplasm.

ergosterol. A plant sterol that acts as a precursor for vitamin D in animals, being converted to this vitamin by ultraviolet radiation.

ergot. *See* sclerotium.

erythroblast. A nucleated cell in bone marrow that gives rise to a red blood cell. Development of the erythroblast is characterized by successive mitoses to produce cells with more haemoglobin and increasingly small nuclei. This eventually results in the formation of a *reticulocyte – an immature red blood cell.

erythrocyte. *See* red blood cell.

erythropoietin. A hormone-like substance that is released by the kidneys and other organs in mammals in response to low oxygen concentrations in the tissues. It stimulates the production of red blood cells in bone marrow.

Escherichia coli. The bacterium most widely used in research in molecular genetics. A member of the Enterobacteriacae, it is rod-shaped, motile, and Gram-negative and does not form spores. It contains a single chromosomal DNA molecule, 1.3 mm long. *E. coli* is a normal inhabitant of the colon of man. Though usually harmless, it can cause urinary-tract infections and certain strains cause acute diarrhoea in infants. *See also lac* operon.

essential amino acids. The amino acids that cannot be synthesized by higher vertebrates and must therefore form a part of the diet. The essential amino acids for man are methionine, tryptophan, threonine, valine, isoleucine, lysine, leucine, and phenylalanine; the albino rat requires these eight amino acids plus arginine and histidine.

essential element. *See* macronutrient.

essential fatty acids. Three unsaturated fatty acids, *linoleic acid* ($C_{17}H_{31}COOH$), *linolenic acid* ($C_{17}H_{29}COOH$), and *arachidonic acid* ($C_{19}H_{31}COOH$), that are essential for the growth of mammals. As constituents of phospholipids and glycerides, they are vital for membrane production and fat metabolism. Only linoleic acid is required in the diet as the other two fatty acids can be synthesized from it.

etaerio. A collection of fruits formed from a single flower in which the gynoecium is apocarpous. The etaerio may consist of drupes, e.g. raspberry; follicles, e.g. larkspur; or achenes, e.g. travellers' joy. *See* fruit.

Ethiopian. (Designating) a zoogeographical region of *Arctogea that consists of Africa south of the Sahara. Some authorities regard Madagascar as a separate region.

ethology. *See* animal behaviour.

ethylene. An unsaturated hydrocarbon gas, C_2H_4, released from most plant organs in varying concentrations, most obviously from ripening fruits. It probably triggers ripening and is responsible for the accompanying climacteric rise in respiration typical of some fruits, e.g. tomato, avocado. Ethylene may also sometimes play a role in the breaking of seed dormancy. It can retard growth of some plant organs, e.g. pea epicotyls. *See* climacteric.

etiolation. A type of growth characteristic of plants grown in darkness, which ensures, under natural conditions, that the shoot is carried as rapidly as possible towards light. A typical etiolated plant lacks chlorophyll, giving it a yellow or white appearance. It has reduced unexpanded leaves if a dicot (rolled, sometimes elongated, leaves if a monocot), elongated and often thin internodes (including mesocotyl in monocots; hypocotyl or epicotyl, with a hooked plumule, in dicots), and reduced lignification. Light reverses the effects of darkness, favouring leaf growth, retarding internode (stem) growth, and stimulating chloroplasts to undergo *greening*, i.e. chlorophyll synthesis (*see* etioplast). Greening and associated events are mediated, at least partially, by *phytochrome.

etioplast. The type of chloroplast that is formed in the absence of light and is thus found in etiolated leaves as well as occasionally in dark-grown organs such as roots and hypocotyls. Its chief structural feature is a highly symmetrical (pseudocrystalline) array of tubular and vesicular membranes called the *prolamellar body*. On exposure to light, this body rapidly disperses and develops into the lamellar system typical of the mature chloroplast. During the accompanying greening process, new or increased synthesis of chloroplast components such as RNA, proteins, lipids, ribosomes, and pigments occurs.

Euascomycetidae. *See* Ascomycetes.

eubacteria. A group of *bacteria that are characterized by a rigid cell wall and, in motile forms, by the possession of flagella. Eubacteria are sometimes known as the true bacteria; they comprise the vast majority of species.

eucaryote. *See* eukaryote.

euchromatin. The chief constituent of *chromatin in the nuclei of plant and animal cells. It is distinguished from the smaller chromatin fraction (*see* heterochromatin) by its state of condensation, staining properties, and genetic character.

eugenics. The branch of biology concerned with human heredity. It advocates the possibility of improving the human race by encouraging and promoting the interbreeding of people having 'good' genes and discouraging or preventing the interbreeding of those with 'bad' ones. The difficulty lies in deciding which genes are desirable; in addition, the influence of the environment can never entirely be excluded as a factor in their expression.

Euglenophyta. Unicellular motile algae (*see* Contophora) with no cell wall (the outer protoplast forms a *pellicle). There are basically two flagella but one is usually extremely reduced and may be absent; they are rooted in a gullet at one end of the cell. The pigments present are chlorophylls a and b and β-carotene, and the storage product is *paramylum* (a polysaccharide similar to starch). Some forms, however, lack chlorophyll and are heterotrophic. There is no known sexual reproduction. *See also* Mastigophora.

eukaryote (eucaryote). An organism whose cells contain their genetic material within nuclei, separated from the cytoplasm by the two membranes of the nuclear envelope. Eukaryotic cells are characteristic of most organisms except the bacteria and blue-green algae. *Compare* prokaryote. *See* cell.

Eumycophyta (Eumycotina). The true fungi, comprising four groups: the Deuteromycetes (*Fungi Imperfecti), *Phycomycetes, *Ascomycetes, and *Basidiomycetes. In schemes of classification that exclude the plasmodial slime fungi (i.e. Myxomycetes and Plasmodiophorales), the true fungi are all mycelial; in schemes that include the slime fungi, the true fungi include all the mycelial fungi plus those plasmodial fungi that may produce flagellate zoospores under certain conditions. *Compare* Myxomycophyta.

euphotic zone. The *photic zone of a sea or lake, especially the upper part of this zone.

euploidy. The condition in which the chromosome number of a nucleus, cell, or organism is an exact multiple of the haploid number, so that all chromosomes are present in the diploid, triploid, tetraploid (etc.) state and there are no extra unpaired ones. Therefore when the haploid number is n, the euploid number $2n$, $3n$, $4n$, etc. Most normal nuclei other than haploid ones are euploid. *Compare* aneuploidy.

Euryapsida. *See* Synaptosauria.

euryhaline. Designating aquatic organisms that can tolerate a wide range of salinity. Euryhaline organisms may be found in an estuary (salt content approximately 14 parts per 1000) or in the open sea (salt content 35 parts per 1000). *Compare* stenohaline.

eusporangiate. Designating ferns in which the sporangium develops from the inner daughter cell produced by periclinal division of a superficial cell in the lamina (adjacent cells may also contribute to the sporangium). The eusporangiate condition is regarded as primitive: it is important taxonomically and characterizes the Eusporangiatae (Marattiales and Ophioglossales). *Compare* leptosporangiate.

Eustachian tube. A tube that connects the cavity of the middle ear of tetrapods to the pharynx, permitting equalization of air pressure across the tympanum.

eustele. *See* stele.

Eutheria (Placentalia). The infraclass or subclass of the Mammalia that contains the most advanced and the majority of living mammals. Placental mammals are characterized by the birth of the young at a comparatively advanced stage of development after a long gestation period in the maternal uterus, where they are nourished by the placenta. They have a highly organized brain with large cerebral hemispheres and a dentition consisting primitively of three incisors, one canine, four premolars, and three molars on each side of both jaws. Placental mammals appeared in the Cretaceous and underwent great adaptive radiation in the early Cenozoic (*see* Tertiary). The group includes the extant orders *Insectivora, *Dermoptera, *Chiroptera, *Primates, *Edentata, *Pholidota, *Lagomorpha, *Rodentia, *Cetacea, *Carnivora, *Pinnipedia, *Tubulidentata, *Proboscidea, *Hyracoidea, *Sirenia, *Perissodactyla, and *Artiodactyla and the extinct *Creodonta, *Condylarthra, and *Notoungulata. *Compare* Metatheria, Prototheria.

eutrophic. Designating a lake or river with a high concentration of nutrient salts and a high rate of primary production. Eutrophic lakes are relatively old and shallow, with a well-developed littoral and sublittoral vegetation (including a dense growth of plankton) but a less extensive profundal zone, with few fish. Eutrophication can be artificially increased by the addition of agricultural fertilizers, animal excrement, etc., to the water (*see* pollution). *Compare* oligotrophic.

evergreen. (Designating) vascular plants that produce and shed leaves all the year round, so that the branches are never bare. Each leaf often lasts for several years. The condition of being evergreen is not an indicator of taxonomic status. *Compare* deciduous.

evocation. The induction of a particular type of development or cellular differentiation in an embryonic animal tissue by a natural substance (*evocator*) that diffuses from the neighbouring cells of an *organizer in the embryo. The process can be artificially induced by means of a tissue implant or by various chemical substances.

evolution. The gradual development of complex organisms from simpler ancestral types over the course of geological time. It is caused by gradual changes in a population resulting from inherited variations in individuals in successive generations. Evolution begins with the production of new species, which gradually differ more and more from each other until new genera, families, classes, etc., have evolved.

The alternative doctrine to evolution is that of *Special Creation, generally accepted by most biologists until the 18th century. The possibility of evolution was recognized in ancient times, but the speculations of Empedocles and Aristotle were not seriously considered until naturalists such as Buffon (1707–88) and Erasmus Darwin (1731–1802) challenged the theory of Special Creation. Lamarck was the first biologist to propose a theory of evolution (*see* Lamarckism) but his suggestion that characteristics acquired during the lifetime of an organism, by use and disuse of its organs, could be inherited by its offspring was not generally accepted. The first satisfactory explanation of the mechanism by which evolution takes place was proposed by Charles Darwin (1809–82) and Alfred Russel Wallace (1823–1913) in the 19th century (*see* Darwinism). Today their theory of natural selection acting on random inherited variations has been modified by recent advances in genetics (*see* genetic drift, isolating mechanisms).

exarate. *See* pupa.

exarch. Designating a stele in which the metaxylem develops to the inside of the protoxylem, i.e. centripetal to it. *Compare* centrarch, endarch, mesarch.

exchange diffusion. A type of carrier-mediated transport of molecules across a biological membrane. *See* active transport.

excitation-contraction coupling. The process by which excitation of a motor neurone activates the contractile apparatus of muscle. In *striated muscle it depends on an ordered system of membranes within the cell. The sarcoplasmic reticulum concentrates calcium ions by active transport across its membrane. At regular positions it becomes closely apposed in a triad pattern to deep infoldings of the cell membrane known as the *T system*. Depolarization of the muscle cell membrane occurs when an impulse in the motor neurone causes release of neurotransmitter at the motor end plate. Excitation in the T system causes the sarcoplasmic reticulum to release calcium into the cytoplasm. Temporary attachment of calcium to the regulatory proteins troponin and tropomyosin in the muscle structure deinhibits cross-bridge attachment and thus permits contraction. Reabsorption of calcium by the sarcoplasmic reticulum brings about relaxation.

excitatory postsynaptic potential (EPSP). The graded local depolarization of the postsynaptic membrane that is elicited by neurotransmitter released from the presynaptic membrane of an excitatory *synapse.

excretion. The elimination by an organism of the waste products of metabolism, chiefly water, carbon dioxide, and nitrogenous compounds (urea, uric acid, etc.). In unicellular and simple multicellular animals excretion occurs by diffusion through the cell membrane or epidermis. In higher plants waste products diffuse out through the leaves. Animals excrete carbon dioxide during respiration, often via respiratory organs; most animals have special excretory organs for the elimination of other waste substances, e.g. *nephridia (many invertebrates), *Malpighian tubules (arthropods), and *kidneys (vertebrates).

exine. The outer layer of the *perispore.

exocarp (epicarp). *See* pericarp.

exocrine gland. A vertebrate gland, epithelial in origin, possessing a duct that carries its secretions to an epithelial surface. The classification of exocrine glands is based on the type of duct system and the nature of the secretory part of the gland. Glands with single secretory passages and single unbranched ducts are called *simple glands*; those with elaborately branched passages and ducts are *compound glands*. Glands whose secretory component is a tubule of uniform diameter are *tubular glands*; those with a saclike secretory part are *acinar (alveolar* or *saccular) glands*. Many glands are intermediate in type and are termed *tubuloacinar*. For example, pyloric glands are simple tubular glands; sebaceous glands are simple acinar glands; the exocrine pancreas is a compound tubuloacinar gland. *Compare* endocrine gland.

exocytosis. The reverse process of *endocytosis, by which materials (e.g. undigestible or waste materials from Protozoa) and secretory products (such as zymogen granules) are extruded from the cell. *See* secretion.

exodermis. A subepidermal protective layer of the root, one to several cells thick. It is equivalent in position to the hypodermis of the stem but is structurally and physiologically more similar to the *endodermis, often possessing Casparian strips.

exogamy. The fusion of gametes from parents that are not closely related to one another. *See* outbreeding.

exo-intine (medine). The middle layer of the *perispore.

exon. An essential coding sequence in a gene. The coding sequences of many eukaryotic genes consist of a series of exons interrupted by *intron sequences. After the gene is transcribed into *HnRNA, the introns are excised and the transcripts of the exon sequences are spliced together to form messenger RNA, which is translated into protein.

exonuclease. An enzyme (*see* DNase) that cuts a nucleic acid sequence externally, so removing terminal nucleotides. *Compare* endonuclease.

exopodite. *See* biramous appendage.

Exopterygota (Heterometabola). A group of the Pterygota (winged insects) in which metamorphosis is incomplete, with no pupal stage, and the wings develop outside the body of the larva (*nymph*), which resembles the adult in structure and habits. The Exopterygota contains the orders *Ephemeroptera (mayflies), *Odonata (dragonflies), *Plecoptera (stoneflies), *Orthoptera (grasshoppers), *Phasmida (stick insects), *Dermaptera (earwigs), *Embioptera (foot spinners), *Dictyoptera (cockroaches and mantids), *Isoptera (termites), *Psocoptera (book-lice), *Mallophaga (biting lice), *Anoplura (sucking lice), *Hemiptera (bugs), *Thysanoptera (thrips), *Grylloblattodea, and *Zoraptera.

exoscopic development (in plants). *See* embryo.

exoskeleton. A skeleton that lies outside the body tissues of an animal. It protects and supports the internal organs and may provide attachment for muscles. Examples are the strengthened cuticle of arthropods and the shell of molluscs. Some exoskeletons are formed within the skin, e.g. the bony plates of chelonians and armadillos. *See also* cuticle, carapace, plastron. *Compare* endoskeleton.

exosporic. Designating spore production external to the sex organ or sporangium. It occurs in certain fungi, such as the Basidiomycetes and some slime fungi. *Compare* endosporic.

exotoxin. A potent toxin that is excreted by a bacterium and has toxic effects on the infected host, often affecting the central nervous system. Exotoxins are produced in diphtheria, tetanus, and botulism; when purified, they are the most powerful poisons known. *Compare* endotoxin.

explantation. *See* tissue culture.

exploratory behaviour. Any pattern of animal behaviour that is not governed by the drive to satisfy a need but enables the animal to increase its awareness of its environment. An animal will explore new surroundings in which it finds itself even if it is not searching for food, drink, etc. The information it gains from the exploration may be used in the future, in specific goal-orientated behaviour. *Compare* appetitive behaviour.

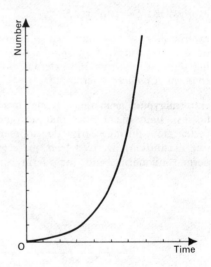

Exponential growth

exponential growth. A type of growth occurring when populations multiply in such a way that the rate of increase in numbers at any time is proportional to the number of individuals present. When this occurs the population increases slowly in the initial stages of growth, when the population is low. As the population rises, the rate at which it multiplies also increases, so a graph of number against time (see illustration) shows a characteristic sharp rise. Exponential growth follows an equation of the type $N = N_0 e^{-Ct}$, where N is the number of organisms, N_0 the initial number, C a constant, t the time, and e is the exponential constant, equal to 2.718. It can occur in a variety of biological systems, as in the growth of a population of bacteria or other unicellular organisms, the doubling of cells in an organism, or the increase in a plant or animal population. In theory the exponential increase would continue indefinitely but in practice other factors affect the growth rate. The rate at which organisms die also increases as they exhaust their supplies, accumulate waste, etc., and the increase tails off to reach a steady value. The practical curve has a sigmoid (S-shaped) form.

expressivity. *See* penetrance.

exteroceptor. A *receptor that is located on the integument of an animal, collecting information from the external environment. *Compare* interoceptor.

extraembryonic membranes (foetal membranes). Four membranes that surround vertebrates during early development (see illustration). Derived from the ectoderm, endoderm, and mesoderm and associated with the placenta, they assist in the respiration, nutrition, excretion, and protection of the embryo (or foetus).

The *yolk sac* forms as a ventral outgrowth of the embryonic gut of most fish, reptiles, and birds. As the yolk is absorbed the sac is withdrawn into the embryo. In mammals, in which there is no yolk, the outer layer of the sac forms part of the chorion and is delivered as part of the afterbirth at parturition. The *allantois* is a sac formed as a ventral outgrowth from the hind part of the embryonic gut of amniotes. In reptiles and birds it functions primarily as a bladder for the storage of excretory products but it also acts as a respiratory surface. In mammals it is more important in the nourishment of the foetus, becoming closely associated with the chorionic villi of the placenta. The *amnion*, present only in amniotes, is a membrane that encloses the protective *amniotic fluid* in which the foetus develops. When fully formed it generally fuses with the chorion. The *chorion*, a superficial membrane that surrounds the embryo of amniote vertebrates, is formed by overlapping of the ectodermal and mesodermal layers of the late blastula. Its outer epithelium develops from the trophoblast. Later it forms external villi, which become variously

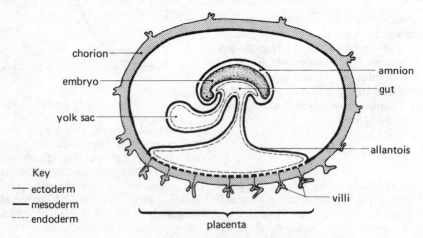

Key
— ectoderm
— mesoderm
---- endoderm

Extraembryonic membranes in a mammal

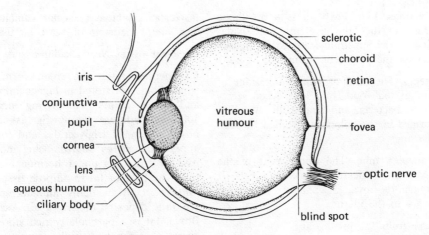

Cross-section of mammalian eye

developed and eroded to form the placenta.

extrorse. Designating anthers that dehisce towards the outside of the flower.

eye. A sense organ responding to light. The simplest type of eye is the *ocellus, which is present in many invertebrates. More complex eyes, having numerous accessory structures and capable of forming an image, are found in insects and crustaceans (*see* compound eye) and in vertebrates and molluscs (see illustration).

eyespot (stigma). 1. A light-sensitive organelle of many flagellate algae and gametes and of the zoospores of non-motile algae. It consists basically of one to four rows of globules containing carotenoid pigments (orange or red), associated with, or found in, a chloroplast and often close the flagellum. 2. A light-sensitive spot of pigment in various lower animals, including some Protozoa, jellyfish, and flatworms.

F

F$_1$. The first filial generation obtained in breeding experiments: the progeny pro-

duced by crossing the parental generation (P$_1$).

F$_2$. The second filial generation obtained in breeding experiments: the progeny produced by crossing the F$_1$ generation.

facial nerve. *See* cranial nerves.

facilitated diffusion. A type of carrier-mediated transport of molecules across a biological membrane. *See* active transport.

facilitation. The phenomenon of increasing the postsynaptic response of a synapse to successive stimuli. Each stimulus leaves the synapse more responsive to the next stimulus, so that one stimulus eventually evokes a postsynaptic potential (EPSP or EPP; *see* synapse) of sufficient magnitude to trigger an impulse. Facilitation therefore differs from temporal *summation in that the threshold postsynaptic potential is not the sum of several subthreshold potentials. Facilitation and the reverse effect, *antifacilitation* (*depression, synaptic fatigue*), occur at synapses and neuromuscular junctions and are an important mechanism of nervous *integration.

FAD (flavin adenine dinucleotide). A derivative of riboflavin that functions as a coenzyme in many oxidation-reduction reactions. Like FMN, it is a prosthetic group of the *flavoproteins, and oxidation of the substrate leads to the reduction of the prosthetic group.

faeces. The solid or semisolid residue of undigested food, bile and other secretions, bacteria, and dead cells, which is formed in the colon and voided through the anus.

Fallopian tube. The upper part of the *Müllerian duct of female mammals. It transports ova discharged from the ovary to the uterus.

false fruit. *See* pseudocarp.

family A unit used in the *classification of plants and animals. A family consists of a number of closely related or similar genera or occasionally of only one genus. Family names end in *-aceae* or *-ae* in botany and in *-ideae* in zoology. In botany, families were formerly called *natural orders*. Families are named after a *type genus*, which is characteristic of the whole family. For example, the family Rosaceae is named from the genus *Rosa* (roses); the family Pongidae from the genus *Pongo* (orang-utan). Unlike the names of species and genera, family names are not printed in italic type. In animal classification, families are divided into *subfamilies* whose names end in *-inae* and are grouped into *superfamilies* ending in *-oidea*. For example, the families Pongidae (apes) and Hominidae (man) are grouped into the superfamily Hominoidea; the Pongidae is split into the subfamilies Hylobatinae (gibbons) and Ponginae (great apes). Plant families are divided into subfamilies whose names end in *-oideae*; the subfamilies are themselves divided into tribes, which end in *-eae*. For example, the family Rosaceae is divided into the subfamily Rosoideae and the tribe Roseae. Superfamilies are rarely used in botany. Above the level of the superfamily, families are grouped into orders.

fascia. A sheet of connective tissue, commonly investing muscles.

fascicular cambium (vascular cambium). The lateral meristem of *vascular tissue.

fascicular tissue. *See* vascular tissue.

fat (neutral fat). The main form in which lipids are stored in higher animals and some plants, comprising nearly 100% of *adipose tissue. Fat is composed chiefly of triglycerides and forms a potential energy source, being mobilized by *lipolysis under hormonal control. The bulk of fat in adipose tissue is *white fat*, but in many animals small separate deposits of *brown fat* occur. Brown fat is a particularly rich store of energy that can be rapidly converted to heat, and hibernating animals probably use brown-fat metabolism in the recovery from hibernation. There is also speculation that in man excess food intake is normally balanced by the rapid turnover of brown fat, so preventing the unnecessary production of white fat.

fat body. 1. One of a pair of branched masses of adipose tissue in amphibians, situated in the abdomen just anterior to each kidney. The fat bodies provide a reserve of fat that is used during hibernation (and, in the males, during the breeding season) and they may help to nourish the maturing gametes.
2. A loose network of tissue in insects that fills the spaces between the organs of the body. It contains fat, protein, glycogen, and other food reserves used by the insect before metamorphosis, during hibernation, etc.

fate map. A map of an egg or embryo in which cells or parts of cells that will give rise to specific adult organs and tissues are separately identified. Such a map is most easily constructed for highly mosaic eggs and embryos, in which fate is determined early, as compared with highly regulative eggs, in which commitment is relatively late and some plasticity is evident. Fate maps of *Drosophila* blastoderms and mouse eggs have been drawn, but those of frog eggs are perhaps the best known.

fatty acid. One of a group of carboxylic acids with long hydrocarbon chains that are the basic components of many important lipids, including the glycerides. In this form they occur abundantly although they are found only in trace amounts as free fatty acids. The most common naturally occurring fatty acids have even numbers of carbon atoms (C_{14} to C_{24}). Of the animal saturated fatty acids, *palmitic acid*, $CH_3(CH_2)_{14}COOH$, and *stearic acid*, $CH_3(CH_2)_{16}COOH$, are the most abundant; of the unsaturated fatty acids, *oleic acid*, $CH_3(CH_2)_7CH:$ $CH(CH_2)_7COOH$, is the most widely distributed (*see also* essential fatty acids).

Although long-chain fatty acids are insoluble in water, their sodium and potassium salts are water-soluble and function as soaps (*see* saponification).

Fatty acids are synthesized in the cell cytoplasm from acetyl CoA and malonyl CoA in the presence of a complex of seven enzymes (*fatty-acid synthetase complex*). The acetyl CoA comes from the mitochondria, being formed during *fatty-acid oxidation, and serves as a precursor of malonyl CoA in a reaction catalysed by *acetyl CoA carboxylase*, utilizing biotin as a coenzyme. The fatty-acid chain is built up by the successive addition of two carbon units from malonyl CoA to one molecule of acetyl CoA.

fatty-acid oxidation (beta-oxidation). The process by which fatty acids are oxidized via acetyl coenzyme A (CoA), occurring in the mitochondria of higher animals and plants that store neutral fat as an energy reserve. The sequence of reactions involved is shown in the diagram. The fatty acid is activated at the mitochondrial membrane by a reaction involving ATP and CoA; passage of the activated fatty acid (which is in the form of a CoA ester) across the mitochondrial membrane is facilitated by carnitine, with which it forms a fatty acyl carnitine derivative. Within the mitochondrial matrix fatty acyl CoA is reformed and undergoes the successive removal of two carbon units from the carboxyl end; the products of each of these oxidations are acetyl CoA, a fatty acyl CoA with two carbon units fewer than the starting material, and reduced coenzymes ($FADH_2$ and NADH). The acetyl CoA may then either enter the Krebs cycle or, by further oxidations, produce more reduced coenzymes, which (with those previously formed) enter the electron transport chain and are used to synthesize ATP.

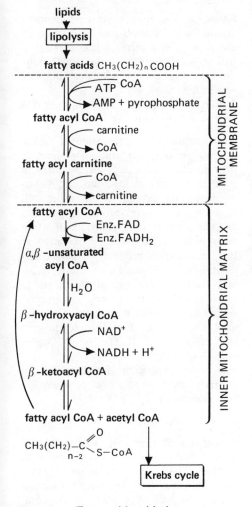

Fatty-acid oxidation

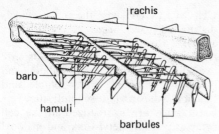

Part of a contour feather

feathers. Epidermal structures forming the body covering of birds. There are three main types: the contour feathers, the smaller down feathers, and the hair-like filoplumes.

Contour feathers are arranged in regular rows and give the body its general shape. A typical contour feather consists of a central horny shaft (*rachis*) bearing two flattened *vanes* made up of rows of *barbs*. Each barb bears two rows of *barbules*, which interlock with the barbules of adjacent barbs by means of small hooks (*hamuli* or *barbicels*) (see illustration). This unites the barbs and ensures that the surface of the vane remains smooth and unbroken. Arising from the base of the rachis is a second and usually smaller feather – the *afterfeather*.

Down feathers (or *plumulae*) form the sole body covering of nestlings; in most adult birds they lie between and beneath the contour feathers. The shaft bears a crown of free barbs (the barbules lack interlocking hooks), giving the feather a fluffy appearance.

Filoplumes are small hairlike feathers lacking vanes; they are scattered over the body between the contour feathers.

feedback inhibition (end-product inhibition). The inhibition of an *enzyme in a reaction sequence, often the first enzyme in the pathway, by the product of the reaction. Feedback inhibition is a type of allosteric regulation; *catabolite repression is an example.

Fehling's test. A biochemical test for reducing sugars, such as glucose and fructose (monosaccharides) and maltose and lactose (disaccharides), and also for aldehydes. Fehling's solution is an aqueous solution of cupric sulphate (Fehling's I) and potassium sodium tartrate and Rochelle salt (Fehling's II). Equal quantities of Fehling's I and II are added to the suspected sugar and the solution is boiled. A positive result is a brick red precipitate, produced by the reduction of the cupric sulphate to red insoluble cuprous oxide. The negative result is a blue solution. Fehling's test is not very sensitive for very dilute solutions of sugars. To detect these, and to obtain quantitative results, *Benedict's test should be used.

femur. 1. The long bone of the upper section of a tetrapod rear limb. It articulates with the pelvic girdle through a ball-and-socket joint at the acetabulum. Distally it articulates with the tibia. *See* pentadactyl limb.
2. The section of an insect's limb that is nearest to the body.

fermentation. The degradation of carbohydrate or other organic substances to provide chemical energy in the form of ATP by a series of reactions not requiring molecular oxygen. In anaerobic cells it is the only energy-producing process; in facultative aerobic cells it is the first stage, which is followed by oxidation of the fermentation products. *Alcoholic fermentation* takes place in certain yeasts and bacteria. Glucose is degraded to pyruvic acid by the process of glycolysis, with the eventual production of ethanol and carbon dioxide according to the equation: $C_6H_{12}O_6 = 2CO_2 + C_2H_5OH$.
The most common fermentation in animal cells is *lactic acid fermentation* (*see* glycolysis).

ferns. *See* Pteropsida.

ferredoxins. A group of red-brown proteins containing iron in association with sulphur. They have very negative redox potentials, i.e. they are strong reducing agents. As such they are common components of electron transport chains in most organisms, functioning, for example, in photosynthesis (light reaction).

fertilization (syngamy). The fusion of the cytoplasmic material (*plasmogamy*) and nuclear material (*karyogamy*) of two gametes to produce a cell, the zygote. It is the vital and significant feature of *sexual reproduction. Fertilization usually provides the stimulation for embryo development; some organisms, however, become dormant after fertilization.

Fertilization in plants primitively involves the fusion of two similar flagellate gametes (*isogamy*), which are attracted to each other chemically. From this, *oogamy* has evolved, in which one gamete is nonmotile. Oogamy occurs in most plants, including many algae and fungi and all bryophytes, pteridophytes, and seed plants. In most gymnosperms and all angiosperms neither gamete possesses flagella and fertilization is achieved by means of a *pollen tube, formed from the pollen grain, which brings the male nucleus adjacent to the ovum (*compare* pollination). Some lower plants (e.g. many phycomycete fungi) that possess male gametes without flagella produce a *fertilization tube*, a protrusion from the male organ (antheridium) that fuses with the female oogonium and through which the male gametes pass.

Fertilization in animals is very varied. In some animals, e.g. *Ascaris* (a nematode) and *Rana* (frog), the mature male spermatozoon enters the ovum before the latter has completed meiosis; in certain species its entry is necessary for the ovum to complete its development. Occasionally several sperms may enter an ovum; this is termed *polyspermy* and all but one of the sperms degenerate. After fertilization the ovum forms a *fertilization membrane* around itself, which prevents entry of further sperm (*see also* egg membrane). The point of entry of the sperm is influenced by egg structure (e.g. yolk distribution) and itself influences the development of the zygote (it can be altered experimentally and its effects observed). Fertilization is accomplished in one of two ways. In *external fertilization* the gametes are expelled from the bodies of the parents and meet by chance; this is most common in aquatic or amphibious animals. In *internal fertilization* the ova are fertilized within the female and various devices are used to introduce the sperm into the body of the female, including *spermatophores and various types of *intromittent organ.

Feulgen. *See* staining.

F factor (fertility factor, sex factor). A genetic element present in certain bacteria, enabling them to undergo *conjugation. F factor is a *plasmid and, since it is capable of integration into the host cell genome, may also be called an *episome. F factors have been observed in *Escherichia, Shigella, Salmonella*, and related genera and have been particularly studied in *E. coli*. During conjugation a copy of the F factor is transferred from the donor cell, termed the F^+ (or male) cell, to the recipient, the F^- (or female) cell. Very rarely the F factor may undergo recombination with the chromosome of the F^+ cell and become integrated into it. When this happens, the F factor causes transfer of part of the chromosome (rarely, the whole chromosome) to the F^-. Strains with integrated F factors are called *Hfr*; in contrast to F^+ strains they do not transmit the F factor to F^- recipients.

fibre. 1. (in botany). An elongated sclerenchyma cell with very tapered ends and simple pits, which provides mechanical support for the plant. Fibres may be classified as *xylary fibres* (in the xylem) or *extraxylary fibres* (all other fibres). Xylary fibres are found only in angiosperm xylem and are of two sorts, *fibre-tracheids and *libriform fibres*, both of which arise from the same meristematic cells as the xylem and are regarded as having evolved from xylem tracheids. Libriform fibres are much shorter than tracheids and have considerably thicker walls. Extraxylary fibres are produced in a variety of positions,

e.g. as bundle sheaths or caps, scattered in the phloem, etc. The term *bast fibres* is sometimes used for all extraxylary fibres but is more usually restricted to phloem fibres (the terms *hard* and *soft bast* refer to phloem fibres and the rest of the phloem tissue, respectively). Extraxylary fibres may or may not be lignified. The important fibres of commerce (flax, hemp, ramie) are almost entirely cellulose.
2. (in zoology). A fine, often microscopic, thread-shaped structure, e.g. a muscle fibre, nerve fibre, or a collagen or elastin fibre.

fibre-tracheid. A type of *tracheary element occurring in the xylem of angiosperms that is intermediate in form between a *fibre and a *tracheid. It is usually classified as a fibre. Fibre-tracheids are shorter than tracheids and longer than fibres and usually have both simple and bordered pits.

fibrin. The insoluble fibrous protein that forms the gel matrix of blood clots. It is produced when the enzyme thrombin acts on the plasma protein fibrinogen, which releases two small polypeptides leaving the fibrin monomer. This molecule then polymerizes to form the fibrin network characteristic of blood clots.

fibrinogen. The inactive precursor of *fibrin, which is a normal constituent of blood plasma. It is a soluble dimeric protein consisting of three pairs of polypeptide chains and is converted into fibrin by the enzyme thrombin.

fibrinolysis. The process by which sterile blood clots are dissolved as a result of fibrin degradation. It can occur a few hours or days after clotting and is mediated by the proteolytic enzyme *plasmin.

fibroblast. A flat spindle-shaped cell, present in large numbers in vertebrate connective tissue, that is responsible for the production of collagen and of the mucopolysaccharides of the connective tissue ground substance. Fibroblasts synthesize and secrete the inactive collagen precursor tropocollagen (*see* collagen), which is polymerized into mature collagen fibrils extracellularly.

fibula. One of the two long bones of the lower hind limb of tetrapods (*compare* tibia). It bears little weight and is consequently often reduced. *See also* pentadactyl limb.

filament. Any slender threadlike structure, such as the stalk of an angiosperm stamen, an algal or fungal hypha, a chain of cells (algae, bacteria, etc.), the rachis of a down feather in birds, or one of the fine processes on the gills of fish and aquatic molluscs.

filial generation. *See* F_1, F_2.

filoplumes. *See* feathers.

filter feeding. A method of feeding, found in many aquatic invertebrates, in which minute food particles are ingested from the surrounding water. Filter feeders are common in plankton and benthos communities.

fimbriae. *See* pili.

fingerprinting. The technique in which a macromolecule is enzymatically broken to yield small fragments. These are then separated by chromatography or electrophoresis to give a characteristic pattern (a *fingerprint*). This pattern can be used to compare similar molecules and to show small differences due, for example, to mutation or to species differences.

fins. Locomotory organs of fish and of some other aquatic animals.
The fins of all fishes (Chondrichthyes and Osteichthyes) are supported by flexible *fin rays*, which are fibrous, cartilaginous, horny, or bony. Fishes have two pairs of lateral fins, the *pectoral* and *pelvic fins*, which are homologous with the fore and hind limbs, respectively, of tetrapods. They are usually used in steering. There are three basic types of paired fins. The *lobed fin*, characteristic of the Choanichthyes, has a central axis of bony or cartilaginous elements articulating with the pectoral or pelvic girdle.

The *fin-fold fin*, typical of the Chondrichthyes, has a broad fleshy basal attachment. In the *ray fin*, characteristic of the Actinopterygii, the basal lobe and skeletal elements have become reduced or lost so that in teleosts the fin is supported only by the fin rays.

In addition to the paired fins there are several unpaired *median fins*: the *dorsal* and *anal fins*, used principally in balancing, and the *caudal* (or *tail*) *fin*, which provides the main propulsive movement (*see* homocercal, heterocercal, diphycercal).

fish. *See* Agnatha (jawless fish), Chondrichthyes (cartilaginous fish), Osteichthyes (bony fish).

fission. Asexual reproduction in unicellular organisms in which a single cell divides to produce two (or more) daughter cells that are similar to the parent. First the nucleus divides, followed by the cytoplasm. Fission is common in Protozoa and bacteria. For example, *Paramecium*, *Amoeba*, and many bacteria undergo *binary fission*, in which two daughter cells are formed; the Sporozoa (e.g. *Plasmodium*) reproduce by *multiple fission* (or *sporulation*), in which repeated divisions of the nucleus are followed by subdivision of the cytoplasm to produce many daughter cells, which form spores.

fitness (in ecology). The potential for survival, conferred on an organism by its genetic composition. It determines its performance under the pressures of natural selection.

fixation. A process used in the preparation of microscope slides of organisms or tissues. The material is exposed to a *fixing agent*, the most important of which are alcohol, acetic alcohol (a mixture of acetic acid and ethanol), formalin-alcohol, and solutions containing osmium tetroxide. This agent kills the tissue and ensures that its original shape is maintained, prepares it for *staining, and hardens it so that thin sections can be cut. After fixation, tissues undergo *dehydration, *clearing, *embedding, and sectioning by *microtome.

Flagellata. *See* Mastigophora.

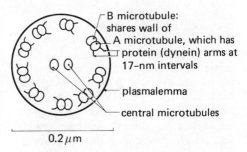

B microtubule: shares wall of A microtubule, which has protein (dynein) arms at 17-nm intervals

plasmalemma

central microtubules

0.2 μm

Cross-section of a flagellum

flagellum. A long fine hairlike organelle that projects from the cell surface and whose beat causes movement of the cell or the external medium.

The flagella of bacteria are used exclusively for locomotion. They have a hollow rodlike structure, the walls being rows (helices) of identical spherical subunits of a protein, *flagellin*.

The flagella of eukaryotes are larger (mostly up to 150 μm) and have a fundamentally different structure, which is identical to eukaryote cilia (see illustration). The nine outer pairs of A + B microtubules are continuous with the A and B microtubules of the *basal body (or *blepharoplast*), which is always found at the base of the flagellum (and cilium). The two central microtubules end in a complex transition zone between flagellum and basal body. Flagella, unlike cilia, usually beat with a wavelike motion propagated from tip to base or vice versa. Occasionally, helical waves are formed. Flagella are of two types, *whiplash* and *tinsel*, the latter bearing hairs called *mastigonemes. Flagella of some algae (notably Prasinophyceae) bear sheaths of tiny scales. Flagella are absent from flowering plants and most conifers and present only on the antherozoids of other land plants. In motile reproductive stages (antherozoids, spermatozoa, zoospores) of plants and animals, in flagellate protozoans, and in many unicellular and colonial algae flagella are locomotory organelles. In some multicellular organisms, e.g. sponges, they are used for circulation of the external medium.

flame cell (solenocyte). A hollow cell at the end of a protonephridium tubule, within the tissues of an animal, whose central cavity is continuous with that of the tubule. Slender processes from the cell reach into the tissue spaces. The flame cell contains cilia or flagella whose beating directs excretory products, which diffuse into the cell through the processes from the surrounding tissues, down the protonephridium to the exterior. Flame cells occur in the Platyhelminthes, Rotifera, some Annelida, and Cephalochordata. *See* nephridium.

flatworms. *See* Platyhelminthes.

flavin. A derivative of riboflavin, either FAD or FMN, that is the prosthetic group of the *flavoproteins.

flavin adenine dinucleotide. *See* FAD.

flavin mononucleotide. *See* FMN.

Flavone

flavonoid. A compound containing the $C_6-C_3-C_6$ skeleton:

where C_6 is a benzene ring. Flavonoids are common plant products and are classified according to the structure of the C_3 portion. This usually forms a ring containing oxygen, as in flavone.

The flavonoids and their glycosides (formed by adding sugar) are widely distributed as water-soluble pigments in plant vacuoles: the anthocyanins (*see* anthocyans), which are red, blue, and purple, are particularly prominent. The *aurones* (benzalcoumarones) and *chalcones* are yellow and the *flavones* and *flavonols* and their glycosides tend to be pale yellow and ivory. Among the exclusively colourless flavonoids are the *catechins*, *leucoanthocyanidins*, and *isoflavones*.

flavoprotein. One of a group of conjugated proteins in which a derivative of riboflavin (either *FAD or *FMN, known as *flavins*) is bound to the protein component as the prosthetic group. Flavoproteins function as dehydrogenases in the *electron transport chain in aerobic respiration.

fleas. *See* Siphonaptera.

floral formula. A representation of the structure of a flower by means of abbreviations and symbols. The parts of the flower are represented by the abbreviations K (calyx), C (corolla), P (perianth), A (androecium), and G (gynoecium), each of which is followed by a number indicating the number of parts in each whorl (bracketed numbers denote that the parts are fused, and the symbol ∞ indicates there are more than 12 parts). A line above or below the letter G and its number indicates the gynoecium is superior or inferior, respectively. The symbols ⊕ and ·|· indicate that the flower is actinomorphic or zygomorphic, respectively.

florigen (flowering hormone). A hypothetical plant hormone postulated to transmit the flowering stimulus from the leaves, where it is perceived, to the apical meristems. Gibberellins and auxins have also been implicated in floral initiation in certain cases, but no consistent mechanism has emerged. *See* photoperiodism.

flower. The sexual reproductive body of an angiosperm, consisting of modified sporophylls that form the perianth, androecium, and gynoecium, all of which arise from the receptacle.

flowering hormone. *See* florigen.

fluctuation test. A test, originally designed by Luria and Delbruck in 1943, to determine whether or not mutation in bacteria is spontaneous and nonadaptive. They compared the numbers of a particular favourable mutation occurring in numerous small parallel cultures with those in one large culture. The numbers in the small cultures were highly variable (hence the name fluctuation test), indicating the random nature of the mutational event.

flukes. *See* Trematoda.

FMN (flavin mononucleotide). A derivative of riboflavin that, like *FAD, is a prosthetic group of the flavoproteins and functions as a coenzyme in oxidation-reduction reactions.

foetal membranes. *See* extraembryonic membranes.

foetus. The embryo of a mammal after it has developed the main features of its adult form, i.e. in humans after two to three months of gestation.

foldback DNA. A sequence of DNA that, as a result of its possessing an *inverted repeat sequence of bases, is able to fold back and hybridize with itself. Such self-hybridization occurs very rapidly when DNA is placed in conditions that favour renaturation. *See also* nucleic acid hybridization, palindromic sequence.

Folic acid

folic acid (pteroylglutamic acid). A vitamin of the B complex whose deficiency leads to megaloblastic anaemia in mammals. It consists of glutamate and p-aminobenzoic acid linked to a substituted pterin (see formula). Folic acid is the precursor of *tetrahydrofolic acid*, a coenzyme that functions in the transfer of.1-carbon groups in methylation and purine and pyrimidine synthesis.
The term folic acid is also used for the group of derivatives of pteroylglutamic acid.

follicle. 1. (in zoology). A small sac, cavity, or gland. *See* Graafian follicle, hair follicle.
2. (in botany). A dry dehiscent *fruit that is formed from a monocarpellary ovary and splits along one side only at maturity.

follicle-stimulating hormone (FSH). A glycoprotein hormone (*see* gonadotrophin) secreted by the pars distalis of the pituitary gland under hypothalamic regulation (*see* neurohormone). FSH and *luteinizing hormone are usually released together and act synergistically. In female mammals FSH stimulates growth of young Graafian follicles in the ovary; in males it stimulates sperm production in the seminiferous tubules.

fontanelle. A dorsal gap in the vertebrate chondrocranium or in its membrane bone roofing. A conspicuous fontanelle is present in newborn babies, on the top of the head between the frontal and parietal bones, but it closes at about 18 months of age.

food chain. A food relationship in an ecosystem in which energy is transferred from plants through a series of organisms by each stage feeding on the preceding stage and providing food for the succeeding one. Each stage of the food chain is known as a *trophic level*. The first trophic level is occupied by plants (the *producers*), which obtain their energy from the sun. These plants are eaten by herbivores, which form the second trophic level and are in turn eaten by carnivores. There may be one or more species of carnivore occupying successively higher trophic levels in a food chain. The herbivores and carnivores are known as the *consumers* (primary, secondary, tertiary, etc.). There are seldom more than six trophic levels in a food chain, and the organisms at the base of the chain are typically smaller and more numerous than those at the top (*see* pyramid of numbers, pyramid of biomass). Simple food chains are rare; there is usually a variety of plants and animals at each level, forming a more complicated *food web*. This range of organisms is necessary as the sole species occupying a particular trophic level in a simple food chain could easily be completely consumed, which would adversely affect the organisms in the next and succeeding stages.

foot spinners. *See* Embioptera.

foramen. A natural opening or passage in the animal body. There are numerous foramina in vertebrates, many of which are associated with the skull (*see* foramen magnum).

foramen magnum. The opening in the occiput of the vertebrate skull through which the spinal cord passes.

Foraminifera. An order of mostly marine Protozoa of the class Sarcodina characterized by a simple or chambered shell, constructed of lime, chitin, or silica and perforated by numerous pores through which the pseudopodia protrude. The order, which has been in existence since Cambrian times, includes *Globigerina*, whose shells form a deposit (*globigerina ooze*) covering large areas of the ocean floor, and the extinct *Nummulites*, whose shells are the principal constituent of European Tertiary limestones.

forebrain (prosencephalon). The most anterior of the three hollow dilations of the neural tube that constitute the brain of embryonic vertebrates. It is primitively associated with olfaction and gives rise during development to the eyes. In higher vertebrates the dorsal region is elaborated to form the *cerebral hemi-

spheres anteriorly and the *thalamus posteriorly; the ventral region gives rise to the *hypothalamus.

foregut. 1. The region of the alimentary canal of vertebrates anterior to the bile duct, which is primarily responsible for the reception and storage of foodstuffs.
2. The anterior ectodermal section of the gut of arthropods, which is derived from the stomodaeum and lined with cuticle.
Compare midgut, hindgut.

form. A unit used in the classification of plants and animals. It comprises a loose group within a species whose members show variation, usually qualitative variation, from the typical members of the species. These variants may be seasonal, such as a white form of an arctic animal in winter; they may be one of several polymorphic types, such as melanistic forms of animals or different flower colours in plants; or they may be a group whose taxonomic position within the species is uncertain.

fossil. The remains or traces of an organism that existed in former times, usually up to the end of the Pleistocene Ice Age, 20 000 years ago.
Occasionally an entire organism or part of an organism is preserved. Such fossils may be found in ice, amber, tar, volcanic ash, or peat. The soft parts of organisms may be preserved by desiccation in dry air, resulting in mummification, or as impressions or films of carbon on the surrounding rock. The carbonized outlines of leaves have been found in coal, the more volatile constituents of the leaf having been lost.
Most fossils, however, consist only of the persistent hard parts of organisms, such as teeth, shells, and skeletons. Most of these fossils are preserved in aquatic environments. The organism falls to the lake, river, or sea bed and the soft parts rot. The hard parts are then buried in the sediment and become part of the rock formed; the fossil is lithified with the sediment and is often distorted and compressed. The softer

and less compressed the rock, the better the fossil. Many fossils occur only in harder older rocks, in which other changes have followed lithification. These changes result in the formation of petrifications, moulds, or casts. *Petrification* is the replacement of molecules of the material of the shell, skeleton, etc., by another molecule, such as iron pyrites, calcite, or silica. For example, fossil wood is produced when the carbon of the tree is replaced by silica. *Moulds* are formed when, after lithification, the original fossil dissolves away or is otherwise lost, leaving a mould of its outline in the surrounding rock. The palaeontologist can fill this with latex solution to obtain a cast of the original fossil. *Casts* can also be made naturally when secondary material such as silica percolates through the rock and fills up the mould. As well as the fossils of actual organisms, *trace fossils* exist, providing indirect evidence of a former animal. These include tracts, trails, footprints, *coprolites* (fossil faeces), and *gastroliths* (polished pebbles that are thought to have been the gizzard stones of dinosaurs). Fossils are used as time markers in comparisons of geological strata and as evidence of evolution and of life in the past; they are also indicators of oil- or ore-rich strata. *See also* chemical fossils, living fossil.

fossil hominid. Any of the fossil primates that are regarded as the forerunners of modern man. These fossils were found mainly in the Old World, from deposits of Miocene to late Pleistocene age. The forerunners of the fossil hominids belonged to the genera *Dryopithecus* and *Ramapithecus*. In the early Pleistocene some hominids appeared that have now been placed in the genus *Australopithecus*. From the mid Pleistocene, fossils occur that can be placed in the genus *Homo*, the only member of which to survive to the present day is *Homo sapiens*. *See also* Piltdown man.

founder effect. A situation in which a new population, showing *genetic drift, is established by only a few founding individuals. Colonies of individuals on isolated oceanic islands are frequently the descendants of very few initial colonizing members, and such populations rapidly become genetically distinct from the parent population from which the colonizing individuals were themselves derived.

fovea. A depression in the retina of some vertebrates that contains closely packed cone cells only and is therefore specialized for acute vision. It is free of blood vessels and internal layers of cells and is situated at the centre of the visual field. Some birds have two foveas in each eye, which enables acuity of both forward and lateral vision. *See also* binocular vision, macula.

frameshift. A shift in the positions of the bases read as codons in messenger RNA caused by the addition or deletion

	codon				
	1	2	3	4	5
normal mRNA	AUG	AGA	CUG	ACC	GUA
	↓	↓	↓	↓	↓
polypeptide	met —	arg —	leu —	thr —	val – ...
with frameshift	AUG	AGG	ACU	GAC	CGUA
	↓	↓	↓	↓	↓
polypeptide	met —	arg —	thr —	asp —	arg – ...

Frameshift

of one or more bases in the gene coding for that message. This leads to a nonsensical series of amino acids in the polypeptide synthesized. The diagram shows a frameshift in which an extra base (guanine) has been inserted at codon 2.

fraternal twins (dizygotic twins). Twins produced by the simultaneous fertilization of two ova by two sperms. These twins are no more genetically alike than brothers and sisters and can be of different sexes. *Compare* identical twins.

free energy (Gibb's free energy function). Symbol: G. A thermodynamic function that represents the energy that would be absorbed or evolved during a reversible process. It is defined by the equation $G = H - TS$, where H is the *enthalpy, T the thermodynamic temperature, and S the *entropy. For chemical processes the change in G (ΔG) is important rather than the absolute value of G. At constant pressure (p), therefore, $\Delta G = \Delta H - T\Delta S = \Delta U + p\Delta V - T\Delta S$, where ΔU is the change in internal energy and ΔV is the change in volume. For biological reactions that take place in solution, $p\Delta V$ is negligible and $\Delta G = \Delta U - T\Delta S$.
Where the ΔG for a reaction is negative, the reaction proceeds to equilibrium spontaneously and where it is positive, the reaction occurs in the reverse direction. When equilibrium has been attained $\Delta G = 0$. The value of ΔG varies with the conditions of the system, e.g. concentration of reactants, temperature, etc. For example, a block of ice will melt into a liquid above 0°C, as $T\Delta S$ is larger than ΔH. However, below 0°C, $T\Delta S$ is less than ΔU and the ice remains a solid.

freemartin. An abnormal female member of a pair of unlike-sexed twins in cattle and some other ungulates. The female is an *intersex, being sterile and showing some male characteristics, and is thought to have developed after receiving male hormones from her twin brother via their joined placental circulations in the uterus.

freeze etching. *See* freeze fracturing.

freeze fracturing. A method of preparing specimens for electron microscopy. The specimen is frozen, then fractured with a knife under vacuum. The fracture plane usually reveals surfaces of membranes and organelles. A shadowed replica of the surface is made, often after a thin layer of ice has been sublimed from the surface (*freeze etching*). The final image is thought to represent the natural state of the living cell since no chemical fixatives or solvents are employed.

frequency-dependent selection. Selection by a predator of a morph in a polymorphic population of prey individuals so that the proportion of a morph killed is greater when it comprises a large proportion of the population than when it is rare. *See* apostatic selection.

Freund's adjuvant. The *adjuvant most commonly used in experiments with animals. Complete Freund's adjuvant consists of waxes, mineral oil, and killed tubercle bacilli and is administered in an oil/water emulsion with aqueous antigen. Injected subcutaneously, it forms a granulomatous lesion consisting mainly of histiocytes, lymphocytes, and epithelioid cells. Severe reactions occur when Freund's adjuvant is injected into humans as its constituents are not easily metabolized.

Friend cell. A leukaemic cell in the mouse discovered by Dr Charlotte Friend. The leukaemia occurs in certain mouse strains after injection with a specific virus and can be readily maintained in culture. It is an erythroid cell line that can frequently be induced to synthesize haemoglobin when treated with the drug dimethyl sulphoxide. For this reason Friend cells have been widely used for studies on differentiation.

frogs. *See* Anura.

147

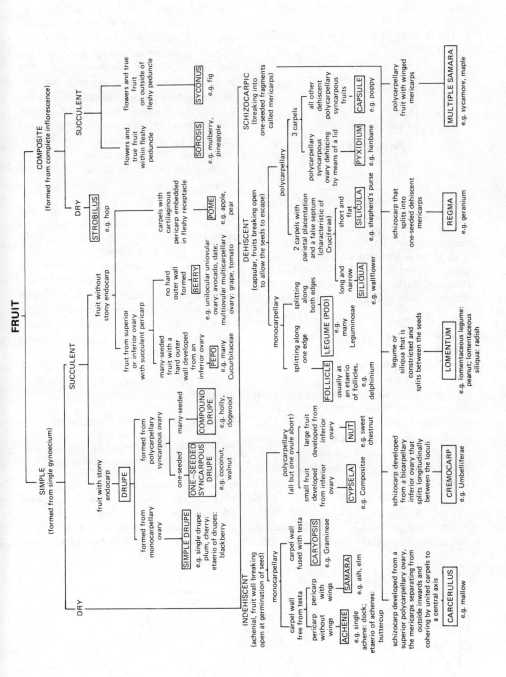

Classification of the principal types of fruits

frond. 1. A large usually divided leaf, especially the megaphyll of a fern or palm.
2. The leaflike thallus of some algae and lichens.

α-D-fructofuranose

fructose. A ketohexose sugar, $C_6H_{12}O_6$. Free fructose usually exists in the laevorotatory pyranose form (*L-fructopyranose*) but in combination, e.g. with glucose to form sucrose, fructose is more common in the dextrorotatory furanose form, *α-D-fructofuranose* (see formula). *See also* monosaccharides.

fruit. The ripened ovary of a flower, together with any accessory parts associated with it. The ovary wall is termed the *pericarp (or fruit wall)* and is distinct in superior ovaries. In inferior ovaries the ovary wall is usually fused with the receptacle (the term fruit wall is sometimes also applied to this joint structure). Formerly, fruits that incorporate structures other than the ovary were called *false fruits* (or *pseudocarps*), those formed from an inflorescence being called *composite fruits*; fruits formed from the ovary alone were termed *true fruits*. This is a misleading distinction suggesting, for example, that fruits formed from an inferior ovary are false since the carpels are adherent to the receptacle. Fruit formation usually follows fertilization of the ovules and occurs simultaneously with seed ripening (*see also* apomixis, parthenocarpy). The type of fruit formed depends on the seed dispersal mechanism of the species, e.g. most succulent fruits are dispersed by animal consumption; dry fruits (dehiscent or indehiscent) by wind, water, etc. The classification of the principal types of fruits is shown in the chart.

frustule. The siliceous cell wall of the Bacillariophyceae (diatoms), which is composed of two halves (*valves*) that fit together like a pill box. In some diatoms the valve face has a narrow slit (*raphe*) with three round apertures (*nodules*) along its length, one at each end and one in the middle. Cytoplasm streams out of the raphe and returns via the nodules, producing a gliding motion in these diatoms.
The term frustule is occasionally used to include the valves plus the cytoplasm of the cell.

FSH. *See* follicle-stimulating hormone.

fucoxanthin. A brown xanthophyll pigment. *See* photosynthetic pigments.

functional response. The relationship between the number of prey consumed by one predator or *parasitoid under specified conditions and the density of its prey or hosts. Of the three basic

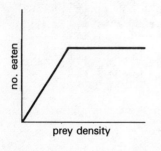
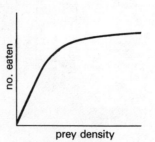
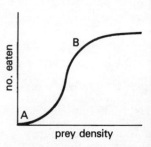

Functional response

types illustrated, only the third exhibits *density dependence (between A and B) and hence has the potential to regulate the numbers of the prey.

fundamental tissues. *See* ground tissues.

Fungi (Mycota). A group of thallophytes whose plant body is typically a mycelium (in a few small groups it is an amoeba-like cell, a plasmodium, or a pseudoplasmodium). Fungi lack chlorophyll and are not photosynthetic; their walls usually consist of chitin, although a few fungi produce cellulose as well (cell walls are absent in the nonmycelial groups). The fungi are usually divided into two subgroups: the *Myxomycophyta and *Eumycophyta.

Fungi Imperfecti (Deuteromycetes). A group of fungi with septate mycelia in which sexual reproduction (the *perfect stage*) is either lacking or is not known. Many of these fungi are of great importance as they cause diseases in plants, animals, and man.

funicle (funiculus). The stalk by which the ovule is attached to the placenta in the ovary of angiosperms.

furanose. A monosaccharide that exists in the form of a five-membered ring of four carbon atoms and one oxygen atom. An example is α-D-fructofuranose, one form of *fructose. *Compare* pyranose.

6-furfurylaminopurine. *See* kinin.

G

GABA (gamma-aminobutyric acid). An amino acid, $NH_3CH_2CH_2CH_2COOH$, found predominantly in nervous tissue, especially the brain. GABA is a potent hyperpolarizing agent and is thought to act as an inhibitory neurotransmitter in the regions where it is active.

galactose. An aldohexose sugar whose dextrorotatory form (D-galactose) is an epimer of D-glucose and a component of the disaccharide *lactose. D-galactose also occurs in glycolipids and glycoproteins.

gall bladder. A muscular diverticulum of the bile duct in which bile is stored. The gall bladder expels its bile under the influence of the hormone cholecystokinin, which is released in response to the presence of food in the duodenum. A gall bladder is absent in many birds and mammals.

gametangium. A gamete-producing structure or sex organ in plants, i.e. an *antheridium, *oogonium, or *archegonium.

gamete (germ cell). A specialized haploid cell, concerned with sexual reproduction, that undergoes *karyogamy with another gamete to produce a *zygote, from which the next generation arises.

gametogenesis. The formation of gametes, i.e. ova and spermatozoa. *See* oogenesis, spermatogenesis.

gametophore. A special branch in some thallose liverworts bearing either archegonia (an *archegoniophore*) or antheridia (an *antheridiophore*).

gametophyte. The generation in the life cycle of a plant that bears the sex organs (and thus the gametes). It forms the dominant plant in the life cycle of the bryophytes and the prothallus of pteridophytes. *Compare* sporophyte.

gamma-aminobutyric acid. *See* GABA.

gamma globulin. One of a group of serum proteins with distinct electrophoretic mobility. The group includes serum immunoglobulins and other globulins, without antibody activity.

ganglion. 1. A mass of nervous tissue that is encapsulated in connective tissue and contains many synapses and cell bodies. Ganglia are close to areas of high sensory input or motor output and act as integrative centres for such regions. In invertebrates, the ganglia and their connectives constitute the *central nervous system.
2. *cerebral ganglia.* The most anterior pair of ganglia of the invertebrate central nervous system. They are associated with the primary sense organs and are usually the dominant centre of the nervous system, analogous to the vertebrate brain.
3. *basal ganglia. See* corpus striatum.
4. *spinal ganglion.* An enlargement of the dorsal *root of the vertebrate spinal cord that contains the cell bodies of the afferent spinal neurones.
5. *autonomic (sympathetic* and *parasympathetic) ganglia.* Peripheral ganglia of the vertebrate *autonomic nervous system.

ganglioside. One of a group of glycolipids found especially in nerve-cell membranes. They consist of a fatty-acid substituted sphingosine molecule together with an oligosaccharide, which commonly contains D-glucose, D-galactose, N-acetylgalactosamine, and N-acetylneuraminic acid.

ganoid scale. The bony scale characteristic of primitive fishes of the subclass Actinopterygii. It is composed of a basal layer of dense laminated bone (*isopedin*), a layer of spongy vascular bone, a thin layer of dentine, and a thick outer layer of enamel (*ganoine*), forming a shiny surface on the scale. As the Actinopterygii evolved there was a reduction in the thickness of the various layers; in modern teleosts the scales are composed only of thin bone and in some, e.g. *Anguilla* (eel), they are lost altogether. *Compare* cosmoid scale, placoid scale.

gastric juice. A mixture of hydrochloric acid, proteolytic enzymes, and mucus secreted by cells within folds of the stomach mucosa (*gastric glands*).

gastric mill. *See* gizzard.

gastrin. A polypeptide hormone secreted from the mucosa of the pyloric region of the mammalian stomach in the presence of certain foods, peptones, bile, alcohol, and water. Gastrin stimulates secretion of hydrochloric acid from the stomach, a hormone action first demonstrated in 1906. Gastrins show some similarities in structure to cholecystokinin-pancreozymin and will similarly promote secretion from the pancreas.

Gastropoda. A large class of the Mollusca characterized by a well-developed head bearing eyes and tentacles, a single shell, and a large flattened foot. Gastropods undergo torsion during development, i.e. the visceral hump becomes twisted through 180° so that the mantle cavity, gills, and anus are anterior and the other organs are asymmetrically arranged (torsion becomes secondarily reversed in many forms). In addition, the visceral hump and shell are spirally coiled. The subclass Prosobranchia, e.g. *Patella* (limpets), are mostly marine forms in which full torsion is retained. The shell is closed by an operculum. In the marine Opisthobranchia, e.g. *Aplysia* (sea hare), the shell is reduced or absent and the visceral hump has undergone partial or complete detorsion. The Pulmonata, e.g. *Helix* (land snail) and *Limax* (slug), are freshwater or terrestrial forms that rarely undergo detorsion. The mantle cavity is modified as an air-breathing lung (there are no gills).

Gastrotricha. A small phylum of minute pseudocoelomate invertebrates found in marine and fresh waters. The ventral surface of the body is covered with cilia used in swimming and the dorsal surface bears scales, spines, or bristles. The gut is a straight tube with a muscular sucking pharynx. *See also* Aschelminthes.

gastrula. The stage in the development of animal embryos that follows the blastula and results from gastrulation. The cells of a gastrula are differentiated into the *germ layers and the central cavity (*archenteron) opens to the exterior by the blastopore. *Compare* neurula.

gastrulation. The process in the animal embryo by which a blastula is converted into a gastrula, with the laying down of the germ layers. Gastrulation involves a complex migration of the cells of the blastula, a process that includes *invagination in many species and *epiboly and *involution in vertebrates.

gel electrophoresis. A separative technique using precast gels of starch, agar, or *polyacrylamide as a porous medium. The gel is made in a buffered salt solution of chosen pH, the molecules to be separated are applied to the top of the gel, and an electric potential is applied to the gel. The speed of movement of the molecules is related to their charge. Proteins and nucleic acids are both amenable to delicate subfractionation by gel electrophoresis. *See also* electrophoresis.

gel filtration. A chromatographic technique (*see* chromatography) for separating molecules of different sizes by the use of a column of an insoluble gel in the form of small hydrophilic beads. Large molecules are not retarded by the gel and pass rapidly through the column but smaller molecules can enter the spaces between the beads and are retarded to a degree dependent on the size of the molecule and the properties of the particular gel being used. Cross-linked chains of the polysaccharide dextran (Sephadex®) are used for the gel. Different degrees of cross-linking permit different types of separation to be carried out.

gemma. A small superficially formed uni- or multicellular propagule that differs in structure from the parent plant. Gemmae are produced by many land plants, including most bryophytes (e.g. lenticular gemmae are produced in cupules on the thallus of *Marchantia polymorpha*) and some pteridophytes (e.g. small nodular gemmae are produced on the rhizoids of *Psilotum trique-*

trum). The term gemma sometimes also includes vegetative propagules that are modified organs of the parent plant, such as the small lateral bulbils produced by the mosses *Pohlia* and *Bryum* and by the angiosperm *Agave americana* (century plant).

gemmation. 1. (in plants). The production of gemmae.
2. (in animals). *See* budding.

gemmule. An internal bud produced by all freshwater sponges and some marine forms. It consists of a number of cells enclosed in a protective coat that often contains spicules. On death and decay of the parent, the gemmules are released and can survive unfavourable conditions in a state of dormancy. In suitable conditions the cells are released from their coat and give rise to a new sponge.

gene. One of the basic units of heredity, each of which forms a discrete part of the *chromosomes of eukaryote cells. The theory of the gene requires a distinction between the *phenotype, the physical characteristics of the individual, and the *genotype, the inherited factors determining these characteristics. It also requires that inheritance is particulate, rather than blending. Particulate inheritance assumes that characters mixed in a genetic cross can be segregated out again and are not lost in an inseparable blend. The features of particulate inheritance were defined in *Mendel's laws, published in 1866. For his work, Mendel chose characteristics that were determined by alternative forms of the same genes in pea plants, e.g. smooth and wrinkled seed coats, white and purple flowers. These different forms of the same gene are now known as *alleles and arise by low-frequency mutations of the genes. The significance of Mendel's work was not realized until 1900 and the location of the genes in the chromosomes was suggested by Sutton and Boveri in 1903. The characters chosen by Mendel for his studies showed *independent assortment because the alleles determining them were located on different chromosomes. Characters determined by genes on the same chromosome, however, do not segregate readily: they show *linkage. Linked genes can be separated by the process of *crossing over during meiosis, which gives rise to a new assortment of genes, the recombinant (see recombination). The frequency of occurrence of recombinants is termed recombination frequency, and independent assortment corresponds to a recombination frequency of 50%. A frequency much less than this indicates that the genes are linked on the same chromosome; a very low frequency that they are closely linked, since the probability of crossing over occurring is assumed to be constant for a unit length of chromosome. Using this recombination frequency, Morgan and his coworkers, in the 1920s, constructed a *genetic map for the fruit fly Drosophila, placing the genes in linear order on the chromosomes. Four distinct linkage groups were found, corresponding to the four pairs of chromosomes observed under the microscope.

The gene was now defined either as the unit of recombination, the gene being the shortest length of chromosome separable from neighbouring chromosome segments on either side by recombination, or as the shortest chromosomal segment that could undergo mutation. A third definition of the gene as a unit of function was suggested by Beadle in 1945, in the *one gene–one enzyme hypothesis. Later work showed that functional genes occupied a much greater chromosome length than genes defined by mutation or recombination. With bacteria and viruses it is easy to grow large numbers of individuals and select out the rare recombinants, thus enabling detailed analysis of genes and gene sequences. Both the recombination unit and the smallest mutation unit are recognized as being one base pair of the DNA nucleotide sequence. The gene as a unit of function is now defined by the *cis-trans test.

Many different classes of genes are now recognized, some coding for transfer RNA or ribosomal RNA; some, the so-called structural genes (or *cistrons), coding for protein; and some having a role in regulating other genes (see operon). Many gene sequences are known to be interrupted by lengths of noncoding DNA known as *introns. These and many other features of gene fine structure have been revealed by the application of modern techniques involving *genetic engineering and *DNA sequencing.

gene amplification. A temporary dramatic increase in the numbers of a particular gene in a genome during one developmental period. (Loosely, the term may be applied to any increase in the numbers of a specific gene.) The best-known of the few naturally occurring examples is the large increase in the numbers of the major ribosomal RNA genes in the early development of many insects, molluscs, fish, and amphibians, in which the normal number of these genes in the genome is raised up to 1000 fold. Forced gene amplification can be accomplished by powerful selection techniques applied to tissue-culture cells over long periods. Thus treatment of mammalian cells with methotrexate in gradually increasing concentrations has been used to force amplification of the gene for dihydrofolate reductase. The product of this gene confers resistance to methotrexate.

genecology. The branch of biology that is concerned with the genetics of populations of plants and animals in relation to the ecological niches they occupy.

gene dosage. The effective number of copies of an individual gene present in the genome of a cell or an organism. For most structural genes in diploid organisms this number is two, but for those genes coding for histone or ribosomal RNA, for example, the dosage may be much higher. See also dosage compensation.

gene flow. The introduction of new alleles from one population to another by the interbreeding of their members. This changes the composition of the gene pool of the receptive population and therefore increases genetic variation within that population.

gene frequency. The frequency with which a particular allele occurs in a population.

gene pool. The sum total of the genes of an interbreeding population at a given time.

generation time. The average period of time from the prophase of one cell division to that of the next in a population of eukaryotic cells or from one cell division to the next in a population of bacterial cells. Generation times of cells in culture vary from 20 minutes for a fast-growing bacterium to 24 hours or more for mammalian cells in tissue culture.

generative nucleus. *See* pollen tube.

genetic code. The code controlling the inheritance of characteristics from one generation to the next. It is expressed by the linear sequence of nitrogenous bases in *messenger RNA, which is transcribed from the DNA of the chromosomes. The four bases adenine, guanine, cytosine, and uracil are arranged as a series of nonoverlapping base triplets (*codons*) from a defined starting point; the sequence of codons determines the sequence of amino acids during protein synthesis. There are 20 amino acids commonly found in proteins and 64 codons in the mRNA, since some amino acids are represented by more than one codon (i.e. the code is *degenerate*) and some codons have other functions (see table).

genetic drift (Sewall Wright effect). The principle that variation in gene frequen-

first base in codon	second base in codon				third base in codon
	U	C	A	G	
U	phe	ser	tyr	cys	U
	phe	ser	tyr	cys	C
	leu	ser	STOP	STOP	A
	leu	ser	STOP	trp	G
C	leu	pro	his	arg	U
	leu	pro	his	arg	C
	leu	pro	gln	arg	A
	leu	pro	gln	arg	G
A	ile	thr	asn	ser	U
	ile	thr	asn	ser	C
	ile	thr	lys	arg	A
	met (START)	thr	lys	arg	G
G	val	ala	asp	gly	U
	val	ala	asp	gly	C
	val	ala	glu	gly	A
	val	ala	glu	gly	G

STOP = codon signalling termination of polypeptide chain
START = codon signalling start of polypeptide chain

The genetic code

cies in populations can occur by chance, rather than by *natural selection. It is usually thought to be important only in small and isolated populations, but one school of thought considers that it may be of greater importance than was previously believed, especially for genes, such as those for blood groups, that appear to have no selective advantage.

genetic engineering (recombinant DNA technology). The technology involved in altering genotypes by artificial means. The most general form of such experiments is the isolation or production of a gene sequence, the insertion of such a sequence into a bacterial *plasmid, and the large-scale growth of the plasmid in a suitable bacterial host. The appropriate gene (or its protein product) may then be recovered from the bacterial cultures in bulk. Potentially, any gene can be cloned in this way in bacterial cells and the technique has recently been extended to eukaryotic cells, particularly yeast. DNA sequences used in gene cloning work are obtained in two ways. They may be isolated using *restriction endonuclease enzymes and then inserted into chosen plasmids by the use of suitable endonucleases, *ligases, and *polymerases. Such sequences give rise to clones of genomic DNA. Alternatively, messenger RNA may be isolated from tissues and DNA prepared from it by the use of the enzyme *reverse transcriptase. The DNA produced by this second method is *complementary DNA (cDNA)*; it differs from the genomic DNA of the same general DNA region in lacking all the *intron and *promoter sequences.

Genetic engineering has many potential uses. It may be used to introduce foreign (e.g. human) genes into bacteria and yeasts in order to obtain large quantities of their gene products. Thus such products as insulin and interferon – all available formerly only at great expense and usually from nonhuman sources – may be obtained from cells grown cheaply in large cultures in fermentors. It is also used to improve crop plants; for example, by introducing the genes necessary for producing nitrogen-fixing enzymes, so eliminating the need for costly nitrogenous fertilizers. A longer-term objective is the insertion of 'good' genes into humans to counteract harmful mutations and treat such genetic disorders as sickle-cell anaemia, diabetes, and phenylketonuria.

genetic map (chromosome map). A graphic representation of the relative positions of genes on chromosomes, plasmids, or viral genomes. Distances between genes are estimated by a number of different methods. In some eukaryotes (e.g. *Drosophila* and certain other dipterans) a *cytological map* can be produced from observation of the giant *polytene chromosomes in the salivary glands. Alternatively, *linkage maps* can be obtained by measuring *cross-over values (recombination frequencies), which indicates the degree of linkage (and therefore the physical distance) between genes.

Bacterial chromosomes can be mapped by interrupted mating, *transduction (transfer of DNA from one bacterial cell to another inside a virus), or *transfection (uptake of naked DNA by a bacterium). In interrupted mating, genes are transferred from one bacterium to another on a single DNA molecule, and the time taken for them to appear in the recipient bacterium indicates their relative positions. Maps constructed by transduction or transfection use the principle that the closer two genes are on the chromosome, the more likely they are to be transferred into the same recipient cell. Recombination frequencies are used to map genes in viruses and bacteriophages. Fine-structure mapping (determination of the order of sites within genes) is possible in organisms with short life cycles and producing large numbers of offspring. Such maps have been constructed for genes in fruit flies and viruses.

Genetic mapping has now become more precise with the advent of radioactive *complementary DNA (cDNA) but is frequently complicated by such phenomena as multiple copies of individual gene sequences, *pseudogenes, and the interrupted nature of the many gene sequences that contain *introns.

genetics. The branch of biology concerned with the study of heredity and variation. The term was defined in 1905, by Bateson, following the rediscovery of Mendel's work in 1900 by de Vries and others, working independently.
Classical (or *Mendelian*) *genetics* is based on *Mendel's laws concerning particulate inheritance and includes both the observation of Mendelian patterns of heredity in experimental crosses and the observed structure of chromosomes and sequence of genes (*cytogenetics*). *Ecological genetics* is concerned with the study of heredity at the population level and examines changes in genotype and phenotype from one generation to the next. *Bacterial genetics*, which developed during the 1930s, elucidates the chemical nature of genes, including their manner

of replication and the way in which the genetic information they contain is translated into the phenotypic characteristics of the organism.

genitalia. The external reproductive organs of a male or female animal.

genome (genom). The single haploid set of chromosomes in the nucleus of any cell, organism, or species. *See also* karyotype.

genotype. The genetic complement of an organism, i.e. the particular set of alleles it possesses. The term is often used in contrast to the *phenotype (appearance) of the organism.

gentian violet. *See* staining.

genus (*pl.* **genera**). A unit used in the *classification of plants and animals. A genus consists of a number of closely related species, and members of the same genus often have a number of obvious characteristics in common by which they can clearly be seen to be related. The common name of an animal or plant is often similar to or

Geological Time Scale

era	period	epoch	time*
Cenozoic	Quaternary	Holocene	
		Pleistocene	1
	Tertiary	Pliocene	11
		Miocene	25
		Oligocene	40
		Eocene	60
		Palaeocene	70
Mesozoic	Cretaceous		135
	Jurassic		180
	Triassic		225
Palaeozoic	Permian		270
	Carboniferous		350
	Devonian		400
	Silurian		440
	Ordovician		500
	Cambrian		600

*Time = approximate age of beginning of period in millions of years

identical with the name of the genus. For example, roses all belong to the genus *Rosa*; gorillas are placed in the genus *Gorilla*. Genera are grouped into families.

geochronology. *See* varve dating.

geological time	geological strata
era	group
period	system
epoch	series
age	stage
chron	zone

Geological units

geological time scale. The method of subdividing the times of past geological ages (see chart). This time chart starts at the Cambrian, when structural fossils first became abundant. The time before this is known as the *Pre-Cambrian, from which few structural fossils are known and during which life is believed to have originated (*see* origin of life). The dates given have been determined by *radioactive dating techniques and are only approximate. Some authorities, especially in Europe, divide the Cenozoic era into two separate eras, the Tertiary and Quaternary; the epochs from the Palaeocene onwards are then regarded as periods.

The main divisions of the scale are known as *eras*, the subdivisions as *periods*, and the subdivisions of these as *epochs*. There are also further subdivisions known as *ages* and *chrons*. Each period is often subdivided into Lower and Upper (or sometimes into Lower, Middle, and Upper) periods. The rock strata deposited in past geological ages are subdivided according to the time scale but the names of the subdivisions are different; each unit of time has a corresponding unit of rock formation (see table).

geophyte (in *Raunkiaer's classification). A herbaceous plant whose winter buds are situated well below the surface of the soil. Geophytes are plants with perennating organs such as bulbs, corms, and rhizomes; examples are bluebell and lesser celandine.

geotropism. Tropic movement in response to gravity (*see* tropism). Roots are positively geotropic; primary roots grow vertically downwards, penetrating the soil. The stimulus is perceived by the root tip, which controls auxin distribution. In horizontal roots auxin accumulates on the lower side in concentrations that inhibit growth; cells on the upper side elongate more rapidly, causing downward growth. The main lateral roots are plagiotropic to gravity (*plagiogeotropism*), growing downwards at an angle, whereas the finer laterals are insensitive; this results in widespread penetration of the soil by the roots. The shoot system may spread similarly. The main stem is negatively geotropic, growing vertically upwards in the absence of light (towards light otherwise); lateral branches are plagiogeotropic, angled upwards; leaves are plagiogeotropic, growing at right angles to gravity (horizontally). Stem structures that grow horizontally, such as rhizomes and runners, are described as *diageotropic* (a special kind of plagiogeotropism). Monocotyledon leaves and some others grow almost vertically (negatively geotropic and orthotropic to gravity).

germ cell. *See* gamete.

germinal epithelium. *See* ovary, testis.

germinal vesicle. The grossly enlarged nucleus of the vertebrate *oocyte prior to the first meiotic division. At this stage the nucleus is particularly rich in polymerase enzymes and in some species the chromosomes can be seen to have adopted a characteristic appearance (*see* lampbrush chromosome).

germination. The onset of growth of a seed or spore, often following a period of dormancy and usually in response to suitable environmental conditions. The latter generally include warmth, availability of oxygen, and sometimes the presence of light (required, for example, by the seeds of mistletoe and some varieties of lettuce). *See also* after-ripening.

germ layer. One of the main layers of cells found in animal embryos at the gastrulation stage. Triploblastic embryos have three germ layers: the *ectoderm, *mesoderm, and *endoderm; diploblastic animals have only the ectoderm and endoderm.

germ plasm. A substance thought to be transmitted in the gametes (germ cells) in an unchanged form from generation to generation. The germ plasm was believed to be unaffected by the environment and to give rise to the body cells. The theory of the *continuity of the germ plasm* was put forward by Weismann, towards the end of the, 19th century, and can be loosely correlated with the theory of genes.

gestation. The period of time from conception to birth (parturition) in viviparous animals.

giant chromosome. *See* polytene.

giant fibre (giant axon). A nerve axon of exceptionally large diameter. Giant fibres may either arise from a single cell or develop by fusion of several smaller units. As their large diameter results in a low internal resistance, they provide rapid conduction pathways and frequently mediate escape responses. They occur in many invertebrates, including the Annelida and Cephalopoda, and in some vertebrates.

Gibberellic acid

gibberellin. One of a class of plant growth substances. The name is derived from the fungus *Gibberella fujikuroi,*

which makes infected rice seedlings grow taller and from which the first gibberellins, GA_1, GA_2, and GA_3, were isolated; GA_3 is known as *gibberellic acid* (see formula).

More than thirty gibberellins are now known; all are diterpenoids and all contain the skeleton:

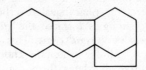

Addition of gibberellin often promotes stem elongation and it makes genetically dwarf plant varieties, e.g. of maize and pea, grow normally. Gibberellin stimulates flowering in certain long-day plants, e.g. cabbage, spinach. It can also stimulate leaf and fruit growth, break dormancy in some seeds and tubers, and stimulate the synthesis of α-amylase in germinating barley seeds. Because of these properties, gibberellins are widely used in agriculture and horticulture.

gill. 1. A respiratory organ characterized by highly vascular tissue appendages, usually specialized for gaseous exchange in water. Gills may be irrigated by the action of cilia, as in some polychaete worms, or by the respiratory movement of other organs, as in crustaceans and fishes. The *internal gills* of fish are derived from endoderm and project from the wall of the pharynx, lying in *gill slits. *External gills*, present in amphibian larvae, etc., are ectodermal in origin but may be protected by folds of the body wall.
2. One of the radiating lamellae on the underside of the pileus of agaric fungi (mushrooms and toadstools), upon which the basidia are produced.

gill bar. One of the skeletal elements in the wall of the pharynx of cephalochordates, which supports the tissue separating the gill slits.

gill books. The respiratory organs of some aquatic arachnids, including *Limulus* (*see* Merostomata). They consist of piles of vascular lamellae borne on the hindmost abdominal appendages.

gill pouch (pharyngeal or **visceral pouch).** One of a series of paired outpushings of the endoderm of the pharynx, present in all chordates at some stage of their development. A corresponding ingrowth of the ectoderm of the surface of the body meets the pharyngeal diverticulum and an opening is formed: the *gill cleft* (*pharyngeal* or *visceral cleft*). This develops into a *gill slit in aquatic chordates. In terrestrial chordates the gill pouches are soon lost and some of them never perforate the pharyngeal wall. The first gill pouch develops into the Eustachian tube and middle ear cavity in tetrapods.

gill slit. One of a series of paired openings in the pharynx of aquatic chordates, connecting the pharynx with the exterior. In protochordates they are concerned with feeding; in cyclostomes, fish, and amphibians they function in respiration and bear the internal gills (the first gill slit is modified as the *spiracle). The gill slits of cyclostomes are saclike and sometimes known as *gill pouches*. Gill slits develop from the embryonic *gill pouches.

gingiva (gum). The portion of the epithelium of the oral cavity that surrounds the teeth.

Ginkgo. See Coniferopsida.

gizzard (gastric mill). A region of the gut in animals eating hard foods that is specialized for grinding and breaking up food. It has thick muscular walls and hard grinding surfaces, e.g. swallowed stones in grain-eating birds; chitin patches in insects. In reptiles and birds it is a modification of the pyloric end of the stomach; in invertebrates it is formed in the foregut.

gland. A structure concerned with the secretion of a specific chemical substance.
Animal glands secrete their products either onto an epithelial surface, usually through a duct (*see* exocrine gland), or directly into the bloodstream (*see* endocrine gland).
Plant glands are unicellular or multicellular and can be internal or external. For example, the stinging hairs of *Urtica dioica* (stinging nettle) are external unicellular glands; *nectaries and *hydathodes are external multicellular glands. Many plants possess single cells containing gums, crystals, tannins, etc.; others have multicellular organs secreting latex, resin, etc.

gleba. The fertile inner portion that produces the basidiospores in the fruit body of the Gasteromycetes (puffballs, stinkhorns, earthstars, and bird's-nest fungi).

glenoid cavity. The hollow in the tetrapod pectoral girdle in which the head of the humerus articulates. It is formed from the scapula and (except in placental mammals) the coracoid.

glia (glial cells, neuroglia). Accessory non-nervous cells that are derived from embryonic neural tissue and invest the neurones of the nervous system. Their functions include the mechanical and metabolic support of the nervous tissue and they are implicated in the regenerative process of damaged neurones. Specialized glia, the *Schwann cells*, form the *myelin sheath.

globulin. One of a group of simple proteins that are soluble in aqueous salt solution but mostly insoluble in water and are coagulated by heat. The group includes the serum globulins (*gamma globulins*), e.g. *immunoglobulin.

glomerulus. A knot of capillaries encapsulated by the expanded end (*Bowman's capsule*) of a uriniferous tubule in the vertebrate *kidney. It filters water, salts, etc., from the bloodstream.

glossopharyngeal nerve. *See* cranial nerves.

glottis. The slitlike opening of the *larynx into the pharynx of vertebrates.

glucagon. A straight-chain polypeptide hormone of 29 amino acid residues, syn-

REACTIONS
SPECIFIC TO
GLYCOLYSIS

REACTIONS
COMMON

REACTIONS
SPECIFIC TO
GLUCONEOGENESIS

Key
① glucose–6–phosphatase
② fructose diphosphatase
③ phosphoenolpyruvate carboxykinase
④ pyruvate carboxylase
⑤ hexokinase
⑥ phosphofructokinase
⑦ pyruvate kinase
Pi = PO₃H
Ⓟ = phosphate
GDP guanosine diphosphate
GTP guanosine triphosphate

glucose → Pi ①
glucose–6–Ⓟ ← H₂O
fructose–6–Ⓟ → Pi ②
fructose–1,6–diⓅ ← H₂O
dihydroxy– acetone Ⓟ + glyceraldehyde 3–Ⓟ
+NADH
1,3–diphospho- glycerate
+ATP
3–phosphoglycerate
2–phosphoglycerate
+H₂O
phosphoenolpyruvate
⑦ CO₂ GDP ③
Mg²⁺ GTP
pyruvate oxaloacetate ⇌ malate
+NADH

oxaloacetate ⇌ malate
ADP + Pi
ATP ④
pyruvate CO₂ MITOCHONDRIA

Gluconeogenesis

thesized and secreted by the α-cells of the islets of Langerhans of the mammalian pancreas in response to low blood-glucose levels (hypoglycaemia). This hormone was first identified as a contaminant of insulin extracts that antagonized the action of insulin. It was isolated in 1955 and finally characterized in 1957. Glucagon produces high blood-glucose levels (hyperglycaemia) primarily by stimulating glycogenolysis, gluconeogenesis from protein, lipolysis, and ketogenesis in the liver. Large amounts of the hormone stimulate lipolysis in adipose tissue and insulin secretion from the β-cells of the islets of Langerhans.

glucocorticoid. Any of a group of *corticosteroid hormones that possess ketonic (C=O) or hydroxyl (–OH) groups at C3 and C20 and whose principal action is on carbohydrate, fat, and protein metabolism. They promote the deposition of glycogen in the liver, the formation of glucose from tissue protein, and the mobilization of fat. They inhibit carbohydrate utilization by tissues and immune and inflammatory responses. The main naturally occurring glucocorticoids are *cortisol, *corticosterone, and *cortisone; several synthetic glucocorticoids have been used therapeutically. *Compare* mineralocorticoid.

gluconeogenesis. The formation of glucose from noncarbohydrate precursors. Krebs cycle intermediates, amino acids, lactate, pyruvate, and glycerol can serve as precursors for glucose in most organisms. The common pathway into which the precursors converge is a reversal of glycolysis from pyruvate to glucose or glucose-6-phosphate. The sequence utilizes the reversible reactions of glycolysis, together with bypass reactions for the three irreversible steps (see illustration). These three steps are the sites of regulation of gluconeogenesis. In vertebrates gluconeogenesis occurs chiefly in the liver and kidneys.

glucosamine. An amino sugar, $CH_2OH(CHOH)_3CHNH_2CHO$, whose dextrorotatory form (D-glucosamine) is found in heparin and a number of other polysaccharides, including hyaluronic acid.

α—D—glucopyranose   β—D—glucopyranose

D-glucose

glucose. The most widely distributed monosaccharide in its dextrorotatory form (*D-glucose* or *dextrose*). It is an aldohexose, $C_6H_{12}O_6$, existing in two principal forms: *α-D-glucopyranose* and *β-D-glucopyranose* (see formulae). D-glucose is a major energy source in metabolism, undergoing oxidation to carbon dioxide and water ($C_6H_{12}O_6 + O_2 = 6CO_2 + 6H_2O$). It is a component of sucrose and of the most abundant polysaccharides, e.g. cellulose, starch, and glycogen.

glutamic acid (glutamate, glu). An amino acid, $HOOCCH_2CH_2CH(NH_2)COOH$, one of the 20 common *amino acids found in proteins. Glutamate is important in intermediary metabolism and commonly contains an amino group derived from the degradation of other amino acids (*see* transamination, deamination). Glutamate has a potent depolarizing action on neurones in the central nervous system of mammals and in crustaceans and thus may function as a neurotransmitter or modulator of neurotransmission.

glutamine (gln). An amino acid, $H_2NCOCH_2CH_2CH(NH_2)COOH$, one of the 20 common *amino acids occurring in proteins. Glutamine is used as a source of amino groups in purine biosynthesis. In most fish the amino groups derived from amino-acid degradation are transferred to glutamic acid to yield glu-

tamine, which is then hydrolysed back to glutamic acid in the kidney with the production of ammonia for excretion.

glutathione. A sulphur-containing tripeptide coenzyme of glutamic acid, cysteine, and glycine. It serves as a hydrogen acceptor in a number of reactions, e.g. in the formation of disulphide bridges ($-S-S-$) from thiol groups ($-S-H$) in the biosynthesis of *insulin.

glutelin. One of a group of simple plant proteins that are soluble only in dilute acids and bases. The group includes *glutenin*, a constituent of *gluten.

gluten. A reserve protein occurring in cereal grains, especially wheat, consisting of a mixture of glutenin (a glutelin) and gliadin (a prolamine). Sensitivity to gluten results in coeliac disease in children, characterized by inability to absorb fat; such cases must be treated with a gluten-free diet.

glycans. *See* polysaccharides.

glycerides (acyl glycerols). Fatty-acid esters of glycerol. One, two, or three of the hydroxyl groups of glycerol may be esterified; the most abundant glycerides are the *triglycerides* (or *triacyl glycerols*), the major components of plant and animal storage fat.

glycerol. A trihydric sugar alcohol, $CH_2OHCHOHCH_2OH$, important as a component of many lipids, including phosphoglycerides (*see* phospholipids) and fats.

glycine (gly). An amino acid, CH_2NH_2COOH, one of the 20 common *amino acids occurring in proteins. Glycine serves as a precursor in the biosynthesis of purines, porphyrins, and creatine and is a component of glutathione and the bile salt glycocholate. It is probably also a neurotransmitter at inhibitory synapses in the vertebrate CNS.

glycogen. A polysaccharide, consisting of branched chains of D-glucose molecules, that is the form in which carbohydrate

161

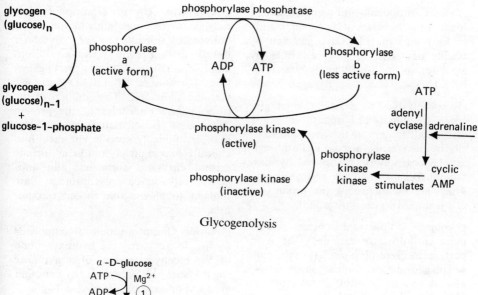

Glycogenolysis

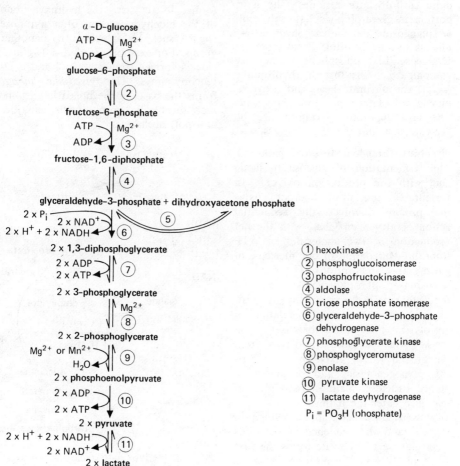

① hexokinase
② phosphoglucoisomerase
③ phosphofructokinase
④ aldolase
⑤ triose phosphate isomerase
⑥ glyceraldehyde-3-phosphate dehydrogenase
⑦ phosphoglycerate kinase
⑧ phosphoglyceromutase
⑨ enolase
⑩ pyruvate kinase
⑪ lactate deyhydrogenase

P_i = PO_3H (phosphate)

Glycolysis

is stored in animals and some algae and fungi. In vertebrates it is found mainly in liver and muscle. Glycogen can be readily degraded to glucose, either by amylases, in the same way as *starch, or by a phosphorylase (see glycogenolysis).

glycogenolysis. The degradation of glycogen to glucose-l-phosphate, which is carried out mainly in the liver and muscles by the enzyme glycogen phosphorylase. Glycogenolysis is activated by such hormones as adrenaline and glucagon, which act by increasing the production of cyclic AMP (see illustration).

glycolipid. A lipid that contains one or more carbohydrate residues. The lipid portion is glycerol phosphate, glycerol, or sphingosine and the carbohydrate residue is usually inositol, D-galactose, or D-glucose. Like phospholipids they are *amphipathic, having a hydrophilic (polar) carbohydrate head and a hydrophobic tail of fatty acid or sphingosine. The most important glycolipids are the *cerebrosides and the *gangliosides.

glycolysis (Embden-Meyerhof pathway). The fermentation of glucose to lactic acid with the production of ATP. In vertebrates and most microorganisms the process involves the sequential action of eleven enzymes, with the net production of two molecules of ATP from the degradation of one molecule of glucose (see illustration). The enzymes hexokinase, phosphofructokinase, and pyruvate kinase are essentially irreversible and are the sites of regulation of glycolysis, phosphofructokinase being the key site. The glucose is derived from the breakdown of glycogen in animals (see glycogenolysis) and of starch in plants. Fructose, mannose, and glycerol may also enter the pathway.
Glycolysis takes place in the cytoplasm of cells and the sequence of reactions from glucose to pyruvate forms the first stage of *aerobic respiration in many organisms. In facultative anaerobic cells glycolysis provides a short-term energy supply in conditions of oxygen shortage.

glycoprotein. Any of a group of naturally occurring compounds in which carbohydrate side-chains are covalently linked to a protein backbone. Commonly occurring side-chains are D-galactose, D-mannose, N-acetyl-D-glucosamine, and sialic acid. The addition of the carbohydrate molecules to the protein component is mediated by a large number of highly specific enzymes. Biologically important glycoproteins include certain enzymes, hormones, and antigens; cell-surface glycoproteins are thought to play a role in cell recognition.

glycoside. One of a group of compounds formed by replacing the hydroxyl group of the aldehyde carbon of a pyranose sugar, such as glucose, by another group. For example, methyl α-D-glucoside is formed from methanol and α-D-glucopyranose. This glycosidic linkage forms the basis of the bonds linking the monosaccharide units of disaccharides and polysaccharides.

Glyoxylate cycle

glyoxylate cycle. A modified form of *Krebs cycle (see illustration) in which two molecules of acetyl coenzyme A are converted to one molecule of succinate and two atoms of hydrogen (the latter are passed on to the electron transport chain). The cycle occurs only in certain microorganisms, algae, and higher plants, in regions where fats are being rapidly consumed. For example, it occurs in fat-storing seeds during germination in special microbodies called *glyoxysomes*. The fatty acids are broken down to acetyl groups, which, after passing through the cycle, are mostly converted to carbohydrates.

glyoxysome. A *microbody containing enzymes of the *glyoxylate cycle.

Gnathostomata. A subphylum or super-class containing all the vertebrate classes whose members possess jaws, i.e. the *Placodermi, *Acanthodii, *Amphibia, *Reptilia, *Aves, and *Mammalia, as distinct from the jawless vertebrates (*Agnatha).

Gnetopsida (Gnetophyta, Chlamydospermae). A very small and unusual group of gymnosperms, with a very short fossil history. They differ from other gymnosperms in having vessels in the secondary wood, a very long bristle-like micropyle, and one or two extra envelopes (possibly integuments) around the ovule. There are three living genera, each with its own family: *Gnetum*, *Ephedra*, and *Welwitschia*.

goblet cell. An epithelial cell specialized for the synthesis and secretion of mucus glycoproteins. Goblet cells are widely distributed in vertebrates, particularly in the intestinal and respiratory tracts of mammals and in the epidermis of fish. They are characteristically pear-shaped, with glycoprotein-containing vesicles and basally located nuclei.

Golgi apparatus (Golgi body, Golgi complex). An organelle in the cytoplasm of virtually all eukaryote cells (see illustration at *cell). Discovered by the Italian pathologist Camillo Golgi (1843–1926) in 1898, it consists of a stack (*dictyosome*) of flattened membrane-bounded sacs (*cisternae*), together with vesicles that bud off laterally from one end of the stack; new cisternae are added as required at the opposite end. The Golgi apparatus is of very diverse shape and size; in many secretory cells it appears to ramify throughout the cytoplasm whereas in some animal and many higher plant cells it appears to consist of discrete dictyosomes, numbering up to several hundred per cell.

The functions of the Golgi apparatus usually involve intracellular segregation, concentration, and transport of materials collected first in the cisternae and transported later in the vesicles. In plant cells, Golgi bodies are involved in cell wall formation, synthesizing polysaccharides for the wall matrix and transporting them to the plasmalemma. They also contribute to *cell plate formation after mitosis. The slime, wax, gum, and mucilage secretions of many cells are released from Golgi vesicles. In the secretory cells of animals Golgi vesicles commonly accumulate the secretory products; when these are proteins the Golgi apparatus often works in association with the *endoplasmic reticulum, e.g. in the formation of zymogen granules in the pancreas. The Golgi apparatus sometimes stores absorbed products, e.g. lipids in cells of the digestive tract. Golgi vesicles form primary *lysosomes in animal, and probably also in plant, cells.

gonad. Any organ in animals in which ova or spermatozoa are formed. *See* ovary, testis, ovotestis.

gonadotrophin. One of several mammalian hormones that stimulate the gonads and regulate reproductive activity. The three *pituitary gonadotrophins* are secreted by the pars distalis of the pituitary gland. Two are glycoproteins, *luteinizing hormone (LH) and *follicle-stimulating hormone (FSH), both of which are structurally related to thyroid-stimulating hormone; and one is a protein, *prolactin. The association of the pituitary with reproductive activity was first demonstrated in 1910 and the three hormone activities were separated in the 1930s. The same pituitary gonadotrophins are secreted by both sexes but in different amounts. Secretion is regulated by separate hypothalamic mechanisms (*see* neuroendocrine systems) but LH and FSH are usually released together and act synergistically. *Chorionic gonadotrophin* is a glycoprotein hormone secreted by the chorionic villi of the placenta in higher mammals. Its chief action is the early maintenance of the corpus luteum. Human chorionic gonadotrophin (HCG) was first demonstrated in the urine of pregnant women in 1927. Its highest urine levels occur 40 days after implantation, and an immunological estimation of HCG in the urine provides a widely used pregnancy test.

Gondwanaland. The ancient land mass comprising the present-day continents of South America, Africa, India, Australia, and Antarctica. Gondwanaland was named in the 19th century after an Indian kingdom where fossil plants typical of the whole supercontinent were first described. *See* continental drift.

gonimocarp (cystocarp). *See* carpogonium.

G$_1$ phase. A phase of the *cell cycle.

G$_2$ phase. A phase of the *cell cycle.

Graafian follicle. A fluid-filled spherical body of cells in the mammalian ovary inside which an *oocyte develops. Regulated by pituitary gonadotrophins, a Graafian follicle periodically matures from a follicle produced by the ovary (many other follicles are present, but these do not mature and eventually degenerate). Graafian follicles produce oestrogens and finally become attached to the germinal epithelium of the ovary and release the oocyte (or ovum) (*see* ovulation). The follicle then forms the corpus luteum (*see* oestrous cycle).

graft. The transplantation of a small part of one plant or animal onto the body of another, or the material so transplanted. In animals the individual from which the part is transferred is called the *donor* and the individual receiving it is the *recipient*. In plants, the individual from which the part is transferred is called the *scion* and the one receiving it is the *stock*.

In animal grafts, a small part of one individual is usually grafted onto a whole live animal. Such transplants are not compatible if the graft contains antigens not shared by the recipient. In this case the recipient makes antibodies against the graft, which it recognizes as foreign tissue, and the graft is rejected. For this reason the graft must be of compatible tissue, preferably of the same genotype as the recipient. The grafts that are least likely to be rejected are *autografts*, which are derived from the tissues of the recipients. For example, pieces of skin can be transplanted from one part of the body to replace damaged tissue in another part. If this is not possible, the next most successful type of graft is an *isograft* (*syngraft*), in which the donor is of the same genotype as the recipient (such as an identical, twin) or the donor and recipient are members of a highly inbred strain of animals. A *homograft* (*allograft*) is tissue transplanted from a donor to a recipient of the same species. In practice this type of graft is used in most human organ transplants. If the donor and recipient are related the graft has more chance of success. In *heterografts* (*xenografts*) the tissues are transplanted from a donor of one species to a recipient of a different species. It is a common type of graft in plants, but has less likelihood of success in animals.

In plants, a shoot or a bud of the scion is usually grafted onto the lower part of the shoot of the stock, which is cut off above the graft. The resulting plant normally has its root system made of the stock and its shoot system of the scion. Many cultivated varieties of roses and fruit trees are propagated in this way as it is a very fast method of marketing new material. The scion and stock are usually of two different species of the same genus or members of the same species. Incompatibility can occur, but grafts between more distantly related individuals are less likely to be rejected than the corresponding grafts in animals. If, abnormally, the tissue of the scion and the stock intermingle, a *graft hybrid is produced. In some cases, only a bud of the scion is grafted onto the stock; this is known as *budding* (or *bud grafting*).

graft hybrid. An unusual plant *chimaera produced by grafting, in which a mingling of the tissue of the scion and stock occurs. In some cases one side of the plant consists of cells of the scion and the other side those of the stock. In other instances the tissue of one forms a 'skin' over the other, giving a type of periclinal chimaera. The commonest example of this type of graft hybrid is made by grafting the purple broom (*Cytisus purpureus*) and the laburnum (*Laburnum anagyroides*). The resulting tree has the shape of a laburnum but its flowers are purple, as the outer pigmented layer of the petals consists of a 'skin' of the broom over the laburnum tissue. In binomial nomenclature the graft is written as *Cytisus purpureus* + *Laburnum anagyroides*, and the graft hybrid as +*Laburnocytisus adami*; + denotes a graft hybrid and × a true hybrid.

Gram's stain. A differential staining technique used to distinguish two major groups of bacteria. It was named after H. C. J. Gram (1853–1938), the Danish bacteriologist who first discovered it, in 1884. A heat-fixed smear of bacteria is stained with crystal violet or some other basic dye and then with a dilute iodine solution. The stained smear is then washed with alcohol or acetone. *Gram-negative* bacteria are decolorized, while *Gram-positive* bacteria retain a deep purple colour. The decolorized Gram-negative cells are usually counterstained with the red dye safranin.
The technique is based on the different structure and composition of the cell walls of the bacteria. In both groups the protoplasts take up the stain; in the Gram-positive group the structure of the cell wall is such that the stain is not washed out by alcohol (or acetone).

grana (*sing.* **granum**). Stacks of circular thylakoids arranged like piles of coins within a *chloroplast. This arrangement is thought to increase the efficiency by which light energy is trapped and converted to chemical energy during photosynthesis. Grana were originally observed under the light microscope as dark-green granules within the chloroplast; their lamellar structure was not revealed until the advent of electron microscopy.

granulocyte. One of a group of white blood cells having distinct cytoplasmic granules, which are visible with the light microscope and stain with acid or basic dyes. All granulocytes are *polymorphs, which include neutrophils, basophils, and eosinophils.

graptolites. Extinct Palaeozoic marine colonial animals whose chitinous outer skeletons, in the form of simple or branched stems, are common fossils in strata from the Upper Cambrian to the Carboniferous. The polyp-like individuals lived within cups (*thecae*) on the stems. Graptolites are usually regarded as related to the Coelenterata.

grasshoppers. *See* Orthoptera.

green algae. *See* Chlorophyta.

greenhouse effect. The rise in temperature that occurs in the earth's atmosphere by an effect similar to that occurring inside a greenhouse as a result of the ultraviolet radiation that enters it through its glass roof. Short-wave radiation from the sun passes through the atmosphere (which is analogous to the glass roof of a greenhouse) and is absorbed by the surface of earth, which emits long-wave radiation. This radiation is absorbed by carbon dioxide molecules in the atmosphere, thus some of the solar energy is trapped by the earth's atmosphere, causing a rise in temperature.

greening. *See* etiolation.

grey matter. The region of the vertebrate *central nervous system that contains the cell bodies, dendrites, and axon terminals of neurones, as well as glia and blood vessels. It lacks myelinated fibres and is therefore grey in colour. Because most of the synapses lie in the grey matter, it forms the integration areas of the nervous system. Primitively, grey matter forms a core around the central canal of the spinal cord and mediates spinal reflexes; in higher vertebrates additional dorsal superficial layers of grey matter are developed in the brain and elaborated anatomically and functionally to form dominant coordination centres, such as the *cerebral cortex. *Compare* white matter.

grooming. The actions of an animal involved in cleaning fur or feathers, including licking, scratching, rubbing, picking off dirt or parasites, etc. An animal may groom itself or other members of the same species; social grooming may improve efficiency or act secondarily to increase the cohesiveness of the social group. Grooming is often shown as a *displacement activity.

ground meristem. The meristematic tissue of an *apical meristem that gives rise to the ground tissues.

ground tissues (conjunctive tissues, fundamental tissues). Plant tissues comprising the cortex, medullary rays, and pith of stems and roots and the mesophyll of leaves, together with any derivatives of these. They usually consist of parenchymatous cells but frequently contain cells of other types, such as sclerenchyma and collenchyma. This tissue system is sometimes regarded as a packing tissue in the interstices between other types of tissues; however, because its cells usually retain their living contents, it is also the site of most of the vital activities of the plant, providing, for

example, the only living tissue in the secondary xylem.

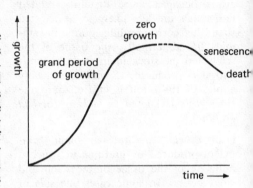

Sigmoid growth curve

growth. The increase in bulk (dry weight and/or size) of an organism that accompanies the developmental processes of differentiation and morphogenesis. The term is sometimes used in a looser sense to include only the latter processes. Growth usually involves cell division and cell expansion. It excludes such phenomena as cell division without expansion (as occurs during cleavage of a zygote to form a blastula), expansion due to absorption of water (as in seed imbibition), and short-term fluctuations of water content and storage products. In all but the most primitive plants cell division is confined to meristems, whereas in animals few cells lose the capacity to divide and growth is not localized. The rate of growth during the lifespan of an organism or organ varies, often following a sigmoid (S-shaped) curve (see diagram). The *grand period of growth* is characterized by an initially slow rate, which increases with increasing cell population, reaching a maximum rate. This rate is maintained until cells cease to divide and expand, when growth gradually ceases and may even become negative as degradation outpaces synthesis during the *senescence phase that precedes death. Such growth curves are typical of many multicellular organisms (e.g. annual plants, insects, birds, mammals), organs (e.g. leaves), and colonies of unicellular organisms (e.g. bacteria, yeast). Some organisms, however, never entirely cease growing; they include woody perennials, algae, fungi, and many animals (particularly invertebrates, fishes, and reptiles).

growth hormone (somatotrophin). A protein hormone that is secreted by the pars distalis of the mammalian pituitary gland and stimulates skeletal and general body growth. In 1921 Evans and Long first showed that anterior pituitary extracts of cattle stimulated growth when injected into rats. Such extracts were later shown to maintain normal growth in hypophysectomized animals and the active protein was isolated in 1944, by Li and Evans. Human growth hormone (HGH), characterized in 1971, has a molecular weight of 21 700 and consists of 190 amino acids with two disulphide bonds. Growth hormones of other species appear to be similar but, unlike ACTH and other pituitary hormones, they do not demonstrate inter-species activity.
The metabolic effects of growth hormone include the stimulation of nitrogen and protein anabolism, mobilization of fat stores, and promotion of carbohydrate storage. Growth hormone also potentiates the effects of other pituitary hormones and affects aldosterone secretion. All these effects are thought to be mediated by *somatomedin.

growth retardant. Any of various natural or synthetic substances that inhibit plant growth, such as abscisic acid or Amo-68. Many have been shown to act by interfering with gibberellin synthesis. Some growth retardants promote flowering in certain plant species.

growth ring (annual ring). The wood produced in one season in trees showing seasonal fluctuations in vascular cambium activity (e.g. in tropical and temperate climates). The rings are visible due to structural differences in the cells: those formed early in the season (*early wood*) are larger and thinner-walled than the later-formed ones (*late wood*). In

dicotyledons the distribution of vessels may also vary: *ring-porous* woods have most of the vessels aggregated in the early wood; in *diffuse-porous* woods the vessels are evenly distributed in the growth ring.

growth substance. An organic compound that is essential for growth or differentiation and acts at very low concentrations. The term is often used as a more accurate description of certain compounds otherwise known as plant hormones (*phytohormones*), which are not strictly hormones since they do not always act at sites remote from their synthesis. It is often the balance between two or more growth substances that determines the response of a given plant tissue. *See* abscisic acid, auxin, florigen, gibberellin, kinin.

Grylloblattodea. A small order of wingless soil-dwelling exopterygote insects, constituting six species found in mountainous regions of North America, Japan, and Russia. They resemble the Diplura and may represent a remnant of the ancestral stock from which the Dictyoptera and Orthoptera evolved.

Guanine

guanine. A purine base (see formula) that is an essential constituent of the nucleic acids (*see* DNA, RNA). *See also* nucleotide, nucleoside.

guanosine. A *nucleoside consisting of D-ribose and guanine linked with a β-glycoside bond.

guard cell. One of a pair of kidney-shaped epidermal cells that surround a *stoma. Each guard cell contains chloroplasts in the cytoplasm together with a nucleus and sap vacuole. The cellulose cell walls of each guard cell are unevenly thickened: the walls adjacent to the pore are rigid and thick, the outer walls are thinner and more elastic. Changes in the turgidity of the guard cells, brought about as a result of metabolic changes in the plant, cause the stoma to open and close.

gum. A substance that swells in water to form a gel or a sticky or slimy solution. A gum that forms a slimy solution is called a *mucilage*. Most plant gums consist of large open flexible polysaccharide molecules; they occur in some algae as well as in higher plants. Plant gums are often produced in specialized secretory cells and may be released in response to injury, forming hard glassy exudates (such as gum arabic from *Acacia* species). Mucilages are produced in slimy masses in cells of succulent xerophytic plants to increase their water-holding power.

gut. Those parts of the alimentary canal having a primarily digestive function: often used as a synonym for the entire alimentary canal.

guttation. The exudation from plants of water in a liquid (rather than a vapour) form. Guttation usually occurs from *hydathodes.

Gymnospermae. A diverse group of vascular plants (a subdivision of the Spermatophyta) whose sole consistent characteristic is that they possess seeds borne naked on a sporophyll (or on a frond in the pteridosperms) and not in an ovary. There are three subgroups: the *Cycadopsida (which includes the pteridosperms), *Coniferopsida, and a small unusual group, the *Gnetopsida.

gynandromorph. An organism, usually an insect, in which one part of the body is male and the other part is female. It is typically produced by one of the sex chromosomes of a female being lost during cell division. Those cells that have not lost an X chromosome contain XX and give rise to female tissue, while those that have lost this chromosome contain XO and produce male tissue.

The proportion of the male and female parts depends on the stage of development at which the X chromosome is lost; if this happens at a very early stage, an organism having one side male and the other side female may be produced. *Compare* intersex.

gynodioecious. Designating a plant species in which bisexual and female flowers are produced on separate plants.

gynoecium. The female reproductive organs of a flower, i.e. the carpels collectively.

gynomonoecious. Designating a plant species in which bisexual and female flowers are produced on the same plant.

H

habitat. The locality in which a plant or animal lives. The organism is adapted to the particular physical conditions within the habitat, which may be a hedgerow, freshwater pond, etc. *Compare* ecological niche.

habituated culture (anergized culture). A plant tissue culture that has spontaneously and irreversibly acquired the ability to synthesize auxin and can thus continue to proliferate without exogenous supplies in the culture medium. Such cultures resemble tumorous plant tissues, such as the growths caused by the crown-gall bacterium, *Agrobacterium tumefaciens*.

habituation. A *learning process in an animal in which continuous repetition of a stimulus without reinforcement gradually produces a diminished response to it.

haem (heme, protohaem, ferroprotoporphyrin). An iron-containing *porphyrin (protoporphyrin IX) that is the prosthetic group of proteins such as haemoglobin, myoglobin, and many cytochromes. The four pyrrole nitrogen atoms of protoporphyrin IX are chelated to divalent iron (FeII); this leaves two other coordination positions of FeII, which, in haemoglobin, may be occupied by oxygen and histidine to form oxyhaemoglobin. The free haem group bears no net charge but is rapidly oxidized to the trivalent complex (FeIII), which bears a positive charge and is known as *haemin* (*hemin, ferriprotoporphyrin*) (see formulae).

Haem   Haemin

haemalum. *See* staining.

haematoxylin. *See* staining.

haemerythrin. A *respiratory pigment found in the corpuscles of the circulatory system of various invertebrate groups. It contains two iron ions, bound directly to polypeptide chains, which are oxidized when oxygen is bound. *Compare* haemoglobin.

haemin (hemin). A complex formed between the porphyrin protoporphyrin IX and trivalent iron (FeIII). *See* haem.

haemocoel. A blood-filled expansion of the blood vascular system in molluscs and arthropods. It functionally replaces the coelom as the main body cavity and hydrostatic skeleton but does not contain germ cells. In arthropods the heart is situated within the haemocoel.

haemocyanin. A blue *respiratory pigment found free in the plasma of some molluscs, arachnids, and crustaceans. Haemocyanin contains two copper ions, directly linked to a polypeptide chain, which are oxidized when oxygen is bound. Haemocyanin may exhibit a *Bohr effect.

haemocytometer. A microscope slide designed for counting cells (e.g. blood cells or bacteria) in a chamber of known volume.

haemoglobin. A pigment of vertebrate red blood cells that is responsible for the transport of oxygen and carbon dioxide (*see* respiratory pigment). It also occurs in some lower animals and in the root nodules of leguminous plants. The haemoglobin molecule consists of two pairs of associated polypeptide chains and has a molecular weight of about 67 000. Due to small variations in the structure of the polypeptide chains, many different types of haemoglobin exist in different animal species and human populations. All types of human haemoglobin contain a common pair of chains, the α-chains. The other pair varies: in *haemoglobin A* (98% of adult haemoglobin) they are termed β-chains; in *haemoglobin A_2* (comprising 2% of adult haemoglobin) δ-chains; and in *haemoglobin F* (found only in the foetus) γ-chains. The four chain types vary only slightly in their content and position of amino acid residues. Each polypeptide chain contains a *haem group. The iron atom in haem is in the ferrous state (FeII) and binds molecular oxygen without any change in valency to form *oxyhaemoglobin*. This is bright red but acquires a bluish tinge as the oxygen is lost. Treatment of haemoglobin with mild oxidizing agents oxidizes the ferrous ion to its ferric (FeIII) state, forming the stable molecule *methaemoglobin*, which is incapable of binding oxygen. Carbon dioxide is bound to haemoglobin at the ends of the polypeptide chains.

haemolysis. The rupture of the plasma membrane of a red blood cell and the consequent release of haemoglobin. Haemolysis can occur for various reasons, e.g. the presence of *haemolysin* (an antibody that can specifically activate complement to cause lysis of a red blood cell), toxic chemicals, mechanical disruption, osmotic shock, or incompatible blood transfusions.

haemophilia. A hereditary disease in which the blood fails to clot normally and any injury results in profuse bleeding. The most common form, haemophilia A, is due to a defect in clotting factor VIII, one of the proteins required for blood to clot. Since the gene for this protein is on the X chromosome, haemophilia mainly affects males, who inherit the mutant X chromosome from their carrier mothers (*see* sex linkage).

haemopoiesis. The process of formation of red and white blood cells by differentiation of mother cells in bone marrow and lymphoid tissue. Bone marrow is the site of formation of red blood cells, which are derived from primitive nucleated types (*see* erythroblast), and polymorphs, which are differentiated from a single granular cell type (*myelocyte*). Lymphocytes and monocytes are formed from precursor cells in lymphoid tissue.

hagfish. *See* Cyclostomata.

hair. 1. One of numerous cornified elastic threads that develop from the epidermis of mammals. Each hair consists of two portions: the *shaft*, which protrudes above the skin surface, and the *root*, which is embedded in the skin, within the *hair follicle. The lower end of the root is enlarged into a knob, the *hair bulb*. Hairs are composed mainly of cuboidal epithelial cells that become increasingly cornified towards the skin surface. Their colour depends on the amount of pigment (melanin) present and also on the presence of air bubbles, which increase with age and are responsible for the white colour of hair in old age. The primary function of hair is to reduce heat loss from the skin but it may also have sensory and protective roles.
2. Any delicate filamentous projection in plants, including such structures as fine trichomes, paraphyses, and root hairs.

hair follicle. The sheath of epidermal cells and connective tissue that encloses the root of a hair. The portion derived from epidermis lies adjacent to the hair and consists of three layers (the inner *cuticle*, *Henle's layer*, and *Huxley's layer*). It is surrounded by a connective tissue sheath derived from the dermis.

hallux. The digit on the inner side of the tetrapod hind limb. It is often shorter than the other digits and in many terrestrial mammals it is absent. It is turned to the rear in most birds as an adaptation to perching. *Compare* pollex.

halophyte. A plant that inhabits places of high salinity, such as salt marshes. Halophytes possess xeromorphic characters but, unlike xerophytes, are not able to withstand long periods of drought and show stunted growth in dry summers. Many halophytes inhabiting salt marshes develop large numbers of water-storing cells, which results in a succulent appearance. Examples of halophytes are *Salicornia* and *Sueda* (sea blite).

halosere. *See* sere.

haltere. A sense organ of the Diptera that detects aerodynamic forces and thus provides information for the maintenance of stability in flight. It consists of a modified hind wing, which is reduced to a highly innervated club-shaped projection that oscillates rapidly during flight.

haplobiont. An organism having only one somatic state, either haploid or diploid. *See also* life cycle.

haploid. (Designating) any nucleus, cell, or organism that possesses a single set of unpaired chromosomes. The number of chromosomes in such a set is known as the *haploid number*, which is usually written as n: in man $n = 23$. A haploid cell cannot undergo meiosis. Haploidy is found in the gametes of both plants and animals; among animals, it also occurs in some protozoans and in the males of certain insects, including bees. In plants, the spores and gametophyte generation of types with alternation of generations are haploid, as are the spores of many fungi and algae. *Compare* diploid.

haplont. An organism having a haploid somatic state. *See also* life cycle.

haplostele. *See* stele.

hapten. A small chemical molecule that reacts specifically with an *antibody but does not stimulate antibody production itself unless complexed with a carrier protein molecule. For example, the hapten p-azo-succinanilate coupled to sheep globulin by a diazo linkage and injected into rabbits forms antibodies that are specific to both p-azo-succinanilate and to sheep globulin. *See also* antigen.

hapteron (holdfast). A structure serving as an anchoring device, especially for submerged water plants. During growth, the basal region of the plant closely adheres to the substrate and becomes cemented to it so that the plant can withstand considerable mechanical battering (e.g. by wave action) without being dislodged. The best-known haptera are those of the larger Phaeophyta of the littoral and sublittoral zones, but similar structures are produced from the rooting systems of members of the angiosperm family Podostemaceae that grow submerged in tropical waterfalls. The term *holdfast* is also used for any of the adventitious anchoring roots of *Hedera helix* (ivy).

haptonasty. *Nastic movement in response to touch. It is characteristic of certain insectivorous plants and of the so-called sensitive plants. An example of the former is the Venus' fly trap, where an insect stimulating sensitive bristles on a leaf is imprisoned by closing of the two halves of the leaf in response to haptonastic turgor changes. The best-known sensitive plant is *Mimosa pudica*, whose leaflets and petioles have pulvini at their bases that are extremely sensitive to touch, injury, and shock, such as sudden change of light intensity or temperature. The leaflets react by folding

upwards and the petioles droop. Response to shock is called *seismonasty*.

Haptophyceae. A group of chrysophyte algae previously classified as *Chrysophyceae and similar to them in most respects. Their distinguishing feature is a special flagellum-like attachment organ called a *haptonema*.

haptotropism (thigmotropism). Tropic movement in response to contact with a solid object (*see* tropism). The stimulus causes cells to grow shorter on the contact side of the plant part, while those on the opposite side grow normally, which results in the part coiling around the object. Tendrils of climbing plants are familiar examples; unmodified organs, such as the petiole of *Clematis*, may also be haptotropic.

Hardy-Weinberg law. A law stating that the frequencies of alternative alleles of the same gene in a population are constant from one generation to the next provided that certain conditions are fulfilled. The conditions are that: (1) the population is infinitely large; (2) mating is at random (i.e. there is no tendency for like or unlike genotypes to mate selectively with each other); (3) there is no selection (i.e. no genotype is more genetically fit than any other); (4) there is no mutation; and (5) there is no migration. This ideal situation (the *Hardy-Weinberg equilibrium*) never exists in reality but the concept is useful in predicting or assessing the effects of (for example) mutation alone on an otherwise ideal population and in assessing selection pressures.

In a population at equilibrium, genotype frequencies for a single gene with two alleles A and a can be expressed as follows. If the frequency of allele A is p and of allele a is q and each individual is diploid and can be AA, Aa, or aa, the frequency of AA individuals is p^2, of Aa individuals 2pq, and of aa individuals q^2 and $p^2 + 2pq + q^2 = 100\%$ (or $p^2 + 2pq + q^2 = 1$). This is the *Hardy-Weinberg equation* and it can be used to calculate the frequency of, say, AA individuals, if only the frequency of *aa* individuals is known.

hares. *See* Lagomorpha.

harlequin chromosome. A chromosome that can be stained by the Hoechst/Giemsa method after exposure to bromouracil and nitrogen mustard in the previous two cell cycles. Following nitrogen mustard treatments, numerous *sister chromatid exchanges occur, and since the staining method darkens only one of each sister-chromatid pair, this leads to a chequered appearance along the length of each bivalent chromosome (hence the name).

Hartig net. *See* mycorrhiza.

harvestmen. *See* Opiliones.

Hatch-Slack pathway. *See* photosynthesis.

haustorium. An outgrowth produced by some parasitic plants that penetrates the host tissues and acts as an absorptive organ. For example, haustoria are produced from the hyphae of some parasitic fungi and from the roots of some parasitic angiosperms. Haustorial structures are sometimes produced in young seedlings for mobilizing food reserves from the seed. For example, in *Allium cepa* (onion) the tip of the cotyledon remains inside the seed to absorb the endosperm.

Haversian canals. The intercommunicating series of canals that occurs throughout compact bone and provides channels for the bone's blood and nerve supply. Each canal is between 20 and 100 μm in diameter and is surrounded by a cylindrical unit of bone made up of concentric lamellae of bony tissue. These units, with their canals, are known as the *Haversian systems*.

heart. A muscular organ, consisting of a specialized section of blood vessel, that pumps blood around the body by means of coordinated rhythmic contractions. Vertebrate hearts are composed of *cardiac muscle, which contracts rhythmically and is subject to only indirect nervous control (*see* pacemaker). In most invertebrates the contractions are initiated by nerves of a heart ganglion. Lower invertebrates, e.g. annelids, may have one principal and several accessory hearts. Insects and most other arthropods have a long tubular heart with many small holes (*ostia*). It undergoes waves of contraction, which drive the blood forward into the blood vessels, and relaxation, during which blood enters the heart through the ostia. Vertebrates, some crustaceans, and many molluscs have short chambered hearts that exhibit discrete phases of contraction (*systole) and relaxation (*diastole). In all hearts unidirectional blood flow is maintained by valves (*see* mitral valve, tricuspid valve). *See also* atrium, ventricle, sinus venosus, ductus arteriosus.

heartwood (duramen). *See* wood.

heat-shock genes. A set of genes in *Drosophila* that can be induced to become puffed in the salivary glands when larvae are exposed to a heat shock of 37°C. Thus a sudden change in gene expression can be visualized under the light microscope. *See also* polytene, puff.

hedgehogs. *See* Insectivora.

Heidelberg jaw. *See Homo.*

HeLa cell. A widely used human tissue cell line. The cells are said to have been derived from a carcinoma of the cervix in a woman patient named *Helen Lane* in 1952. They are a transformed cell line, easily grown in culture, and often found as contaminants in other supposedly pure lines of mammalian cells.

helical thickening. *See* spiral thickening.

heliotropism. *See* phototropism.

helophyte (in *Raunkiaer's classification). A herbaceous plant whose winter buds are situated in mud.

heme. *See* haem.

hemiamphitropous. *See* ovule.

Hemiascomycetidae. *See* Ascomycetes.

hemicampylotropous. *See* ovule.

hemicellulose. One of a heterogeneous group of alkali-soluble polysaccharides, including xylans, galactans, mannans, glucans, and glucomannans, that comprise those parts of the cell wall matrix that are not pectic substances or lignin. Like cellulose, they form chainlike molecules but the chains are noncrystalline, usually shorter, and may have short branches. They transfer stress to cellulose microfibrils, i.e. they act as keying material. They are used as food reserves in some plants.

Hemichordata. A phylum of marine invertebrates in which the body and coelom are divided into three regions, the middle section bearing gill slits. Development is via a *tornaria larva, which shows similarities to the larvae of the Echinodermata. The class Enteropneusta (acorn worms, e.g. *Balanoglossus*) are free-living, having a wormlike body with many gill slits. The Pterobranchia, e.g. *Cephalodiscus*, live in colonies or aggregations within a self-secreted gelatinous case. They have a single pair of gill slits and tentacles for feeding.

hemicryptophyte (in *Raunkiaer's classification). A herbaceous plant whose winter buds are covered, e.g. by leaf litter, but are not embedded deeply in the soil.

hemipenes. The intromittent organs of the Squamata (snakes and lizards). They consist of a pair of erectile grooved saclike outgrowths of the proctodaeum.

Hemiptera. A very large order of exopterygote insects, the bugs, characterized by piercing and sucking mouthparts modified into a beak (*rostrum*). Most bugs feed on plant sap and are serious pests, by both damaging plants and carrying disease. The suborder Heteroptera have forewings that are tough and leathery at the base and are folded over the transparent membranous hind wings at rest. This suborder contains both blood-sucking and herbivorous land bugs, e.g. *Cimex* (bedbug) and *Lygus* (capsid), and the carnivorous water bugs, e.g. *Gerris* (pondskater) and *Notonecta* (backswimmer). The Homoptera have similar semitransparent wings, which are folded over the back at rest. The suborder includes *Cicadetta* (cicada), *Aphis* (aphid), and *Planococcus* (scale insect).

hemitropous. *See* ovule.

hemizygous. Designating a gene or region of a chromosome that is not paired in the diploid state, such as the unpaired region of the X chromosome in the heterogametic sex and all the genes on the X chromosome when no Y chromosome is present. In haploid organisms all genes are hemizygous.

heparin. An anticoagulant present in all mammalian tissues, particularly the lung. Heparin is produced, stored, and secreted by the mast cells of connective tissues. Heparin is a mucopolysaccharide composed of D-glucosamine, D-glucuronic acid, and sulphate. It acts mainly by neutralizing the action of thrombin and by preventing the activation of prothrombin to thrombin.

Hepaticae. A group of bryophytes comprising the liverworts (*compare* Musci). They are characterized by the lack of a distinct protonemal stage, a capsule that lacks a columella and stomata but usually possesses elaters, and unicellular rhizoids. In the *leafy liverworts* the plant body is differentiated into stems and leaves; in the *thallose* (or *thalloid*) liverworts it is a thallus. True roots are absent in both types. One group of thalloid liverworts, Anthocerotales, are sometimes separated from the Hepaticae and placed in a group of equivalent rank, the Anthocerotae, as they differ from the rest in having a meristematic zone at the base of the sporophyte and a columella and stomata in the capsule.

hepatic portal system. A vein in vertebrates carrying blood from the capillary bed of the intestine to that of the liver sinusoids. It provides a short cut for absorbed food (except fats) to the liver, where they are metabolized.

herbivore. A plant-eating animal. *See also* food chain. *Compare* carnivore, omnivore.

hermaphrodite (bisexual). (Designating) a plant or animal species that bears both male and female reproductive organs on the same individual. *Compare* unisexual.

herpesvirus. *See* virus.

heteroblastic development. Progressive change in the size and shape of successive organs during the development from seedling to mature plant. For example, in certain plants with segmented leaves, the later-formed leaves are often more segmented than the first-formed ones. Such changes are believed to be related to the progressive increase in size of the shoot apex.

heterocaryosis. *See* heterokaryosis.

heterocercal. Designating the type of tail characteristic of the Chondrichthyes (cartilaginous fish) and the more primitive members of the Actinopterygii (ray-finned fish). The tip of the vertebral column turns upwards and extends into the dorsal lobe of the caudal fin, which is larger than the ventral lobe. *Compare* diphycercal, homocercal.

heterochromatin. A fraction of chromatin that has characteristics distinct from the bulk of the chromosomal material, the *euchromatin. Heterochromatin is distinguished by its highly condensed state and by its tendency to stain strongly with basic dyes, to remain condensed through interphase (when the euchromatin is decondensed sufficiently to render the form of the chromosomes unresolvable), and to have few (if any) gene coding sequences within it. Examples of heterochromatin are found in the human Y chromosome, the *centromere,

and the *Barr body, although all of these types of heterochromatin are somewhat different from one another.

heterocyst. A cell produced in the filament of certain blue-green algae that develops from an ordinary vegetative cell, which becomes thick-walled and empty. Heterocysts are the points at which the filaments fragment into short lengths termed *hormogones*, which act as a means of vegetative reproduction.

heterodont. *See* dentition.

heteroduplex. A DNA double helix in which the complementary strands are derived from different molecules, so that there may be small regions of mismatching. Heteroduplex molecules occur naturally during genetic recombination between homologous chromosomes and can be produced artificially *in vitro* to estimate the degree of similarity between two molecules from different sources.

heteroecious. **1.** Designating rust fungi that require two host species to complete their life cycle. An example is *Puccinia graminis.*
2. Designating insect species that show an annual alternation between primary and secondary host plants.
Compare autoecious.

heterogametic sex. The sex whose somatic cells do not contain two X chromosomes and whose gonads therefore produce gametes that do not all contain an X chromosome. In many cases the somatic cells contain X and Y chromosomes; when gametes are formed, 50% of the gametes contain X and 50% contain Y. In other cases there is no Y chromosome and the somatic cells contain one X chromosome only (XO); when gametes are formed, 50% contain X and the other 50% do not contain a sex chromosome. The heterogametic sex is the male in man and many mammals. *Compare* homogametic sex. *See* sex determination.

Heterogeneratae. *See* Phaeophyta.

heterograft (xenograft). A *graft derived from a donor of a different species from the recipient. The strength of the rejection of the graft is directly proportional to the degree of relationship between the donor and recipient.

heterokaryosis (heterocaryosis). The existence of more than one type of nucleus in a cell: a condition occurring in some fungi (the cell itself, or the fungal hypha or mycelium containing such cells, is known as a *heterokaryon*). Heterokaryosis results from the plasmogamy without karyogamy of mycelia of different strains and may be a prerequisite for proceeding to the sexual stage of the life cycle. The most usual type of heterokaryotic mycelium is a *dikaryon*, with two nuclei per cell (this condition is called *dikaryosis*). In the sexual phase of the life cycle these nuclei act as gametic nuclei and undergo karyogamy, as in most Ascomycetes and Basidiomycetes. *See also* parasexual cycle.

heterokont. Designating a flagellate spore or cell in which the flagella are of unequal lengths: also used to describe the flagella themselves. *Compare* isokont.

Heterometabola. *See* Exopterygota.

heteromorphism. The production of different morphological forms of individuals, parts, or organs within a species. It is seen, for example, in the different forms of the chromosomes and in the different generations in a life cycle. *See also* dimorphism, heterophylly, polymorphism. *Compare* isomorphism.

heterophylly. The production of different leaf forms in a plant species. In some plants the juvenile leaves differ from the adult foliage (*developmental heterophylly*); in others variable leaf forms are produced in response to environmental factors (*environmental heterophylly*). For example, some aquatic species have submerged leaves that differ from the aerial ones and certain plants show seasonal variation in the leaf form. Other plants, e.g. *Artocarpus* species, habitually produce variable forms of leaf (*habitual heterophylly*).

Heteroptera. *See* Hemiptera.

heteropyknosis. The condition in which certain chromosomes or regions of chromosomes show irregularities in staining properties or condensation as compared with the bulk of the chromosomes and chromatin in the same nucleus. Chromatin that displays heteropyknosis usually stains differentially with basic dyes and is known as *heterochromatin.

heterosis. *See* hybrid vigour.

heterospory. The condition in vascular plants in which the spores are of two sizes: the smaller producing male prothalli, the larger producing female prothalli. It is regarded as an important step in the evolution of the *seed habit. In certain plants, such as the horsetail *Equisetum arvense*, a condition known as *incipient heterospory* occurs: the distribution curve of spore size shows two distinct peaks without discontinuity, the smaller spores producing male prothalli, the larger spores producing hermaphrodite prothalli. This appears to be an early stage in the development of true heterospory. *Compare* homospory.

Heterostraci (Pteraspida). An extinct order of the Agnatha, arising in the Ordovician and abundant in the Silurian and Devonian, containing large flattened bottom-dwelling vertebrates and small actively swimming forms, e.g. *Pteraspis*. The head and front of the body were covered with a heavy shield of plates and the hind part by smaller rhombic scales; there were no finlike appendages. *Compare* Osteostraci.

heterostyly. The condition in which flowers of the same species have styles of two (*distyly*) or sometimes three (*tristyly*) different lengths. It is a method of encouraging or ensuring cross-pollination by insect vectors. For example, primroses have long styles and short anthers (pin-eyed flowers) or short styles and long anthers (thrum-eyed flowers).

Pollination can be effective only between anthers and stigmas of the same length, thus ensuring crossing and preventing selfing. *Compare* homostyly.

heterothallism. The condition in which cross-fertilization between thalli is necessary whether each thallus bears both sex organs or not (the thalli are self-sterile if they produce both sex organs). *Compare* homothallism.

heterotrichous. Designating filamentous algae that produce both an upright and a prostrate system of filaments.

heterotrophic (organotrophic). Designating organisms (*heterotrophs*) that synthesize their organic requirements from organic precursors. Most heterotrophs are chemotrophic (*chemoheterotrophic* organisms), i.e. they use the organic substances as an energy source and are therefore dependent directly or indirectly on the synthetic activities of photosynthetic organisms or of chemoautotrophs. Chemoheterotrophs include all animals and fungi and most bacteria. A few heterotrophs, including the purple nonsulphur bacteria, are phototrophic (*photoheterotrophic* organisms), i.e. they use light energy to synthesize their organic requirements from organic precursors. Organisms, such as green algae, that are autotrophic except for trace requirements (e.g. vitamin B_{12}) for organic carbon are not usually regarded as heterotrophs. *See also* autotrophic (for classification).

heteroxylic. Designating xylem that contains vessels and fibres as well as tracheids and parenchyma, as in most angiosperms. *Compare* homoxylic.

heterozygous. Designating a diploid nucleus, cell, or organism that contains two different alleles for any one gene. For example, if a gene exists in two allelic forms A and a, the heterozygous form is Aa. When two such heterozygous organisms are crossed, the genotype of the F_1 progeny is 25% double dominant AA, 50% heterozygous Aa, and 25% double recessive aa. In the F_1

phenotype, 75% show the dominant A and 25% the recessive a. Heterozygous organisms (*heterozygotes*) are sometimes known as hybrids, since the parents are genetically dissimilar for the gene considered. They frequently survive better than homozygotes, with increased vigour known as *heterozygous advantage*. In the long run heterozygotes allow recessives, which would be unsuccessful in an external environment, to be retained in the genotype and so provide a potential future source of variation. *Compare* homozygous.

hexacanth. *See* onchosphere.

Hexapoda. *See* Insecta.

hexose. A *monosaccharide with six carbon atoms, e.g. glucose.

hexose monophosphate shunt. *See* pentose phosphate pathway.

hibernation. A period of inactivity caused by physiological changes that occurs in many mammals and lower vertebrates during winter. It is an adaptation to conserve energy when little food is available and enables the animal to survive at a reduced metabolic rate. *See also* diapause, aestivation.

high-mobility-group protein. *See* HMG protein.

Hill reaction. The light-induced evolution of oxygen by chloroplasts, caused by noncyclic electron flow between water (an electron donor, i.e. reductant) and an electron acceptor (oxidant), either natural ($NADP^+$) or artificial (e.g. an indophenol dye, ferricyanide). It was originally demonstrated by Robert Hill in 1937.

hilum. The scar on the outer integument of a seed which, in angiosperms, marks the point of attachment of the seed to the funicle.

hindbrain (rhombencephalon). The most posterior of the three hollow dilations of the neural tube that constitute the brain of embryonic vertebrates; it is primitively associated with auditory sensations. The hindbrain develops into the medulla oblongata of the brain stem and is elaborated dorsally to form the cerebellum.

hindgut. 1. The posterior section of the colon of vertebrates, which is primarily absorptive in function.
2. The posterior ectodermal section of the gut of arthropods. It is derived from the proctodaeum and lined with cuticle. *Compare* foregut, midgut.

hip girdle. *See* pelvic girdle.

Hirudinea. The class of the Annelida that contains the leeches – carnivorous or blood-sucking animals mostly found in freshwater or terrestrial habitats. The body is shortened and flattened, each segment being subdivided externally into narrow rings (*annuli*), and it bears anterior and posterior suckers. There are no chaetae or parapodia and the coelom is reduced to sinuses within connective tissue. Leeches are hermaphrodite and their eggs develop in a cocoon produced by the *clitellum.

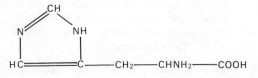

Histamine

histamine. An amine (see formula) released from tissues during injury. It has powerful physiological actions, causing dilation of blood vessels (and hence inflammation), contraction of smooth muscle, and stimulation of gastric secretion. Histamine can be obtained from the amino acid histidine by decarboxylation.

histidine (his). An amino acid (see formula), one of the 20 common *amino acids occurring in proteins. Histidine is a precursor of histamine.

histiocyte. A phagocytic cell, found principally in connective tissue, that is usu-

Histidine

ally stationary but under normal conditions can become converted into a free-moving amoeboid cell (*macrophage). Histiocytes are irregular in shape and have vacuolated and granular cytoplasm that stains with neutral red. They are extremely active in inflammatory conditions and are found in large numbers near tissue haemorrhages.

histochemistry. The study of the chemistry of living cells, especially the distribution of different chemicals within and between the cells, using techniques such as staining, microdissection, chemical analysis, chromatography, and autoradiography.

histocompatibility antigen (transplantation antigen). An antigen that initiates the immune response leading to rejection of a tissue or organ homograft. Histocompatibility antigens, which are genetically determined, are glycoproteins typically occurring in cell membranes, particularly of lymphocytes and macrophages. In man, the group of these antigens that provokes the strongest immunological response is known as the *HL-A system.*

histogenesis. The process by which undifferentiated cells of the germ layers develop into the specialized cells constituting a tissue. *See* ectoderm, endoderm, mesoderm.

histogen theory. The theory of Hanstein (1868, 1870) proposing that the *apical meristem of vascular plants consists of three distinct parts, the *histogens*, each of which has its own apical initial cells and gives rise to different tissues in the plant body. The outer *dermatogen* gives rise to the epidermis; the middle *periblem* gives rise to the cortex; and the inner *plerome* gives rise to all the tissues internal to the cortex. Each of these terms is now often used for descriptive purposes out of context of the original theory. *Compare* tunica-corpus theory.

histology. The study of tissue structure. Originally all histological information was derived from the examination of thin stained sections with the light microscope, but the science has been enhanced by the introduction of the electron microscope, which has enabled intracellular features to be distinguished.

histone. One of a group of simple proteins that have a high content of the basic amino acids arginine or lysine and are found associated with nucleic acids in the chromatin of eukaryotic cells. There are five major groups of histones: *H1* (very lysine-rich, mol. wt. 21 500); *H2A* (lysine-rich, mol. wt. 14 000); *H2B* (lysine-rich, mol. wt. 14 000); *H3* (arginine-rich, mol. wt. 15 000); *H4* (arginine-rich, mol. wt. 11 000). Histones H2A, H2B, H3, and H4 form the cores of the *nucleosome units of chromatin, while H1 links the neighbouring nucleosomes.

histone modification. Alterations to the structure of certain histones after initial synthesis. The modifications are of three kinds: methylation, acetylation, and phosphorylation. All these modifications affect only side chains of particular amino acids in the polypeptide chain. Some of the modifications are thought to be important mechanisms of gene regulation, since the histones of active and inactive chromatin often show differing patterns of modification.

HL-A system. *See* histocompatibility antigen.

HMG protein (high-mobility-group protein). Any of a group of nonhistone proteins of low molecular weight that are believed to play a role in the organization of chromosome architecture. The high mobility of these proteins is evidenced in their behaviour in size-separative techniques and results partly from

their having only about 250 amino acid residues. They bind strongly to DNA.

HnRNA (heterogeneous nuclear RNA). A type of RNA that is the primary transcription product of the structural genes. It is often of very high molecular weight since it includes transcripts of both *exon and *intron sequences. Processing of HnRNA by cleavage and splicing leads to elimination of the intron transcripts and eventual production of *messenger RNA (mRNA). HnRNA, which occurs exclusively in the nuclei of eukaryotic cells, may include many molecules that are not actually mRNA precursors. Like mRNA, much HnRNA is modified by *capping and *tailing.

Hogness box. *See* TATA box.

Holarctic. (Designating) a zoogeographical region of *Arctogea that consists of the Palaearctic and Nearctic.

Holliday model. A model for general chromosome recombination in eukaryotic organisms proposed by Holliday in 1964 (the model has now been broadly substantiated). It proposes that exchange of single strands of DNA occurs between homologous chromatids during *crossing over at meiosis and that, as a result, a cross-bridged structure, or *Holliday intermediate*, is created. Cutting of the single strands permits the intermediate cross-bridge structure to be resolved and to yield recombined sections of DNA lying in parallel. *See also* chiasma-type theory.

holoblastic. *See* cleavage.

Holocene (Recent). The second epoch of the Quaternary period, extending from the Pleistocene to the present day, in which the flora and fauna are in their present-day forms. *See* geological time scale.

Holocephali. The subclass of the Chondrichthyes that contains the modern *Chimaera* ('king of the herrings') and various extinct fishes common in the Jurassic. Chimaeras are deep-sea swimmers characterized by autodiastylic jaw suspension, large fanlike pectoral fins, and a whiplike tail; the skin lacks placoid scales. *Compare* Elasmobranchii.

holocrine secretion. *See* secretion.

holoenzyme. *See* cofactor.

Holometabola. *See* Endopterygota.

holophytic. Designating organisms that synthesize complex organic compounds from simple inorganic substances by the process of photosynthesis. All green plants are holophytic. *Compare* holozoic.

Holostei. A group of bony fishes of the subclass Actinopterygii containing numerous extinct marine forms (the dominant fishes of the middle Mesozoic) and the modern freshwater species of *Lepidosteus* (garpike) and *Amia* (bowfin). They are intermediate in structure between the primitive Chondrostei and the Teleostei, having a partly cartilaginous endoskeleton, no spiracle, and shortened jaws with reduced cheek bones: a modification to allow a wider gap that is further developed in teleosts.

Holothuroidea. The class of the Echinodermata that contains the sea cucumbers, e.g. *Cucumaria*. The body is elongated and cylindrical and shows secondary bilateral symmetry. It is covered with tough leathery skin in which the skeletal plates are reduced to spicules. There are no arms but the mouth is surrounded by food-catching tentacles. The tube feet function in locomotion and burrowing.

holotype (type specimen). The individual organism that is used in the naming and description of a new species: it is is usually kept afterwards in a preserved form (*see* binomial nomenclature). Because many species were named during the 19th century, some holotypes have been lost or destroyed. When this happens a new specimen, corresponding as closely as possible to the description of the original, must be selected to replace the one lost. This specimen is known as the *neotype*. Sometimes the

original publication of the description of the new species does not specify the holotype from among the specimens presented. In this case, one of the specimens, known as the *lectotype*, must be selected from the original material. A description of a new species may be such that a type specimen cannot be selected, possibly because no single specimen from the original material had all the characteristics of the description or because the species itself is very variable. In this case, several specimens are mentioned in the description of the new species and are known as *syntypes*. If more than one holotype is cited in the original description, all these different specimens are known as *isotypes*. In the original naming of the organism and the description of it, specimens other than the holotype may be cited; these are known as *paratypes*.

holozoic. Designating organisms that feed on other organisms or on solid organic matter. After being ingested, this insoluble organic material is digested, absorbed, and assimilated. Most animals and the insectivorous plants are holozoic. *Compare* holophytic.

homeogenetic induction. The induction of differentiation in an undifferentiated cell by an adjacent differentiated cell. An example is the regeneration of severed vascular tissue in plants from undifferentiated pith cells adjacent to the cut end of the xylem and phloem.

homeostasis. The physiological maintenance of the chemical and physical properties of the body at a constant state. When a change occurs in the extracellular fluid a compensatory mechanism comes into operation to nullify the effect. For example, the level of glucose in the blood is raised by ingestion of carbohydrate, but the body responds to this by secreting insulin, which stimulates the uptake of glucose by the tissues and hence reduces the blood glucose to its normal level. The maintenance of the *acid-base balance is another example of homeostatic regulation. An early exponent of this type of regulation was Claude Bernard (1813–78). *See also* internal environment.

hominid. Any primate of the family Hominidae, which includes modern man. The term is often extended to include any manlike primate, such as *Australopithecus* and any of the fossil species of the genus *Homo*. *See also* fossil hominid.

Homo. The primate genus that contains modern man (*Homo sapiens*), the only living species, as well as the fossil species *H. habilis*, *H. erectus*, and *H. neanderthalensis* (now usually considered as a subspecies of *H. sapiens*).

The earliest species, *H. habilis*, is considered by some authorities to be an australopithecine (*see Australopithecus*). Fossils of *H. erectus* have been found widely distributed in the Old World in Middle Pleistocene times, about 500 000 to 400 000 years ago. These include finds at Trinil (Java man), Choukoutien (Peking man), and Olduvai Gorge. The Java and Peking fossils were originally named *Pithecanthropus*, and all fossils of *H. erectus* are sometimes known collectively as *pithecanthropines*; they may be considered as representing an early human phase, compared with the prehuman australopithecines. Pithecanthropines were altogether bigger than the australopithecines, with larger teeth and brains (the latter ranged from 750 to 1200 cc, compared with modern man (1300 cc) and chimpanzees (390 cc)). They had a marked bipedal gait, used crude stone tools of a definite cultural pattern, and were capable of using fire. There have been several finds that appear to be intermediate between *H. erectus* and the most advanced species of man, *H. sapiens*, in development. These include the Heidelberg jaw (c. 500 000 years old) and the skulls found at Vertesszöllös (400 000–350 000 years old), Swanscombe, and Steinheim (both 250 000 years old). The oldest fossils of *H. sapiens* have been found in Upper Pleistocene deposits, about 50 000 years

old, the most important coming from the Far East, Africa, and Europe. The Far East fossils are from Solo in Java (Solo Man) and from Niah, Borneo. The Solo man skulls have some primitive features but the Borneo fossils, dating back 40 000 years, resemble skulls of modern aboriginals. The African fossils are the skull and limb bones from Broken Hill, Zambia, known as Rhodesian man. The European material, the first fossils of *H. sapiens* to be found, represents the classic Neanderthal man. The first of these remains were discovered in 1856 at the Neander valley near Dusseldorf, in Germany. Neanderthal man was upright and bipedal, differing from modern man in having a shorter and broader skeleton and more primitive teeth. The brain was large, with a capacity of 1200–1600 cc, and the hands were capable of gripping in a manlike way. It is known that Neanderthal man made stone tools to a definite cultural pattern and ritually buried his dead. Neanderthal man disappeared abruptly and was replaced by modern man about 35–40 000 years ago, when the ice receded after the last glaciation. The earliest fossils of modern man in Europe are known as Cro-Magnon man, named after the type site at Cro-Magnon in the Dordogne, near Les Eyzies, in France. These men had modern teeth and jaws and rather long skulls; the brains had a capacity of 1000–2000 cc, with an average of 1300 cc. They reached a high level of *Palaeolithic cultural attainment, using finely worked tools of stone and bone: they hunted and gathered food, used fire, and ceremonially buried their dead. These people also produced the cave paintings of Lascaux and other sites. It is not clear how the Cro-Magnon peoples replaced the Neanderthalers. At Mount Carmel in Israel there are two adjacent sites, one containing a Neanderthal and the other a more modern skeleton; Cro-Magnon man may have displaced Neanderthal man, or interbred with him, or exterminated him, or probably all three. Other sites of modern man have been found in Java, China, and Africa.

homocercal. Designating the type of tail characteristic of most modern actinopterygian fish, in which the caudal fin is supported only by fin rays. It evolved from the more primitive *heterocercal tail; the tip of the vertebral column remains slightly upturned but does not extend into the caudal fin. *Compare* diphycercal.

homodont. *See* dentition.

homogametic sex. The sex whose somatic cells contain two X chromosomes (XX) and that therefore produce gametes each containing one X chromosome. The homogametic sex is the female in some organisms, including man and many mammals, and the male in others, including birds and lepidopterans. *Compare* heterogametic sex. *See* sex determination.

homogamy. The maturation of anthers and stigmas in a flower at the same time. *Compare* dichogamy.

homograft (allograft). A *graft derived from a genetically different donor of the same species as the recipient. If the donor and recipient are not closely related, the graft is more likely to be rejected.

homoiothermy. The condition of maintaining the body temperature at a relatively constant level, usually slightly higher than the temperature of the external environment. Mammals and birds are homoiothermic (or *warm-blooded*). *Compare* poikilothermy.

homologous chromosomes. Any two chromosomes that undergo pairing during the prophase of meiosis. They are very similar in length and shape, have centromeres at the same point, and contain the same gene loci. Homologous chromosomes occur in all diploid organisms and their presence infers that two copies of each gene occur in each cell, although these copies may differ in being allelic forms of the same

sequence. One of each pair of homologues is derived from the male and one from the female. Homologous pairs of chromosomes do not associate during mitosis but attach to the spindle quite independently. *See also* bivalent.

homologous organs. Body organs of different species of animals or plants that have the same evolutionary origin but have come to serve different purposes because the animals possessing them have undergone adaptive radiation. For example, the pentadactyl limb of the mammal has been modified into hand, hoof, flipper, wing, etc., in the various mammal groups; these are all homologous organs. *Compare* analogous organs.

Homoptera. *See* Hemiptera.

homospory. The condition in vascular plants in which the spores are all of one size and produce hermaphrodite prothalli. *Compare* heterospory.

homostyly. The condition of flowers of the same species having styles of the same length. *Compare* heterostyly.

homothallism. The condition in which a thallus is sexually self-fertile. *Compare* heterothallism.

homoxylic. Designating xylem that consists only of tracheids and parenchyma, as in gymnosperms. *Compare* heteroxylic.

homozygous. Designating a diploid nucleus, cell, or organism that contains two identical alleles for any one gene. For example if a gene exists in two allelic forms A and a, a homozygous organism may contain AA (double dominant) or aa (double recessive). If two organisms that are homozygous for the same allele are crossed, the progeny, too, are homozygous and identical to the parents with respect to that gene. The organism is said to breed true, and the progeny from it form a *pure line. If a homozygous dominant is crossed with a homozygous recessive, such as $AA \times aa$, the F_1 progeny are heterozygous Aa. A homozygous organism is known as a *homozygote*. *Compare* heterozygous.

homunculus. *See* preformation.

hormogone. *See* heterocyst.

hormone. 1. (in zoology). The chemical substance secreted by an endocrine gland. It is transported in the blood to certain (target) tissues, on which it exerts a specific effect. The term, derived from a Greek word meaning 'exciting, moving, was coined in 1905 by Bayliss and Starling, who first demonstrated that secretin could function as a hormone independently of nervous stimulation. The first hormone to be isolated in crystalline form was adrenaline, in 1901 (although it was only later shown to function as such).
2. (in botany). *See* growth substance.

horsetails. *See* Sphenopsida.

host. 1. An organism that supports another organism (*parasite) living in or on its body at its own expense. A *primary* (or *definitive*) *host* is one in which an animal parasite becomes sexually mature; a *secondary* (or *intermediate*) *host* supports the young or resting stages of the parasite's life cycle.
2. An organism that supports any organism other than a parasite, such as a commensal.

host restriction. The enzymatic degradation of foreign DNA (e.g. of bacteriophages) introduced into a bacterial cell. Bacteria contain *restriction endonucleases, which recognize certain base sequences, usually 4–6 bases long, in the foreign DNA and cut the DNA containing them. Their own DNA is protected from restriction by modification (e.g. methylation) of certain bases.

humerus. The long bone of the upper forelimb of tetrapods, articulating proximally with the pectoral girdle at the glenoid cavity and distally with both radius and ulna. *See* pentadactyl limb.

humus. Dark-brown to black amorphous colloidal organic material in the soil, consisting of decomposed plant and animal remains. Humus provides nutrients for plant growth and increases the water-absorbing capacity of the soil.

hyaloplasm. The ground substance of *cytoplasm, in which no structure is visible.

hyaluronic acid. A mucopolysaccharide with important lubricating properties, found particularly in extracellular spaces of connective tissue, e.g. in the synovial fluid surrounding joints. Hyaluronic acid consists of a repeating unit of D-glucuronic acid and N-acetyl-D-glucosamine.

hybrid. An organism produced from a cross between parents that are not genotypically identical. In the widest sense, all organisms except those that are totally homozygous can be regarded as hybrids. However, the term is usually restricted to a cross between very unlike parents, such as those of two different strains of a species or of two distinct species. Hybrids between species are usually sterile because their chromosomes are too unlike to pair at meiosis. In animals there is no way of making a sterile hybrid fertile. In plants, fertility of the hybrid can be restored by allopolyploidy (*see* polyploidy). Hybrids are useful in that they often show *hybrid vigour, and for this reason F_1 hybrids are often produced from parental strains again and again. In animals, mules are produced in this way from the horse and donkey. In plants, hybrid maize is grown from new seed produced each year. *Compare* graft hybrid.

hybrid swarm. A group of hybrid organisms, usually living together, that have resulted from the crossing, recrossing, and back-crossing of two species. The members of the group are very variable but cannot readily be classified as separate species.

hybrid vigour (heterosis). The increase in general sturdiness, size, and health seen in many hybrids compared to their parents. Its causes are not entirely understood but are thought to be connected with increased *heterozygous advantage. In many cases it can be of practical value to man. For example, hybrid maize plants show an enormously increased yield over the parents, but as they are sterile the parental cross must be repeated for each new crop. Hybrid vigour can be retained in hybrid plants that reproduce vegetatively, as by bulbs or corms.

hydathode. The secretory organ in plants through which *guttation occurs. It consists of a cluster of thin-walled parenchyma cells, the *epithem*, which is in contact on its proximal side with tracheids at the end of a vascular bundle. On its distal side it is bounded by epidermis perforated by one or more pores, which are formed from undifferentiated stomata that have lost the capacity to open and close. Hydathodes occur most commonly on leaf margins.

hydatid cyst. A very large fluid-filled sac formed by certain tapeworms, notably *Echinococcus*, in any organ of their secondary host (man, cattle, sheep, and other animals). Larval tapeworms develop within the cyst and daughter cysts may be budded off to invade other parts of the body. Infection with these cysts results in serious, often fatal, disease in the host.

hydranth. *See* polyp.

hydrocortisone. *See* cortisol.

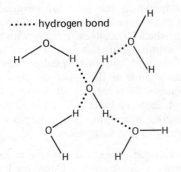

Hydrogen bonds in water

hydrogen bond. A type of bond occurring between an electronegative atom (oxygen, nitrogen, or fluorine) and a hydrogen atom attached to another electronegative atom. The electrostatic attraction between the partially negative atom and the partially positive hydrogen is responsible for the bond. The link is not as strong as a covalent bond but the collective effect of many hydrogen bonds imparts a great degree of stability to a structure. For example, water is stabilized by hydrogen bonds between molecules (see illustration) and this gives it a higher melting point than it would have in the absence of the bonding. Hydrogen bonds between two molecules or parts of the same molecule are important in maintaining the structure of many biological macromolecules, especially proteins and nucleic acids.

hydrolase. One of a group of enzymes that catalyse reactions involving the addition or removal of a molecule of water. This group forms one of the main groups used in *enzyme classification; it has the code number E.C.3.

hydrophily. Pollination with water as the vector carrying pollen from the anther to the stigma. It is rare, many water plants having entomophilous flowers projecting from the water, but it does occur in some pondweeds.

hydrophobic interactions. Attractive forces between nonpolar molecules or parts of molecules in aqueous solution. Such groups or molecules tend to aggregate together, excluding the water molecules from between them, so that the aggregate offers the minimum surface area to the water. This occurs in the formation of *lipid micelles by molecules with hydrophobic tails. Forces between nonpolar molecules are very weak: they are known as *van der Waals forces.*

hydrophyte. 1. A plant that inhabits water or water-ridden places, such as freshwater ponds, rivers, marshes, etc. The plants are adapted by having

divided leaves, little or no cuticle, air-filled cavities, no mechanical or vascular tissue, and reduced root systems. Examples of hydrophytes are water lilies and *Myriophyllum*.
2. (in *Raunkiaer's classification). A herbaceous plant whose winter buds are situated in water.

hydroponics. The technique of growing plants in liquid culture media. Originally the plants were grown with their roots immersed in a solution of water and fertilizer. However, as this resulted in difficulties in maintaining the plants in an upright position and in aerating the solution, they are now grown in a bed of gravel through which the fertilizer solution can be pumped periodically, draining into a tank. The solution, which contains sodium, phosphorus, potassium, and traces of sulphur, magnesium, calcium, etc., can be used indefinitely.
Hydroponics is used in the large-scale cultivation of flowers and vegetables. The yield is the same as for soil-grown plants and the technique saves time by automatically watering and fertilizing the crop.

hydrosere. *See* sere.

hydrotropism. Tropic movement in response to water (*see* tropism): a special type of chemotropism. Roots are generally positively hydrotropic. In most cases the tropic response to water can be stronger than that to gravity.

5-hydroxytryptamine. *See* serotonin.

Hydrozoa. A class of the Cnidaria typically showing well-marked alternation of generations. Most hydrozoans are marine, with a polyp phase that is colonial and usually sessile, as in *Obelia*, but sometimes floating, as in *Physalia* (Portuguese man-of-war). It gives rise, asexually, to free-swimming sexually-reproducing medusae. The best-known exception is *Hydra*, a solitary freshwater species with no medusa phase. Its polyps reproduce both sexually and asexually.

hymenium. The fertile layer in fruiting bodies of ascomycete and basidiomycete fungi. It consists of asci or basidia together with any protective structures, such as paraphyses or cystidia.

Hymenoptera. A large order of endopterygote insects containing the sawflies (e.g. *Nematus*), bees (e.g. *Apis*), wasps (e.g. *Vespula*), and ants (e.g. *Formica*). The hind wings are coupled by small hooks to the larger forewings, enabling a more stable flight. The mouthparts are primarily biting but in some hymenopterans, e.g. bees, there are additional sucking mouthparts. In most species the thorax is joined to the abdomen by a narrow waist. An ovipositor is always present, modified as a saw, drill, or sting. The larvae are usually legless but may be caterpillar-like. Some hymenopterans live in highly organized colonies; others are solitary.

hyoid arch. The *visceral arch lying between the jaw and the spiracle. The dorsal element of the arch is specialized for jaw support in fish (*see* hyomandibular, hyostylic jaw suspension) and for hearing in tetrapods (*see* stapes, columella auris). In tetrapods the ventral elements of the arch form the *hyoid apparatus*, which supports the tongue.

hyomandibular. The dorsal element of the hyoid arch. In modern fish it attaches the jaw to the skull (*see* hyostylic jaw suspension); in tetrapods it becomes the *stapes.

hyostylic jaw suspension. An arrangement in which the jaws are suspended from the cranium by the hyomandibular bone, which articulates dorsally with the neurocranium in the otic region and ventrally with the palatoquadrate bar or quadrate bone of the upper jaw near the jaw hinge. It occurs in all modern fish except the Holocephali and Dipnoi. *Compare* autostylic jaw suspension, amphistylic jaw suspension.

hyperchromic effect. An increase in light absorption displayed by DNA on heating. The effect is due to the separation of the double helix of the molecule into separate single strands, with a resulting alteration in the stacking of the bases. Since DNA absorbs maximally in the ultraviolet at a wavelength of 260 nm, this wavelength is used to measure hyperchromicity. Study of the shape of the melting curve of a DNA sample can be used to provide information about the complexity of the DNA; loss of hyperchromicity on annealing of the DNA is the basis of Cot curve construction (*see* Cot value).

hyperplasia. Increase in the number of cells in a tissue, organ, etc. (due to increased cell division), resulting in the enlargement of the tissue in which they occur. Hyperplasia is a common feature of normal development but also occurs in adult life in more localized situations, such as wound healing, lymph node activity, and tumour growth.

hyperpolarization. An increase in the potential difference across a membrane.

hypertonic. If a solution, A, has a higher osmotic pressure (lower water potential) than another solution, B, it is described as hypertonic to B; B is *hypotonic* to A. If solution A is separated from solution B by a semipermeable membrane, water moves from B to A by osmosis. Solutions of identical osmotic pressure are described as *isotonic*. The terms are often used to describe the osmotic properties of a solution relative to the contents of a cell.

hypertrophy. Increase in the size of cells resulting in an increase in the size of the tissue or organ in which they occur.

hypha. One of the filaments that form the vegetative bodies of most fungi and algae. It is a tubular structure consisting of a cell wall (of cellulose and/or fungal chitin) containing cytoplasm. It may or may not be septate. If it is not septate it is coenocytic (*see* coenocyte); if it is septate it may be coenocytic, as in the green alga *Cladophora*, or dikaryotic (*see* heterokaryosis), as in the Basidiomycetes, or it may consist of ordinary uni-

nucleate cells. In structures such as rhizomorphs and in the bodies of thalloid algae the hyphal filaments become compactly aligned to form dense tissuelike layers, as in the pseudoparenchyma of the larger algae.

hypocotyl. The shoot axis below the cotyledonary node. The transition from the vascular arrangement of the root to that of the stem occurs in a region of the hypocotyl known as the *transition zone*. This zone is between a millimetre and several centimetres long and comprises a part or the whole of the hypocotyl. *Compare* epicotyl.

hypodermis. 1. A subepidermal layer present in the stems and leaves of certain plants that is distinct from the deeper-lying tissues. Together with the outer epidermal layer, it constitutes a multiple *epidermis. It may act as water-storing tissue (as in succulent leaves) or be a protective lignified layer (as in pine leaves).
2. *See* subcutaneous tissue.

hypogeal (in botany). Developing below ground. The term is applied to fungal fruiting bodies such as truffles; seed germination in which the cotyledons remain below ground; and fruit development, as in *Arachis* (peanut), in which the peduncle becomes positively geotropic and buries its apex in the ground, where the fruit develops.

hypoglossal nerve. *See* cranial nerves.

hypogyny. The condition of angiosperm flowers of having the gynoecium above the insertion of the other flower parts, i.e. having a superior gynoecium. *Compare* epigyny, perigyny.

hyponasty. Upward curvature of a plant organ as a result of more rapid growth of its lower side. It is typical of some leaves and petals. *See* nyctinastic movements.

hypophysectomy. The surgical removal of the pituitary gland, undertaken in patients for therapeutic reasons and in animals for research into the endocrine functions of the gland.

hypophysis. *See* pituitary gland.

hypostatic. Designating a gene whose effect is suppressed by the presence of another (nonallelic) gene. The suppression of such a gene is known as *hypostasis*. *See also* epistatic. *Compare* recessive.

hypothalamus. The thickened floor and sides of the posterior part of the vertebrate forebrain, situated below the third ventricle and above the pituitary gland. The hypothalamus is the prime coordinating centre for numerous visceral functions. It is the head of the autonomic nervous system, with separate centres for both sympathetic and parasympathetic regulation, and is the main region for the integration of neural and endocrine functions through its rigorous control of pituitary secretion (*see* neuroendocrine systems). It also contains regions that initiate and control sleep, feeding, drinking, satiety, and certain patterns of behaviour associated with aggression and reproduction. The hypothalamus is the most vascular region of the brain and, by monitoring various aspects of the blood, it regulates such processes as the maintenance of body temperature and water balance.

hypotonic. *See* hypertonic.

Hyracoidea. The order of the Eutheria that contains the hyraxes of Africa, e.g. *Procavia* (rock hyrax) and *Dendrohyrax* (tree hyrax): rabbit-like herbivorous mammals with long hind limbs and a short tail. The digits have hooflike nails and the hind feet have a grooming claw. There are four lower incisors, two strong pointed upper incisors, and a gap (*diastema*) between the incisors and the small grinding cheek teeth.

hyraxes. *See* Hyracoidea.

I

IAA. Indoleacetic acid, the most common naturally occurring *auxin.

IAN. Indoleacetonitrile, a naturally occurring *auxin.

Ice Age. *See* Pleistocene.

Ichthyopterygia. An extinct subclass of large marine reptiles common in the Jurassic and Cretaceous. They were characterized by a *parapsid* skull, i.e. a skull with a single pair of temporal openings high up on the cheek. The single order, Ichthyosauria, contained forms such as *Ichthyosaurus*, which had a streamlined body with short wide paddle-like limbs and median dorsal and caudal fins. Ichthyosaurs probably never left the water and were ovoviviparous. *Compare* Synaptosauria.

ICSH. Interstitial-cell-stimulating hormone. *See* luteinizing hormone.

identical twins (monozygotic twins). Twins produced by the fertilization of one ovum by one sperm to form a zygote that then undergoes mitosis. Each of the products of mitosis develops into an organism. These twins are genetically identical in all respects, including sex. *Compare* fraternal twins.

idioblast. A cell differing markedly in structure or function from neighbouring cells in the same tissue. In plants, sclereids and certain secretory cells often occur as idioblasts. *See also* cystolith.

idiogram. *See* karyotype.

ileum. An indistinctly delimited region of the mammalian small intestine preceding the colon. It is digestive and absorptive in function.

ilium. A paired cartilage bone forming the dorsal element of the tetrapod *pelvic girdle. It articulates with the sacrum.

imago. The adult sexually mature form of an insect.

imbibition. The nonactive (i.e. purely physical) adsorption of water, particularly by substances that form colloids (usually gels) in water. Plant organs contain many such substances, e.g. cellulose, hemicelluloses, pectic substances, starch. As water is imbibed the substance or organ swells, sometimes causing great imbibitional pressures, as in the uptake of water by seeds prior to germination. Increase in volume and fresh weight of expanding nonvacuolated cells (particularly in meristematic regions) is accompanied by imbibition as well as osmosis. Some of the water in soils is held by imbibitional forces.

immune clearance. *See* antigen.

immune response. *See* immunity.

immunity. The ability of an animal or plant to resist and/or overcome harmful infection or agents. There are two principal types of immunity in animals: (1) *nonspecific immunity*, which does not involve the production of antibodies and includes such mechanisms as phagocytosis and the action of interferon and lysozyme; (2) *specifically acquired immunity*, which is due to the presence of antibody in the animal and includes *passive immunity* and *active immunity*. Passive immunity results from the presence of antibody derived from another individual, e.g. from immunoglobulins transferred through the placenta of a mother to her offspring (*passive natural immunity*) or from heterologous antibodies administered to protect the organism from the effects of diseases such as diphtheria and tetanus (*passive induced immunity*). Active immunity is due to the development of an *immune response* following stimulation with an antigen. An immune response may develop after exposure to infection (*active natural immunity*) or it may be induced by *vaccination (*active induced immunity*). It is characterized by the production of either humoral antibody or lymphocytes containing cell-bound antibody (*cell-mediated immunity*).

immunization. The process of rendering an animal resistant to infection or harmful agents. This is achieved by conferring either passive immunity, which provides only temporary protection and is lost when the acquired antibody is catabolized, or active immunity, e.g. by *vaccination, which provides a more effective and permanent protection.

immunoelectrophoresis. A technique for identifying antigens separated from a serum (in a gel or on cellulose acetate paper) by *electrophoresis. A particular antiserum is allowed to diffuse into agar overlaying the chromatogram and forms a visible precipitate when it meets its antibody.

immunofluorescence. The use of antibodies to which a fluorescent dye (e.g. fluorescein) has been bound to stain specific proteins in microscope preparations. The technique can be used, for example, to show the location of a particular enzyme in the cell or to show whether or not a protein is membrane-bound.

immunogenetics. Genetic aspects of the study of *immunoglobulins, the proteins that form *antibodies. The great diversity of antibody structure and specificity renders immunogenetics one of the most complex areas of genetic study.

immunoglobulin (Ig). One of a class of globulins, usually gamma globulins, to which *antibody activity belongs. Immunoglobulins are divided into five classes (reflecting the heterogeneity of the types of antibody molecule), which are abbreviated as follows: *IgG, IgM, IgA, IgD,* and *IgE*. These are further divided into subclasses: IgG into four and IgA and IgM into two each. In their biological properties, IgG and IgM can fix complement; only IgG can cross the placenta and bind to macrophages. The major components of serum antibody are IgG (molecular weight 150 000) and IgM (molecular weight 900 000).

immunological tolerance. Failure of the antibody response in an animal exposed to a potential antigen. It is usually induced by prior exposure to antigens.

There are several forms of immunological tolerance, such as *foetal tolerance*, which is acquired by exposure to antigens during foetal life, *genetic tolerance*, which results from genetic identity, *feeding tolerance* (tolerance to antigens acquired by their ingestion), and *self-tolerance* (tolerance to self-antigens acquired during foetal life).

Impennae. The superorder of the Neornithes that contains the penguins. These birds are confined to the southern hemisphere – most live in sub-Antarctic waters – and are specialized for aquatic life, having wings modified to form flippers. Most penguins come ashore to breed and many do not make nests but incubate their eggs (of which there are one or two) on their feet.

implantation (nidation). Attachment of the fertilized ovum or blastocyst of female vertebrates within the endometrium of the uterus at the start of pregnancy.

imprinting. A *learning process in animals, especially birds, that occurs at an early and usually sensitive stage in their life. The animal learns to react to a certain object, often by following it. Any large moving object can become imprinted; under natural conditions this is usually the parent, but an animal can learn to follow any person, object, or other animal.

impulse. An *all-or-none propagated signal by which information is transmitted rapidly and precisely through the nervous system along the axons of the neurones. An impulse is a sequence of changes in membrane permeability that gives rise to ionic currents and associated voltage changes across the membrane. The characteristic pattern of changes in potential, which can be recorded using microelectrodes and is thus experimentally the most easily observed manifestation of the impulse, is termed the *action potential*. A threshold stimulus is required to initiate an impulse. *In vivo* this is provided by a passive local depolarization called an *end-plate potential, *excitatory postsynaptic potential, or *receptor potential (according to the site). Once initiated, the changes in membrane potential become self-reinforcing and give rise first to an inward current of sodium ions, which reverses the membrane potential from −70 mV to +30 mV, then to an outward current of potassium ions, which restores the *resting potential. Local currents flow along the membrane into the area of the impulse from the resting area ahead of the impulse, which is thus depolarized below the threshold. In this way the impulse is propagated along the membrane as a wave of activity. For a period following the potential changes the membrane is inexcitable, while it recovers its resting state. Because all impulses are the same size, information is conveyed by the frequency and total number of impulses evoked by a stimulus. Impulses are characteristic of all axons, although they appear only at the nodes of myelinated fibres (*see* saltatory conduction), and of vertebrate striated muscle fibre membranes.

inbreeding. The mating of closely related organisms (such as siblings, parents, or cousins in animals): also applied to self-fertilization in plants. Inbreeding results in harmful recessive genes appearing in the phenotype and a decrease in heterozygosity of the population. For both these reasons it tends to be disadvantageous and many organisms have mechanisms, either physical or social, to discourage it and to promote outbreeding. When a stock or variety of animals or plants is selected by man it can be propagated sexually only by inbreeding, at least in the early stages. *Compare* outbreeding.

incisor. A sharp chisel-edged tooth of most mammals that occurs in the front of the mouth. There are usually between one and three incisors on each side of the upper and lower jaws and they are used for gnawing and biting off pieces of food. In rodents they are particularly well developed and continue growing throughout life.

incompatibility. 1. The condition resulting from the action of a mechanism in plants that prevents self-fertilization. The mechanism ensures that pollen from a plant does not grow on the stigma of the same plant or of a genetically identical one and therefore prevents seed from being set. The mechanism is always genetic; genes in the pollen interact in some way with those in the stigma. In some species pollen does not grow on the stigma at all; in others it grows more slowly than compatible pollen, so that self-pollination can occur if cross-pollination fails. In many species incompatibility is brought about by special pollen proteins that interact with those of the stigma. These proteins can sometimes be washed off the pollen and pollination can then be brought about. Also called: **self-sterility.**
2. A genetically determined mechanism in some fungi that prevents sexual reproduction from occurring between individuals of the same strain and results in heterothallism.
3. A physiological interaction between the tissues of two organisms that results in the rejection of a graft or the failure of a blood transfusion in animals or the lack of union of the stock and scion in plants.

incomplete dominance. The condition in which two allelic genes have a different effect when they are together as a heterozygote in a diploid cell than either of them have in the homozygous state. The classic case of incomplete dominance is seen in the Andalusian fowl, in which the feather colour may be black, blue, or white. Two alleles are involved, B and W. When BB is present the fowl is black, when WW occurs it is white; however W is not a recessive, since the progeny of both black and white parents are genotypically BW and phenotypically greyish-blue, due to a mixture of black and white feathers. If two blue fowl are mated, the percentages of progeny are 25% black, 50% blue, and 25% white.

incus. The middle *ear ossicle in mammals, homologous with the quadrate bone of other vertebrates.

indehiscent. Designating plant parts that do not open to release their contents at maturity, especially fruits that do not release their seeds. *Compare* dehiscence.

independent assortment. The segregation of two or more pairs of alleles at meiosis, none of which affects the movement of the others. If two pairs of alleles, Aa and Bb, are present in a diploid heterozygote, four possible types of gametes, AB, Ab, aB, ab, are produced in equal numbers. This will be possible only if A and B are on different chromosomes. Independent assortment does not occur if the genes A and B are linked on the same chromosome. In this case only two possible gametes are found, AB and ab, unless *linkage between the genes is broken down by *crossing over, when a small proportion of gametes Ab and aB can be produced. *See also* Mendel's laws, recombination.

indicator species. A plant or animal species whose presence indicates that a particular combination of environmental conditions is operating. The presence of certain lichen species shows that the level of sulphur dioxide in the air is below a certain threshold, and the presence of some aquatic insect larvae indicates that water-pollution levels have not exceeded a threshold.

indigenous. Designating an organism that is native to a particular habitat, as distinct from one introduced from outside the area.

indoleacetic acid (IAA). The most common naturally occurring *auxin.

indoleacetonitrile (IAN). A naturally occurring *auxin.

inducible enzyme (adaptive enzyme). An enzyme that is synthesized only in the presence of an inducing agent, such as its substrate: a property of the enzyme-synthesizing system and not of the enzyme itself. For example, if the bacterium *Escherichia coli* is grown on a medium containing lactose, it will produce large amounts of β-galactosidase in order to utilize this substrate. *Compare* constitutive enzyme.

induction (in embryology). *See* evocation.

indusium. 1. The protective covering of a fern *sorus, which consists of a small membranous flap of tissue, one cell thick, produced from the epidermis.
2. Any similar protective covering in animals or plants.

industrial melanism. The occurrence of the melanic (dark) form of an organism, typically of some species of moths, in an environment blackened by industrial pollution. Melanic moths are camouflaged in polluted districts and therefore favoured by selection pressures, while the pale forms are selected against as they are conspicuous and readily taken by birds. In unpolluted areas the reverse process occurs; the melanic forms are selected against and the pale forms are selected for. These processes may result in the modification of dominance, the melanic forms becoming dominant in polluted areas and the pale forms in unpolluted ones.

infection. The condition of an organism or part of an organism of being invaded by pathogenic bacteria, viruses, or other microorganisms.

inferior. Designating an angiosperm gynoecium with the other flower parts inserted above it, i.e. the gynoecium of an epigynous flower. *Compare* superior.

inflammation. The early response of an animal to local injury, which contributes to the defence of the organism by providing an unfavourable environment for infection. The response occurs near the site of the injury and consists of dilation of blood capillaries and decrease in blood flow (by the formation of a fibrin

network), the passage of leucocytes and blood proteins and fluids through the capillary walls, and the migration of leucocytes (initially neutrophils, later macrophages and lymphocytes) to the site of the injury.

inflorescence. A group of flowers borne on the same stalk (*peduncle*). Inflorescences are classified according to whether growth of the plant continues by the main axis (*see* racemose inflorescence) or whether the tip of the main axis forms a flower and growth is continued by a lateral bud (*see* cymose inflorescence).

infundibulum. *See* pituitary gland.

inhibition (in the nervous system). The prevention or reduction of effector activity by the action of certain nervous impulses, which occurs by one of two mechanisms. *Presynaptic inhibition* occurs when activity in an inhibitory nerve ending near an excitatory presynaptic membrane reduces the amount of excitatory transmitter released, and hence the size of the postsynaptic response (*excitatory postsynaptic potential or *end-plate potential), without directly affecting the postsynaptic membrane. *Postsynaptic inhibition* occurs when stimulation of an inhibitory neurone induces a postsynaptic potential change (*inhibitory postsynaptic potential), which adds to excitatory potential changes in the same membrane and thus reduces the size of the postsynaptic depolarization. Inhibition by either of these mechanisms is produced either centrally, e.g. the relaxation of an antagonist muscle brought about by a reflex excitation of inhibitory interneurones in the central nervous system simultaneously with excitation of a skeletal muscle; or peripherally, e.g. the control of the strength of crustacean muscle contraction at the neuromuscular junction.

inhibitory postsynaptic potential (IPSP). The graded local hyperpolarization of the postsynaptic membrane that is elicited by neurotransmitter released from the presynaptic membrane of an inhibitory *synapse or neuromuscular junction.

initial (initiating cell). A meristematic cell that divides mitotically into two daughter cells, one of which remains in the meristem while the other joins the cells that will ultimately differentiate into the various organs and tissues of the plant body.

innate behaviour. Any inherited behaviour pattern or patterns exhibited by most of the individual members of a species living under the same conditions. *See also* instinct.

inner ear. The vertebrate organ of equilibrium, secondarily specialized in tetrapods for hearing. It lies within the auditory capsule and consists of a *membranous labyrinth* surrounded by a viscous fluid, the *perilymph. The labyrinth consists of two cavities, the *utriculus* and *sacculus*, each containing an area of sensory epithelium (*macula), which registers both the position of the head relative to gravity and its rate of movement. The utriculus bears three tubes, the *semicircular canals, set at right angles to each other. These are filled with a fluid (*endolymph*) and each canal contains a sensory receptor (*crista), which registers the rate of movement of the head. A diverticulum of the sacculus, the *cochlea, is the organ of hearing.

innervation. The nerve supply of an organ.

innominate artery. A short blood vessel in some birds and mammals that branches from the aorta and divides to form the right carotid and right subclavian arteries.

innominate bone. The bone forming each half of the pelvic girdle of adult amniotes, consisting of the fused ilium, ischium, and pubis.

inositol. A carbohydrate required for the growth of certain animals and microorganisms. The stereoisomer *myo-inositol* (see formula) serves as the precursor of *phosphatidyl inositol*, a phosphoglyceride important as a constituent of animal membranes, muscle, and brain. *See also* vitamin.

Insecta (Hexapoda). The largest class of the phylum Arthropoda and the largest in the animal kingdom. An insect's body is characteristically divided into a head, thorax, and abdomen. The head bears a pair of antennae, a pair of *compound eyes, and one or more *ocelli (simple eyes). The *mouthparts, which are adapted according to the diet, comprise a pair of mandibles and maxillae, a labrum, and a labium. The thorax bears three pairs of five-jointed legs and, in most groups, two pairs of wings, which are strengthened by a vein network. Most insects are terrestrial and respiration is by *tracheae, with segmentally arranged spiracles. Excretion is by *Malpighian tubules. The sexes are separate and most insects undergo metamorphosis during development. There are two subclasses: the *Apterygota (primitively wingless insects) and the *Pterygota (winged insects), the latter being subdivided into the *Exopterygota and the *Endopterygota.

Insectivora. An order of the Eutheria containing small primitive insectivorous or omnivorous and generally nocturnal mammals, e.g. *Sorex* (shrew), *Erinaceus* (hedgehog), and *Talpa* (mole). Insectivores typically have an elongated tapering snout, numerous small teeth with pointed cusps, and a smooth brain with small cerebral hemispheres. The feet

Myo-inositol

have five clawed digits and locomotion is plantigrade.

insertion element (i.s. element). A DNA sequence, found in bacteria (and probably also in eukaryotes), capable of inserting into the genome more or less randomly and also of moving from one chromosome locus to another. The movement of such elements is much more frequent than the base mutation rate: their transposition may lead to a very high mutation rate at the original site or at the new site of insertion. Insertion elements are postulated to be responsible for site-specific plasmid and phage integration (*see* additive recombination) and, together with other longer integrated sequences, to function as *transposons in eukaryotic and prokaryotic cells.

***in-situ* hybridization.** Artificial hybridization of nucleic acids with fixed material on a microscope slide. Most frequently cells are squashed on the slide so that the chromosomes of dividing cells are widely spread, then the DNA in the chromatin is denatured so that it becomes essentially single-stranded. The material is then exposed to a solution containing radioactively labelled DNA or RNA complementary to a specific sequence and held at a temperature that favours DNA annealing. After washing and drying, an autoradiograph is prepared, which should reveal the chromosomal location of DNA sequences involved in the hybridization process. *See also* hyperchromic effect.

instar. A stage in the growth of an arthropod between any two moults (*see* ecdysis). Butterfly larvae (caterpillars) typically have five instars; many beetles have three or four.

instinct. A stereotyped pattern or series of patterns of animal behaviour that is similar in all individuals of the same species and is evoked by certain stimuli. Animals of the same species reared in isolation tend to show similar such patterns of behaviour, often called *fixed*

action patterns. They are assumed to be under genetic control in that they result from some inherited potentiality of the nervous system. Some authorities, however, claim that instinctive behaviour comprises some inherited components and some components that have resulted from interactions with the environment. Young birds of the same species reared in isolation all show a similar basic pattern of bird song; under natural conditions this pattern is modified and made more complex according to the geographical position of the habitat, the influence of other birds, etc.

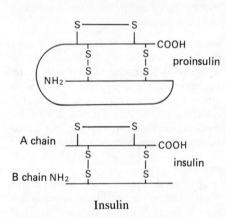

Insulin

insulin. A protein hormone (molecular weight 5800) secreted by the β-cells of the islets of Langerhans in the pancreas in response to high blood-glucose levels (hyperglycaemia). It stimulates glucose utilization by cells and prevents glycogen breakdown (glycogenolysis) in liver and muscle. Insulin was first discovered by Banting and Best (1921) as the component of pancreatic extracts responsible for maintaining depancreatized dogs. Its structure was established in 1955 by Sanger and others; it was the first protein to be fully sequenced. Insulin consists of two polypeptide chains (A and B) of 21 and 30 amino acid residues, respectively, which are linked by disulphide bridges between cystine residues. It is produced from a single-chain precursor, *proinsulin*, which undergoes enzymatic cleavage in the pancreas (see illustration). A deficiency of insulin results in the disease *diabetes mellitus. *Compare* glucagon.

integration. 1. The processes by which the input to the nervous system, i.e. the information collected by the receptors, is treated in such a way that the output, i.e. effector action, is appropriately related to, but not a direct function of, the input. Integration permits coordination and flexibility of behaviour and occurs at a primary level at the *synapses. *See also* reflex, nervous system.
2. The insertion of viral DNA or a plasmid into the chromosomal DNA of a host. The DNA of bacteriophage , for example, becomes integrated into the *E. coli* chromosome after infection.

integument. 1. A protective envelope around the *ovule of seed plants that arises close to the funicle and grows up round the nucellus. Most gymnosperm ovules have one integument; most angiosperms have two. A small pore, the *micropyle, is usually present and represents the limit of closure of the integument(s). After fertilization or agamospermy the integuments form the testa.
2. The outer protective covering of an animal, such as a cuticle, skin, scales, etc.

intention movement. An activity in a sequence of behaviour by an animal that regularly occurs before another activity and can be used to predict it. For example, the nest-building behaviour of the male stickleback always starts with the digging of a pit in the sand. This intention movement is regularly followed by a sequence of other activities: bringing material to the nest, sticking it together, etc.

intercalary meristem. *See* meristem.

intercellular. Occurring between cells.

interfascicular cambium. Part of the lateral meristem of the *vascular tissue.

interferon. A protein that is synthesized by animal cells in response to viral infection and nonspecifically inhibits replication of the viruses. Interferon is assumed to play a significant role in the recovery from viral infection as it is synthesized and found in serum almost at the onset of infection and long before the production of serum antibody. Interferon occurs in a number of slightly variant forms. Human interferon gene sequences have been assembled, largely by artificial synthesis, and attempts are currently under way to produce human interferon from such sequences by gene cloning in suitable bacterial hosts (*see* genetic engineering).

interkinesis. 1. The period between the first and second divisions of meiosis.
2. The period between two mitotic divisions.

intermediate junction. *See* junctional complex.

intermedin. *See* melanocyte-stimulating hormone.

internal energy. Symbol: U. A thermodynamic property of a system defined by the first law of thermodynamics as the difference between the heat absorbed by the system from its surroundings (q) and the work done by the system on the surroundings (w), i.e. $U = q - w$. The internal energy is the sum of the energies of translation, vibration, and rotation of the constituent molecules plus the bond energies. While the absolute value of U is rarely known, changes in U (ΔU) can be measured and are useful in thermodynamic calculations. *See* enthalpy.

internal environment. The extracellular fluid of the body. Its composition is maintained at a constant state by the mechanisms of *homeostasis.

interneurone (intermediate neurone, intercalated neurone, internuncial neurone). A neurone that is neither sensory nor wholly motor and is interpolated between the afferent and efferent neurones of a reflex arc (*see* reflex). In vertebrates interneurones are confined to the central nervous system.

internode. 1. (in botany). The stem axis between two nodes. In the apical meristem the internodes are almost nonexistent; they are developed in the region proximal to the apical meristem by cell divisions below the leaf insertions, i.e. by intercalary growth, the intercalated tissue constituting the internode. *Compare* node.
2. (in zoology). The myelinated region of the axon of a neurone, which separates two nodes of Ranvier. *See* myelin sheath.

interoceptor. A *receptor located in or on an internal organ. *Compare* exteroceptor.

interphase. The stage at which a nucleus is not undergoing mitosis or meiosis. During interphase the nucleus carries out somatic activities, such as protein synthesis and duplication of the chromosomes. A nucleus at this stage is known as a *resting nucleus*; the cell containing it is a *resting cell*.

intersex. An abnormal individual that is not distinctly male or female. It is usually intermediate between the sexes in characteristics but is sometimes completely hermaphrodite. Intersexes are produced in various ways: either by genetic changes and a failure of the sex chromosomes to divide or to operate properly, by the malfunction of sex hormones or other chemicals during development, as in a *freemartin, or by psychological factors.

interstitial cells. *See* testis.

interstitial-cell-stimulating hormone (ICSH). *See* luteinizing hormone.

intestine. The part of the alimentary canal principally concerned with the digestion and absorption of food; in vertebrates it is specifically the part of the gut between the pylorus and the rectum. Primitively a short tube, its secretory and absorptive surface is increased in area to suit the diet and size of the animal. This is achieved by the presence of villi, by folding of the submucosal layer, and by an increase in length through the development of a spiral valve (most fish), pyloric caeca (teleosts), or three-dimensional coiling (teleosts and tetrapods). It may be specialized into an anterior *small intestine* (*see* duodenum, jejunum, ileum), which is digestive and absorptive, and a posterior *large intestine* (*see* colon), in which faeces are formed. The junction between the two regions is marked by a valve and one or more caeca. Food is churned by the action of the muscles in the intestinal wall and chemically digested by secretions of glands in the wall (*see* succus entericus) and of glandular outgrowths of the wall: the pancreas (secreting enzymes) and the liver (secreting bile). The products of digestion are absorbed into the walls of the small intestine: amino acids and monosaccharides into the blood vessels and fats into the lacteals of the villi. Digestion in the large intestine and caeca is largely bacterial. The products – vitamins and monosaccharide derivatives of cellulose – are absorbed, together with water, in the colon; the semisolid indigestible remains form the faeces.

intine. The inner layer of the *perispore.

intracellular. Occurring within a cell or cells.

intraspecific selection. A form of competition occurring between members of the same species resulting in the selection, survival, and breeding of some members and the elimination of others. For example, bright plumage and display behaviour of male birds have evolved in many species due to intraspecific competition of the males for the females and the selection by the females of the males that they find the most attractive. The males with the brightest plumage breed, and the species evolves brighter-coloured males.

introgressive hybridization. The crossing of two species of plants within the same territory with the production of fertile offspring, which then usually cross back to one of the parents. This produces a diffusion (*introgression*) of genes from one species to the other, giving a range of phenotypes of both parental types and a series of hybrids between them.

intromittent organ. An organ in male animals that is specialized for introducing spermatozoa into the reproductive tract of the female: common in species with internal fertilization. Examples of intromittent organs are *claspers (elasmobranchs, insects, etc.), *hemipenes (snakes and lizards), and *penis (mammals).

intron. A sequence of DNA inserted within a gene that is not part of the coding sequence and is therefore not represented in the messenger RNA. Many, though not all, eukaryotic structural genes contain introns; these sequences have not, however, been found in bacterial genes. The initial RNA transcript (*see* HnRNA) from a eukaryotic gene thus contains certain sections complementary to introns and other sections complementary to *exons (the conserved coding sequences). Special enzymes within the cell nuclei are responsible for cutting out the intron sequences within the HnRNA and splicing together the separate exon sequences to yield intact *messenger RNA molecules.

introrse. Designating anthers that dehisce towards the middle of the flower.

intrusive growth (interpositional growth). A method of growth in plants by which a cell forces its way between other cells, causing disruption of their middle lamellae and plasmodesmata. *Compare* symplastic growth, sliding growth.

intussusception. The addition of new cellulose particles between those already present in the cell wall of a plant cell: a type of growth that extends the wall by increasing its surface area.

inulin. A polysaccharide, exclusive to plants, composed of units of fructose. It is one of the less common storage carbohydrates of plants, found particularly in the Compositae, e.g. in the tubers of *Dahlia* and Jerusalem artichoke.

invagination. The folding of one layer of cells within another so that a double-layered pocket is formed. It occurs in the developing animal embryo, particularly during *gastrulation.

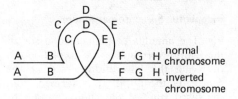

Inversion

inversion. A type of chromosome mutation in which a section of a chromosome breaks off, rotates through 180°, and reattaches. For example, if a chromosome contains the genes ABCDEFGH, the section CDE may become inverted, resulting in ABEDCFGH. Inversions can be recognized when homologous chromosomes pair at prophase of meiosis, as a loop is formed to permit exact pairing of the genes (see illustration).

inverted repeat sequence. A DNA sequence present twice but in opposite orientations with the same molecule. *Transposons contain inverted repeat sequences.

in vitro. Designating biological processes that are made to occur, or investigations that are performed, outside living organisms, traditionally in the test tube.

in vivo. Designating biological processes that occur, or investigations that are performed, within living organisms.

involucre. A protective structure in certain plants, especially the whorls of bracts at the base of a capitulum or umbel or the rings of bracts, scales, etc., surrounding the archegonial and antheridial apparatuses in bryophytes.

involuntary muscle. *See* smooth muscle.

involution. 1. A diminution in the size of an organ. The term can be applied to the return of abnormally enlarged structures to normal or to the decrease in size of normal structures (*atrophy*), as occurs in old age.
2. A turning in of the cells at the dorsal lip of the blastopore, which occurs during *gastrulation in some vertebrates.

iridophore. *See* chromatophore.

iris. The annulus of pigmented tissue in the eye of vertebrates and cephalopods, overlying the lens and pierced at the centre by the pupil. It is formed from the fused rims of the choroid and retinal layers. Except in some fish, the iris is a muscular diaphragm that reflexly controls the amount of light admitted to the eye and so contributes to *accommodation.

irritability. The ability of a cell, tissue, or organism to respond actively to a stimulus – a property of all living protoplasm. In protozoans and plants, the receipt of the stimulus and the production of the response, e.g. changes in cell turgor, are usually confined to the same cell; in metazoans they are usually spatially separated and functionally connected by the *nervous system. *See also* receptor, effector.

ischium. A paired cartilage bone forming the posterior element of the ventral part of the tetrapod *pelvic girdle.

isidium. A small protuberance from a lichen thallus, consisting of closely mixed fungal and algal cells and acting as a vegetative propagule.

islets of Langerhans. Small aggregations of endodermal endocrine cells scattered throughout the vertebrate pancreas (they form a discrete mass in some teleost fish). The islets were named after the young German medical student who first described their structure in 1869.

Histologically, three main cell types have been distinguished: *alpha* (α), *beta* (β), and *D-cells* (α_1). The distribution of the islets and of the cells within them varies with the species: in humans the cells are evenly distributed throughout the tissue although β-cells predominate. The granular α- and β-cells produce glucagon and insulin respectively, and it has been suggested that the α_1-cells may secrete gastrin.

isoantigen (alloantigen). An antigen that stimulates the production of antibodies in genetically different members of the same species.

isoelectric focusing. A method, similar to *gel electrophoresis, for separating different protein molecules from each other. It involves the setting up of a pH gradient within the gel, and the protein molecules assume positions in the gel depending on their net charge.

isoelectric pH. The pH at which there is no net electric charge on a molecule, which will therefore not migrate in an electric field.

isoenzymes (isozymes). Variant forms of an enzyme within an organism that have the same function but can be distinguished by *electrophoresis.

isogamy. The sexual fusion of similar gametes.

Isogeneratae. *See* Phaeophyta.

isograft (syngraft). A *graft derived from a genetically identical or nearly identical donor of the same species as the recipient. Such grafts, e.g. those between identical twins, are unlikely to be rejected.

isokont. Designating a flagellate spore or cell in which the flagella are of equal lengths: also used to describe the flagella themselves. *Compare* heterokont.

isolating mechanisms. Methods that prevent breeding between populations, so that the genes of each do not mix. Isolating mechanisms allow each population to develop independently into separate species, as the genes favourable to one population are not lost by intercrossing with the neighbouring population. The principal mechanism is *geographical isolation*, which ensures that the two populations are not physically in contact with one another. In time this leads to *sexual* and *genetic isolation*, including sexual selection within the different populations, variation in breeding seasons, etc., so that if the two species meet again they do not interbreed. *See also* speciation.

isoleucine (ile). An amino acid, $CH_3CH_2CH(CH_3)CH(NH_2)COOH$, one of the 20 common amino acids found in proteins and an *essential amino acid for man.

isomerase. One of a group of enzymes that catalyse isomerizations (intramolecular rearrangement). This group forms one of the main groups used in *enzyme classification; it has the code number E.C.5.

isomorphism. The condition in plants in which both sexes or all generations in the life cycle are morphologically similar. *Compare* heteromorphism.

Isopoda. An order of the subclass Malacostraca that contains the most successful terrestrial crustaceans, the woodlice (e.g. *Oniscus*), as well as aquatic forms such as *Limnoria* (gribble), a marine wood-borer. Isopods are usually dorso-ventrally flattened and lack a carapace. As the cuticle is not waterproof, the terrestrial woodlice tend to live in areas of high humidity. The thorax bears walking limbs and the abdominal appendages function as respiratory organs (modified for air-breathing in woodlice). Female isopods have a brood pouch in which the eggs hatch directly into miniature adults.

Isoptera. An order of social mostly tropical exopterygote insects, the termites. Termite colonies are based on a caste system, each colony being founded by a winged male and female. After the mating flight the pair lose their wings and copulate. The nymphs develop into either sterile wingless workers or soldiers or winged reproductive forms. The workers build the nest (which is either excavated in wood, often causing great damage, or constructed of mud), tend the other colony members, and search for food (usually wood); the soldiers defend the colony. In some species the young nymphs function as workers.

isotonic. *See* hypertonic.

isotope. Any of two or more atoms of an element having the same numbers of protons but different numbers of neutrons. For example, ^{14}N and ^{15}N are two isotopes of nitrogen; ^{14}N has an atomic mass of 14 and contains 7 protons and 7 neutrons while the *heavy isotope*, ^{15}N, contains 7 protons and 8 neutrons. Some isotopes, such as ^{14}C, ^3H, and ^{32}P, are *unstable* and undergo radioactive decay to a more stable form. Others, such as ^2H, ^{15}N, and ^{13}C, are *stable*. *See also* radioactive labelling.

isotype. *See* holotype.

isozymes. *See* isoenzymes.

J

Java man. *See Homo.*

jejunum. An indistinctly delimited region of the mammalian small intestine between the ileum and the duodenum. It is digestive and absorptive in function.

jellyfish. *See* Scyphozoa.

joint. 1. The structural point of contact between two or more morphologically separate bony elements in vertebrates. Joints vary considerably in their degree of movement: they may be immovable (*synarthroses*), as between the bones of the skull; partially movable (*amphiarthroses*), as between the vertebrae; or

freely movable (*diarthroses*), as between the limb bones. All freely movable joints have cartilage-covered surfaces and are separated by joint cavities (*see* synovial membrane). Immovable and partially movable joints are united directly by cartilage and/or fibrous connective tissue.
2. The point of contact between elements of the body in invertebrates, especially in arthropods.

joule. *See* calorie, SI units.

jugular vein. A paired blood vessel conveying deoxygenated blood from the head of adult mammals. It replaces the lateral head vein and anterior cardinal of other vertebrates.

junctional complex. The region of attachment of neighbouring cells in many epithelia (see illustration at *cell). The lateral walls of the cells are joined near the free surface of the epithelium via three specialized regions of their plasma membranes, each of which may occur independently in other animal tissues. At the *tight junction* (*zonula occludens*), which is nearest the surface, neighbouring plasma membranes are in direct contact in a narrow belt around the cell, which may serve to exclude external substances from the intercellular spaces of the epithelium. The *intermediate junction* (*zonula adherens*) also encircles the cell, below the tight junction, but with a gap of about 20 nm between the plasma membranes. The adjacent cytoplasm of each cell contains a band of filamentous material. The *desmosome* (*macula adherens*) forms a restricted point (rather than a belt) of contact and has a more complex structure. The gap between adjacent membranes is about 10–25 nm and contains a connecting material. Inside the cells numerous microfilaments and dense material converge on the area of contact and end in an amorphous layer on the membranes. The microfilaments may direct or regulate the movement of communicating substances across desmosomes in, for example, develop-

mental processes and tissue regeneration. Desmosomes are usually numerous and scattered.

Jurassic. The second period of the Mesozoic era, extending from 180 to 135 million years ago. It was named after the Jura mountains, where rocks of this period were first recognized. The marine deposits of the Jurassic contain many ammonite fossils, also bivalves, crinoids, corals, and sponges. The Jurassic, together with the following period, the Cretaceous, make up the Age of Reptiles. In the deltaic deposits there are many plant fossils, which are mainly gymnosperms. *See* geological time scale.

Juvenile hormone of *Hyalophora cecropia*

juvenile hormone. One of a group of hormones secreted by the *corpora allata of insects when stimulated by a substance from the brain at specific times during development. They inhibit metamorphosis and promote the growth of larval structures in the presence of ecdysone; when secreted alone, ecdysone promotes growth and differentiation to the adult stage. Juvenile hormone was first extracted from *Hyalophora* moths in 1965 and its terpenoid-like structure characterized in 1967 (see formula).

juvenility. The phenomenon seen in certain plants in which the young plant differs morphologically or physiologically from the mature plant. Leaf shape may differ markedly between juvenile and adult stages, as occurs in ivy and eucalyptus. Certain trees, such as beech, retain the dead leaves on the young plant over the winter, but shed them normally on reaching maturity. Other plants, such as the cultivated brassicas, do not respond to *vernalization until they have reached a minimum size.

K

kairomone. A *pheromone excreted by an animal that is perceived by an individual of a different species. For example, a caterpillar's excretory product contains a chemical that attracts a parasitoid and therefore may lead it to its host.

kappa particles. Particles found within the cells of some strains of the ciliate protozoan *Paremecium* and now known to be commensal bacteria. Such strains may kill other sensitive strains of *Paramecium* placed in the same medium by the release of a soluble substance, *paramecin*, from the kappa particles. Sensitive organisms may become 'killers' by conjugation with a kappa strain. Nuclear genes in the genome of the *Paramecium* are known to be involved in the ability of a cell to retain kappa particles. Commensal relationships of this kind are often cited as evidence supporting the hypothesis that mitochondria have evolved from commensal bacteria living within eukaryotic cells.

karyogamy. The fusion of the nuclear material of cells: the essential feature of sexual reproduction. It usually occurs in the nuclei of the gametes but can also occur in the heterokaryotic cells of some fungi.

karyokinesis. *See* mitosis.

karyotype. The appearance of the chromosome complement of an organism or cell. As chromosomes differ in size, shape, and number in different species, the karyotype provides a distinctive and characteristic feature of an organism. A diagram or photograph of the karyotype is known as a *karyogram* (or *idiogram*) and can be used in precise identification of a species.

keel (carina). The ventral projection of the sternum of birds and bats, providing a large surface area for the attachment of flight muscles.

Kenyapithecus. A genus of Miocene fossil apes found by Dr. L. S. B. Leakey (1903–73) in Kenya in 1962. These apes have hominid teeth and are considered by some authorities to be true early hominids. *See also* fossil hominid.

keratin. A fibrous sulphur-containing protein that is the structural protein of hair, wool, nails, claws, beaks, feathers, and horn and also of the outer cell layers of the vertebrate epidermis. Cells accumulate keratin, i.e. they become *cornified* (or *keratinized*), by the process of *cornification (or *keratinization*).

keratinization. *See* cornification.

ketogenesis. The formation of *ketone bodies.

ketone bodies. Compounds, e.g. acetoacetate (CH_3COCH_2COOH), β-hydroxybutyrate (CH_3COHCH_2COOH), and acetone (CH_3COCH_3), formed, mainly in the liver, by the condensation of the acetyl CoA produced by *fatty-acid oxidation. They pass into the blood and are normally further catabolized in peripheral tissue. *Ketosis*, the production of more ketone bodies than an organism can use, occurs in man during starvation and diabetes; the condition leads to acidosis and can ultimately cause coma.

ketose. A *monosaccharide, such as fructose, that possesses a keto group ($-C = O$).

kidney. The paired excretory organ of vertebrates, also functioning in *osmoregulation. The kidneys are made up of units called *nephrons*, each of which consists of a narrow tube (*uriniferous tubule*) terminating at a cup-shaped *Bowman's capsule*, which encloses a knot of capillaries (*glomerulus*). The capsule and glomerulus constitute the *Malpighian body* (or *corpuscle*). Each glomerulus is supplied by an afferent arteriole arising from a branch of the dorsal aorta; emerging from the glomerulus is an efferent arteriole, which leads to a capillary network surrounding the tubule. Venules from this capillary bed join the renal vein. The uriniferous tubules all drain (via collecting tubules) into a longitudinal duct (*Wolffian duct or *ureter), which opens into the cloaca or bladder. The mammalian kidney is divided into an outer *cortex*, in which the Malpighian bodies are concentrated, and an inner *medulla*, containing the tubules and collecting ducts. These drain into the *renal pelvis*, from which the ureter leads. The high blood pressure in the glomerulus causes many constituents of the blood, including water and nitrogenous waste but excluding colloidal substances, to be filtered into the Bowman's capsule. Much of the water, together with mineral salts, glucose, etc., is reabsorbed into the capillaries surrounding the tubule; the remaining water and nitrogenous products are excreted as *urine.

The tubules comprising the kidney differentiate from embryonic mesoderm in an anterior to posterior sequence (*see* pronephros, mesonephros, metanephros).

kilobase. A sequence of 1000 bases or base pairs of DNA.

kilocalorie. *See* calorie.

kinase. A biological agent, such as a protein or an ion, that can convert the inactive form of an enzyme (*zymogen*) into the active form.

kinesis. A locomotory response of an organism or cell to a stimulus such that the rate of movement (or turning) depends on the intensity of the stimulus but is not related to the direction of the source of stimulation. For example, a woodlouse moves slowly or not at all in a damp atmosphere (e.g. under logs) and quickly in a dry atmosphere. *Compare* taxis, tropism.

kinetin. A synthetic plant *kinin.

kinetochore. *See* centromere.

kinetosome (kinetosomal unit). The *basal body of various structures, particularly of cilia.

Zeatin

kinin. 1. One of a class of plant growth substances, usually purine derivatives, that stimulate cell division. Naturally occurring kinins are called *cytokinins* (or *phytokinins*) and include *zeatin* (see formula).

Commonly used synthetic kinins include *kinetin* (*6-furfurylaminopurine*) and *benzyladenine* (*6-benzylaminopurine*). Kinins are nonacidic and relatively nonmobile. They work synergistically with auxins in controlling cell division; their balance with auxins also affects cell enlargement and morphogenesis, including bud initiation. Kinetin applied to certain leaves delays senescence in its vicinity and attracts nutrients. Kinin-like substances have been found in coconut milk, which is commonly used in culture media.

2. One of a group of polypeptides, including *bradykinin*, that occur in the blood and cause contraction of smooth muscle and dilatation of blood vessels. Their function is uncertain; they may regulate the rate of blood flow or have a role in inflammatory responses.

kinomere. *See* centromere.

kin selection. *See* altruism.

Klinefelter's syndrome. A syndrome in men that results from the presence of an extra X chromosome, giving a karyotype of XXY instead of the normal XY. (Very occasionally more than one extra X chromosome is present, to give

XXXY, XXXXY, etc.) The physical signs of the syndrome include underdeveloped testes, some female characteristics (such as enlarged breasts), and sometimes some degree of mental retardation.

Krebs cycle (citric acid cycle, tricarboxylic acid cycle). A final common pathway in the oxidative catabolism of carbohydrates, proteins, and lipids in *aerobic respiration. A cyclic sequence of enzyme reactions in the mitochondria catalyses the conversion of one molecule of acetate (activated as the coenzyme A (CoA) derivative) to four pairs of hydrogen atoms and two molecules of carbon dioxide. The hydrogen atoms (or their electron equivalents) pass on to an *electron transport chain (respiratory chain), where ATP is produced. Acetate enters the cycle by condensing with oxaloacetate, and during one turn of the cycle one molecule of oxaloacetate is regenerated and is thus available to

react with another acetate molecule (see illustration).

The acetyl CoA required for the cycle is formed by the oxidative decarboxylation of pyruvate, produced in glycolysis; from amino-acid oxidation; and from fatty-acid oxidation. Some of the Krebs cycle intermediates (α-ketoglutarate, oxaloacetate, succinic acid) also serve as precursors of amino acids.

***k*-value.** A logarithmic killing power, originated by Haldane, that is often calculated from age-specific *life tables. It is calculated by subtracting the log of the numbers of organisms after a mortality has occurred from the log of the numbers preceding the mortality. For example, the *k*-value for 1000 moth eggs half of which survive to produce larvae is $3.0 - 2.7 = 0.3$. *k*-values may be added to give overall generation mortality (K) and, because they are a proportional measure, plotting them against the density on which they act may reveal *density dependence.

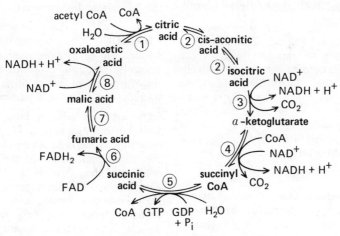

① citrate synthetase   ④ α-ketoglutarate dehydrogenase ⑦ fumarase

② aconitase   ⑤ succinyl CoA synthetase   ⑧ malic dehydrogenase

③ isocitrate dehydrogenase   ⑥ succinic dehydrogenase P_i = PO_3H (phosphate)

GDP guanosine diphosphate   GTP guanosine triphosphate

Krebs cycle

L

labium. The modified second maxilla of an insect, often known as the lower lip, which assists in feeding. *See* mouthparts.

labrum. A flat hinged plate immediately above the mouth in insects. Known as the upper lip, it assists in feeding. *See* mouthparts.

Labyrinthodontia. A subclass of extinct Amphibia, in existence from the Upper Devonian to the Triassic. Like their rhipidistian ancestors, these large amphibians were characterized by hollow teeth, convoluted (*labyrinthine*) in cross section, and a complete roofing of membrane bones to the skull. An early semiaquatic group, the Anthracosauria (Embolomeri), probably gave rise to the modern Anura (frogs) and are thought to have been the ancestral stock of the reptiles. The Permian *Seymouria*, though believed not to have been a direct ancestor, has both amphibian and reptilian characteristics.

Labyrinthulales. The net slime moulds: a small group of aquatic fungi whose plant body consists of amoeboid cells connected by slime filaments along which the cells move (this body is sometimes termed a *net plasmodium* or *filoplasmodium*). These fungi are of uncertain affinities but are usually classified as *Myxomycophyta.

lacewings. *See* Neuroptera.

lachrymal gland. One of several glands in the eyelids of terrestrial vertebrates that secretes a watery liquid (tears), which moistens and cleans the cornea.

***lac* operon.** The sequence of DNA in the bacterium *Escherichia coli* that regulates and codes for three genes involved in the lactose pathway. β-galactosidase and two other enzymes in the pathway are synthesized coordinately when the

*operon is switched on. This activation is accomplished by a derepression process involving the *effector molecule, usually allolactose, binding with the repressor protein and so permitting transcription of the operon.

lactation. The process of milk production by the mammary gland, which involves the action of hormones produced by the pituitary, placenta, ovaries, and adrenal and thyroid glands. Milk secretion is stimulated primarily by pituitary *prolactin and adrenal corticosteroids, while milk ejection involves the action of *oxytocin (and to a lesser degree vasopressin) on the cells that surround the alveoli of the mammary gland. These processes are maintained for long periods by means of the sucking stimulus at the nipple, which initiates a feedback neurohormonal reflex to stimulate further hormone secretion.

lacteal. One of a number of blind-ending lymph vessels in vertebrates, each of which drains a villus of the small intestine and discharges into the thoracic duct. Digested fats are absorbed into the lacteals as fine droplets.

lactic acid. An organic acid, $CH_3CHOHCOOH$, produced during the breakdown of glucose (*see* glycolysis, anaerobic respiration). Lactic acid is the major product of fermentation in certain bacteria (*see* lactic acid bacteria).

lactic acid bacteria. A large group of rod-shaped or spherical Gram-positive anaerobic bacteria in which lactic acid is the major (and sometimes the only) end product of their fermentation. They have complex growth requirements, reflecting their limited biosynthetic abilities. The group includes the genera *Streptococcus*, *Diplococcus*, and *Lactobacillus*. Lactic acid bacteria are of economic importance in the production of cheese, yoghurt, etc., from milk.

lactogenic hormone. *See* prolactin.

lactose. A disaccharide of galactose and glucose (see formula) found in milk.

Lactose

lacuna. 1. (in botany). A cavity within a tissue or organ that contains water or secreted gases and often acts as a water-storage device or provides buoyancy (*compare* loculus). The term is also used as a synonym for *leaf gap.
2. (in zoology). Any small cavity, such as one of the cavities containing bone cells within the bone matrix.

Lagomorpha. The order of the Eutheria that contains the hares (e.g. *Lepus*), rabbits (e.g. *Oryctolagus*), and pikas (*Ochotona*). These herbivores differ from rodents principally by possessing two pairs of completely enamelled incisor teeth in the upper jaw (the second pair are small and nonfunctional).

lag phase. The initial phase in the growth of a cell culture, immediately after inoculation of the growth medium, during which there is no increase in cell numbers. During this time certain enzymes are induced and the cells adapt for growth in the new medium. *See also* log phase.

Lamarckism. The theory of *evolution put forward by Jean-Baptiste Lamarck (1744–1829) at the beginning of the 19th century. It proposes the origin of new species by the inheritance of *acquired characteristics*, i.e. characteristics developed during life by use and disuse are transmitted to the gametes and inherited by the offspring. This theory has lost support in the western world because it lacks definite proof and because a mechanism for the inheritance of acquired characteristics is difficult to postulate. However, in the Soviet

Union a modern version of the theory has gained acceptance. Known as *neo-Lamarckism* (or *Lysenkoism*), its chief proponent being the Russian geneticist T. D. Lysenko (1898–1976), it stresses the importance of the inheritance of changes brought about by environmental influences. *Compare* Darwinism.

lamella. 1. A layer of one, or several closely appressed, thylakoids. Series of photosynthetic lamellae (*lamellar system*) occur in *chloroplasts and in the cytoplasm of photosynthetic bacteria and blue-green algae. The lamellae are arranged to trap light efficiently. In chloroplasts they are typically arranged in stacks called *grana* (*grana lamellae*) linked by *inter-grana* (or *stroma*) *lamellae*. Some algal chloroplasts lack grana; each lamella is then either simple (i.e. one thylakoid, as in red algae) or compound (between two and four thylakoids). In some photosynthetic bacteria the lamellae are stacked, while in blue-green algae they comprise single thylakoids only.
2. Any thin platelike structure, such as one of the gills of an agaric fungus (mushroom or toadstool) or one of the concentric layers of tissue surrounding each Haversian canal in bone.

Lamellibranchia. *See* Bivalvia.

lamina. 1. The flattened photosynthetic blade of a leaf that is attached to the petiole.
2. The flattened terminal portion of the thallus of some algae.

laminarin. The chief carbohydrate reserve of brown algae, which is stored in solution and is exclusive to this group. It consists of about 20 linked glucose units. Some laminarins may contain *mannitol.

lampbrush chromosome. A type of chromosome, found in the oocytes of many vertebrates, that is much larger and less condensed than normal chromosomes. The long axis of the chromosome bears large numbers of paired loops, each loop arising from a chromomere, giving the chromosome a structure resembling a Victorian lampbrush. Lampbrush chromosomes persist for many months throughout the long diplotene stage of meiosis and, unlike other chromosomes (except the giant *polytene chromosomes of Diptera) remain active in transcription.

lampreys. *See* Cyclostomata.

lamp shells. *See* Brachiopoda.

large intestine. *See* colon.

larva. The immature form in which many animals exist after hatching from the egg and before undergoing metamorphosis to the adult form. The larva is self-supporting and differs from the adult in structure and mode of life; it is usually incapable of sexual reproduction (*see* neoteny). Larval stages occur in anamniote vertebrates, e.g. the tadpole of frogs, and in most invertebrates, e.g. the caterpillar of butterflies and the ciliated planktonic larvae of many marine phyla. *See* ammocoete, dipleurula, leptocephalus, nauplius, planula, tornaria, trochophore, veliger.

larynx. A dilated region at the upper end of the trachea of tetrapods, opening into the pharynx through the glottis. It is specialized to close the glottis during swallowing, which prevents food from entering the lungs. Primitively the glottis is closed by a muscular sphincter but in most tetrapods the larynx contains a complex arrangement of muscles and cartilages, which causes the glottis to be blocked by the epiglottis. Further modifications of the larynx in animals with a keen sense of smell enable breathing to continue during swallowing. In amphibians, reptiles, and mammals the larynx is secondarily specialized for sound production, with the development of a pair of elastic *vocal cords, which vibrate as air is expelled.

latent period (reaction time). The time that elapses between the reception of a stimulus and the beginning of the appropriate response by an irritable tissue.

latent virus. A virus that can remain in the host organism for long periods without any observable effect. It may be induced (by 'helper' viruses, a chemical, or radiation) to multiply and produce disease symptoms long after the initial invasion of the host. Probably only the genomes are retained, untranscribed, during the latent period. Latent viruses include herpes simplex, which causes cold sores, and chickenpox virus (varicella), which can become latent and recur later as shingles (herpes zoster).

lateral line system. Part of the *acoustico-lateralis system.

lateral meristem. *See* cambium.

lateral plate. *See* mesoderm.

latex. A liquid found in the laticifers of certain plants. It is usually milky, as in the dandelion, but may be colourless or orange to brown. It can contain a variety of substances. For example, the latex of the rubber tree (*Hevea brasiliensis*) contains all the enzymes and intermediates needed for rubber synthesis and the latex of the opium poppy contains alkaloids. Other constituents of latex include sugars, starch grains, waxes, and tannins.

laticifers. Latex-containing structures occurring in vascular plants. They vary structurally from single parenchyma cells to tubules ramifying throughout the plant. *Simple laticifers* are either single cells or are derived from single cells; *compound laticifers* are derived from several cells. *Articulate laticifers* are compound and consist of chains of cells in which contiguous end walls may break down, resulting in so-called *latex vessels*. *Nonarticulated laticifers* are simple and derive from single cells by growth and ramification. They have been termed *latex tubes* or *laticiferous cells*.

Laurasia. The ancient land mass comprising the present-day continents of

North America, Europe, and Asia. *See* continental drift.

LD$_{50}$. Lethal dose 50: the dose of a drug, radiation treatment, or titre of a virus at which 50% of the organisms exposed to it are killed. It is used as a standard measure of toxicity.

L-DOPA (L-dihydroxyphenylalanine). An amino acid intermediate in the synthesis of the catecholamines dopamine, noradrenaline, and adrenaline. L-DOPA is administered therapeutically in the treatment of Parkinson's disease in order to raise the levels of brain dopamine, which are deficient in this condition.

leaf. The principal lateral appendage of the stem of a plant, which functions in photosynthesis and transpiration and produces lateral buds in its axil. Leaves of vascular plants are often classified into two types: *microphylls and *megaphylls. The leaves of bryophytes are simple organs similar to microphylls but not homologous, as they are borne on the gametophyte. The megaphyll usually consists of three parts: the *leaf base* (or *phyllopodium), by which the leaf is attached to the stem, the *leaf stalk* (or *petiole*), and the flattened *leaf blade* (or *lamina*), whose *mesophyll tissue carries out the functions of the leaf.
Most plants produce several types of leaf during their lifespan. These include *cotyledons (or *seed leaves*), protective *scale leaves*, e.g. on buds, and *bracts and *floral leaves* (*see* petal, sepal) on the inflorescence as well as the *foliage leaves*, which may themselves be variable in form (*see* heterophylly). Leaves may be either *simple*, with a leaf blade that is entire, or *compound*, with the blade divided into separate segments (*leaflets*) that arise either from a single point at the tip of the petiole (in *palmate leaves*) or serially along the rachis (in *pinnate leaves*).
The arrangement of leaves on a stem is termed the *phyllotaxis, while the pattern formed by the combination of phyllotaxis and the leaves' orientation to the

light is the *leaf mosaic*. The arrangement of the vascular tissue in the lamina is termed the *venation. The orientation of the tissues within the vascular bundles of the lamina is fairly constant, with the phloem on the abaxial side and the xylem on the adaxial side. Certain plants may have *bundle sheaths around the veins.
In some plants leaf functions are taken over by some other organ, such as a phyllode or cladode.

leaf buttress. The small lateral prominence on a shoot apex that marks the initiation of a leaf and from which the leaf develops.

leaf gap. A short discontinuity in the primary vascular system of a stem that marks the point of departure of a *leaf trace, where parenchyma cells differentiate instead of stelar tissue. Leaf gaps are present in the steles of ferns and fern allies other than those with protosteles and in angiosperms; they are probably absent in gymnosperms (see illustration at *stele).

leaf trace. A vascular bundle to a leaf after its departure from the stem stele and before entering the leaf base. The vascular tissues of a leaf consist of primary xylem and phloem and connect with the vascular tissues of the stem before secondary thickening occurs. The leaf trace differentiates centripetally (i.e. from the outside inwards) from a locus in the leaf base via the cortex to join the stem stele. The leaf trace is often associated with a *leaf gap and there may be more than one trace per leaf.

learning. The acquisition of new patterns of behaviour in an animal or the modification of existing patterns as a result of experience. Learning may be brought about by *conditioning, *habituation, or *imprinting.

lecithin. *See* phospholipids.

lectin. A protein of plant origin that binds to specific carbohydrates in cell surfaces and causes agglutination. Certain lectins agglutinate red cells of specific blood groups and can therefore be used for blood typing. *See also* concanavalin A, phytohaemagglutinin.

lectotype. *See* holotype.

leeches. *See* Hirudinea.

leghaemoglobin. A haemoglobin-like molecule found in the root nodules of leguminous plants. This iron-containing protein is able to bind oxygen and so keep the oxygen tension of the nodule tissue very low. Such conditions favour the nitrogen-fixing activity of the symbiotic bacteria present in the nodule.

legume (pod). A dry dehiscent *fruit that is formed from a monocarpellary ovary and splits along two sides at maturity. It is characteristic of the Leguminosae.

Leishman's stain. *See* staining.

lemurs. *See* Dermoptera (flying lemurs), Primates.

lens. A biconvex transparent body responsible for focusing light onto the sense cells of many photoreceptors, e.g. the retina of the eye. In vertebrate eyes it is composed of cells containing *crystallin*, a collagen-like protein. In aquatic species it is solely responsible for the refraction of light and is of a fixed spherical shape; accommodation is achieved by the backward or forward movement of the lens. In most terrestrial vertebrates it is used only for the fine adjustment of focus, changing its shape by means of the ciliary body.

lenticel. One of a number of areas, usually 0.5–1 mm in diameter, consisting of loosely packed cells and occurring at intervals in the periderm. They probably function in gaseous exchange.

Lepidodendrales. *See* Lycopsida.

Lepidoptera. A large order of endopterygote insects, the butterflies and moths. They are characterized by a covering of scales, often brightly coloured, over the wings and body. Mandibles are usually absent and the maxillae form an extensible tube (*proboscis*) for sucking nectar or fruit juices. The larvae (caterpillars) typically have eight pairs of legs and well-developed mandibles. The majority feed on plant stems and leaves and some are serious plant pests. Butterflies, which are diurnal, have slim bodies and clubbed antennae and rest with the wings folded over the back, the hind wings almost covering the forewings. Moths, which are mostly nocturnal, never have clubbed antennae and rest with the wings in various positions.

Lepidosauria. A subclass of reptiles characterized by a diapsid skull, a median eye, and a body covering of overlapping horny scales. They first appeared in the Upper Permian and are divided into three orders: the extinct *Eosuchia, the *Rhynchocephalia (tuatara), and the *Squamata (lizards and snakes).

Lepospondyli. A subclass of extinct Amphibia of the Carboniferous and Permian, characterized by vertebrae with a single spool-shaped centrum surrounding the notochord, as in modern forms. Some members of the order Microsauria, e.g. *Cardiocephalus* of the Lower Permian, had well-developed limbs and are thought to have been possible ancestors of the modern Urodela. *Compare* Labyrinthodontia.

leptocaul. Designating angiosperms that have a small primary structure, providing many small easily replaced buds and leaves. *Compare* pachycaul.

leptocephalus. The marine larva of the eel. It has a small thin transparent leaf-like body with a small head and long fragile teeth for feeding on plankton. Leptocephali hatch in the Sargasso Sea in the west Atlantic and migrate eastwards, taking about 2.5 years, to European waters, where they undergo metamorphosis into elvers (young eels).

leptosporangiate. Designating ferns in which the sporangium develops from the outer daughter cell produced by periclinal division of a superficial cell in the lamina. The leptosporangiate condition is regarded as advanced: it is important taxonomically and characterizes the Leptosporangiatae (Filicales, Marsileales, and Salviniales). *Compare* eusporangiate.

leptotene. A stage of the prophase of the first division of *meiosis.

lethal dose. *See* LD_{50}.

leucine (leu). An amino acid, $(CH_3)_2CHCH_2CH(NH_2)COOH$, one of the 20 common amino acids found in proteins and an *essential amino acid for man. In vertebrates, it is the only amino acid that is not capable of yielding glucose through *gluconeogenesis.

leucocyte. *See* white blood cell.

leucoplast. A *plastid that lacks pigment.

leucosin. *See* chrysolaminarin.

leukaemia. A malignant disease characterized by a high proportion of abnormal white cells in the blood. The disease is sometimes associated with a leukaemia virus. Certain chemical and physical agents, such as high doses of X-rays, can sometimes induce leukaemia, possibly by causing activation of a latent leukaemia virus already present.

L-forms. Forms of certain bacteria (e.g. some streptococci) in which the cell wall has been lost. L-forms can multiply and give rise to L-form colonies in suitable media. Some can revert to normal cells but others are stable. Their importance in nature is unknown but it is thought that they may persist in tissues for long periods and be responsible for relapses in certain diseases.

LH. *See* luteinizing hormone.

lice. *See* Anoplura (sucking lice), Mallophaga (biting lice), Psocoptera (booklice).

Lichenes. Thallophyte plants composed of a fungus and an alga in such close symbiosis that they form a vegetative plant body that is morphologically different from either of the constituents. The fungal constituent (*mycobiont*) is either an ascomycete or a basidiomycete, while the alga (*phycobiont*) may be one of a variety of free-living forms (*see also* cephalodium). The lichens are divided into two groups in the basis of their fungal constituent: Ascolichenes (having ascomycetes) and Hymenolichenes (having basidiomycetes).

life cycle. The various stages of development through which organisms of a species may pass from the fertilized egg cell of one generation to the same stage in the next generation. There are often various alternatives by which the adult stage is reached, and the term therefore describes the reproductive potential of the species. The term is less commonly used for the various stages through which an individual organism may pass from birth to death.

In the simplest life cycles, an individual gives rise to offspring similar to itself, e.g. by asexual reproduction; the most complex life cycles, e.g. in parasites, involve the development of many different morphological and reproductive stages (generations), i.e. there is *alternation of generations. Sexual reproduction provides the means for great variation in the more complex life cycles. Two genetic states exist in such life cycles: the haploid and the diploid. Either may be dominant, or both may play a distinct role in the life cycle. A number of terms (originally devised by Svedelius for the algae) are now in general usage for these variations:

haplont, a sexual haploid organism in which only the zygote is diploid, meiosis occurring at zygote germination;

diplont, a sexual diploid organism in which only the gametes are haploid, meiosis occurring at gametogenesis;

haplobiont, an organism with only one cytological type in its life cycle, either haploid or diploid;

Monomorphic haplont
e.g. *Chlamydomonas*
     Volvox
     Spirogyra

Trimorphic diplont
e.g. *Aurelia*
     (scyphozoan
     jellyfish)

Dimorphic haplont
e.g. *Nemalion*
     (red alga)

Monomorphic
diplobiont
e.g. *Ulva*
     Ectocarpus
     (brown alga)

Trimorphic haplont
e.g. *Batrachospermum*
     (red alga)

Dimorphic
diplobiont
e.g. *Laminaria*
     (brown alga)
     pteridophytes
     seed plants
     (with very
     reduced
     gametophyte
     generation)

Monomorphic diplont
e.g. *Fucus*
     Pelvetia (brown alga)
     (seed plants appear to
     belong to this but are
     actually dimorphic
     diplobionts)
     vertebrates

Dimorphic
diplobiont
e.g. *Corallina*
     (red alga)
     Polysiphonia
     (red alga)

Key

☐ ◯ △ – different morphological forms   V – vegetative generation

S – sporophyte (vegetative) generation   G – gametophyte generation

ⓩ – zygote   n – haploid   2n – diploid

Common types of life cycle

diplobiont (or *diplohaplont*), an organism with two cytological types in its life cycle.

In many species the different cytological generations are represented by different morphological forms; in addition each cytological type may also exhibit more than one morphological form. These organisms are known as *polymorphic*, as distinct from *monomorphic*, i.e. having only one morphological type in the life cycle.

All these terms can be combined to describe any kind of life cycle; representative life cycles are shown in the illustration.

life table. A table in which mortality and survival in an animal or plant population are catalogued and their causes identified. An *age-specific life table* is used for organisms whose generations do not overlap; a cohort, e.g. of a butterfly's eggs, is followed through the generation and the numbers dying and the cause of death identified at each stage. A *time-specific life table* is effectively a cross-section of a population in which generations overlap and birth rate equals death rate, as in man, fish, and long-lived plants. Such a table can be used to calculate average survival and mortality rates and life expectancy.

ligament. A nonextensible band of white fibrous connective tissue connecting the bones in movable vertebrate joints. The ligaments strengthen the joint and restrain its movements in certain directions; they are composed of bundles of collagen fibres and lie either inside or outside the capsule enclosing the joint.

ligase (synthetase). One of a group of enzymes that catalyse the condensation of two molecules coupled with the breakdown of ATP or another triphosphate. This group forms one of the major groups used in *enzyme classification; it has the code number E.C.6. *See also* DNA ligase.

light green. *See* staining.

light microscope. *See* microscope.

light reaction. *See* photosynthesis.

lignin. A complex three-dimensional polymer of variable composition whose basic units include sugars, phenolic substances, aromatic amino acids, and alcohols. It is a common constituent of cell walls, particularly secondary walls, in which its presence in the matrix provides resistance to compression. It is the major constituent of wood.

ligule. 1. A small flap of tissue of unknown function produced on the adaxial surface of the leaves and sporophylls of certain pteridophytes of the group Lycopsida, namely the orders Lepidodendrales (all extinct), Isoetales (quillworts), and Selaginellales.
2. A thin dry membrane extending above the leaf sheath and formed from the tip of the fused stipules, found in both dicotyledons and monocotyledons, especially in the Gramineae (grasses).
3. A strap-shaped extension of the corolla of certain flowers, such as the ray florets of the Compositae.

limiting factor. Any environmental factor that tends to inhibit the growth or activity of an organism or population, either by being below the level necessary for normal growth or by exceeding the limits of tolerance for the species. For example, for plants carrying out photosynthesis on a sunny day, when water, light, etc., are in good supply, carbon dioxide is usually the limiting factor; if the amount of carbon dioxide is increased, the photosynthetic rate increases.

limiting layer. *See* meristoderm.

limnology. The study of fresh waters, especially lakes and ponds, including their physical, geographical, and biological characteristics.

Limulus. *See* Merostomata.

linkage. The phenomenon of two or more genes being on the same chromosome. The genes are said to be *linked*, and the term *linkage group* is applied to all the genes on the same chromosome. The number of linkage groups in an organism is therefore equal to the haploid number of chromosomes. Linkage can be broken down by crossing over during meiosis. This leads to fresh linkage groups being formed in the gametes and therefore new combinations of genes (*see* recombination) in the progeny. Genes that are in the same linkage group do not show *independent assortment. *See also* cross-over value, genetic map, sex linkage.

linkage map. *See* genetic map.

linoleic acid. *See* essential fatty acids.

linolenic acid. *See* essential fatty acids.

lipase. An enzyme that hydrolyses triglyceride fats into glycerol and fatty acids. In vertebrates it is secreted by the pancreas and intestinal glands.

lipid. One of a large heterogeneous group of organic compounds, occurring widely in living organisms, that are characterized by their solubility in nonpolar solvents such as alcohol and diethyl ether. Lipids vary from simple straight-chain hydrocarbons, such as *fats and *waxes, to the more complex *phospholipids, *glycolipids, *terpenes, and *steroids.

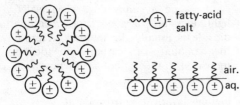

Fig. 1: Lipid micelle   Fig. 2: Monolayer

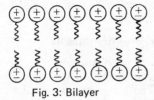

Fig. 3: Bilayer

Lipid micelle and associated forms

lipid micelle. An aggregation of molecules of fatty-acid salts (soaps) or phospholipids in aqueous solution, the hydrophobic fatty acid chains orientated together at the centre of a sphere or oblong with the polar groups directed outwards (see Fig. 1). Monolayers (one

molecule thick) form on aqueous surfaces, the hydrocarbon chains pointing up into the air and the polar groups into the liquid (see Fig. 2). Similarly, at an aperture separating two aqueous compartments, bilayers 7 nm thick are spontaneously formed; due to their similarity to natural membranes bilayers are used experimentally as model membranes (see Fig. 3). *See also* membrane.

lipogenesis. The biosynthesis of *fatty acids. Substrates, such as glucose, that are able to yield acetyl CoA provide precursors for this process.

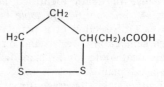

Lipoic acid

lipoic acid. A substance required for the growth of a number of microorganisms. It consists of a fatty-acid chain with a disulphide bridge (see formula) and takes part in the enzyme sequences catalysing the oxidative decarboxylation of α-ketoglutarate and pyruvate in carbohydrate metabolism. *See also* vitamin.

lipolysis. The hydrolysis of lipids, especially of the triglycerides in fat by lipases, to produce fatty acids for oxidative catabolism (*see* fatty-acid oxidation). Triglycerides, which are stored in adipose tissue, may be transported in the plasma to the liver where degradation occurs; alternatively they are first hydrolysed and the free fatty acids, noncovalently bound to albumin, are transported to the liver. Hormones such as adrenaline and ACTH increase adipose tissue lipolysis and hence increase the plasma levels of free fatty acids.

lipolytic hormone (LPH). *See* lipotrophin.

lipopolysaccharide. One of the main constituents, with lipoprotein, of the cell wall of Gram-negative bacteria (see

PROPERTY OF TVEI

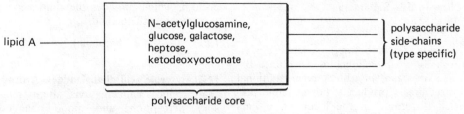

Lipopolysaccharide

illustration): these two substances comprise 80% (dry weight) of the cell wall. The lipopolysaccharide is responsible for the antigenic specificity of the bacterium, the polysaccharide side-chains acting as the determinant sites.

lipoprotein. One of a group of conjugated proteins having polar lipids as the non-amino-acid group. They occur in the blood and lymph, where they function in the transport of lipids from the small intestine to the liver and from the liver to the site of fat deposition.

lipotrophin (lipolytic hormone, LPH). One of at least two peptide factors (β- and α-*LPH*) produced by the pars distalis of the mammalian pituitary gland that are structurally related to β-melanocyte-stimulating hormone (β-MSH) stimulate and lipolysis. β-LPH, first isolated in 1964, may be the precursor of β-MSH but it may also function as a hormone since it has been found in the blood.

Lissamphibia. The subclass of the Amphibia that contains the living members, which differ from primitive amphibians in having a greatly reduced dermal skull roofing and postcranial skeleton. Adults typically have a moist scaleless skin, which restricts them to damp environments and acts as a respiratory surface, supplementing the limited supply of oxygen drawn into the lungs by the pumping action of the floor of the mouth. The structure of the heart does not allow the complete separation of oxygenated and deoxygenated blood. There are three orders: *Anura (frogs and toads), *Urodela (newts and salamanders), and *Apoda.

lithotrophic. *See* autotrophic.

littoral. 1. Designating or living on the seashore between the extreme low and high tide marks. Littoral organisms form part of the benthos.
2. Designating the zone of a lake or large pond from the water's edge down to a depth of about 6 metres. The rooted vegetation is limited to this zone. *Compare* sublittoral, profundal.

liver. The largest organ of the vertebrate body, arising as a diverticulum of the gut. It functions as a gland by producing bile, which is stored in the gall bladder and discharged into the duodenum through the bile duct. The principal function of the liver is as a site of intermediary metabolism; it receives the absorbed products of digestion via the hepatic portal vein. Carbohydrates are stored in the form of glycogen and metabolized to provide chemical energy. Fats are also stored and metabolized. Amino acids are deaminated, with the consequent formation of nitrogenous excretory compounds such as urea. Other functions of the liver include the detoxification of poisonous substances, the breakdown of red blood cells in the adult (*see* bile pigments) and their synthesis in the embryo, and the synthesis of fibrinogen and prothrombin.

liverworts. *See* Hepaticae.

living fossil. Any organism alive today whose closest relatives are known only as fossils and which was formerly thought to be extinct itself. *Latimeria* (a coelacanth) is a well-known animal living fossil; *Ginkgo* is a notable plant example.

lizards. *See* Squamata.

loculicidal. *See* dehiscence.

loculus. 1. (in botany). A small cavity, usually completely enclosed within a tissue or organ, in which some additional structure is produced. For example pollen is formed in the loculi of anthers and asci in the loculi of some ascocarps. *Compare* lacuna.
2. (in zoology). Any small chamber or cavity, such as one of the divisions of a foraminiferan shell.

locus (gene locus). The region of a chromosome occupied by a particular gene and therefore determining a single biochemical function. The alleles of any one gene occupy the same loci on homologous chromosomes.

locusts. *See* Orthoptera.

log phase (exponential phase). The phase in the growth of a cell culture following the *lag phase, when the increase in cell numbers is exponential, i.e. numbers double at regular intervals.

lomasome. A structure in certain plants (particularly fungi) consisting of membranous vesicles situated outside the plasmalemma, either in a space between the cell wall and plasmalemma or embedded in the wall. It has been suggested that they are formed particularly during wall synthesis when plasmalemma production is not balanced by cell expansion.

lomentum. A type of *fruit: a legume or siliqua constricted transversely between the seeds.

long-day plant. *See* photoperiodism.

loop of Henle. *See* uriniferous tubule.

lophophore. A circular or horseshoe-shaped filter-feeding organ possessed by members of the phyla Ectoprocta, Phoronida, and Brachiopoda (sedentary aquatic invertebrates). It is composed of ciliated tentacles surrounding the mouth but not the anus (the gut is U-shaped); the tentacles are continuous with the

coelom, which provides the fluid necessary to keep them rigid.

LPH (lipolytic hormone). *See* lipotrophin.

LSD (lysergic acid diethylamide). A drug that produces hallucinations, altered sensory perception, and mood changes when taken in very small doses. LSD acts by increasing the concentration of *serotonin in the brain.

luciferin. The light-emitting compound responsible for the luminescent properties of many organisms. *See* bioluminescence.

lumbar vertebrae. The bones of the lower back region of the *vertebral column.

lumen. 1. The space enclosed by the cell wall of a plant cell that has lost its living contents.
2. The central cavity of a duct, tube, etc.

lung. A respiratory organ characterized by an invaginated moist epithelial surface for gas exchange, usually with the air. Among the vertebrates, lungs are found in many fossil fish, in Dipnoi, and in tetrapods, arising as a ventral diverticulum of the pharynx and homologous with the *swim bladder of the Actinopterygii. The lungs are saclike and highly elastic to permit changes in volume during ventilation, the air being forced in by swallowing (amphibians) or by suction (amniotes). The walls are greatly subdivided to increase the area of the respiratory surface. In amphibians, reptiles, and mammals the respiratory surface is confined to blind-ending sacs (*see* alveolus). In birds the respiratory surface forms the inner surface of anastomosing air capillaries, which, in combination with extensive *air sacs, allow the free circulation of air.
The lung of molluscs is a highly vascular section of the mantle cavity, which is ventilated by muscular action or is aerated by diffusion.

lung book. The respiratory organ of some air-breathing arachnids, consisting of leaflike vascular invaginations of ectoderm sunk in a pit in the body wall. Exchange of gases takes place by diffusion across the invaginations. *Compare* gill book.

lungfish. *See* Dipnoi.

lutein. A xanthophyll pigment. *See* photosynthetic pigments.

luteinizing hormone (interstitial-cell-stimulating hormone, LH, ICSH). A glycoprotein hormone (*see* gonadotrophin) secreted, with *follicle-stimulating hormone, by the pars distalis of the pituitary gland under hypothalamic regulation. In female mammals LH promotes the maturation of Graafian follicles and stimulates them to produce oestrogens; its presence is also required for ovulation and the formation of corpora lutea. In males it stimulates the interstitial cells of the testis to produce androgens.

luteotrop(h)ic hormone (LTH). *See* prolactin.

lyase. One of a group of enzymes that catalyse the addition of groups to double bonds or the formation of double bonds. This group forms one of the main groups used in *enzyme classification; it has the code number E.C.4.

Lycopsida (Lycophyta). A group of homosporous or heterosporous pteridophytes differentiated into roots, stems, and leaves, the aerial branches being densely covered with spirally arranged *microphylls. The sporangia are thick-walled and borne either in the axil of, or on, a sporophyll. The lycopsids reached their peak in the Carboniferous and Permian; some extinct tree forms, e.g. *Lepidodendron*, possessed secondary thickening and were co-dominants (with the sphenopsids) in the forests that formed the Carboniferous coal seams. The group contains the Lycopodiales (including the club moss *Lycopodium*), the extinct Lepidodendrales (e.g. *Lepidodendron*), Selaginellales (e.g. *Sela-*

ginella), Isoetales (including *Isoetes* (quillworts)), and Protolepidodendrales, a primitive group of extinct plants. The lycopsids are sometimes split into two groups on the possession or otherwise of a ligule: the heterosporous Ligulatae (Lepidodendrales, Selaginellales, and Isoetales) and the homosporous Eligulatae (Protolepidodendrales and Lycopodiales) respectively.

lymph. The colourless fluid, derived from the interstitial fluid of vertebrates, that is contained within the vessels of the *lymphatic system. While having the same salt concentration as plasma, it has a lower protein concentration and its cells are chiefly lymphocytes.

lymphatic system. A closed system of tubes (*lymphatic vessels*) through which lymph is transported from the interstitial fluid into the bloodstream. The smallest peripheral lymphatic vessels, the lymphatic capillaries, are thin-walled tubes of endothelium supported by fibrous tissue. The larger collecting vessels have smooth muscle fibres in their walls and also contain valves. The flow of lymph through the vessels is maintained by muscular and respiratory movements in mammals and by the pumping action of *lymph hearts in other vertebrates. Closely associated with the lymphatic vessels are *lymph nodes.

lymphatic tissue. *See* lymphoid tissue.

lymph heart. One of a number of small two-chambered muscular structures, situated at various points along the lymphatic vessels, that actively pump lymph through the *lymphatic system. Lymph hearts are characteristic of amphibians and are occasionally present in teleosts and reptiles; they are absent in mammals.

lymph node (lymph gland). A flat oval structure that consists of lymphoid tissue and lies in the course of a main lymphatic vessel (*see* lymphatic system). It is usually supplied by several afferent vessels but is drained by a single efferent vessel. Lymph nodes act as filters of foreign bodies, particularly by preventing bacteria from entering the bloodstream, and as a result may themselves become inflamed and enlarged. Within the cortex of lymph nodes are germinal centres that give rise to lymphocytes.

lymphocyte. One of two types of agranular white blood cell. The more common type is the small lymphocyte, a round cell, 6–8 μm in diameter, with a densely staining nucleus and little cytoplasm. The large lymphocyte is 10–20 μm in diameter; it has relatively more cytoplasm and a less densely staining nucleus than the small lymphocyte. Lymphocytes are found in all tissues except those of the central nervous system and have a very variable lifespan (between 2 and 200 days). They originate in the thymus and lymphoid tissues, the latter also being the probable site of their destruction. They exhibit a slight degree of amoeboid movement but have little phagocytic activity. Lymphocytes are the immediate ancestors of all antibody-forming cells; small lymphocytes have also been shown to be responsible for humoral (*B-lymphocytes*) and cell-mediated (*T-lymphocytes*) *antibody reactions.

lymphoid tissue (lymphatic tissue). The vertebrate tissue that is responsible for the production of lymphocytes and occurs in the form of diffuse or dense aggregations of lymphocytes. In some parts of the body, lymphoid tissue exists as identifiable organs, e.g. the tonsils, spleen, thymus, and lymph nodes, although in other areas, especially in the respiratory and gastrointestinal tracts, diffuse lymphoid aggregations occur that are not structurally separated from the surrounding connective tissue.

lymphoma. Any malignant tumour that arises in the lymph nodes. *See* cancer.

Lysenkoism. *See* Lamarckism.

lysine (lys). An amino acid, $H_2NCH_2CH_2CH_2CH_2CH(NH_2)COOH$, one of the 20 common amino acids occurring in proteins and an *essential amino acid for man. Lysine is a precursor of the polyamine cadaverine.

lysis. The destruction of a cell, usually by rupture of its membrane. Under normal conditions lysis of cellular constituents of the body may be initiated by the cell itself (*see* autolysis) or by *phagocytes, which also lyse invading cells. Most *bacteriophages cause lysis of their bacterial host cells after infection.

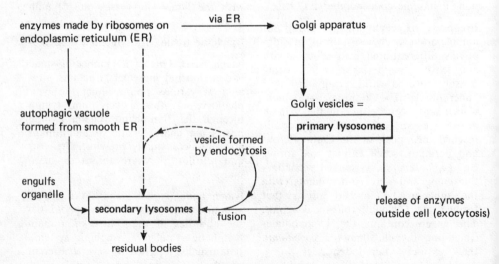

Origin of lysosomes

lysogeny. 1. (in botany). The formation of any structure by the disintegration of cells, as in the formation of the gum ducts of *Eucalyptus* by disintegration of the gum-containing cells. *Compare* schizogeny.
2. The relationship between a temperate bacteriophage and its host, in which the viral DNA is incorporated into the bacterial DNA and is reproduced with it; the viral genes are repressed and the host cell is not destroyed. The viral DNA is known as the *prophage*. If a lysogenic bacterium is exposed to ultraviolet radiation or similar treatment the viral genes are derepressed and complete phage DNA is produced, with subsequent lysis of the bacterial cell.

lysosome. An organelle of eukaryotes, bounded by a single membrane, that contains hydrolytic enzymes, such as acid phosphatases, proteases, nucleases, and lipases. In animal cells lysosomes are commonly 0.1–0.5 μm in diameter and have homogeneous contents. They are often derived from vesicles of the Golgi apparatus as shown in the diagram. Lysosomes have many functions, mostly involving intracellular digestive (degradative) processes. Digestion usually occurs within the organelle, but its enzymes are sometimes released. Its most important functions are the digestion of material taken in by *endocytosis (e.g. food by some protozoans, bacteria by mammalian white blood cells); the destruction of redundant organelles (see autophagy); the release of enzymes to destroy cellular and extracellular materials, particularly after death (see autolysis); the release of enzymes outside the cell (see exocytosis), e.g. during the replacement of cartilage by bone in ossification; and the storage of indigestible residues in secondary lysosomes (called *residual bodies*), occurring in such tissues as human heart, nerve, and liver. In plant cells the cell vacuoles may also act as lysosomes.

lysozyme. An enzyme that catalyses the destruction of the cell walls of many bacteria, by hydrolysing the *mucopeptide. Bacteria exposed to lysozyme swell and burst in their usual hypotonic enviroment. Lysozyme specifically attacks the β 1–4 glycosidic bonds between the N-acetylmuramic acid and N-acetylglucosamine residues of the mucopeptide, weakening its covalent structure and hence the resistance of the wall to osmotic swelling. Lysozyme is found in tears, saliva, mucus, and egg white.

M

macromolecule. A giant molecule made up of smaller subunits linked together. For example, proteins (made up of amino acids) are macromolecules, as are nucleic acids and polysaccharides.

macronucleus (meganucleus). *See* nucleus.

macronutrient (essential element). An element that is essential for the life of an organism and is required in relatively large amounts. There are ten macronutrients: carbon, hydrogen, oxygen, nitrogen, sulphur, phosphorus, potassium, magnesium, calcium, and iron.

macrophage. A motile phagocytic cell, found throughout vertebrate tissues, that can be identified by its ability to store certain vital dyes, e.g. trypan blue and Indian ink. Macrophages occur principally as resting cells in connective tissue (*see* histiocyte), in the spleen and lymph nodes, in the endothelial lining of blood vessels and sinusoids of bone marrow, in the liver, adrenal glands, and the anterior lobe of the pituitary, and in the blood as *monocytes.

macrophyll. *See* megaphyll.

macrospore. *See* megaspore.

macrosporophyll. *See* megasporophyll.

macula. 1. A spot of sensory epithelium in the sacculus and utriculus of the ver-

tebrate inner ear. The macula consists of supporting and sensory cells; the latter are connected to the auditory (vestibulocochlear) nerve and bear hairs embedded in an *otolith. The bending of the hairs registers the tilt and rate of movement of the head. *Compare* neuromast, statocyst.
2. A region of the vertebrate retina rich in cone cells and hence specialized for acute perception of detail. It often surrounds a fovea.

madreporite. *See* water vascular system.

Malacostraca. The largest and most successful subclass of the Crustacea, including marine, freshwater, and terrestrial members. The head has *compound eyes, usually on movable stalks. The thoracic appendages bear gills for respiration and are used for walking or swimming and (in some) for feeding; the abdominal appendages are used for swimming and (in the females) for carrying eggs. In many malacostracans development is direct. The subclass contains five orders, including the *Amphipoda (e.g. *Gammarus*), *Isopoda (woodlice), and *Decapoda (crabs, lobsters, etc.).

malleus. An *ear ossicle in mammals, attached to the tympanum and homologous with the articular bone of other vertebrates.

Mallophaga. An order of small ectoparasitic exopterygote insects, the biting lice (or bird lice). They have flattened wingless bodies with clawed legs for clinging to the host. Most species live among the feathers of birds, on which both the nymphs and adults feed using their biting mouthparts; some feed on the host's blood. Each species is restricted to a particular species of host.

Malpighian body. The part of a nephron comprising a Bowman's capsule together with its glomerulus. *See* kidney.

Malpighian layer (stratum Malpighii). The layer of cells in the vertebrate *epidermis that lies adjacent to the base-

ment membrane. It consists of two distinct cell layers: (1) the lower *stratum germinativum* (*stratum basale*), whose cells are usually in active mitosis and are continually migrating towards the surface, and (2) the overlying *stratum spinosum*, whose cells contain fine keratin filaments. The cells of the Malpighian layer often contain granules of the pigment melanin, which is responsible for skin colour.

Malpighian tubules. Slender blind-ending excretory tubes opening into the alimentary canal near the junction of the midgut and hindgut in the Arachnida, Insecta, Chilopoda (centipedes), and Diplopoda (millipedes). They lie in the haemocoel and extract from the blood the excretory products (mainly uric acid) that pass into the hindgut and exit with the faeces. The number of Malpighian tubules varies from two to about 150.

β-maltose

maltose. A disaccharide consisting of two glucose molecules in a glycosidic link (see formula). Maltose is formed in the enzymic degradation of *starch and occurs in germinating cereal seeds, especially barley.

Mammalia. The class of vertebrates that contains the most successful tetrapods, most of whose characteristics evolved as adaptations to an active carnivorous life. Mammals are homoiothermic, typically having an insulating body covering of hair and sweat and sebaceous glands in the skin. Their socketed teeth are differentiated into incisors, canines, and cusped premolars and molars, and a bony secondary palate allows the retention of food in the mouth while breathing. A four-chambered heart allows the complete separation of oxygenated and deoxygenated blood and a diaphragm assists in respiratory movements. Mammals (except the Monotremata) are viviparous, with *mammary glands secreting milk for the young. They have a relatively large brain with a corresponding high degree of intelligence. The class arose in the Triassic from active carnivorous reptiles (*see* Synapsida), from which they are distinguished by a squamosal-dentary jaw articulation, the lower jaw being formed from a single pair of bones (the dentaries), and three ossicles in the middle ear. The group underwent great adaptive radiation in the *Tertiary period. There are several fossil orders: the *Docodonta, *Multituberculata, *Pantotheria, *Symmetrodonta, and *Triconodonta, and three living groups: the *Prototheria (monotremes), *Metatheria (marsupials), and *Eutheria (placentals).

mammary gland. The milk-producing gland that is characteristic of all female mammals. One or more pairs of these glands develop on the ventral surface of the body and are thought to have evolved from sweat glands. Although the state of the gland fluctuates during the oestrous cycle, its complete development and functioning (*see* lactation) generally occurs only after parturition, for the purpose of suckling the young. The mature gland consists of several lobes of multiple branching ducts embedded in fatty tissue. The ducts lead from numerous alveoli of milk-secreting cells and in most mammals drain into sinuses that open to the exterior via pores at the nipple. In the Monotremata nipples are absent and the milk is secreted directly from the sinuses onto the surface of the body.

manatee. *See* Sirenia.

mandible. 1. The lower jaw of vertebrates.
2. One of a pair of appendages in crustaceans, insects, and myriapods, usually specialized for biting food. *See* mouthparts.

mandibular arch. The most anterior visceral arch, modified in all jawed vertebrates to form the cartilaginous elements of the jaw, i.e. the *palatoquadrate bar and *Meckel's cartilage.

mannitol. An alcohol derived from the sugars mannose or fructose that, like laminarin, is a major reserve carbohydrate of brown algae and is stored in solution. It also occurs in some higher plants, e.g. carrot, celery, asparagus.

mannose. An aldohexose sugar whose dextrorotatory form (D-mannose) is an epimer of D-glucose and a component of many polysaccharides and mannitol.

manoxylic. Designating gymnosperm wood, such as that produced by the Cycadopsida, that has wide parenchyma rays and is therefore soft and spongy. *Compare* pycnoxylic.

mantis (*pl.* **mantids**). *See* Dictyoptera.

mantle. 1. A fold of epidermal tissue covering the dorsal and lateral surfaces of the body of the Mollusca. It secretes the shell (when present) and protects the gills (which lie in the *mantle cavity*, between the mantle and the body); in the Cephalopoda the mantle is muscular and functions in locomotion and respiration.
2. A similar fold of tissue in the Brachiopoda.
3. The body wall of the Urochordata, lying beneath the outer test.

margo. The part of a pit membrane surrounding a *torus.

Marsupialia. The sole order of the *Metatheria (pouched mammals), confined now to Australasia and to North and South America. The more primitive marsupials, the polyprotodonts, have numerous small incisor teeth. They include all the American and some of the Australasian marsupials. The more specialized Australasian herbivores, the diprotodonts, never have more than three large incisors on each side of the jaws and the hind foot is typically *syndactylous*, i.e. the second and third toes are encased in a sheath of skin at their base forming a comb for grooming. Diprotodonts include *Macropus* (kangaroo) and the phalangers.

marsupium. A pouch on the abdomen of female marsupials (*see* Metatheria) and some monotremes (e.g. *Tachyglossus*) that covers the mammary glands and in which the immature young complete their development.

mass flow. The bulk transport of materials by hydrostatic pressure, postulated as a mechanism for *translocation through phloem. It is suggested that high sucrose concentrations at the loading end of sieve tubes induce high hydrostatic pressures via osmosis, and that the unloading sites (the *sinks*), where sucrose is consumed or converted for storage, have low hydrostatic pressures. The resulting gradients of hydrostatic pressure in the phloem cause mass flow of solutions from source to sink. This theory cannot, however, entirely account for the high flow rate observed and it has been suggested that mass flow is supplemented by an electrically driven osmosis (*electroosmosis*) across the sieve plates, where electrical potentials are developed.

mast cell. One of a number of cells in connective tissue that have strongly basophilic cytoplasmic granules that store histamine, heparin, and serotonin. These substances are thought to be released from the granules during inflammation, anaphylaxis, and immune response.

mastigoneme. One of a series of fine short hairs that project laterally, usually in one or two rows, from eukaryotic flagella. There are two main types: hollow stiff mastigonemes, which have the effect of reversing the direction of locomotion (as on the forward projecting flagella of heterokont flagellates); and thin flexible solid mastigonemes, as in *Euglena*, which are comparable in structure to entire bacterial flagella and whose function is unknown.

Mastigophora (Flagellata). A class of Protozoa whose members possess one or more *flagella for locomotion. They are probably not far removed from the ancestors of both plants and animals and some are practically indistinguishable from the algae and often classed with them (*see* Euglenophyta). The subclass Phytomastigina (Phytoflagellata), e.g. *Euglena*, carry out photosynthesis using a pigment in the chromatophores. Some members, e.g. *Volvox*, form large colonies. The Zoomastigina (Zooflagellata) have a holozoic nutrition and some of them, e.g. *Trypanosoma*, are parasites.

mastoid process. The exposed end of the mammalian auditory capsule, which is not covered by membrane bones. It contains air spaces that connect with the middle ear.

mating type. Either of the two strains of a heterothallic fungus that are needed for fertilization to take place. Since the two mating types and their gametes are morphologically identical, they are designated *plus* and *minus* rather than male and female.

maxilla. 1. A tooth-bearing membrane bone of the upper jaw of vertebrates. In mammals it bears all the teeth except the incisors.
2. A paired appendage in the Myriapoda, Crustacea, and Insecta, used for feeding. *See* mouthparts.

mayflies. *See* Ephemeroptera.

MCPA. 4-chloro-2-methylphenoxyacetic acid: a synthetic *auxin widely used as a weedkiller.

meatus. An anatomical passage, e.g. the *external auditory meatus* of the outer ear: a short tube leading from the ear orifice to the tympanum.

mechanoreceptor. A *receptor that normally responds to mechanical stimuli, either direct (e.g. touch) or indirect (e.g. sound, gravity).

Meckel's cartilage. A paired cartilage, derived from the mandibular arch, that forms the lower jaw of adult Chondrichthyes and embryo Osteichthyes and tetrapods. It hinges with the palato-quadrate bar. In adult teleosts and nonmammalian tetrapods it ossifies as the articular bone; in mammals it is represented by the malleus.

meconium. The contents of the intestine of the mammalian foetus, consisting of a black fluid produced from an interaction of glandular secretions on swallowed amniotic fluid. It forms the first faeces of the newborn mammal.

Mecoptera. A small order of endopterygote insects, the scorpion flies, first known as fossils in the Lower Permian. Scorpion flies have a slender body with two pairs of membranous wings and are mostly carnivorous, feeding on other insects with their biting and chewing mouthparts, which are carried on a beaklike *rostrum*. In the male the tip of the abdomen is often turned up, like a scorpion's tail. The larvae resemble caterpillars.

median eye. A third eye, present in the top of the head of many early vertebrates, derived from a diverticulum of the brain either anteriorly (*parietal eye*) or posteriorly (*pineal eye*). It is found in a degenerate form in modern lampreys, *Sphenodon*, and some lizards and is represented in higher vertebrates by the *pineal gland.

mediastinum. The space between the pleural sacs in the mammalian thorax, in which the heart, thymus, oesophagus, trachea, etc., are situated.

medine. *See* exo-intine.

medulla. 1. The central part of an animal organ or tissue, particularly of the *adrenal glands and mammalian *kidney.
2. *See* medulla oblongata.
3. *See* pith.
4. The central mass of hyphae in some fungal structures, e.g. the stipe of *Psalliota*.

medulla oblongata (medulla). The hindbrain portion of the brain stem, which is continuous with the spinal cord and gives rise to most of the segmental *cranial nerves. It contains centres for the regulation of respiration, blood pressure, etc., via the *autonomic nervous system.

medullary plate. *See* neural plate.

medullary ray (pith ray). A vertical plate of parenchymatous tissue extending between the pith (medulla) and cortex across the vascular region (*see* parenchyma). *Primary medullary rays* occur in plants in which the primary vascular tissue is a ring of bundles; they occur between the bundles and are formed from the primary ground-tissue meristem. *Secondary medullary rays* are formed in plants with secondary thickening from the ray initials of the vascular cambium (*see* vascular tissue). Such rays can be classified as *uniseriate* or *multiseriate* (one or several-to-many cells wide, respectively, when viewed in tangential section) and as *homogeneous* (consisting of one cell type) or *heterogeneous* (of more than one type).

medullated nerve fibre (myelinated nerve fibre). A nerve fibre that is mostly enclosed in a myelin sheath.

medusa. The free-swimming form of the Cnidaria, which resembles an umbrella, convex side up, with the mouth in the centre underneath and tentacles hanging down from the margin. A continuous upward pulsating movement is produced by contraction of a band of muscle around the umbrella margin, forcing water downwards. In the class Hydrozoa medusae produce polyps by sexual reproduction and are themselves produced asexually by polyps; in the Scyphozoa (jellyfish) the polyp stage is reduced or absent and in the Anthozoa (sea anemones and corals) medusae are absent. *Compare* polyp.

Megaloptera. An order of endopterygote insects containing the alder flies (e.g. *Sialis)* and snake flies (e.g. *Raphidia).* They are often classified with the

*Neuroptera (lacewings) but are distinguished by their wings, whose veins are not excessively branched at the margins, and their larvae, which have biting mouthparts. Alder flies are found near fresh water and their larvae are aquatic; snake flies are terrestrial.

meganucleus (macronucleus). *See* nucleus.

megaphyll (macrophyll). One of the two types of leaves produced by pteridophytes: it is usually large and often pinnately divided. The megaphyll is charac-terized by a complex vascular system of branching veins that typically leave one or more leaf gaps in the stem stele. It is regarded as having an evolutionary line separate from that of the *microphyll (*see* telome theory). The leaves of gymnosperms and angiosperms are usually also classified as megaphylls.

megasporangium. The sporangium borne on the *megasporophyll of heterosporous plants, in which the larger spores (*megaspores*) are formed. In pteridophytes the megaspore gives rise the gametophyte prothallus that produces

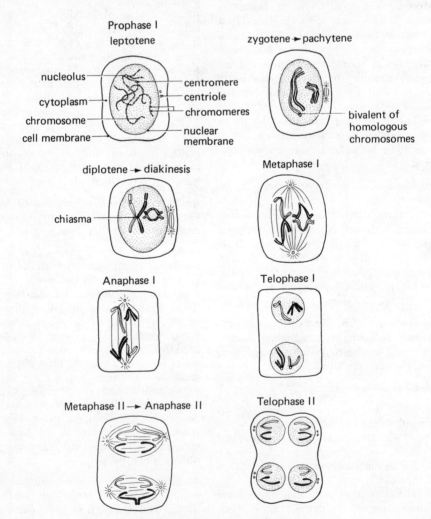

Meiosis in a gamete-forming cell

the female sex organs (archegonia). In seed plants the megasporangium is modified to form an ovule (*see also* seed). *Compare* microsporangium.

megaspore (macrospore). A spore formed within a *megasporangium.

megasporophyll (macrosporophyll). The sporophyll of heterosporous plants that bears the megasporangia. In pteridophytes and gymnosperms it usually forms part of a cone (*see* strobilus). The megasporophyll of the Coniferales is the *ovuliferous scale and that of angiosperms is the *carpel.

meiosis (reduction division). The process by which a nucleus divides into four daughter nuclei, each containing half the number of chromosomes of the parent nucleus. Meiosis has two functions: firstly the reduction of the chromosome number from diploid to haploid, and secondly the exchange of genetic material by the process of *crossing over, allowing genetic diversity to be produced. There are two successive divisions, known as division I and division II. Each division may be divided into four stages, which are not distinct and grade into each other (see illustration).
The first stage (*prophase*) of the first division is subdivided into five phases. In the first phase, *leptotene*, the chromosomes appear as thin threads that are not divided into two chromatids and have a visible centromere. This is followed by *zygotene*, when homologous chromosomes are attracted to each other and come together. They pair, forming a *bivalent*, starting at one end and zipping up like a zip fastener, a process known as *pairing* (or *synapsis*). Zygotene is followed by *pachytene*, when the chromosomes become shorter and thicker by coiling; they also coil around each other and each divides into two chromatids. In *diplotene* crossing over occurs: breaks occur in homologous chromatids due to the strain of their coiling; they then join up crosswise with the chromatid of the homologous chromosome. This grades into *diakinesis*, when the chromatids of

homologous chromosomes, no longer attracted to each other, try to move apart but are held together at the point where they crossed over. This point, known as a *chiasma*, appears as a visible cross. By the end of prophase, the nucleolus and nuclear membrane have broken down and in animals and lower plants a *spindle is organized in the cytoplasm by the centrioles. In the second stage (*metaphase*) of division I, the bivalents orientate themselves on the spindle. Their centromeres come to lie on either side of the equatorial plate and equidistant from it. The homologous chromosomes strain to separate but are held together by their chiasmata, which may begin to slip towards the ends of the chromosomes, a process known as *terminalization*. This stage is followed by *anaphase*, when the spindle contracts and elongates. The pairs of homologous centromeres finally separate and move towards their respective poles, pulling the rest of the chromosome after them. *Telophase* follows, during which the spindle disperses and a nuclear membrane usually forms around each group of half-bivalents. The length of telophase varies in different species: two complete interphase nuclei may form and cell division may occur, or telophase may be very short with only partial elongation of the chromosomes.
The second division is mechanically very similar to mitosis, except that the two cells are dividing synchronously. The length of the second prophase is inversely proportional to that of telophase I; at the end of it the chromosomes have appeared, the nuclear membrane has broken down, and a spindle is organized. In metaphase II the chromosomes come to lie on the equatorial plate; they separate in anaphase II and form separate nuclei in telophase II, resulting in four nuclei that go into interphase.
Meiosis can occur only in diploid or polyploid cells. It occurs in the process of gamete formation in animals, in the production of the pollen grain and embryo sac in higher plants, and in the

formation of spores in plants with alternation of generations. In fungi meiosis results in the production of sexual spores, such as ascospores and basidiospores. *Compare* mitosis.

melanin. One of the pigments occurring in the hair, skin, integument, etc., of many animals. It is contained in melanophores (*see* chromatophore) and consists of complex polymers of tyrosine derivatives and proteins, either *eumelanins* (brown or black) or *phaeomelanins* (yellow, orange, or red).

melanism. The existence, in a population of animals, of individuals that are black (melanic) due to excessive production of the pigment melanin. For example, the black panther is a melanic form of leopard. Several species of moths exist in a melanic form (*see* industrial melanism).

melanocyte-stimulating hormone (MSH, intermedin). One of several peptide hormones that stimulate pigment cells (*see* chromatophore). They are secreted by the pars intermedia of the mammalian pituitary gland and by homologous structures in other vertebrates. Two types, structurally resembling the N-terminal portion of ACTH, have been isolated from a number of species. *α-MSH* (13 amino acid residues) is present in most mammals but is thought not to be secreted into the blood in significant amounts. Since the early 1960s various *β-MSHs* (18–22 amino acid residues) have been described and measured in the blood. The precise role of MSH in mammals remains to be established, but in lower vertebrates it regulates changes in skin colour by acting on the chromatophores, as was first shown in Amphibia by Hogben in 1922. The best-known action of MSH is on the dispersion of melanin in melanophores, an effect mediated by cyclic AMP. The production and secretion of MSH is under hypothalamic control (*see* neuroendocrine systems).

melanophore. *See* chromatophore.

Melatonin

melatonin. A substance synthesized from serotonin and secreted mainly by the vertebrate pineal gland (see formula). It causes melanin to be less widely dispersed in dermal melanophores, as was first demonstrated in 1917, when pineal glands fed to tadpoles resulted in extreme lightening of the skin. It is also implicated in reproductive function and the photoperiodic regulation of the gonads. Melatonin was isolated and identified as the active principle of beef pineals in 1958.

membrane. Most organelle and plasma (cell) membranes are about 7.5 nm thick (the thickness varies between 5 and 10 nm). Biological membranes consist of predominantly polar lipids and protein, usually in the approximate ratio of 2:3. The major lipids are the *phospholipids phosphatidyl ethanolamine (cephalin) and phosphatidyl choline (lecithin), together with *cholesterol and sphingomyelin in the plasma membrane of higher animals. Cholesterol is absent from bacteria. The proteins are typically large molecules, providing mechanical strength and elasticity, and are sometimes enzymic. In plasma membranes (and therefore on cell surfaces) glycoproteins are important as antigens. Membranes differ in lipid and protein constituents according to their site and function. The *unit membrane hypothesis* of Davson and Danielli, and later Robertson, proposed that biological membranes consist of bilayers of lipids orientated with their polar groups exposed at the upper and lower surfaces of the bilayer and their hydrophobic portions in the centre (*see* lipid micelle). The protein components of the membrane cover the outside of the bilayer. Alternative bilayer schemes have subsequently been proposed, and most evidence now favours the fluid mosaic model, originally proposed by Singer and Nicholson in 1972. According to this model the unit membrane is a lipid bilayer structure but the protein molecules, rather than spreading as a continuous layer over both surfaces of the inner lipids, are believed to be suspended as individual floating units within the bilayer. The distribution of both lipid and protein molecules in the unit membrane is now known to be asymmetric and to vary according to the particular type of membrane being studied. Some membranes (e.g. chloroplast thylakoids) have been shown to contain or be composed of globular subunits, either scattered or in 'cobblestone' arrangements. Whereas cells are bounded at the cell surface by a single unit membrane, two unit membranes form an enveloped structure at the surfaces of nuclei, mitochondria, and chloroplasts. The two membranes of the envelope often differ in their structure and composition.

Membranes are permeable to water and lipophilic (fat-soluble or nonpolar) substances, slightly permeable to small ions, and relatively impermeable to polar substances, e.g. sugars. Movement of ions and polar molecules across membranes can be effected by *active transport and other carrier-mediated systems or may sometimes occur through minute protein-lined pores; macromolecules can be taken up by phagocytosis or pinocytosis (see endocytosis). Membranes control and direct movement of substances in and out of cells and within cells; they can act as electrical insulators (as in the *myelin sheath of certain nerve fibres); and they are the sites of protein synthesis (in rough endoplasmic reticulum) and other enzyme-controlled reactions and electron transport (in mitochondria, chromoplasts, and endoplasmic reticulum).

membrane bone (dermal bone). A bone formed by intramembranous *ossification, i.e. it is laid down directly in connective tissue with no cartilage precursor. Membrane bones occur throughout the vertebrates; examples are the bones of the skull and face, the clavicle, and the bony plates providing the superficial armour of some primitive fish. *Compare* cartilage bone.

membranous labyrinth. The vertebrate organ of equilibrium, consisting of a closed system of fluid-filled cavities and tubes enclosed in the auditory capsule. *See* inner ear.

Mendelism. The branch of genetics concerned with the transmission of characteristics from parents to offspring, as studied in breeding experiments. The characteristics chosen for study must be produced by pairs of alleles, typically with one allele of each pair dominant to the other. The ratios of dominant to recessive characteristics observed in the progeny are used to deduce the genotypes of parents and progeny. This technique was elucidated by Gregor Mendel (1822–84) in the 1860s, who stated the principles governing the transmission of his alleles in two laws (*see* Mendel's laws).

Mendel's laws. The two laws proposed by Gregor Mendel (1822–84) to explain the behaviour of factors (now known as genes) that govern the transmission of inherited characters from generation to generation.

Mendel's first law, the *Law of Segregation*, states that factors are present in pairs in somatic cells. When an organism forms gametes, the pairs separate so that each gamete contains only one factor. It is now known that genes are arranged on chromosomes, which are present in homologous pairs in somatic diploid cells. When the haploid gametes are formed, homologous chromosomes are separated by meiosis so that each gamete contains one chromosome of each pair. Thus genes present in pairs in somatic cells are present singly in gametes. To this extent Mendel's first law is always true. However, it implies that genes are entirely discrete particles, which do not blend with or modify each other, whereas in fact the action of genes can be modified in various ways.

Mendel's second law, the *Law of Independent Assortment*, states that when more than one pair of factors are considered, each pair segregates independently of every other pair. This law is not always true; it does apply to genes on different chromosomes but the segregation of genes on the same chromosome is affected by linkage (*see* independent assortment).

meninges. The layers of tissue that invest the vertebrate brain and spinal cord. Fish have a single layer; tetrapods have a stout outer layer, the *dura mater, and two soft inner layers, the *arachnoid mater and the *pia mater, separated by the *subarachnoid space. The meninges are homologous with the choroid and sclerotic coats of the vertebrate eye.

menstrual cycle. The type of oestrous cycle that occurs in higher primates (Old World monkeys, apes, and humans). It is characterized by a rapid breakdown of the uterine endometrium after metoestrus, which results in bleeding (*menstruation*). In addition, the animal remains sexually receptive throughout the cycle.

mericarp. A one-seeded fragment formed from the breaking up of a schizocarpic *fruit.

meristele. *See* stele.

meristem. A tissue responsible for plant growth whose cells divide mitotically, the derivatives differentiating into the new tissues of the plant body. Meristematic activity is generalized in the embryo but in vascular plants it becomes restricted principally to the apices of the shoots and roots (*see* apical meristem) and, later, to the *lateral meristem* (*see* cambium). Meristematic tissue may be interspersed between more-or-less differentiated tissues, as in the internodes and leaf sheaths of many monocotyledons: this is termed *intercalary meristem*. In nonvascular plants the position of the meristem varies; for example it is apical in the bryophytes

and intercalary in some large brown seaweeds, such as *Laminaria*.

The term *primary meristem* is used for tissue, such as apical meristem, that has at no stage undergone differentiation; the term *secondary meristem* is applied to meristems, such as the cambia, that occur on the older parts of the plant.

meristoderm (limiting layer). The meristematic outer layer of some Phaeophyta (brown algae), e.g. *Fucus* species, that supplements the activities of the apical meristematic cell.

meroblastic. *See* cleavage.

merocrine secretion. *See* secretion.

merosporangium. The asexual sporangium of some phycomycete fungi, which superficially resembles a chain of conidia but is actually a single sporangium containing several *merospores*, around each of which the sporangium wall becomes constricted.

Merostomata. A class of the Arthropoda previously classified as an order (Xiphosura) of the Arachnida, to which they are related. All members, except five species of the marine genus *Limulus* (horseshoe or king crabs), are extinct. Horseshoe crabs are found only in Asia and North America. The cephalothorax is covered with a horseshoe-shaped heavily armoured carapace and the abdomen ends in a long spine. The mouth is situated among the legs, which have crushing bases for mastication, and is surrounded by small pincer-like chelicerae and masticatory pedipalps. Respiration is by *gill books.

merozygote. A partially diploid bacterial cell arising as a result of *conjugation, *transformation, or *transduction. Since the basic bacterial cell is haploid and such processes as conjugation involve only a partial transfer of the bacterial genome, the resulting recipient cell is only partially diploid.

mesarch. Designating a stele in which the protoxylem is completely surrounded

225

by metaxylem. *Compare* centrarch, endarch, exarch.

mesencephalon. *See* midbrain.

mesenchyme. Embryonic mesodermal tissue, loosely arranged and widely scattered, that develops into adult connective tissue, blood, lymphoid tissue, cartilage, etc.

mesentery. 1. The double layer of peritoneum by which the stomach and intestines hang from the dorsal body wall. It contains the nerves, blood vessels, and lymph vessels that pass to and from the gut.
2. One of the vertical membranes that divides up the body cavity of the Anthozoa (sea anemones, etc.).

mesocarp. *See* pericarp.

mesocotyl. The shoot axis between the scutellum and coleoptile in the embryo of Gramineae (grasses).

mesoderm. The middle layer of the three *germ layers of triploblastic animal embryos. It develops into cartilage, bone, muscle, blood, kidneys, and gonads. In coelomates the mesoderm arises as two layers: the outer *somatic mesoderm* and the inner *splanchnic mesoderm*. In vertebrates the dorsal somatic mesoderm consists of segmented mesodermal *somites*, each of which is made up of three regions: *myotome*, which gives rise to striated muscle; *sclerotome*, which develops into the vertebral column and proximal parts of the ribs; and *dermatome*, which gives rise to the dermis (*see also* mesenchyme). The splanchnic mesoderm develops into many visceral organs. *Lateral-plate mesoderm*, present in vertebrates, is unsegmented and consists of somatic and splanchnic components; it gives rise to the sternum and limb girdles, peritoneum, smooth muscle, etc.

mesoglea. The gelatinous layer between the ectoderm and endoderm in the body wall of the Coelenterata. It varies from a thin noncellular membrane, as in *Hydra*, to a thick fibrous material forming the bulk of the animal, as in jellyfish. Except in the class Hydrozoa, it contains cells that have migrated from the other layers, but these do not form tissues and organs as in the triploblastic animals.

mesonephros. The second part of the *kidney to appear in the embryonic development of vertebrates. Drained by the *Wolffian duct, it is the functional kidney of adult fishes and amphibians and of embryo amniotes. In adult amniotes it is functionally replaced by the *metanephros, part of it becoming incorporated into the male reproductive system. *Compare* pronephros.

mesophilic. Designating microorganisms that require an optimum temperature of 30–40°C for growth, with a minimum growing temperature of 10–15°C. *Compare* thermophilic, psychrophilic.

mesophyll. The region of a leaf between the two epidermal layers. It consists mainly of parenchyma cells but may also contain collenchyma and sclerenchyma cells, which support the veins. In the dorsi-ventral leaves of dicotyledonous plants the parenchyma is differentiated into two layers. The upper *palisade mesophyll* (or *layer*) is the main photosynthesizing region of the leaf. It consists of long columnar cells that contain many chloroplasts and fit closely together, their longitudinal axes at right angles to the leaf surface. The lower *spongy mesophyll* (or *layer*) contains irregularly shaped cells with fewer chloroplasts. Air spaces between the cells communicate with the stomata, permitting exchange of gases between the leaf and the atmosphere.
The leaves of monocotyledons are not usually differentiated into these layers.

mesophyte. A plant that inhabits places where the water supply is adequate, i.e. the conditions are neither too wet nor too dry. Water lost by transpiration can by replaced by uptake from the soil. Mesophytes will wilt even if a comparatively small amount of water is lost. The majority of angiosperm plants are mesophytes.

mesosome. A membranous structure found in the cells of some Gram-positive bacteria, such as *Bacillus subtilis*. The mesosome consists of whorled membranes infolded from the plasma membrane at the cell surface. It is rich in respiratory enzymes and often closely associated with a developing cross-septum of the cell wall, but its precise function remains unclear.

mesothelium. A sheet of cells that is derived from mesoderm and lines the coelom, synovial sacs, etc.

Mesozoic. The second era of the *geological time scale, beginning with the Triassic period and ending with the Cretaceous and extending in time from 225 million to 70 million years ago.

messenger RNA (mRNA). A type of RNA, often between 10^3 and 10^4 nucleotides long, by which the coding information from the structural genes is conveyed to the site of protein synthesis, the ribosomes. A single strand of the DNA acts as a template for its synthesis (*see* transcription). Although messenger RNA comprises a linear sequence of bases complementary to to the DNA coding sequence, in eukaryotic cells the RNA sequence is not entirely colinear with the DNA sequence because the latter contains *introns. The introns are transcribed along with the exon coding sequences to yield an intermediate product, *HnRNA, from which the introns are removed to produce messenger RNA. On the ribosome the messenger RNA code is translated (*see* translation) into the polypeptide sequence of a protein molecule by the action of *transfer RNA. *See also* genetic code.

mestom sheath. An inner layer of the *bundle sheath occurring in the leaves of some Gramineae (grasses).

Metabola. *See* Pterygota.

metabolism. The sum of the physical and chemical changes that constantly take place in living organisms. These changes include the building up of the constituents of the organism (*see* anabolism) and the breakdown of molecules to provide energy for anabolic processes (*see* catabolism). The term also refers to the metabolic changes undergone by a particular constituent of an organism, e.g. carbohydrate metabolism. *See also* basal metabolic rate.

metabolite. A substance that takes part in any of the processes of metabolism. Metabolites are either produced by the organism during metabolism or are taken in from the environment.

metacarpal bones. The rod-shaped bones of the fore foot of tetrapods, articulating with the carpal bones proximally and with the phalanges distally. They are greatly elongated in running mammals. *See* pentadactyl limb.

metacarpus. The complex of metacarpal bones, forming the palm of the hand in man.

metacentric. *See* centromere.

metachromatic stains. *See* staining.

metachronal rhythm. A rhythm of beating characteristic of groups of cilia and of the parapodia of certain Polychaeta. It results in a wavelike progression of beating of successive cilia or limbs and a smooth continuous movement of fluid past the surface of the organism or epithelium. *See* cilium.

metameric segmentation (metamerism, segmentation). The arrangement of the organs of an animal in a series of similar units along the longitudinal axis of the body. It occurs in varying degrees in the Annelida, Arthropoda, and Chordata and is often obscured in the anterior region of the body by cephalization. Metameric segmentation is most clearly marked in annelids, in which the body is divided both externally and internally into a number of segments (*metameres*). In arthropods external segmentation is often obscured, but internally the body organs are repeated to an extent similar to that found in annelids. In the Chordata external segmentation is lost and internal metamerism is most clearly seen in the embryo. For example, vertebrate embryos show clear segmentation of the myotome muscles (*see* mesoderm).

There are various theories of the origin of metameric segmentation. It may have arisen as an adaptation to more efficient locomotion: the passage of rhythmic waves of muscular contraction along the body would have been aided by the division of the muscles into separately controlled units.

metamorphosis. The stage in the life history of some animals during which the larval form undergoes rapid transformation to the adult form. Metamorphosis is characteristic of amphibians, in which it is controlled by thyroid hormone, and insects, in which it is also under hormonal control. The process generally involves the involution of larval tissues by lysosomal enzymes.

metanephridium. *See* nephridium.

metanephros. The last (posterior) part of the *kidney to develop in amniotes (it never develops in anamniotes), becoming functional at birth or after hatching. It is drained by the *ureter.

metaphase. The second stage of *mitosis and *meiosis.

metaphloem. The part of the primary phloem that is laid down after the axis or structure in which it occurs has finished elongating. *Compare* protophloem.

metaplasia. The transformation of certain types of cell into others not normally associated with the same anatomical loci. It is essentially an abnormal process resulting from disease, e.g. tumour formation, or exposure to unusual conditions, e.g. epithelial metaplasia in the respiratory tract, which occurs in response to irritants such as smoke and sulphur dioxide.

metatarsal bones. The rod-shaped bones of the hind foot of tetrapods, articulating with the tarsal bones proximally and

with the phalanges distally. They are greatly elongated in running mammals. *See* pentadactyl limb.

metatarsus. The complex of metatarsal bones, forming part of the arch of the foot in man.

Metatheria. The infraclass or subclass of the Mammalia that contains the pouched mammals, included in a single order, the *Marsupialia. Marsupials are more primitive than the placentals and constitute a specialized side-branch. The young, born after a brief gestation period and in a very immature state, complete their development in a *marsupium. *Compare* Eutheria, Prototheria.

metaxylem. The part of the primary xylem that is laid down after the axis or structure in which it occurs has finished elongating. *Compare* protoxylem.

Metazoa. A subkingdom of animals whose bodies are composed of many specialized cells grouped together to form tissues and that possess a coordinating nervous system. This subkingdom includes all animals except the Protozoa and Parazoa (sponges).

methaemoglobin. *Haemoglobin in which the ferrous atoms of the haem group have been oxidized to their ferric states. Methaemoglobin is incapable of binding molecular oxygen.

methionine (met). An amino acid, $CH_3SCH_2CH_2CH(NH_2)COOH$, one of the 20 common amino acids occurring in proteins and an *essential amino acid for man.

methyl blue. *See* staining.

methylene blue. *See* staining.

methyl violet. *See* staining.

metoestrus. *See* oestrous cycle.

microbody. A small ($0.3-1.5$ μm) roughly spherical organelle of many plant and animal cells that is bounded by a single membrane and often has dense homogeneous contents, though crystalloids and filaments are sometimes present. Microbodies perform oxidation processes and are classified according to function. *Peroxisomes* produce hydrogen peroxide as a by-product and an enzyme, catalase, that breaks it down. In liver and kidney cells peroxisomes may be important in degrading purines. In higher plants they are functionally and spatially associated with chloroplasts and mitochondria, oxidizing excess glycollate produced in the chloroplasts during *photorespiration and passing products to the mitochondria. In certain animals and higher plants fats may be converted to carbohydrates (gluconeogenesis) in peroxisomes. A special type of fat conversion to carbohydrate takes place during germination of many fat-storing seeds via the *glyoxylate cycle in special peroxisomes called *glyoxysomes*.

microdissection. The technique used for the dissection of small organisms or parts of organisms that are clearly visible only through a microscope. The specimen is dissected while being viewed under a microscope using instruments controlled indirectly by mechanical or thermal means.

microfilament. A fine protein filament, 5–8 nm in thickness, found scattered or in bundles in the cytoplasm of all eukaryote cells. Microfilaments resemble the actin-containing filaments of muscle and are involved in cytoplasmic streaming, amoeboid movements, and morphogenetic changes. They occur in epithelial cells, often associated with desmosomes (*see* junctional complex), and in absorptive cells of vertebrate intestines, where they form supporting cores to the microvilli.

micrograph. A photograph of an image produced by a microscope, either by a light microscope (*light micrograph*) or an electron microscope (*electron micrograph*).

micrometre. Symbol: μm. A unit of microscopic distance equal to one thousandth of a millimetre. The radius of many cells is about 1–20 μm, and many bacteria are about 1 μm across. Formerly a micrometre was called a *micron* and was written μ. *See also* nanometre, SI units.

micron. *See* micrometre.

micronucleus. *See* nucleus.

micronutrient. A chemical in the environment that is necessary for the healthy growth of an organism but is needed only in small amounts. Micronutrients include the *trace elements and the *vitamins. *Compare* macronutrient.

microphyll. One of the two types of leaves produced by pteridophytes: it is usually a few millimetres long though it may be larger; for example, the microphylls of *Isoetes* are about 10 cm long. It is characterized by a very simple vascular system consisting of a simple midvein that leaves no leaf gap in the stem stele. The microphyll is regarded as having an evolutionary line separate from that of the *megaphyll. The most commonly accepted theory of its evolution is the *enation theory* of Bower (1935), which suggests that a small enation devoid of vascular supply (such as occurs in *Psilophyton princeps*) gradually acquired a vascular supply.

micropyle. 1. A small pore in the outer coat of an *ovule or *seed that remains from the incomplete closure of the integuments. It is frequently the site of entry of the pollen tube to the ovule and of imbibition of water in the seed. **2.** A small pore in the chorion (shell) of an insect's egg, through which the spermatozoa enter.

microscope. An instrument used to magnify material for examination of structure invisible to the naked eye.
The *light microscope* uses light as a radiation source for viewing the specimen. The usual type is a *compound microscope*, i.e. one that possesses two (rather than one) short-focal-length converging lenses that combine to give high magnification (the product of the magnifica-

	transmission e.m.	*light microscope*
radiation source	electrons	light
wavelength	e.g. 0·005 nm at 50 kV	400–700 nm
max. useful magnification	× 250 000 (on screen)	× 1500
max. resolution		
in practice	0·5 nm	200 nm–250 nm
in theory	0·2 nm	200 nm
lenses	electromagnets	glass (or quartz for UV radiation)
specimen	nonliving, dehydrated, relatively small/thin	living or nonliving
common stains	contain heavy metals to reflect electrons	coloured dyes
image	black and white	usually coloured

Comparison of light and electron microscopes

tion of the two lenses). An enlarged image of the specimen is formed by an *objective lens* and this is magnified further by the second lens, the *eyepiece lens*. When the specimen is thin enough to be viewed by transmitted light, a condenser situated below the specimen focuses light through it. *Resolution* is the ability to distinguish (*resolve*) two adjacent and separate points or objects. Two objects lying closer together than the *limit of resolution* of a microscope cannot be distinguished as two separate objects. The theoretical limit of resolution of a microscope (see table) is about half the wavelength of the radiation used to view the specimen and resolution is therefore higher the shorter the wavelength. Magnification up to the limit of resolution reveals further detail but further magnification increases blurring as well as size of the image. The best light microscopes give a magnification of about × 1500 using green light (higher using ultraviolet light). Contrast of material examined can be improved by *staining, either of living material

(*see* vital staining) or of material preserved in its living state by appropriate *fixation procedures. Examination of material, particularly living material (which often lacks contrast), can also be improved by the use of the following specialized forms of light microscope.

The *phase-contrast* and *interference microscopes* make use of the fact that cells contain regions of different refractive index, which change the light path (refractive index × thickness) and hence retard light to varying degrees. These differences in refractive index are translated by special optical systems into differences in contrast (of brightness or colour). In phase-contrast microscopy, two light rays differing by a quarter of one wavelength in phase are added (made in phase so that they reinforce each other) to give a brighter image (*bright contrast phase*) or subtracted (made out of phase by half a wavelength so that they partially cancel each other) to give a darker image (*dark contrast phase*). In interference microscopy the relative phase of the two beams is continuously variable so that contrast of an object can be heightened or reduced at will. Both phase-contrast and interference microscopy can be used for quantitative determinations of amounts of materials present in specific areas of cells, as well as visualizing structures otherwise difficult or impossible to see, particularly in living cells, e.g. flagella, chromosome movements.

In the *polarizing microscope* plane-polarized light, produced by a *polarizer*, is passed through the specimen. Plane-polarized light (in which the wavelike vibrations of light are confined to one direction only) can interact with areas of the specimen that are highly oriented (e.g. crystalline areas) and the interaction can be translated into contrast by means of an *analyser*. Ordered (*birefringent* or *anisotropic*) areas can be made to look brighter or darker than surrounding material. Polarizing optics have been used in, for example, the study of biological membranes, fibrillar structures, and cell division.

The *ultraviolet microscope* uses ultraviolet (UV) radiation as a light source. It has the advantage of greater resolution since UV radiation has a shorter wavelength (as short as 220 nm) than visible radiation (390–780 nm). The radiation is made visible by projecting it onto a fluorescent screen or is recorded photographically. UV radiation is damaging to living cells, so these can be studied only for a short time. An additional advantage is the visualization of certain biological molecules that strongly absorb UV light; areas in which these are concentrated (e.g. DNA in chromosomes) appear dark.

The *dark-field microscope* is fitted with a special condenser that passes an oblique beam of light through the specimen. This is not visible in the eyepiece (hence a dark field or background is seen) but light reflected or scattered from interfaces is visible. Thus cell outlines, organelles (such as nuclei and mitochondria), chromosomes and spindles in dividing cells, oil droplets, and other inclusions are visible as bright objects against a dark background. Dark-field microscopy provides more contrast between unstained objects than is possible by normal light microscopy and sometimes allows detection (but not resolution) of objects too small to be seen by normal light microscopy.

The *electron microscope (e.m.)* uses electrons as a radiation source. Since the wavelength associated with a beam of electrons is much shorter than that of light, the e.m. has much greater resolution than the light microscope (see table). It is operated under high vacuum to minimize electron scattering through collision with air molecules. In the *transmission e.m.* electrons pass through the specimen and are focused either onto a fluorescent screen for a visible image or onto a photographic plate or film for a permanent photograph (*electron micrograph*). Specimens are commonly ultrathin sections (*see* microtome), large macromolecules (e.g. DNA), small particles (e.g. viruses, ribosomes), fragments (e.g. membranes, cell walls), or thin replicas of the surface features of larger objects. Various techniques for providing contrast include heavy-metal staining, negative staining, and shadowing. *High-voltage electron microscopes* are a new generation of transmission e.ms. in which the electron beam is accelerated at very high voltage (e.g. 1000 kV, as compared to 40–80 kV in a conventional electron microscope). It can therefore penetrate thick sections and even whole cells or organelles to give information on three-dimensional structure.

In the *scanning e.m.* a narrow beam of electrons scans to and fro across the specimen and reflected electrons control the production of a television-like image on a cathode-ray tube. Features are viewed with great depth of field, giving a three-dimensional effect. Resolution is, so far, lower than for the transmission e.m. (5–20 nm) but specimens can be larger and thicker. It is particularly useful for studying surface features, for example of pollen grains, diatoms, and leaves, and certain other structures, e.g. wood (including fossil woods).

microsome. A composite structure consisting of ribosomes associated with vesicular fragments of endoplasmic reticulum. The term was originally applied to small particles (*microsomal fraction*) isolated from tissue homogenates by differential centrifugation, which, under appropriate conditions, would synthesize proteins. This was later shown to be a property of the ribosomes alone, the microsomes being largely artefacts.

microsporangium. The sporangium borne on the *microsporophyll of heterosporous plants, in which the smaller spores (*microspores*) are formed. In pteridophytes the microspore gives rise to the gametophyte prothallus that produces the male sex organs (antheridia). In seed plants the microspores are the *pollen grains* and the microsporangia are termed *pollen sacs* (or, in angiosperms, *anthers*). *Compare* megasporangium.

microspore. A spore formed within a *microsporangium.

microsporophyll. The sporophyll of heterosporous plants that bears the microsporangia or pollen sacs. The microsporophyll of pteridophytes and gymnosperms is usually borne on a cone (*see* strobilus); the microsporophyll of angiosperms is the *stamen.

microtome. An instrument for cutting sections (thin slices) of biological material for microscopic examination. For light microscopy, where sections of a few micrometres thick are required, a steel knife is used. The material is usually embedded in a medium such as paraffin wax for support (*see* embedding); alternatively a *freezing microtome* is used, which keeps the specimen frozen, and thus rigid, while cutting. The *ultramicrotome* is used for cutting extremely thin sections (20–100 nm) for electron microscopy. The material is embedded, usually in a hard resin, and cut with a glass or diamond knife.

microtubule. A minute unbranched tubule occurring in groups in the cytoplasm of virtually all eukaryote cells. They usually have an external diameter of about 24 nm and their walls, about 5 nm thick, are composed of globular protein subunits. At intervals cross-bridges (arms), probably involved in motility and in linking adjacent microtubules, project from the walls. Microtubules function passively in cell support and shape (cytoskeletal role), particularly in asymmetric cells, developing cells, and in elongate cell processes, e.g. axons of neurones. A layer of microtubules is commonly found in the outermost layers of the cytoplasm of plant cells. Microtubules are also associated with cellular motion: they form *spindle fibres and are responsible for chromosome movements during nuclear division (in plants a band of microtubules also encircles the cell before prophase in the future plane of division); they are also found in cilia and flagella. Elsewhere they may have a role in orienting the movement of cytoplasmic constituents, as in phragmoplasts (where microtubules are involved in cell-plate formation) and in melanophores (where they are associated with movement of pigment granules). Microtubules are found in basal bodies and centrioles, often in close association with these structures (as in asters). They may sometimes define channels of cytoplasmic streaming.

microvilli. Microscopic projections of cytoplasm, usually 2–4 μm high, that protrude above the free surface of epithelial cells and increase their absorptive area. Each cell usually has many regularly arranged microvilli. They are particularly prolific in the linings of the intestinal and respiratory tracts; such regions of dense regularly arranged microvilli are called *brush borders*.

midbrain (mesencephalon). The middle one of the three hollow dilations of the neural tube that constitute the brain of embryonic vertebrates. It is primitively concerned with the processing of visual information passed backwards from the forebrain. Except in those vertebrates in which the *tectum is developed as a dominant integrative centre, the midbrain remains as a largely unelaborated *brain stem, which gives rise to some cranial nerves.

middle ear (tympanic cavity). The air-filled cavity between the tympanum and the fenestra ovalis, present in most tetrapods and encased in the bulla of the skull in mammals. It is homologous with the gill pouch of the fish spiracle. Sound is conducted across the cavity by vibrations of the *ear ossicles. The middle ear cavity is connected to the pharynx by the Eustachian tube, by means of which damaging differences in air pressure across the tympanum can be equalized.

middle lamella. The thin intercellular layer of *pectic substances (calcium and magnesium pectates) that acts as a cement between neighbouring plant cell walls. *See* cell plate.

midgut. 1. The region of the alimentary canal of vertebrates between the bile duct and the middle of the colon. It is responsible for the digestion and absorption of foodstuffs.
2. The endodermal section of the gut of arthropods: it is not lined with cuticle. *Compare* foregut, hindgut.

migration. The periodic movement of populations of animals between one region and another, usually brought about by seasonal changes in the climate resulting in lower temperatures and a reduced food supply (in many species migration is the alternative to hibernation).
Migration occurs in many animal groups, including mammals (such as whales and caribou), fish (such as eels and salmon), a few reptiles, and some insects; it is especially prevalent in birds, whose migrations are spectacular. The longest migration is performed by a bird, the Arctic tern, which breeds in the circumpolar regions of the Arctic and a few months later migrates to the Antarctic: a distance of 17 600 km. Animals that migrate must have great powers of orientation in order to navigate, but their methods of orientation are poorly understood. In aquatic animals sea currents may be important. Various mechanisms have been suggested for land and aerial migrants, including orientation to the sun's rays. In some birds, following coastlines may be important for part of the route.
Migration is a very regular process; all members of the same species migrate at about the same time. Several stimuli have been suggested as causing the onset of migration. Seasonal changes in temperature and food supply are very variable; the more regular seasonal change of day length is a more likely stimulus (*see* photoperiodism). Several theories have been proposed to explain the evolution of migratory behaviour, especially in birds. One of the more recent is the continental drift theory, which suggests that birds originally undertook short flights between their breeding and winter feeding ranges. As the continents drifted apart, birds continued to fly from one range to the other, although these ranges had become widely separated.

milk teeth. *See* deciduous teeth.

millipedes. *See* Diplopoda.

Millon's test. A biochemical test for protein. The suspected protein is heated with Millon's reagent – a solution of mercuric nitrate and nitrous acid. The positive result is a pink or dark red precipitate of coagulated proteins; the negative result is a clear solution.

mimicry. The phenomenon of one species of animal (especially an insect) resembling another, sometimes to the benefit of both species and sometimes to the benefit of only the mimic. In *Müllerian mimicry*, two or more predator-resistant species, e.g. species that are distasteful, poisonous, or stinging, have similar *warning coloration. Thus when a predator has found a few individuals distasteful, it will leave all similarly coloured insects alone. Therefore fewer individuals of each species are taken before the bird learns to avoid all such insects. In *Batesian mimicry*, one palatable or harmless species resembles a predator-resistant one by mimicking its warning coloration. Once the predator has learnt to avoid the distasteful species, it also avoids the harmless one. Batesian mimicry can work only if the harmless species is less numerous than the predator-resistant one.

mineralocorticoid. Any of a group of *corticosteroid hormones whose principal action is on electrolyte and water metabolism, chiefly involving the stimulation of sodium and water reabsorption by the distal tubules of the kidney. The most potent mineralocorticoid is *aldosterone, but other corticosteroids that are secreted in larger amounts and contain no oxygen at C11 also show significant mineralocorticoid activity. *Compare* glucocorticoid.

minichromosome. The chromatin structure within which the DNA of some eukaryotic viruses occurs. Viruses, such as *SV40, that replicate within the nuclei of eukaryotic cells derive histone molecules from the host cell; these, together with their own DNA, form the viral nucleosomes. The minichromosome of SV40 occurs not only within infected cells but also persists within the free virus.

Miocene. An epoch of the *Tertiary period.

miracidium. The first larval stage of endoparasitic flukes (*see* Trematoda), which hatches from eggs passed out with the vertebrate host's excreta and swims by means of the cilia covering its flat body. It enters the secondary host, a snail, in which it develops into a *sporocyst. *See also* redia, cercaria.

mismatch (in DNA). The presence of noncomplementary bases opposite each other in the double helix. *See* heteroduplex.

Mississippian. A subdivision of the *Carboniferous period in America that is equivalent to the Lower Carboniferous in Britain and continental countries.

mites. *See* Acari.

mitochondrion   (chondriosome). An organelle in the cytoplasm of all those eukaryotic cells that carry out aerobic respiration. The number per cell varies from one to about 10 000, depending on the organism and on the stage of development of the cell. Morphology and size is extremely variable; spherical to cylindrical types are common in higher plants and animals, the much studied liver mitochondrion being approximately 3 μm $\times$ 1 μm. In some cells mitochondria continually move and change shape; splitting and fusion can also occur. In some cells they are precisely arranged: in insect flight muscle they are aligned in long rows between the myofibrils for efficient supply of the ATP needed for muscular contraction. Such concentration of mitochondria at sites of energy consumption is often observed. At other times they may be located near sources of substrate, such as fat globules.

The mitochondrion is surrounded by an envelope consisting of two membranes (see illustration at *cell). The surface area of the inner membrane is increased by involutions called *cristae*, which project into the gel-like matrix. The components of *oxidative phosphorylation and *electron transport are located in the cristae, which also contain the *elementary particles*. These are small knoblike particles consisting of the enzyme ATPase, which is involved in phosphorylation. They protrude on short stalks from the inner surface of the membrane when treated for negative staining but *in vivo* they probably lie within the membrane. The number of cristae varies; in general, the more active the mitochondrion in respiration, the more numerous the cristae.

The matrix of the mitochondrion contains various enzymes of the *Krebs cycle and *fatty-acid oxidation. It also contains one or more closed circles of double-stranded DNA, which constitute the genome of the mitochondrion. No copy of the mitochondrial genome exists in the nuclear DNA, thus indicating that these organelles are distinct self-replicating factors with considerable genetic autonomy. Many mitochondrial proteins are, however, coded on the nuclear rather than the mitochondrial genome. The possession of a separate genome and many other attributes suggest that mitochondria, like *chloroplasts, may have originated as symbiotic prokaryotic organisms within eukaryotic cells.

mitosis (karyokinesis). The process by which a cell nucleus divides into two daughter nuclei, each containing exactly the same chromosomes, and therefore genes, as the parent nucleus. The nuclear division is usually followed by cell division. Mitosis may be divided into four active stages: prophase, metaphase, anaphase, and telophase, which are not distinct but grade into each other (see illustration). When it is not undergoing mitosis, the cell is in

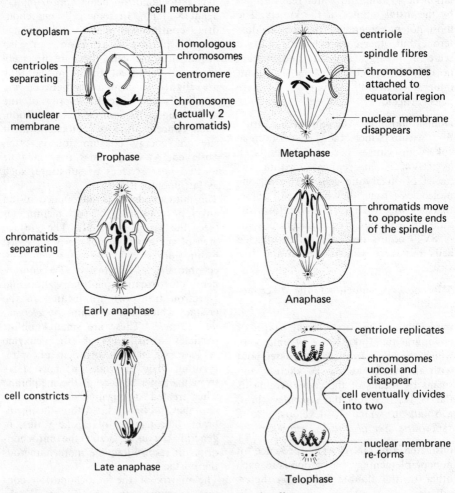

Mitosis in an animal cell

interphase (the *resting nucleus*) and carries out activities such as duplication of chromosomes and protein synthesis. At the beginning of *prophase* the chromosomes appear as very long threads, which are tangled together and can be stained by basic dyes. They gradually become shorter and thicker by coiling into a spiral, a process known as *spiralization*. Each chromosome then appears as a double thread; each of the threads is called a *chromatid. The chromatids are joined together at the centromere, a nonstaining region of the chromosome. Towards the end of prophase the nucleolus, which has been diminishing, disappears. The nuclear membrane begins to break down and by the end of prophase the chromosomes are dispersed in the cytoplasm. In *metaphase* (or, according to some authorities, at the end of prophase) a *spindle is formed in the cytoplasm; in animals and lower plants it is associated with the *centrioles. The chromosomes come to lie on the *equatorial plate of the spindle, to which they are attached by their centromeres. In *anaphase* the centromeres divide into two, the chromatids separate, and the spindle elongates. This results in each chromatid being pulled to its respective pole, led by the centromere. *Telophase* is in many ways the reverse of prophase. The chromosomes become longer and less distinct as they uncoil, the nuclear membrane re-forms, and the nucleolus reappears. After telophase the cytoplasm usually also divides and two new cells are formed. Mitosis occurs whenever cell division is necessary for growth or nonsexual reproduction; it is found in most animals and plants in either the haploid or diploid phase. *Compare* amitosis, endomitosis, meiosis.

mitotic index. The proportion of cells in a population that are observed in mitosis. Mitotic indices vary from more than 10% for some cells in culture to less than 1% for tissues *in vivo*. A mitotic index of 0.1 means that 10% of the cell population are observed in mitosis.

mitral valve (bicuspid valve). A valve comprising two membranous flaps between the atrium and ventricle of the left side of the heart in birds and mammals.

molar. A ridged multiple-rooted tooth of mammals, two or more of which are situated in the back of the mouth adjacent to the premolars. They are used for grinding and pounding food and are structurally similar to the premolars, from which they differ in not being represented in the deciduous teeth.

moles. *See* Insectivora.

Molisch test. A biochemical test for carbohydrate. A few drops of α-naphthol are added to a solution or suspension of the suspected carbohydrate and concentrated sulphuric acid is slowly poured down the side of the test tube. A violet ring at the juncture of the two solutions indicates carbohydrate.

Mollusca. A phylum of bilaterally symmetrical unsegmented invertebrates in which the body is typically divided into a head, a ventral muscular locomotory organ (*foot*), and a dorsal visceral hump. The latter is covered by a layer of tissue (*mantle*), which can secrete a calcareous shell. The edges of the mantle overlap into flaps, which enclose a cavity containing the gills. The coelom is reduced to the pericardial, gonad, and kidney cavities. The feeding organ is typically a *radula. Development usually occurs via *trochophore and *veliger larval stages. Most molluscs inhabit marine or freshwater environments but some are terrestrial; the phylum includes the classes *Monoplacophora, *Amphineura, *Gastropoda, *Scaphopoda, *Bivalvia, and *Cephalopoda.

mongolism. *See* Down's syndrome.

monkeys. *See* Primates.

monochasium. *See* cymose inflorescence.

monoclonal antibody. An antibody produced by a cell clone and therefore comprising only a single species of immunoglobulin molecule. Such cell clones are produced by the artificial fusion of antibody-forming cells from mouse spleen with mouse myeloma cells (which are cancerous). The hybrid cells multiply rapidly and are grown *in vitro* as clones of cells, each clone producing only a single type of antibody molecule.

Monocotyledonae. The smaller of the two subgroups of angiosperms (*compare* Dicotyledonae). Monocotyledons are characterized by the possession of a single cotyledon in the embryo. The vascular bundles form two or more rings or are scattered through the axis; there is usually no vascular cambium (arboreal forms such as palms achieve their stature by primary growth, although a few monocotyledons possess anomalous secondary thickening). The leaves generally have parallel veins; the floral parts, if not numerous, are typically in threes (or multiples of three), rarely fours, never fives; and the pollen grains are *unicolpate* (i.e. with one germ pore). The group includes the palms, grasses, orchids, lilies, etc.

monocyte. A large agranulocytic vertebrate white blood cell, 10–12 μm in diameter, that has an oval nucleus and stains with basic dyes, e.g. methylene blue. Monocytes comprise up to 7% of the white cells in human blood and have pronounced phagocytic properties, ingesting large particles and bacteria. In inflammatory conditions they migrate from the blood to the tissues and are thought to be identical with tissue macrophages.

monoecious. 1. Designating a plant species in which separate male and female flowers are produced on the same plant. *Compare* dioecious.
2. *See* autoecious.

Monogenea. An order of the *Trematoda (flukes), sometimes regarded as a separate class of Platyhelminthes.

monohybrid. An organism considered as heterozygous for one pair of alleles, such as *Aa. Compare* dihybrid.

mononucleotide. *See* nucleotide.

monophyletic. Designating a group of species, genera, etc., that have descended from a common ancestor. All natural groups in classification are monophyletic. *Compare* polyphyletic.

monophyodont. *See* dentition.

Monoplacophora. The most primitive class of the Mollusca, known only from Cambrian fossils until 1952, when *Neopilina* was discovered. *Neopilina* is a rare deep-sea mollusc with a large fragile limpet-like shell. Adaptations for adhesion to rock surfaces include a reduced head and a broad flat circular foot.

monopodium (in botany). A branching system in which the apex of the primary axis continues to grow indefinitely. This type of branching is sometimes called *indefinite* (or *racemose*) branching and is characteristic of a *racemose inflorescence. *Compare* dichotomy, sympodium.

monosaccharides. The simplest group of carbohydrate sugars, with a general formula $C_nH_{2n}O_n$. They are classified according to the number of carbon atoms in the molecule (a *triose* has three carbon atoms, a *tetrose* has four, a *pentose* has five, a *hexose* has six, etc.) and also according to the nature of the carbonyl group: those with an aldehyde group are termed *aldoses*; those with a keto group are *ketoses*. For example, ribose is an *aldopentose*; fructose is a *ketohexose* (see table). All monosaccharides (except dihydroxyacetone) contain one or more asymmetric carbon atoms, i.e. a carbon atom to which four different atoms or groups of atoms are attached, and they can therefore exist in a number of different forms called *stereoisomers. Monosaccharides can also exist in a cyclic form, due to the interaction of the carbonyl group with the hydroxyl group on carbon 4 (to form a *furanose) or carbon 5 (to form a *pyranose). The most widely distributed

D– aldoses

D– ketoses

a triose   D– glyceraldehyde

a triose   dihydroxyacetone

a tetrose   D– erythrose

a pentose   D– xylulose

a pentose   D– ribose

a hexose   D– fructose

Monosaccharides

monosaccharide is the dextrorotatory form of the hexose *glucose (D-glucose).

monosomy. The condition in which one or more chromosomes are represented only once in a nucleus, cell, or organism, so that the diploid chromosome complement is $2n - 1$, where n is the haploid number. Monosomy is the normal condition for the males of some grasshoppers, which have only one sex chromosome and therefore a chromosome complement of $2n + X$. *See also* aneuploidy.

monospore. An asexual spore produced for vegetative reproduction by some algae, such as certain Phaeophyta and the sexual and Chantransia stages of some Rhodophyta. Monospores are produced singly in *monosporangia* and on

germination give rise to plants similar to the parent.

Monotremata. The sole order of the subclass *Prototheria: primitive, but highly specialized, mammals confined to Australasia. The aquatic *Ornithorhynchus* (duck-billed platypus) has webbed feet and a bill containing horny pads used for crushing invertebrates. *Tachyglossus* and *Zaglossus* (echidnas or spiny anteaters) are terrestrial insectivores with sharp spines protecting the body, a long toothless snout and tongue for catching ants and termites, and powerful limbs and claws for opening insect nests.

monozygotic twins. *See* identical twins.

morph. *See* polymorphism.

morphactin. One of a group of plant growth regulators consisting of variously modified fluorene-9-carboxylic acids. Morphactins ('morphologically active substances') profoundly affect growth and development (morphogenesis). Morphactins usually inhibit shoot elongation and cell division of apical meristems; the plane of division (polarity), and hence growth pattern, is also severely affected. Organs therefore grow slowly and tend to have fused parts (e.g. funnel-shaped leaves and flowers). In contrast, emergence of lateral buds is often stimulated. The net effect is dwarfism (compact bushy growth) and loss of apical dominance. In roots an opposite reaction occurs: the primary roots are often stimulated but elongation of lateral roots is inhibited. Other effects of morphactins include complete inhibition of photo- and geotropism, the occasional stimulation of cambial activity, retardation of leaf senescence, and inhibition of germination of most seeds. All these effects probably involve synergistic or antagonistic interaction with endogenous growth substances.

morphallaxis. *See* regeneration.

morphogenesis. The development of form and structure of an organism or part of an organism.

morphology. The study of the structure of animals, plants, and microorganisms, especially the form, arrangement, and interrelationships of their internal parts. *Anatomy* is also the study of biological structure and is sometimes used as a synonym for morphology; however anatomy is usually concerned with the details of gross or microscopical structure of organs or parts. *See also* histology, cytology. *Compare* physiology.

morula. An animal embryo during cleavage, which comprises a solid group of cells that will later form the *blastula.

mosaic. An organism consisting of two or more lines of genetically different cells. The term is almost synonymous with *chimaera, but the latter should be reserved for organisms in which the multiple cell lines have arisen from different zygotes.

mosaic egg. A fertilized ovum in which the direction of development of the cells of the embryo is determined in the early stages of cleavage (in some species, e.g. amphioxus, even before fertilization). *Compare* regulation egg. *See also* fate map.

mosses. *See* Musci.

moths. *See* Lepidoptera.

motor neurone (motoneuron). An efferent neurone whose axon connects with a muscle or other effector.

moulting. 1. *See* ecdysis.
2. The periodic shedding of hair or feathers by mammals or birds.

moulting hormone. *See* ecdysone.

mouthparts. Paired appendages on the head of arthropods that are modified for feeding. Crustacea, Chilopoda, and Diplopoda have a pair of *mandibles* and two pairs of *maxillae*, which are used for grasping and shredding the food. Crustaceans also have three pairs of *maxillipedes*. Insects have one pair each of mandibles and maxillae; the second pair of maxillae are specialized as the *labium* (*lower lip*). There is also a *labrum* (*upper lip*), which is developed from a flat exoskeletal secondarily hinged plate immediately above the mouth.

M phase. The phase of the *cell cycle in which mitosis occurs.

MSH. *See* melanocyte-stimulating hormone.

mucilage. A slimy substance consisting of complex carbohydrate derivatives, produced by many plants and animals. *See* gum.

mucin. A glycoprotein that is the chief constituent of mucus.

mucopeptide (murein, peptidoglycan). A macromolecule unique to the *cell wall of prokaryotes, though often present in small amounts (less than 10% in Gram-negative bacteria). It is a complex heter-opolymer of two amino sugars, N-acetylglucosamine and N-acetylmuramic acid, and the amino acids alanine, glutamic acid, and either diaminopimelic acid or lysine. Half the alanine and all the glutamic acid residues are of the D isomer. Mucopeptide is formed as a continuous molecular net around the cell membrane, conferring both shape and the strength to resist osmotic burst-ing in the usual hypotonic environment.

mucopolysaccharides. A group of polysaccharides that are present in animal connective tissue and consist of disaccharide repeating units, one mono-mer of which is always an amino sugar, such as glucosamine. The most abun-dant mucopolysaccharides are *hyaluronic acid, *chondroitin, and *heparin.

mucosa. *See* mucous membrane.

mucous membrane (mucosa). The layer of moist surface epithelium and underly-ing connective tissue lining many verte-brate internal cavities that are continu-ous with the external environment. It occurs in the intestinal, respiratory, and urinogenital tracts. The term is mislead-ing in that some so-called mucous mem-branes, e.g. most of the urinogenital tract, contain no mucus-secreting cells. *Compare* serous membrane.

mucus. The slimy viscous sticky sub-stance produced by the epithelial cells of mucous membranes, which can be dispersed but not dissolved in water. The main components of mucus are gly-coproteins, secreted by *goblet cells and containing large amounts of carbohy-drate, which are responsible for the high viscosity of these protective and lubrica-ting fluids. The mucus produced by invertebrates also contains glycoproteins, but of unknown composition.

Müllerian duct. The oviduct of vertebrates (except the Agnatha). It was named after the German physiologist J. P. Müller (1801–58), who first accu-rately described its function. In both sexes the duct develops from embryonic mesoderm in association with the Wolff-ian duct, but in males it becomes vestig-ial. One end of the duct, forming a cili-ated funnel, opens into the coelom and captures ova discharged from the ovary. The ova are transported down the duct towards the cloaca by muscular and cili-ary movements; in higher vertebrates fertilization occurs in the duct during this process. In most vertebrates the Müllerian duct is paired (it is single in birds); in mammals the upper part con-sists of two *Fallopian tubes*, which lead into paired uteri (as in the rat) or a sin-gle uterus (as in humans). The duct usu-ally fuses posteriorly into a single medial vagina, which opens to the exte-rior.

multicellular. Designating organisms or parts that consist of many cells.

multiple alleles (multiple allelomorphs). Several (three or more) alleles, any two of which occupy the same relative posi-tion on homologous chromosomes in diploid cells. In some cases one of the alleles is dominant to the others; for example in *Drosophila*, the allele for red eye colour is dominant to that for cher-ry, eosin, apricot, etc. In other cases there is no dominance. In some plants, e.g. *Nicotiana* (tobacco), the presence of a series of multiple alleles, S_1 S_2 S_3 etc., produces *incompatibility: if the same allele is present in the pollen grain and in the ovary the pollen grain cannot grow. The term *multiple allelomorph* is also used for the characteristic produced by a multiple allele.

Multituberculata. An extinct order of Jurassic to early Tertiary mammals con-taining the first herbivorous mammals, characterized by a gap (*diastema*) between the strong incisor teeth and molars with rows of cusps for grinding. The dentition and jaw musculature were similar to those of later placental herbi-vores but multituberculates were not ancestral to later groups.

murein. *See* mucopeptide.

Musci. A group of bryophytes comprising the mosses (*compare* Hepaticae). They are characterized by the possession of a well-developed filamentous or thalloid protonema, a capsule that has a columella and stomata but lacks elaters, and the presence of multicellular rhizoids.

muscle. Tissue specialized to contract, thus producing tension, movement, and mechanical energy. Muscles are usually classified as *striated (voluntary) muscle, *smooth (involuntary) muscle, or *cardiac muscle, based on the appearance of their cells under the microscope and on their mechanical behaviour.

muscle spindle. A stretch receptor of vertebrate muscle, consisting of modified muscle fibres with both sensory and motor innervation. The muscle spindle monitors both the static and the dynamic components of contraction, which enables continuous adjustment of the level of stimulation of the muscle via a feedback loop. Differences in loading and other factors affecting the degree of contraction are thus automatically compensated for. Passive stretching of the muscle stimulates the muscle spindle and initiates reflex contraction, so that the muscle returns to its previous length (the *myotactic reflex*, which maintains posture). Voluntary contraction of the muscle involves motor activation of the spindle from the higher centres to reset it to maintain a new length. Crustaceans possess a similar receptor, the *muscle receptor organ*, in the intersegmental abdominal flexor muscles.

mutagen. Any agent capable of causing a *mutation or increasing the rate of mutation. Chemical mutagens cause chemical changes in DNA molecules leading to either changing of a base pair or addition or deletion of a base pair. Nitrous acid, for example, removes an amino group from cytosine, converting it to uracil. This ultimately leads to substitution of an adenine–thymine base pair for a guanine–cytosine base pair at DNA synthesis. Other chemical mutagens include alkylating agents, such as nitrogen mustard and ethyl methanesulphonate, which can produce base pair changes; and *acridines, which cause deletions or additions of base pairs. Electromagnetic radiation can also induce mutation. X-rays, gamma rays, and beta particles all increase the frequency of mutation and ultraviolet light is known to produce pyrimidine dimers by covalent bonding between adjacent pyrimidine bases on the DNA chain.

mutation. A change in the amount or structure of DNA in the chromosomes or the resultant change in a characteristic of the organism. If this change occurs in the gametes the mutation is inherited by subsequent generations of offspring. If it occurs in any other cells (somatic cells) it is not inherited, except by the daughter cells produced by mitosis of the mutated cell, and is known as a *somatic mutation*. Inherited mutations produced by a change in the amount of DNA are known as *chromosome mutations* and are usually visible under the microscope. Inherited mutations produced by a change in the structure of DNA (by a change in one or more bases) are known as *gene mutations* and are not visible under the microscope. There are various types of chromosome mutations, including *polyploidy, *aneuploidy, *deficiency, *duplication, *inversion, and *translocation. Gene mutations are probably more common and result in the misreading of one or more codons in DNA leading to one or more wrong amino acids being substituted in the protein being made. This results in the formation of an ineffective protein or a protein that differs from the original.

The occurrence of mutations is one way of providing variations in a population on which natural selection can act, bringing about evolution of the species. When first produced, mutations are usually recessive and deleterious; if they are advantageous natural selection eventually causes them to become dominant. Gene mutations usually occur only in one chromosome of a homologous pair, and the mutated gene is allelomorphic to the unmutated one. Mutations are brought about by various means: some occur naturally, others can be induced by *mutagens.

mutualism. An association between two organisms in which both benefit. For example, a certain species of hermit crab always has a sea anemone attached to its shell. The sea anemone receives food and transport from the crab, which is itself protected by the stinging cells of the anemone. The sea anemone cannot survive unless it is attached to the shell of a crab; if the anemone is removed from its position the crab will find another and place it on its shell. *See also* symbiosis.

mycelium. The tangled mass of hyphae that forms the vegetative body (sometimes termed a *thallus*) of a fungus.

mycetocyte. A specialized cell of certain insects that contains symbiotic microorganisms (bacteria and yeasts). Mycetocytes are sometimes concentrated in groups known as *mycetomes*.

mycobiont. The fungal constituent of a lichen. *Compare* phycobiont.

mycoplasmas. A group of minute nonmotile bacteria with a flexible cell wall. The shape of the cell varies according to the stage of the life cycle. The group includes *Mycoplasma*, which causes various diseases in animals, and the nonpathogenic microorganisms formerly known as *pleuropneumonia-like organisms* (*PPLO*).

mycorrhiza. An association between fungal hyphae and a higher plant, commonly occurring in the roots of vascular plants. Fairy rings, an association between a basidiomycete fungus (such as *Marasmius oreades*) and a grass, are an example of this type of association. A close physiological interaction occurs between two constituents of a mycorrhiza. The fungus obtains sugars and other nutrients plus hormonal material from the host, while the latter receives materials synthesized by the fungus, which also supplies a greater surface area for absorption.

Mycorrhizae are of two main types: ectotrophic and endotrophic. *Ectotrophic mycorrhizae* develop between a basidiomycete fungus and a woody plant. The root tips become invested in fungal hyphae, which suppress root-hair production. The hyphae penetrate between the cells of the cortex to form a meshwork termed the *Hartig net*. The infection causes morphological changes in the roots; for example they may become coralloid or dichotomously branching. *Endotrophic mycorrhizae* occur between fungi of various groups and woody and herbaceous plants. The fungal hyphae penetrate the cortex both intra- and intercellularly and frequently become dissociated and partially digested in the inner regions of the cortex.

Mycota. *See* Fungi.

myelin sheath. An insulating jacket surrounding the axon of most vertebrate and some invertebrate neurones. It is composed of closely packed double layers of plasma membrane that are derived from and continuous with the membranes of the Schwann cells and spiral tightly round the axon. The cytoplasm of the Schwann cells forms columns between the membrane lamellae. The regions of the axon ensheathed with myelin are termed the *internodes*; the unmyelinated spaces between the adjacent Schwann cells are the *nodes of Ranvier*. *See also* saltatory conduction.

myelocyte. *See* haemopoiesis.

myeloid tissue. The vertebrate tissue that produces red blood cells and polymorphs. The principal myeloid tissues in foetal life are the liver and spleen, but in the adult their function is taken over by the red marrow of certain skeletal bones (ribs, vertebrae, sternum, and skull).

myofibril. The structural unit of a *striated muscle cell, consisting of the contractile apparatus, i.e. sarcomeres, surrounded by sarcoplasmic reticulum and mitochondria.

myoglobin. A protein in the fibres of vertebrate muscles that binds molecular oxygen. It consists of a single polypeptide chain that carries a haem group and bears many similarities to the individual chains comprising the *haemoglobin molecule. It has a molecular weight of 17 000 and each molecule can bind one atom of oxygen by means of the haem group.

myo-inositol. *See* inositol.

myoneme. A contractile fibril in the ectoplasm of some Protozoa, including the ciliates *Stentor* and *Vorticella*.

myosin. A protein that, with actin, constitutes the principal element of the contractile apparatus of muscle. The myosin molecule consists of a tail, by which it aggregates with other myosin molecules to form filaments, and a globular head with sites for the attachment of actin and ATP. *See* striated muscle.

myotome. *See* mesoderm.

Myriapoda. A group of terrestrial arthropods whose members have a distinct head, typically bearing antennae, mandibles, and maxillae (*see* mouthparts), and numerous pairs of walking legs. It includes four classes, the two principal ones being the *Chilopoda (centipedes) and the *Diplopoda (millipedes).

myxamoeba. The product of a germinating zoospore of the *Myxomycetes.

myxobacteria. A group of bacteria that lack a rigid cell wall and show a gliding movement in contact with a solid surface. They occur in soil, rotting wood, etc., and form loose colonies that, under certain conditions, produce stalked fruiting bodies.

Myxomycetes. The true slime fungi (or moulds): a group of free-living fungi characterized by a plant body consisting of a *plasmodium. Under certain conditions they will produce flagellate zoospores, which germinate to release one to four uninucleate amoeboid cells (*myxamoebae*). The Myxomycetes are usually placed with the mycelial fungi in the *Eumycophyta but are sometimes classified as *Myxomycophyta. The term Myxomycetes is sometimes used as a synonym for the Myxomycophyta.

Myxomycophyta (**Myxomycotina, Archimycetes**). The slime fungi (or moulds): fungi whose plant body is either an amoeba-like cell, a pseudoplasmodium, or a plasmodium. The fungi included in this group vary. In its broadest sense the group includes the *Acrasiales, *Labyrinthulales, *Myxomycetes, and *Plasmodiophorales. However, the latter two subgroups are often placed in the *Eumycophyta as they both produce flagellate zoospores under certain conditions (the first two groups never do this).

Myxophyta. *See* Cyanophyta.

myxovirus. *See* virus.

N

NAA. α-naphthaleneacetic acid, a synthetic *auxin.

NAD (nicotinamide adenine dinucleotide). A coenzyme functioning as a hydrogen carrier in oxidation-reduction reactions, for example in those of the electron transport chain in aerobic respiration. NAD and the closely related coenzyme *NADP* (*nicotinamide adenine dinucleotide phosphate*) are both derived from nicotinic acid. They are reduced to NADH and NADPH, respectively, when hydrogen atoms are transferred from the substrates to the coenzymes in reactions catalysed by substrate-specific dehydrogenases.

NAD was the first coenzyme to be recognized; its structure (and that of NADP) was elucidated in the 1930s. NAD was formerly termed *DPN* (*diphosphopyridine nucleotide*), and NADP *TPN* (*triphosphopyridine nucleotide*).

NADP. *See* NAD.

nanometre. Symbol: nm. A unit of microscopic distance equal to one thousandth of a *micrometre (i.e. 10 angstrom units). *See* SI units.

naphthaleneacetic acid (NAA). A synthetic *auxin.

nares (nostrils). The paired openings by which the nasal cavity of vertebrates communicates with the exterior. The *external nares* open onto the surface of the head, while the *internal nares* (*see* choanae), present only in tetrapods and crossopterygians, open into the mouth.

nasal cavity. A cavity in the head of vertebrates that contains the *olfactory organs. Its epithelium is differentiated into sensory, secretory, and supporting cells and it opens to the exterior via the external nares. In most fish the cavity is blind-ending, but in crossopterygians and tetrapods it communicates with the pharynx via the *choanae and therefore becomes a route for respiratory air. It contains salt glands in birds.

nascent. Designating DNA or RNA that is newly synthesized.

nastic movements (nasties). Nondirectional movements of plant parts in response to external stimuli: a type of *paratonic movement. The stimulus is usually universal, i.e. of equal intensity around the plant, but can be unilateral. Movement is directed not by the stimulus but by the inherent properties of the plant part. Nasties may be growth movements, in which case they are slow and confined to growing plants, or relatively rapid movements caused by turgor changes. They are typical of many

leaves and petals. *See* nyctinastic movements, haptonasty.

natural group. A group of organisms of any taxonomic rank that are thought to be descended from a common ancestor.

natural order (in botany). A former name for *family.

natural selection. The main mechanism bringing about evolution according to Darwinian theory. Competition for food and space, the action of predators, etc., influence the composition of a population, resulting in the survival of organisms having variations advantageous to their environment and the elimination of those with unfavourable variations. When survivors of these selection pressures breed, their advantageous variations are passed on to the next generation, which eventually results in evolutionary change. *Compare* sexual selection, genetic drift.

nature and nuture. The genotype and environment, respectively, of an organism. The interaction beween the two produces the phenotype (appearance of the organism).

nauplius. The larva of many Crustacea. Its tiny unsegmented oval body is covered in a protective chitinous armour and bears a single eye and three pairs of limbs used for swimming; the first pair of limbs are unbranched and the others are biramous.

nautilus. *See* Cephalopoda.

Neanderthal man. *See Homo.*

Nearctic. (Designating) a zoogeographical region of *Arctogea consisting of Greenland and North America as far south as Mexico. This region has a basically similar fauna as the land masses are practically interconnected; differences are due mainly to climatic variations.

nectar. The sugary fluid secreted from the nectaries of a flower, which attracts the animals (insects in temperate regions but also birds and bats in the tropics) that cause pollination.

nectary. A glandular structure in a flower from which nectar is secreted.

negative interference (in genetic mapping). The effect that a cross-over event appears to have of reducing the probability of another cross-over in its vicinity. Thus double cross-overs within a short region of a chromosome are much less frequent than would be predicted from the frequencies of observed single cross-overs.

negative staining. A method of staining for light or electron microscopy in which only the background is stained, so that the unstained specimen shows up clearly against it.

nekton. The animals actively swimming in a sea or lake, e.g. fish. *Compare* benthos, plankton.

nematocyst. The functional part of a stinging cell (*see* cnidoblast) of the Cnidaria.

Nematoda. A very large phylum of pseudocoelomate invertebrates, the roundworms, distributed universally in marine and fresh waters, soil, and in other organisms. Nematodes are not closely related to any other phylum. They are bilaterally symmetrical, with an unsegmented elongated cylindrical body, pointed at both ends and covered with a tough cuticle. The muscular and excretory systems and embryonic development are unusual. The phylum includes free-living nematodes such as *Anguillula* (vinegar eel) and parasites such as *Heterodera* (eelworm of potatoes) and *Ascaris* (in the intestines of pig and man). Some, such as *Wuchereria* (filaria) and *Dracunculus* (Guinea worm), cause serious diseases in man. *See also* Aschelminthes.

Nematomorpha. A small phylum of very long thin pseudocoelomate worms, the thread or hair worms. They have a reduced digestive system and the sexes are separate. The adults are free-living

in fresh water but the young are parasites of arthropods and have a protrusible spiny proboscis used to enter the host. *See also* Aschelminthes.

Nemertina (Nemertea, Rhynchocoela). A small phylum of acoelomate triploblastic mostly marine worms, the proboscis (or ribbon) worms. These unsegmented bilaterally symmetrical animals have a threadlike proboscis, used in defence and food capture, which can be everted rapidly by contraction of the surrounding fluid-filled cavity (*rhynchocoel*). There is a blood vascular system and the gut has a mouth and anus.

neo-Darwinism. *See* Darwinism.

Neogea. A zoogeographical region comprising the Neotropical region of Central and South America. *See* zoogeography.

Neogene. A collective name for the Miocene, Pliocene, and Pleistocene epochs of the *geological time scale.

Neognathae. The superorder of the Neornithes that contains most modern birds. They have been numerous since the Cretaceous and many orders have been known since the Eocene. The order Passeriformes (perching birds) contains about half the known bird species and includes the Oscines (songbirds). The feet of perching birds characteristically have four toes, of which the hallux has the longest claw and is directed backwards for perching.

neo-Lamarckism. *See* Lamarckism.

Neolithic. The New Stone Age of human history, which succeeded the *Palaeolithic about 10 000 years ago in Mesopotamia. It was characterized by advanced stone implements, following the invention of techniques of grinding and polishing to make very fine arrowheads, axes, knives, etc. Farming replaced hunting and gathering as a method of obtaining food, with the cultivation of cereals and the development of animal husbandry.

neomycin. An antibiotic, obtained from the bacterium *Streptomyces fradiae* and similar to *streptomycin, that acts by binding to bacterial ribosomes to cause misreading of the genetic code. It is used to treat intestinal bacterial infections and infectious dermatitis.

neopallium. An area of the *cerebral cortex of the vertebrate brain. It is highly developed in mammals, in which it is the dominant centre for all nervous activities.

Neopilina. See Monoplacophora.

neoplasm. See tumour.

Neornithes. The subclass of the Aves that contains the majority of extinct and living birds. Characteristics include a short tail with a fan of feathers, pneumatic bones, a reduced hand with fused bones, and powerful flight muscles attached to a large keeled sternum. Teeth are present only in a few extinct forms and the beak and feet are modified according to the way of life. There are four superorders: the extinct *Odontognathae, the *Palaeognathae (ratites), *Impennae (penguins), and *Neognathae (most modern birds). Compare Archaeornithes.

neoteny. The persistence in an animal of juvenile or larval features, or of the entire juvenile form, beyond the normal juvenile stage of development. It is thought that the evolution of some groups is due to neoteny; for example the Chordata are thought to be descended from neotenous echinoderm larvae, and man is thought to be a neotenous form of ape. Neoteny is also seen in certain ostriches bred for their plumes. Selected to retain their juvenile downy plumage, these birds also have juvenile characteristics of head and beak. See also paedogenesis.

Neotropical. (Designating) the region of South America and Central America as far north as Mexico. It forms the zoogeographical region of Neogea and sup-ports a very distinctive fauna. See zoogeography.

neotype. See holotype.

nephridium. An excretory organ of many invertebrates that consists of an ingrowth of ectoderm forming a simple or branched tube with an intracellular lumen and cilia at the inner end. Excretory products diffuse into the nephridium and are wafted to the exterior by ciliary action. The most primitive type of nephridium, the *protonephridium*, ends blindly in a *flame cell; it occurs in the Platyhelminthes and Rotifera. The *metanephridium* secondarily opens into the coelom by combining with a coelomoduct, so that the inner part of the tube is mesodermal; the internal opening is known as the *nephrostome* (or *nephridiostome*) and the external opening is the *nephridiopore*. Metanephridia are found, for example, in some annelids.

nephron. The unit of the vertebrate *kidney, comprising a *Malpighian body* – a knot of capillaries (*glomerulus*) enclosed in a cup-shaped structure (*Bowman's capsule*) – from which leads a *uriniferous tubule* surrounded by blood capillaries.

neritic. Designating or inhabiting sea between the low tide mark and the edge of the continental shelf, i.e. coastal waters, less than 200 metres deep. Compare oceanic.

nerve. A bundle of *nerve fibres and glia encased in a connective tissue sheath. A *mixed nerve* is one containing both sensory and motor nerve fibres. See also neurone, nervous system, cranial nerves, spinal nerves.

nerve cell. See neurone.

nerve cord. The thick longitudinal strand of nervous tissue that forms a prominent part of the *central nervous system. The invertebrate nerve cord is characteristically a double ventral strand connecting segmentally arranged ganglia, while that of vertebrates is single, hollow, and dorsal (*see* spinal cord).

nerve ending. The peripheral ending of a *neurone. The nerve ending of a sensory neurone is the site at which an environmental stimulus is transformed into an electrical signal; it is either a free nerve ending, i.e. a system of ramifying branches, or is associated with accessory structures (*see* receptor). The ending of a motor neurone is the site of transmission of information to an effector, e.g. an end plate on a muscle.

nerve fibre. The axon of a *neurone, together with its myelin sheath (if present). The nerve fibre is the relay unit of the nervous system and is specialized to conduct information accurately in the form of *impulses. The speed of conduction is increased in nerve fibres with a large diameter (*see* giant fibre) and in those with a myelin sheath.

nerve impulse. *See* impulse.

nerve net. A type of simple *nervous system found in the Coelenterata, Echinodermata, and Hemichordata. It consists of many similar neurones connected by fusion or two-way synapses in a diffuse network, so that a wave of excitation spreads radially around the stimulus. As a consequence of *summation and *facilitation at the synapses, the area excited increases with the stimulus strength. Conduction velocity is low, but rapid through-conducting pathways are often present.

nervous system. A network of cells that is present in all Metazoa and is specialized to form communication channels between the receptors, which sense the environment, and effectors, which produce responses to stimuli. Nervous tissue consists of *neurones, which receive, transmit, and pass on information, and supportive *glia. Information is propagated throughout the nervous system as a train of impulses travelling along the axons of neurones. It is the frequency of these impulses, rather than variations in their magnitude, that conveys the information. Between neurones – at the *synapse – the information is conveyed chemically.

Some synapses relay information without modification, so that an input stimulus evokes a fixed output (*see* reflex). However, most neurones make synaptic contact with many other neurones. Excitation at the synapses produces small graded electrical responses in the postsynaptic membrane (*excitatory or *inhibitory postsynaptic potential). In most neurones, one such response will not initiate an impulse and the eventual information relayed depends on the interaction of postsynaptic responses at different synapses on a neurone (*see* summation, facilitation, inhibition). The synapse is thus the primary site of decision-making in the nervous system, permitting an appropriate response to diverse stimuli to be selected. This enables flexible and complex behaviour to develop. Fixed rhythmical behaviour patterns are generated, without sensory input, by *pacemaker units in the nervous system. Synaptic mechanisms are also involved in more complex forms of behaviour, such as learning, in which information can be stored in a short- or long-term memory, retrieved, and used to modify existing behaviour patterns. The responses of the nervous system depend in part on its general level of excitability, which is influenced by the activity of hormones. The simplest type of nervous system, the *nerve net, contains all the elements and physiological properties found in more advanced systems. It is capable of some integrative activity, but its capabilities are limited by the restricted range of the receptors and the diffuse and localized nature of conduction through the net. More advanced nervous systems are characterized by an increase in the range and specificity of the information collected by the receptors, the development of distinct communication tracts (such as giant fibres), and the localization of synapses in *ganglia. These more advanced nervous systems have developed into two separate but interrelated parts: a *central nervous system, in which integration occurs, and a *peripheral nervous system, through which information is relayed. In most animals the most anterior ganglion, which is associated with the sense organs of the head, collects and interprets most of the sensory input to the nervous system and thus becomes dominant in controlling motor output patterns throughout the system. The dominant centre of the vertebrate nervous system, the brain, is the site of long-term memory and sophisticated learning processes.

neural arch. An arch of bone that arises dorsally from the centrum of a vertebra and encloses the spinal cord. In some vertebrae a median projection from the neural arch, the *neural spine*, is present; it usually serves as an attachment for muscles.

neural crest. A band of ectodermal cells on each side of the neural tube in vertebrate embryos that gives rise to the dorsal root ganglia of the spinal nerves, chromaffin tissue, chromatophores, and many other ectodermal structures.

neural plate (medullary plate). A flat dorsal region of ectoderm in vertebrate embryos that develops after gastrulation and gives rise to the central nervous system. *See* neural tube.

neural tube. A dorsal tube formed in vertebrate embryos after gastrulation by the joining together of the two edges of the neural plate (*neural folds*). The neural tube develops into the brain and spinal cord of adult vertebrates.

neuroblast. An embryonic cell that gives rise to nervous tissue in the adult.

neurocranium. The part of the skull protecting and supporting the brain and sensory organs. It consists of a complex of the chondrocranium and the overlying membrane bones. *Compare* splanchnocranium.

neuroendocrine systems. The neural and endocrine factors that together bring about the coordination or integration of most functions in animals. Processes not controlled by neuroendocrine systems include those with direct nervous stimulation, such as innervation of skeletal muscle, or those with no apparent neural control, such as the circulation of blood cells and calcium homeostasis.

Direct neural stimulation of endocrine secretion occurs in the neurohypophysis of the pituitary gland and in the adrenal medulla of mammals (and homologous tissues in other vertebrates). In other vertebrate systems, however, *neurosecretion* of chemical messengers (*see* neurohormone), particularly from the hypothalamus, brings about integration with more distant endocrine functions. Neurosecretion was first described in invertebrates as early as 1917, following Kopec's experiments on insects, and occurs diffusely from various regions of the brain. Probably all the endocrine secretions under neural control feed back at hypothalamic or other brain regions, where they, in their turn, modulate neural activity together with the sensory inputs to these regions.

neuroglia. *See* glia.

neurohormone. Any substance (often a peptide) that is released from specialized nerve cells (*neurosecretory neurones*) of animals and produces a specific effect at a distant site. Neurohormones are usually manufactured in the cell body and transported down the axon to the nerve ending, where they are released in response to impulses passing down the axon. They are usually transported to their target organs by the bloodstream, although some neurosecretory cells terminate in close proximity to the effector organ.

Following the pioneer work of G. W. Harris in the 1940s, it was established that the hypothalamus is the main region for producing and secreting neurohormones in mammals, birds, and possibly other vertebrates. Several small peptide neurohormones are transported in the blood to the pituitary gland and specifically control hormone synthesis and secretion from the pars distalis and pars intermedia. The first of these releasing (or inhibiting) factors or hormones to be isolated and characterized (in 1969) was a tripeptide, *thyrotrophin-releasing factor* (*TRF*). *Gonadotrophin-releasing factor*, isolated in 1971, was shown to be a decapeptide. Vasopressin and oxytocin are further neurohormones released from the hypothalamus; noradrenaline is secreted by chromaffin tissue in the adrenal medulla.

neurohumour. *See* neurotransmitter.

neurohypophysis. *See* pituitary gland.

neuromast. A sensory receptor of the *acoustico-lateralis system, which resembles the macula of the tetrapod inner ear but lacks an otolith.

neuromuscular junction. The *synapse between a motor neurone and a muscle cell membrane, which is similar in structure and mode of operation to the synapse between neurones. Except in vertebrate striated twitch muscle, *facilitation and *summation at the junction enable finely graded muscle contractions to be made. The area of muscle cell membrane below the nerve ending is called the *end plate*.

neurone (neuron, nerve cell). The principal cell type of the *nervous system, which is specialized for the transmission of information. All neurones have five main structural and functional regions. An expanded *cell body* (*perikaryon, soma*) contains the nucleus and is primarily concerned with the vegetative functions of the cell. The input region, where impinging energy elicits a graded nonconducted change in the membrane potential, is identified with the *nerve ending and its associated receptor structures in sensory neurones and with the *dendrites* – short branching processes arising from the cell body and making synaptic connections with incoming neurones – in other types of neurone. Most neurones bear one or more long unbranched processes: the *axons*. The proximal end of the axon is usually the site at which a self-propagated *impulse

is initiated, by a threshold depolarization produced by activity at the input region (*see also* nerve fibre). The axon forms the conductile region, relaying impulses over long distances. The axon terminals – small branches at the end of the axon – form the output region of the neurone, conveying information to other neurones and to effectors, generally by release of *neurotransmitter compounds from a presynaptic membrane. Neurones are arranged to form an integrated system of communication channels. *See also* nerve net, synapse.

neurone theory. The theory that the nervous system is composed of discrete cells (*neurones*), which do not physically join but become closely apposed at regions called *synapses, which are specialized for the transmission of information from cell to cell. The neurone theory superseded the *reticular hypothesis*, which claimed that a protoplasmic contact existed between nerve cells.

neuropil. A region of neurone axons and dendrites containing many synapses, found in parts of the vertebrate brain and in invertebrate ganglia.

Neuroptera. An order of endopterygote insects containing the lacewings (e.g. *Chrysopa*) and ant-lion flies (e.g. *Myrmeleon*). They are characterized by delicate fine-veined wings and biting mouthparts and are carnivorous, feeding on many insect pests. The larvae, too, are carnivorous and have suctorial mouthparts. Lacewing larvae feed on aphids while ant lions live in pits, feeding on the insects that become trapped there. The alder flies (*Megaloptera) are often included in this order.

neurosecretion. *See* neurohormone, neuroendocrine systems.

neurotransmitter (neurohumour, transmitter). A locally acting chemical compound that is secreted by a neurone and mediates the transmission of nervous excitation across a *synapse from one neurone to another or from a neurone to an effector. The neurotransmitter is manufactured in the cell body and stored in vesicles in the synaptic region. Compounds identified as transmitters include *acetylcholine (at some vertebrate and invertebrate peripheral synapses); adrenaline and *noradrenaline (at some vertebrate peripheral synapses); *dopamine (in the vertebrate brain); *GABA (gamma-aminobutyric acid), at crustacean inhibitory neuromuscular junctions; *serotonin (5-hydroxytryptamine), at synapses in the molluscan central nervous system; and *glycine (at inhibitory synapses in the vertebrate central nervous system).

neurula. The stage of a vertebrate embryo that succeeds the gastrula, when the *neural tube develops from the neural plate and marks the first appearance of the nervous system.

neuter. An organism that does not have sex organs but is otherwise normal. For example, flowers that do not have stamens or pistils and have been produced as ornamentals in cultivation are called neuters.

neutron scattering. A technique employing the emission of neutrons from high-flux neutron generators to determine ordered structure of biological materials containing two or more components. Since scattering-length density is dependent on the elements present in a compound, patterns of neutron scatter can yield useful information about the biological molecules or materials causing the scatter.

neutrophil. A polymorph having fine cytoplasmic granules that stain faintly with acidic or basic dyes. Neutrophils comprise 55–60% of the white cells of human blood. They exhibit amoeboid movement and are highly phagocytic, appearing in large numbers in blood during pyogenic (pus-forming) infections and migrating freely into the tissues during inflammation.

newts. See Urodela.

niacin. See nicotinic acid.

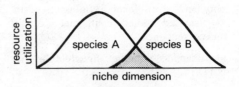

Ecological niches

niche. The sum of the abiotic and biotic components of the environment with which an organism reacts. For each resource, the biological activity of a species can be considered as a bell-shaped curve, whose height indicates the maximum level of activity or rate of resource utilization and whose breadth indicates the variety of resources used. Two such species curves show niche breadth, distance apart, and niche overlap (see illustration): the closer the niches of two species, the more likely it is that interspecific *competition will occur between them.

nicking. The production of single strand breaks in DNA. Some endonucleases nick DNA, and this has been widely exploited as a means of obtaining discrete DNA sequence lengths for sequencing or cloning.

nicking-closing enzyme. A DNA *polymerase involved in *DNA repair. It effects the introduction of a nick in the DNA chain next to an undesirable base, followed by excision of the unwanted base, insertion of an authentic base in its place, and closing of the nick by *DNA ligase action.

nick translation. A technique employed to produce radioactive *probe DNA from double-stranded DNA. The controlled use of DNA polymerase I results in the progressive translation (movement) of a nick (break), one nucleotide at a time, along a length of DNA; the enzyme also has the ability to replace the extruded nucleotides with a new polymer as it moves. If suitable radioactive nucleotides are available as the nick moves along, they will be inserted and polymerized to form a radioactive single-stranded molecule in place of the nicked sequence.

nicotinamide adenine dinucleotide. *See* NAD.

nicotinamide adenine dinucleotide phosphate (NADP). *See* NAD.

nicotinic acid (niacin). A vitamin of the B complex that is essential to man and other animals, who obtain it from such sources as milk, yeast, liver, etc. Deficiency of the vitamin in man results in the disease pellagra. Nicotinic acid is a constituent of the coenzymes NAD and NADP; it has the formula C_5H_4NCOOH (pyridine-3-carboxylic acid).

nictitating membrane. A transparent membrane forming a third eyelid, beneath the lower eyelid, in some amphibians, reptiles, birds, and a few mammals (including the cat). It can be drawn across the eyeball independently of the upper and lower eyelids.

nidation. *See* implantation.

nidicolous. Designating birds that hatch in a comparatively undeveloped state, being naked, blind, and helpless. They remain in the nest for some time and are cared for by the parent(s). *Compare* nidifugous.

nidifugous. Designating birds that hatch in a well-developed state so that they are soon able to leave the nest and fend for themselves. *Compare* nidicolous.

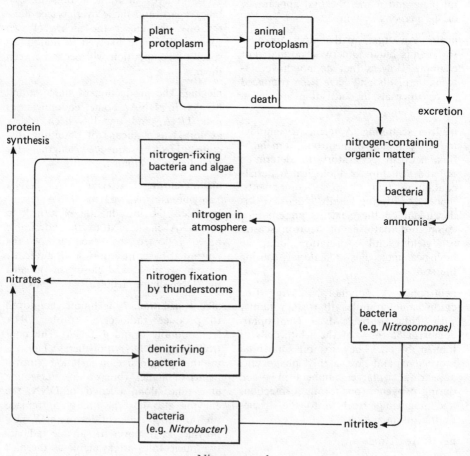

Nitrogen cycle

ninhydrin reaction. A biochemical and chromatographic test for the presence of proteins or amino acids. Ninhydrin (triketohydrindene hydrate) is heated with the test substance and produces a blue colour for a positive result.

nitrification. The process by which *nitrifying bacteria* in the soil convert complex organic compounds containing nitrogen into nitrates, which can be absorbed easily by plants. The process occurs in three stages: the decaying organic matter is converted to ammonia; this is oxidized to nitrites by *Nitrosomonas* bacteria, and the nitrites are converted to nitrates by *Nitrobacter* species.

nitrogen cycle. The circulation of nitrogen and its compounds in nature (see illustration). The cycle involves the activities of nitrifying bacteria (*see* nitrification), which convert organic nitrogenous compounds to nitrates, and nitrogen-fixing microorganisms (*see* nitrogen fixation), which convert free nitrogen to nitrates. Some of the nitrates are reduced to nitrites and nitrogen by the action of denitrifying bacteria (*denitrification*); the rest are utilized by plants in protein synthesis.

nitrogen fixation. The incorporation of gaseous nitrogen into compounds containing nitrogen. In nature this is brought about by some bacteria in the soil and some blue-green algae in the sea. The soil bacteria are either free-living or exist symbiotically in the root nodules of leguminous plants. Nitrifying bacteria bring about the conversion of the dead remains of these microorganisms and plants into nitrates, which can be utilized by plants (*see* nitrogen cycle). A small amount of nitrogen is fixed, as nitric oxide, by the action of thunderstorms in the atmosphere. Gaseous nitrogen is also fixed on a massive scale by industrial chemical processes for the production of nitrate fertilizers used in agriculture.

nm. *See* nanometre.

NMR spectroscopy (nuclear magnetic resonance spectroscopy). A technique used in chemistry and biochemistry to obtain useful absorption spectra for different compounds by induction of small changes in the resonant frequency of the atomic nuclei.

node. The part of a shoot axis to which one or more leaves are attached. In the apical meristem successive leaf primordia are very close together; they (together with their nodes) become separated by cell divisions below the leaf insertion, i.e. by intercalary growth. *Compare* internode.

node of Ranvier. A small region of exposed axon occurring between adjacent Schwann cells of medullated nerve fibres. *See* myelin sheath, saltatory conduction.

nondisjunction. The process of misdivision during meiosis that brings about *aneuploidy in a cell. During anaphase I of meiosis, when homologous chromosomes separate, both members of a bivalent migrate to the same pole instead of separating to opposite poles. Thus one of the daughter nuclei produced gains an extra chromosome and becomes a trisomic $(2n + 1)$ while the other loses a chromosome and becomes a monosomic $(2n - 1)$.

noradrenaline (norepinephrine). A neurotransmitter in the sympathetic nervous system and a neurohormone released from the adrenal medulla. Noradrenaline was first extracted from *adrenergic nerves (splenic nerves) and peripheral tissue (heart) by Von Euler, who concluded from its distribution and physiological activity that it was the transmitter of the sympathetic nervous system. Noradrenaline is present, together with adrenaline, in adrenal tissue and is partly responsible for the action of intravenously injected adrenal extracts in producing increased blood pressure. The excitatory effects of noradrenaline on the sympathetic nervous system include powerful vasoconstriction, in which vascular smooth muscle is the effector. Noradrenaline is widely distributed in sympathetically innervated effectors such as smooth muscle and glandular tissue. It is stored in synaptic vesicles in sympathetic nerve terminals and in chromaffin granules in the adrenal medulla. The release of noradrenaline from nervous tissue and its secretion from the adrenals are analogous, both processes being calcium-dependent and accompanied by the release of ATP and proteins. In the central nervous system, noradrenaline is localized in nerve terminals of the brain stem (as shown by fluorescent histochemistry), especially in the hypothalamus, where local application of noradrenaline inhibits the firing of certain neurones. This suggests that it is functioning here as an inhibitory transmitter.

norepinephrine. *See* noradrenaline.

nostrils. *See* nares.

Nothosauria. An extinct suborder of the Sauropterygia containing small marine amphibious Triassic reptiles, e.g. *Nothosaurus*. They had an elongated body with a long flexible neck, long jaws with numerous sharp teeth, and paddle-like limbs.

notochord. A flexible rod that extends along the entire length of the body of adult and/or embryo members of the Chordata, lying dorsal to the gut and ventral to the nerve cord. It strengthens and supports the body and acts as a protagonist for the swimming muscles of aquatic chordates. It is made up of disc-like vacuolated cells whose turgor pressure acts against the resistance of the surrounding connective tissue sheath, giving the notochord its stiffening and elastic properties. In the development of vertebrates the notochord is partly or wholly replaced by the vertebral column.

Notogea. A zoogeographical region consisting of the continents and islands of the *Australasian region; it has a very distinctive fauna. Notogea is subdivided

by some authorities into the Australian, Polynesian, and Hawaiian regions. *See* zoogeography.

Notoungulata. An extinct order of the Eutheria, in existence from the Palaeocene to the Pleistocene, containing early ungulates (hoofed herbivorous mammals) confined mainly to South America. The group included the small rodent-like typotheres and hegetotheres, e.g. *Pachyrukhos*, as well as the larger toxodonts, such as *Toxodon*.

nucellus. The tissue within an *ovule that is equivalent to the megasporangium (and is thus part of the sporophyte parent). A single cell of the nucellus becomes the megasporocyte while the rest acts as a nutritive tissue for the developing megaspore. In the seeds of some plants, e.g. *Beta vulgaris* (beetroot), the nucellus may be retained to form a food store, the *perisperm*, for the developing embryo.

nuclear magnetic resonance spectroscopy. *See* NMR spectroscopy.

nuclear pore. *See* pore complex.

nucleic acid. Either of two complex organic acids, *DNA or *RNA, made up of *nucleotide units in the form of long chains (i.e. polynucleotide chains). Nucleic acids occur in the cells of all organisms, usually in combination with a protein (*see* nucleoprotein).

nucleic acid hybridization. The technique of associating two complementary nucleic acid sequences *in vitro* (*see* denaturation). Such association, by the formation of hydrogen bonds between complementary bases, may be between DNA and either DNA or RNA. *See also* recombinant DNA, *in situ* hybridization.

nucleoid. The DNA-containing area of a prokaryote cell, analogous to the eukaryote nucleus but not membrane bounded.

nucleolus. A small body one or more of which occur in the interphase nucleus of most eukaryote cells. The function of the nucleolus is ribosome manufacture; it contains protein, DNA, and much of the nuclear RNA, the latter making it strongly basophilic. Two zones are visible: a peripheral zone containing granules resembling ribosomes and a central region containing a dense convoluted fibrillar material (the *nucleolonema*) interspersed with areas of looser fibrils. This central region contains the so-called nucleolar organizing region of the chromosome, comprising the chromatin of the repeated genes for 18 and 28S ribosomal RNA. In some organisms, in which such genes are concentrated in one region of the haploid chromosome set, only two nucleoli are present in each diploid cell. In organisms in which more than one such cluster of repeated genes exists in the haploid state, four or more nucleoli may occur. *Gene amplification of the ribosomal genes during vertebrate early development explains the temporary presence of large numbers of nucleoli in some of these cells.

nucleoprotein. A compound consisting of a nucleic acid (DNA or RNA) combined with a protein. In eukaryotic cells DNA in the nucleus is associated with histones and protamines; RNA in the cytoplasm is associated with protein in the form of the ribosomes. Viruses may be entirely nucleoprotein, consisting of DNA or RNA surrounded by a protein or lipoprotein coat.

nucleoside. A molecule consisting of D-ribose or deoxyribose linked to a purine or pyrimidine base; it is formed by the partial hydrolysis of a nucleotide. Common nucleosides are *adenosine, *guanosine, *cytidine, *thymidine, and *uridine.

nucleosome. The basic unit of chromatin structure in eukaryotic cells. A nucleosome consists of eight *histone molecules of four different types, together with about 140 base pairs of DNA coiled around it. Nucleosomes are arranged at intervals along a length of DNA, approximately one nucleosome per 200 base pairs, and evidence suggests that they are present both on active and inactive chromatin. A fifth type of histone, H1, links neighbouring nucleosomes together. Chromatin consists of stacks of nucleosomes, each stack resembling a solenoid.

nucleotide. A compound consisting of a pentose sugar, phosphoric acid, and a nitrogenous base. Nucleic acids (*see* DNA, RNA) consist of many nucleotides linked covalently to form a *polynucleotide* chain; the base is either a pyrimidine (cytosine, thymine, or uracil) or a purine (adenine or guanine) and the sugar is D-ribose (for RNA) or deoxyribose (for DNA). Two nucleotides can be linked through their phosphate groups to form a *dinucleotide*; two important dinucleotides are the coenzymes *NAD and *FAD. Nucleotides can also occur free in the cell; examples of *mononucleotides* are *AMP and *coenzyme A.

nucleus. 1. The organelle of the eukaryote cell that contains the *chromosomes and hence ultimately controls cellular activity and inheritance through the activity of the genetic material, DNA. It is conspicuously large in most cells, commonly up to 20 μm long and usually spherical to ovoid in shape. It is surrounded by two membranes, forming the *nuclear envelope*; the outer membrane is continuous with the endoplasmic reticulum. The envelope is perforated by complex *nuclear pores*, 40–100 nm in diameter, which control exchange between nucleus and cytoplasm (*see* pore complex). The interphase nucleus contains *chromatin (which condenses during nuclear division into chromosomes), and one or more *nucleoli, in which ribosomes are manufactured, all within a ground substance called the *nucleoplasm* (or *nuclear sap*). True nuclei are absent from prokaryotes (bacteria and blue-green algae). Red blood corpuscles of mammals and sieve-tube elements of higher plants are virtually unique in losing their nuclei as they mature. In ciliates and some other Protozoa two types of nuclei, a *micronucleus* and a *macronucleus* (or *meganucleus*), exist. Cells with a macronucleus normally also possess one or more micronuclei. The macronucleus contains nucleoli and most of the DNA and is polyploid. It controls normal cell metabolism, i.e. the vegetative functions of the cell, and divides amitotically. The micronucleus divides by mitosis and functions in sexual reproduction (*see* conjugation). **2**. An anatomically distinct mass of nerve cell bodies in the vertebrate brain. The nuclei resemble, and are often alternatively termed, *ganglia*.

nullisomy. The condition in which both members of one pair of homologous chromosomes are absent, so that the chromosome complement is $2n - 2$, where n is the haploid number. *See also* aneuploidy.

numerical response. The relationship between the numbers or fecundity of a population of predators or *parasitoids and the density of their prey or hosts. Like *functional response, it may reveal density dependence.

nunatak. A mountain or plateau *refugium.

nut. A dry indehiscent *fruit formed from an inferior ovary.

nutation. An *autonomic growth movement of plants in which the growing stem undergoes slight circular movements. It is particularly pronounced in young climbers and helps them to entwine supports.

nutritional requirements. Essential minimal requirements for the growth and maintenance of an organism. *Macronutrients, elements required in relatively large amounts, include carbon, hydrogen, oxygen, etc.; *micronutrients, substances required in minute amounts, include trace elements and (for most animals and some microorganisms) vitamins. Plants use only carbon dioxide, water, and various inorganic salts as a source of these nutrients. Animals and some microorganisms, however, must ingest organic compounds, derived from plants or other animals, as a source of carbon for energy production, essential amino acids, and vitamins.

nyctinastic movements (nyctinasty, sleep movements). *Nastic movements in response to daily changes of light and/or temperature: the familiar opening and closing responses of certain leaves and flowers. Closing may be from a horizontal to a vertical or drooping position. In flowers it is caused by more rapid growth of the lower sides of petals (*hyponasty*) in the former case and of the upper sides (*epinasty*) in the latter case; in leaves and leaflets it is usually caused by turgor changes of special cells (*pulvini*). Auxins probably control both types of response. Closing usually occurs at night, as with marigold, dandelion, and crocus flowers and *Oxalis* leaves. Opposite movements occur during the day. Some flowers open in the evening, e.g. evening primrose; these are mostly pollinated by night moths. Response to light intensity is *photonasty* (or *photonastic movements*); response to temperature is *thermonasty* (or *thermonastic movements*). Some plant parts, such as crocus petals, exhibit both responses.

nymph. The immature form of exopterygote insects. It resembles the adult in structure except that the wings and reproductive organs are not developed. The wings appear as buds and increase in size with each instar.

O

obtect. *See* pupa.

occipital condyle. A curved surface on the occiput of the tetrapod skull, articulating with the atlas vertebra in such a way as to permit nodding of the head. Reptiles and birds have one condyle, amphibians and mammals two.

occiput. 1. The region of the vertebrate skull around its articulation with the vertebral column.
2. A skeletal plate in insects at the back of the head.

oceanic. Designating or inhabiting the region of the sea beyond the continental shelf, where it is deeper than 200 metres. *Compare* neritic.

ocellus. A simple eye, present in insects and some other invertebrates, that is not capable of forming an image. It typically consists of a small group of photoreceptive cells with few or no accessory structures.

oculomotor nerve. *See* cranial nerves.

Odonata. An order of exopterygote insects containing the dragonflies, in existence since Permian times; some fossil members had a wingspan of 70 cm. These brightly coloured predaceous insects are characterized by a long thin abdomen, two pairs of equally sized elongated wings, very large compound eyes, and reduced antennae. The aquatic nymphs are also carnivorous. The Anisoptera (dragonflies) are strong agile fliers that spread their wings flat at rest. The Zygoptera (damselflies) are smaller and have a fluttering flight, folding their wings over the abdomen when resting.

odontoblast. One of a series of cells that lie along the periphery of the pulp cavity of a tooth, typified by their long cytoplasmic processes (*fibres of Tomes*), which extend into the canals of the surrounding dentine. They are thought to be involved in the formation and nutrition of dentine although the latter does not become necrotic when the odontoblasts are destroyed.

Odontognathae. An extinct superorder of the Neornithes containing two genera of aquatic birds of the Upper Cretaceous. *Ichthyornis* resembled a gull and the larger *Hesperornis* had numerous teeth,

greatly reduced wings, and strong hind limbs used for swimming.

odontoid peg. A projection on the *axis vertebra.

oesophagus. The anterior region of the alimentary canal, primarily a passage by which food passes from the mouth to the digestive regions. In vertebrates it runs from the pharynx to the stomach and transports food, moistened by mucus secreted by the walls, by peristalsis. In birds and some insects it may contain a distended storage region, the *crop.

Oestradiol-17β

oestradiol-17β. The main natural *oestrogen produced and secreted by mammals (see formula). It was first extracted from pig ovaries in 1935 and was later also isolated from cow placental extracts.

Oestriol

oestriol. An *oestrogen isolated in 1930 from the urine of pregnant women (see formula). It is an excretion product of the ovary, but is probably also produced by the placenta.

oestrogen. Any of a group of 18C (carbon) steroid hormones produced from acetate and cholesterol, chiefly by the ovaries and placenta but also by the testes and adrenal cortex in all vertebrates. They are also produced by many species of plants. Oestrogens have metabolic effects on many animal tissues but their best-known action is in female mammals, in which they stimulate the growth and maintenance of the reproductive organs (especially the uterus and vagina) and also of the female secondary sexual characteristics. Oestrogens also affect reproductive function and behaviour by actions on the hypothalamus and other regions of the central nervous system (*see* oestrous cycle). The secretion of oestrogen from mature Graafian follicles is regulated by the pituitary gonadotrophins. Oestrogens have been shown to regulate the expression of genes in target tissues such as the uterus and brain by stimulating the synthesis of specific messenger RNA and protein in these organs: cytoplasmic and nuclear hormone receptors have been isolated. The predominant natural mammalian oestrogens are *oestradiol-17β and *oestrone. Many other oestrogenic substances found in the blood and urine are thought to be metabolites (e.g. *oestriol) produced from the main hormones, although they may also have physiological significance. A number of potent synthetic oestrogens that are not steroids are used therapeutically.

Oestrone

oestrone. The first *oestrogen to be identified (see formula). It was isolated in crystalline form from the urine of pregnant women in 1929 and was later shown to be produced by the ovaries.

oestrous cycle. The reproductive cycle that occurs, either continuously or only during the breeding season, in sexually mature female mammals in the absence of pregnancy. Its length varies in different species from four to sixty days. The process is centrally regulated by the hypothalamus, which periodically releases factors that stimulate the secretion of pituitary gonadotrophins. These, in turn, promote oestrogen and progesterone production, and the gonadal hormones themselves act as a feedback to modulate activity in the central nervous system. The following phases of the cycle generally occur:

(1) *oestrus* (*follicular phase*): the period of heat, during which copulation is permitted. In the ovary Graafian follicles mature and oestrogen secretion is at its highest; the endometrium (lining of the uterus) proliferates. *Ovulation occurs towards the end of this phase (it may be spontaneous, as in the rat, or activated by mating reflexes, as in the rabbit) and is probably triggered by a sharp rise in luteinizing hormone secretion.

(2) *metoestrus* (*luteal phase*): the period shortly after ovulation when mating is no longer permitted. The corpus luteum develops in the ovary and progesterone secretion increases, while the secretion of oestrogen decreases.

(3) *dioestrus*: the beginning of the regression of the corpus luteum and uterine lining as well as the start of new follicular growth. Progesterone secretion diminishes. In some mammals this phase is lengthened if pregnancy does not follow mating and is termed *pseudopregnancy*.

(4) *pro-oestrus*: the involution of the corpora lutea, coupled with the appearance of Graafian follicles, and a decrease in gonadal hormone secretion. It is followed by a slow increase in the secretion of follicle-stimulating hormone and oestrogen in preparation for the next oestrus.

If fertilization occurs following oestrus, the cycle becomes suspended in the luteal phase for the duration of pregnancy. Since the hormonal fluctuations during the cycle cause corresponding histological changes in the epithelium of the vagina, vaginal smears or scrapings of the vaginal wall can be examined under a microscope to determine the phase of the cycle.

oestrus. *See* oestrous cycle.

offset. *See* stolon.

oidium (arthrospore). An asexual spore produced by the fragmentation into individual cells of a fungal hypha, the latter often being modified to form short branches termed *oidiophores*.

Okazaki fragment. A short sequence of DNA that is the primary product of DNA polymerase during DNA *replication. Okazaki fragments, of some 1000 to 2000 bases, are joined together by DNA ligase to yield a continuous new strand. Since synthesis can only proceed from a template strand going from the 3′ end towards the 5′ end, synthesis of short fragments is inevitable using one of the parent strands as template. Although DNA replication could proceed continuously on the other strand, it also seems to be replicated initially as Okazaki fragments.

olecranon process. A projection of the ulna at the elbow joint, to which is attached the main extensor muscle of the tetrapod forelimb.

oleic acid. *See* fatty acid.

olfactory nerve. *See* cranial nerves.

olfactory organs. The organs of smell. In vertebrates a pair of olfactory organs is situated in the *nasal cavity, communicating with the exterior via the external nares. The organs themselves consist of areas of sensory epithelium containing numerous bipolar cells, which respond to chemicals from the environment dissolved in mucus secreted by the epithelium of the nasal cavity. In invertebrates olfactory receptors occur in various positions, e.g. on the antennae in insects.

Oligocene. An epoch of the *Tertiary period.

Oligochaeta. The class of the Annelida containing the terrestrial earthworms (e.g. *Lumbricus*) and freshwater forms (e.g. *Tubifex*). As an adaptation to burrowing, the body lacks parapodia and head appendages and bears only a few chaetae. Oligochaetes are hermaphrodite and their development is direct, with no larval stage. The eggs develop within a cocoon, produced by the *clitellum.

oligopeptide. *See* peptide.

oligotrophic. Designating a lake or river with a low concentration of nutrient salts and therefore low productivity. Oligotrophic lakes are deep and relatively young, with narrow littoral and sublittoral zones and a large population of fish. *Compare* eutrophic.

omasum (psalterium). The third chamber of the stomach of ruminants. *See* Ruminantia.

ommatidium. The unit of which the arthropod *compound eye is composed. Each ommatidium contains a lens, visual pigment, and a sensory axon.

omnivore. An animal that feeds on both plant and animal material. *Compare* carnivore, herbivore.

onchosphere (hexacanth). The embryo of tapeworms (*see* Cestoda). In some genera, e.g. *Taenia*, it has six hooks used to bore through the gut wall of the intermediate host. It is then carried in the bloodstream to the tissues, usually muscle, where it develops into a *cysticercus.

oncogenic virus. A virus associated with cancer (because of the difficulty of establishing absolute causal relationships in biology, it is best not to regard these viruses as representing the cause of the disease). Both DNA and RNA viruses may be oncogenic, including some papovaviruses, adenoviruses, and leukoviruses. The *Rous sarcoma of chickens and feline leukaemia are diseases in which viral causation is particularly likely. Many oncogenic viruses are capable of inducing cell *transformation *in vitro*.

one gene–one enzyme hypothesis. The hypothesis that each gene is concerned with the synthesis of a single enzyme. However, since genes also determine the structure of all nonenzymic proteins, and many enzymes and other proteins are polymeric structures in which each monomer is coded by a separate gene, the concept is better expressed as the *one gene–one polypeptide chain hypothesis*.

ontogeny. The development of an individual during its lifetime. *Compare* phylogeny. *See* recapitulation.

Onychophora. A small phylum of invertebrates having some annelid and some arthropod characteristics, sometimes classified as a class of the Arthropoda. The single genus, *Peripatus*, lives mainly in tropical forests and has an elongated body bearing short unjointed segmentally arranged clawed legs and covered with a thin soft cuticle. The body cavity is a haemocoel and respiration is carried out by tracheae.

oocyte. An egg cell of the animal ovary that undergoes meiosis to form an ovum. After a period of growth, the *primary oocyte* undergoes the first division to form a *polar body* (or *polocyte*), a cell with very little cytoplasm, and a *secondary oocyte*, a cell with a large amount of cytoplasm that undergoes the second division to form a further polar body and an ovum. In many species one of the two oocyte stages is released at ovulation and fertilization occurs without the formation of an ovum. *Compare* spermatocyte.

oogamy. The sexual fusion of two dissimilar gametes. The male gamete is small, often motile, and has little food reserve; the female is larger, sedentary, and contains food reserves for the developing zygote.

oogenesis. The formation of ova from precursor cells (*see* oocyte).

oogonium. 1. The simple female sexual organ of many algae and fungi, containing one to many oospheres.
2. A cell of the animal ovary that divides to produce oocytes.

oosphere (ovum, egg cell). A naked spherical sedentary haploid female gamete in plants, generally containing some food reserve. The term is sometimes restricted to a female gamete developed within an oogonium.

oospore. A fertilized oosphere that develops into a thick-walled resting spore.

operculum. 1. A fold of tissue that covers the gill slits of the Holocephali and Osteichthyes. It arises from the hyoid arch and in the Osteichthyes it is stiffened with plates of membrane bone.
2. A horny disc on the base of the foot of terrestrial gastropod molluscs. It acts as a protective door when the animal retires into its shell.
3. The disc- or dome-shaped lid of a sporangium, ascus, or bryophyte capsule, which opens at maturity to allow dehiscence of the spores.

operon. A group of closely linked genes that behave as a unit in determining the synthesis of the enzymes of a particular catabolic or biosynthetic pathway. It consists of an *operator gene* and one or more *structural genes* and its expression is controlled by a *regulator gene*, which is not part of the operon. The operator gene acts as an on/off switch controlling the transcription of the messenger RNA for the synthesis of all the proteins determined by the structural genes. The regulator gene produces a protein, the *repressor*, which can bind specifically to the DNA of the operator locus and prevent the synthesis of the messenger RNA.

Ophiuroidea. The largest class of the Echinodermata, containing the brittle stars (e.g. *Ophiothrix*). The body, which is covered with articulating skeletal plates, consists of a small central disc from which long fragile radiating arms are sharply delimited. The mouth is on the ventral surface. Locomotion is effected by the arms, the tube feet being used only for feeding.

Opiliones (Phalangida). The order of the Arachnida that contains the harvestmen (e.g. *Phalangium*), in which the cephalothorax and abdomen are broadly joined, forming a small globular body, and the legs are very long and thin. The second pair of legs, which are often the longest, are sensory and the chelicerae are pincer-like.

opsin. *See* rhodopsin.

opsonin. An antibody, present in blood serum, that reacts with the surface antigens of bacteria to promote phagocytosis. *Opsonic adherence*, which involves binding through complement components, is one of the most important defence mechanisms against infection.

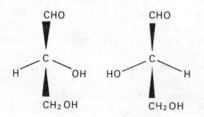

L-glyceraldehyde   D-glyceraldehyde

Enantiomers of glyceraldehyde

optical activity. The property of a molecule that causes rotation of the plane of polarization of polarized light when it is passed through a solution of the compound. Compounds, such as the *monosaccharides, that possess one or more asymmetric carbon atoms (i.e. a carbon atom to which four different atoms or groups of atoms are attached) can exist in two different configurations (*enantiomers*) about the asymmetric carbon atom, one configuration being the mirror image of the other. One enantiomer rotates the beam of polarized light to the left (*laevorotatory* or L-) and the other rotates the light to the right (*dextrorotatory* or D-). For example, glyceraldehyde may have either of the forms shown in the illustration.

optic chiasma. The point of cross-over of the *optic nerve.

optic nerve. The second *cranial nerve of vertebrates, passing from the retina to the brain, of which it is embryologically a part. Primitively, the fibres from the left eye cross over to the right side of the brain (and vice versa) at the *optic chiasma*. In species with *binocular vision the cross-over is incomplete, as fibres from those areas of both retinae that view the same objects go to the same side of the brain.

orbit. The cavity in the vertebrate skull housing the eyeball. It is part of the chondrocranium.

order. A unit used in the *classification of plants and animals. An order consists of a number of similar or closely related families or only one family. Names of orders end typically in -*ales* in plants and in -*a* in animals. Orders are grouped into classes.

Ordovician. The second period of the Palaeozoic era, extending from 500 to 440 million years ago. It was named after a Celtic tribe that lived in the region of Wales where rocks of the period were first recognized. Ordovician fossils consist mainly of trilobites and brachiopods, but there are also gastropods, nautiloid cephalopods, and many echinoderms (including crinoids and some echinoids). *See also* geological time scale.

organ. A part of the body of an organism that forms a structural and functional unit and is composed of more than one tissue. An example of a plant organ is a leaf; animal organs include the heart and liver.

organ culture. The growth of organs, usually embryonic organs, *in vitro*. *See* tissue culture.

organelle. A functionally and structurally discrete part of a living cell, often bounded by a membrane; i.e. an organ of the cell. The metabolism of a cell is apportioned between various organelles and the cytoplasm in which they lie. Examples of organelles are the nucleus, mitochondria, plastids, ribosomes, and endoplasmic reticulum.

organizer. A region of cells in an animal embryo that, by the release of an evocator (*see* evocation), can induce and direct cellular differentiation in another region. For example, if the dorsal lip of the amphibian blastopore (which itself develops into the notochord and somites) is transplanted into a region of prospective epidermis, it will induce prospective epidermal tissue to form a neural tube.

organotrophic. *See* heterotrophic.

Oriental. (Designating) a region of *Arctogea consisting of India and Indochina as far south as Wallace's line.

origin of life. Most modern organisms are dependent, directly or indirectly, on two closely linked metabolic processes: photosynthesis and aerobic respiration. Although opinions differ as to what steps were involved in their evolution, it seems likely that photosynthesis evolved in the first third of the earth's history and aerobic respiration in the last half. Evidence from *chemical fossils, morphological remains of microorganisms, and geochemistry regarding conditions present during rock formation suggests that six main stages of evolution are involved.

(1) *abiogenic production of organic compounds.* The earliest atmosphere probably consisted of ammonia, methane, hydrogen, and water vapour. Such a mixture has been shown to produce many of the organic compounds utilized by living organisms when energy in the form of an electric discharge, ultraviolet radiation, or sunlight is passed through it. These compounds include all the amino acids, some proteins, porphyrins and vitamins, and the precursors of nucleotides. The process of self-replication using DNA or RNA as a coding device for proteins is chemically extremely complex and a satisfactory theory of its evolution has not yet been suggested. However, a compartmentalizing of such self-replicating systems within a membrane-bound unit would have resulted in the first primitive organisms.

(2) *anaerobic heterotrophy.* The first true organisms probably obtained energy by the partial oxidation of organic substances of nonbiotic origin. They evolved into organisms that used gaseous hydrogen for the reduction of carbon dioxide in the atmosphere to produce their carbohydrates, which they could then use as an energy source by partial oxidation.

(3) *anaerobic photoheterotrophy.* The first primitive type of photosynthetic system arose when anaerobic heterotrophs started using the light-absorbing porphyrins present in their cytoplasm for trapping light energy, as well as partially oxidizing hydrocarbons formed chemically.

(4) *anaerobic phototrophy.* Anaerobic photoheterotrophy was followed by the evolution of anaerobic organisms whose only method of organic molecule synthesis depended on light energy.

(5) *lysis of water.* The first oxygen in the atmosphere was produced by the photolysis of water. An important step in photosynthesis evolution occurred when organisms started dissociating water for themselves to yield hydrogen (the importance being that elemental oxygen was released into the atmosphere).

(6) *oxygenation of carbon compounds.* The final important stage occurred with the evolution of organisms capable of using oxygen to oxidize carbohydrates and yield much more energy than primitive fermentation processes.

An approximate time scale for these developments is indicated by the geological formations Banded Iron Formations and Red Beds. The former were laid down $3.4-1.8 \times 10^9$ years ago under

reducing conditions (stages 1–3). The Red Beds have been laid down since 1.8 × 10⁹ years ago in the presence of free oxygen, indicating that oxygen was present in the atmosphere and no longer toxic and that some organisms may have evolved the extra enzyme systems necessary for aerobic respiration (stages 4–5). Following oxygen evolution three levels of concentration in the atmosphere have been suggested as critical for the evolution of higher life forms:
(1) *1% PAL* (present atmospheric level): allowed a completely modern type of metabolic system to function (probably around 6 × 10⁸ years ago, corresponding with the sudden blossoming of forms in the Cambrian).
(2) *10% PAL*: provided enough oxygen in the atmosphere to shield the land against short-wave ultraviolet radiation (prior to this organisms needed the protection of water). This led to the invasion of the land by plants and thus to (a) the establishment of vegetation (providing possible habitats for the later invasion of the land by animals); and (b) increased oxygen production (probably occurring about 4 × 10⁸ years ago – the Devonian expansion).
(3) *20% PAL*: allowed land animals to emerge (about 3.4 × 10⁸ years ago, corresponding with the appearance of the amphibians at the end of the Devonian).

ornithine. A basic amino acid, $H_2N(CH_2)_5CH(NH_2)COOH$, that functions as an intermediate in the *urea cycle and as a precursor of pyrroline alkaloids (e.g. nicotine).

ornithine cycle (urea cycle). *See* urea.

Ornithischia. An extinct order of reptiles of the subclass Archosauria containing dinosaurs of the Jurassic and Cretaceous, characterized by a quadriradiate (i.e. birdlike) pelvic girdle. All ornithischians were herbivorous and most were quadrupedal, e.g. *Stegosaurus*, which had two rows of triangular bony plates down the back and bony spikes on the tail, and *Triceratops*, in which the head bore three large horns. Some forms, e.g. *Igua-*

nodon, could become bipedal for speed. *Compare* Saurischia.

orthoamphitropous (amphitropous). *See* ovule.

orthocampylotropous (campylotropous). *See* ovule.

orthogenesis. The theory that evolution can occur in a definite direction, which is predetermined by inherent factors in the genotype and does not rely on natural selection or genetic drift.

Orthoptera. A large order of exopterygote insects containing the grasshoppers, locusts, and crickets. They are characterized by enlarged hind legs modified for jumping and biting mouthparts. The Ensifera (crickets and long-horned grasshoppers, e.g. *Gryllus*, *Tettigonia*) have long threadlike antennae and stridulate by rubbing together modified veins on their forewings. The hearing organs are on the front legs. The Caelifera (short-horned grasshoppers and locusts, e.g. *Chorthippus*, *Locusta*) have short antennae and stridulate by rubbing pegs on the hind leg against a hardened vein on the forewing. The hearing organs are on the abdomen.

orthostichy. The vertical series formed by certain leaves that occur exactly above each other. It is seen in plants in which the phyllotaxis is not spiral.

orthotropic. *See* tropism.

orthotropous (atropous). *See* ovule.

osculum. The large opening in the body of sponges (*see* Porifera) through which water, which has entered via the numerous tiny inhalent pores (*ostia*), leaves. There may be one or several oscula.

osmiophilic globules. *See* plastoglobuli.

osmium tetroxide. A substance used in aqueous solution as a biochemical test for fat, which it causes to turn black. It is also used as a fixative in light and electron microscopy. Osmium tetroxide is sometimes erroneously called *osmic acid*.

osmoregulation. The means by which animals maintain the concentration of water, salts, and ions in their bodies at the correct level.

Freshwater animals, whose body fluids are hypertonic to the surrounding water, have various adaptations to prevent or counteract the inward diffusion of water. For example, freshwater protozoans have a *contractile vacuole; in other animals nephridia, Malpighian tubules, or kidneys excrete the surplus water that accumulates in the body. The kidneys of freshwater fish have well-developed glomeruli and their principal function is to eliminate water and reabsorb salts rather than to excrete nitrogenous waste (this occurs chiefly via the gills).

Marine animals, on the other hand, must conserve water and eliminate salts. The outer body surface is relatively impermeable; for example the epidermal glands of fish secrete a thick layer of mucus covering the body. The kidneys of marine vertebrates contain few glomeruli and relatively short tubules, which reduces water excretion and restricts the reabsorption of salts.

Terrestrial animals avoid the dangers of desiccation by having a relatively impermeable cuticle, skin, or similar body covering. The kidneys of mammals and birds are characterized by uriniferous tubules that are elongated by the formation of a U-shaped portion (*loop of Henle*) between the distal and proximal regions, which increases the efficiency of salt and water reabsorption.

osmosis. The passage of solvent molecules from a less concentrated to a more concentrated solution through a semipermeable membrane (a membrane that allows passage of solvent, but not solute, molecules). In living organisms the solvent is water and the distribution of water is largely dependent on osmosis. Water enters cells through their plasma membranes. The latter are not true semipermeable membranes since they also selectively admit certain solutes; they are therefore called *selectively* (or *differentially*) *permeable membranes*. In plant cells a second differentially permeable membrane, the *tonoplast, often surrounds a large central vacuole whose contents determine the osmotic properties of the cell. Osmosis into cells (*endosmosis*) or out of cells (*exosmosis*) is determined by the relative osmotic pressures of the internal and external solutions (or, more strictly, the relative *water potentials), water moving from low to high osmotic pressures. *Osmotic pressure* (*OP* or Π) is the maximum pressure that could develop if the solution were separated from pure water by a rigid semipermeable membrane. It is seldom achieved under natural conditions and is therefore often called *osmotic potential*. Osmotic pressure increases as the concentration of solutes (e.g. sugars, salts) increases; it is related to the number of molecules or ions in a given volume rather than to their nature.

ossification. The replacement of embryonic or adult connective tissue by *bone. Ossification that occurs by replacement of cartilage is termed *endochondral (intracartilaginous) ossification* (*see* cartilage bone), in contrast with simple *intramembranous ossification* (*see* membrane bone). The process requires the presence of vitamins A and D and growth hormone. It is characterized by the invasion of connective tissue by *osteoblasts, which deposit successive layers of bone and eventually become trapped in the bone matrix as *osteocytes. During early growth, bones are continually remodelled by resorption of existing bony tissues (a process associated with *osteoclasts) and by the laying down of new bone.

Osteichthyes. The class of vertebrates containing the bony fishes, characterized by an endoskeleton of bone. They have evolved from freshwater Devonian types to become the dominant fishes, invading all types of waters. Primitively, the body was completely encased in heavy bony scales, but in modern forms both the scales and endoskeleton are reduced for lightness. The single external gill opening is covered by an *operculum, and in modern forms the spiracle is greatly reduced or absent. *See* Choanichthyes, Actinopterygii. *Compare* Chondrichthyes.

osteoblast. Any of the bone cells, found in growing bones, that are responsible for bone deposition. They are derived from a connective tissue layer beneath the periosteum. Osteoblast cytoplasm is intensely basophilic, owing to the high RNA content, and stains strongly for alkaline phosphatase during growth. It also contains carbohydrate granules, extensive rough endoplasmic reticulum, and a well-developed Golgi apparatus. *See* ossification.

osteoclast. Any of the multinucleate cells of bone found predominantly in areas of bone resorption, in which they are assumed to play a role. They are derived from osteoblasts and osteocytes and contain a slightly basophilic cytoplasm rich in acid phosphatase. *See* ossification.

osteocyte. Any of the principal cells of fully formed bone, found within the bone matrix and derived from osteoblasts. They are thought to participate in the release of calcium from the bone into the blood.

Osteostraci (Cephalaspida). An extinct order of the Agnatha, common in the late Silurian and early Devonian. They were small fishlike vertebrates, e.g. *Cephalaspis*, with the head covered by a strong flattened bony shield and the body by bony plates. *Compare* Cyclostomata.

ostiole. The aperture to a fruiting body such as an ascocarp or pycnidium, through which the spores escape. It often occurs at the tip of a neck lined with paraphyses.

ostium. 1. One of many tiny apertures in the body wall of sponges (*see* Porifera) through which water, bringing food and oxygen, enters.

2. One of the small apertures in the arthropod heart, through which the blood enters.

Ostracoda. A subclass of small marine and freshwater Crustacea, e.g. *Cypris,* in which the body is completely enclosed in a hinged bivalved carapace. The head is well developed and the abdomen reduced. The second antennae protrude from the carapace and, in some forms, serve in swimming, but most ostracods crawl over the bottom using their limb-like appendages. Most are filter feeders but some are predatory.

Ostracodermi. A group of fossil Agnatha characterized by a heavy armour of bony plates and scales. *See* Osteostraci, Heterostraci.

otic capsule. *See* auditory capsule.

otocyst. *See* statocyst.

otolith. The part of the *macula of the inner ear consisting of a gelatinous mass containing granules of calcium carbonate and in which are embedded the hairs of the sensory cells.

outbreeding. The mating of individuals of the same species that are not closely related: also applied to cross-fertilization in plants. Many plants and animals have mechanisms (either physical or social) that encourage outbreeding, since this tends to be advantageous and to promote heterozygosity. However, extreme outbreeding – the crossing of two different species – is discouraged by various mechanisms because the products of the cross are infertile. *See also* incompatibility. *Compare* inbreeding.

outer ear. Those parts of the tetrapod ear external to the tympanum. An outer ear is absent in amphibians and some reptiles, in which the tympanum is exposed at the surface of the skin. In other tetrapods it consists of a short tube (*external auditory meatus*) with (in mammals) a *pinna.

ovary. 1. (in zoology). The main reproductive organ of female animals. In vertebrates there is a pair of ovaries, which produce both ova and steroid hormones in a cyclic manner (*see* oestrous cycle) under the control of the pituitary *gonadotrophins. In many birds only the left ovary is functional.

The mammalian ovary consists of a surface *germinal epithelium* surrounding numerous follicles contained within a stroma of connective tissue. Each follicle contains many cells surrounding a single *oogonium*. A few of these follicles mature (*see* Graafian follicle) to produce oocytes and ova at *ovulation, after which they form corpora lutea. Oestrogens are secreted by cells within the maturing follicle and also by interstitial cells within the connective tissue. The latter cells also produce small amounts of androgens.

2. (in botany). The hollow basal portion of a carpel, containing one or more ovules borne on a *placenta. This is a *simple* (or *monocarpellary*) ovary of an apocarpous gynoecium (see illustration at *ovule). In syncarpous gynoecia the basal portions of two or more carpels are united to form a single *compound* (or *polycarpellary*) ovary, bearing ovules on placentae corresponding in number to the carpels and possessing either a single loculus (cavity) or several loculi, one for each constituent carpel.

oviduct. The duct or tube in animals that transports ova from the ovary (or from the coelom after discharge from the ovary) to the outside. *See also* Müllerian duct.

oviparity. A type of animal reproduction in which the fertilized eggs are laid or spawned by the mother. The eggs contain poorly developed embryos with a large supply of yolk. Oviparity occurs in many vertebrates, excluding marsupial and placental mammals, and in most invertebrates.

ovipositor. An organ, formed from modified paired appendages, at the hind end of the abdomen of a female insect through which the eggs are laid. In many Hymenoptera it is modified as a sting, saw, or drill.

ovotestis. An organ of certain hermaphrodite animals, e.g. the snail, that produces both ova and spermatozoa.

ovoviviparity. A type of animal reproduction in which the embryos develop within the maternal organism but make no apparent contact with maternal tissues for the purposes of nutrition. Ovoviviparity occurs sporadically in many invertebrate groups, fish, and reptiles.

ovulation. The discharge of an ovum or oocyte from a mature follicle of the vertebrate ovary. The process, although not fully understood, is initiated by hypothalamic factors that stimulate the secretion of luteinizing hormone from the pituitary. A rapid rise in the level of this hormone in the presence of follicle-stimulating hormone causes ovulation.

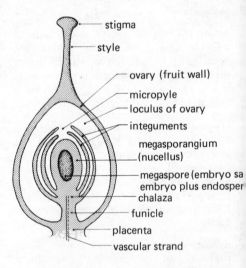

Diagrammatic section through a monocarpellary angiosperm pistil containing a single ovule

ovule. The structure in gymnosperm and angiosperm plants in which meiosis and

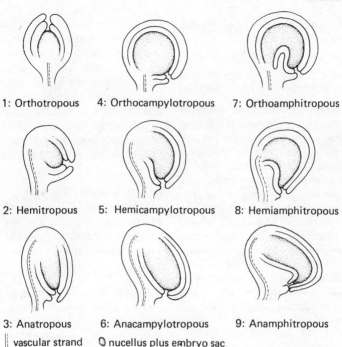

1: Orthotropous   4: Orthocampylotropous   7: Orthoamphitropous

2: Hemitropous   5: Hemicampylotropous   8: Hemiamphitropous

3: Anatropous   6: Anacampylotropous   9: Anamphitropous

‖ vascular strand   ⃝ nucellus plus embryo sac

Types of angiosperm ovules

megaspore formation occurs and which is borne on an *ovuliferous scale in many gymnosperms and on the *placenta within the ovary of angiosperms: an integumented megasporangium. It consists of a short stalk (termed the *funicle* in angiosperms) bearing a small mass of parent (sporophyte) tissue, the *nucellus, which is surrounded by one or two *integuments (see illustration). These arise as folds at the funicular end of the nucellus (this region is known as the *chalaza*) and grow up round the nucellus; the small aperture usually left by their incomplete closure is termed the *micropyle*. A single cell at the micropylar end of the nucellus enlarges to become the megasporocyte and undergoes meiosis to produce four cells, of which three abort and one becomes the functional megaspore. This cell undergoes either free nuclear division (division of the nucleus without division of the cytoplasm) or ordinary cell division to produce the *embryo sac. This structure produces the archegonia (in gymnosperms) or contains the functional

gametic nucleus (in angiosperms) and is usually regarded as a retained gametophyte prothallus. After fertilization of the archegonia or embryo sac, or by agamospermy, the ovule matures into the *seed.

There are nine positions in which the ovule may be borne on the funicle (see illustration). The simplest type (and probably the most primitive, from which the others evolved) is the *orthotropous* (or *atropous*) ovule, from which the *hemitropous* and *anatropous* ovules are derived. The *orthocampylotropous* (or *campylotropus*) ovule gives rise to the *hemicampylotropous* and *anacampylotropous* ovules, and the *orthoamphitropous* (or *amphitropous*) ovule gives rise to the *hemiamphitropous* and *anamphitropous* ovules.

In gymnosperms such a wide variety is not shown; ovules are either erect or anatropous.

ovuliferous scale. The megasporophyll of the Coniferales, borne in the axil of a bract scale on the megasporangiate cone (*see* strobilus). *See also* ovule.

ovum (egg cell). An unfertilized non-motile female gamete. In many animals it is produced in the ovary (*see* oocyte).

oxidative phosphorylation. The synthesis of ATP from phosphate and ADP coupled to electron transport along the respiratory chain (*see* electron transport chain), which occurs in mitochondria during *aerobic respiration. During substrate oxidation reduced coenzymes (e.g. NADH) are formed, which provide the energy to drive the respiratory chain. There are three sites in the chain where ATP can be formed during total oxidation with NADH as hydrogen donor. Thus substrates such as malate, pyruvate, and isocitrate, which yield NADH on oxidation, give a ratio of ATP formed to the amount of oxygen consumed (*P:O ratio*) of 3. $FADH_2$ formed during succinate oxidation bypasses one of the sites of phosphorylation when it enters the chain; thus succinate gives a P:O ratio of 2.

Phosphorylation is controlled by certain proteins in the mitochondrial membrane called *coupling factors*, one of which is a high-molecular-weight ATPase. Oxidative phosphorylation is inhibited (uncoupled) by various *uncoupling agents*, including dinitrophenol and the antibiotic oligomycin.

oxidoreductase. One of a group of enzymes that catalyse oxidation-reduction reactions, i.e. the transfer of hydrogen. This group, which includes the dehydrogenases, forms one of the main groups used in *enzyme classification; it has the code number E.C.1.

oxygen debt. The physiological condition that exists in normally aerobic animals during periods of temporary anoxia (lack of oxygen). Intermediary metabolism is switched to an anaerobic pathway, producing compounds that can be stored until sufficient oxygen becomes available to complete the oxidative process. In mammalian muscle, pyruvate is normally oxidized via the electron transport chain. When insufficient oxygen is available, e.g. during exercise in excess of the capacity of the respiratory system, the enzyme lactate dehydrogenase is activated and pyruvate is converted anaerobically to lactate, building up an oxygen debt. When aerobic metabolism is re-established, the debt is paid off as lactate is moved to the liver and oxidized.

oxygen quotient (Q_{O_2}) The rate of oxygen consumption of an organism or tissue, measured in units of microlitres of O_2 per milligram dry weight per hour. *Compare* respiratory quotient.

oxyhaemoglobin. *See* haemoglobin.

oxytocin. A peptide hormone secreted by the pars nervosa of the pituitary gland of birds and mammals (see formula at *vasotocin). It was the first pituitary hormone to be isolated, characterized, and synthesized (by du Vigneaud in the early 1950s). Its most potent effects involve contraction of the cells surrounding the alveoli of the mammary gland, causing milk ejection, and of the smooth muscle of the uterus, either during coitus to facilitate transport of spermatozoa or during parturition to facilitate expulsion of the foetus. A number of structurally similar peptides, differing by only one or two amino acid residues, have been isolated from the posterior pituitaries of many lower vertebrates. *See also* neurohormone.

P

P_1. The parental generation in breeding experiments, crossed to produce progeny known as the F_1 generation.

P700 and P680. Modified forms of chlorophyll a with peaks of light absorption at wavelengths around 700 nm and 680 nm respectively. P700 molecules comprise the energy traps of Pigment System I (*see* photosynthesis) and P680 molecules are thought to be the traps of Pigment System II.

P$_{FR}$ (P$_{730}$). *See* phytochrome.

P$_R$ (P$_{660}$). *See* phytochrome.

pacemaker. 1. (sinoatrial node) A group of muscle cells in the sinus venosus of the vertebrate heart whose spontaneous rhythmical electrical activity activates and maintains the contractions of the cardiac muscle. The pacemaker cells have no true resting potential; the impulses that drive the muscle are separated, and their frequency controlled, by a period of progressive depolarization known as the *pacemaker potential*.
2. Any similar group of muscle cells or neurones (or any single cell) whose spontaneous electrical activity drives an effector organ that requires continuous cyclic activation.

pachycaul. Designating angiosperms that have a large primary structure in which bud and leaf formation is slow and massive. *Compare* leptocaul.

pachytene. A stage of the prophase of the first division of *meiosis.

paedogenesis. A form of neoteny in which an organism becomes sexually mature while still in the larval or immature state. Paedogenesis is seen in the axolotl, which is the larval stage of the salamander but can breed in this form.

pairing (synapsis). The coming together in close association of the members of each pair of homologous chromosomes at prophase I of *meiosis.

Palaearctic. (Designating) a region of *Arctogea consisting of Europe, north Africa, and Asia as far south as the Himalayas. This region has a basically similar fauna as the land masses are practically interconnected; differences are due mainly to climatic variations.

Palaeocene. An epoch of the *Tertiary period.

palaeoecology. The study of the interrelationships of living organisms and their environment that existed in the past. These relationships can be elucidated by the techniques of palynology and radioactive dating.

Palaeogene. A collective name for the Palaeocene, Eocene, and Oligocene epochs of the *geological time scale.

Palaeognathae (Ratitae). The superorder of the Neornithes that contains the flightless birds. Most ratites are large, heavy, and fast-running, notably *Struthio* (ostrich) of Africa (the largest living bird), *Dromaius* (emu) of Australia, and the recently extinct *Dinornis* (moa) of New Zealand. *Apteryx* (kiwi) of New Zealand is smaller, with a long beak. Ratites have long powerful hind limbs, reduced wings, and no keel on the sternum. The feathers lack barbs. Ratites are descended from flying birds by several different evolutionary lines and are probably not closely related to each other.

Palaeolithic. The Old Stone Age of human prehistory, extending from the Pleistocene to about 7–10 000 years ago. Neanderthal and Cro-Magnon man and other species of *Homo* all contributed to Palaeolithic culture, which was characterized by the use of tools, mainly stones (especially flints) that came to hand. Food was obtained by hunting, fishing, and gathering (there was no agriculture). *Compare* Neolithic.

palaeontology. The study of life in the past, including the structure of fossils, their evolution, and their environment.

Palaeozoic. The first main era of the *geological time scale, beginning with the Cambrian period and ending with the Permian and extending in time from 600 million to 225 million years ago.

palate. The roof of the mouth of vertebrates, which is composed of the palatoquadrate bar and membrane bones and is pierced anteriorly (except in most fish) by the *choanae. In most reptiles and birds it is vaulted to provide a dorsal channel for air. In crocodiles and mammals complete separation of the air and food passages is achieved by development of a secondary palate (*false palate*). This consists of a shelf of membrane bone (*hard palate*) that continues posteriorly as a tissue flap (*soft palate*); the choanae are situated posteriorly. The soft palate is raised during swallowing to prevent entry of food into the nasal cavity. In amphibians the skin of the palate is highly vascular and serves as a respiratory surface.

palatoquadrate bar (pterygoquadrate bar). A paired cartilage derived from the mandibular arch, forming the upper jaw of adult Chondrichthyes and embryo tetrapods. It ossifies as the *quadrate bone. *See also* autostylic jaw suspension, hyostylic jaw suspension.

palindromic sequence. A nucleic acid sequence in which the code reads the same from either end. Such sequences are very common in DNA and their function is unknown. Most of these sequences are only true palindromes when both strands are considered. Thus

–AACTGCAGTT–
–TTGACGTCAA–

is palindromic. Such sequences are significant in two ways. Firstly, since they have a central axis of symmetry, they are capable of adopting special tertiary structures. For example, the sequence shown above can be alternatively folded as shown below and the specific hydrogen bonding requirements remain satisfied.

```
      ⌒
G     C
T     A
C     G
A     T
A     T
 ⨎   ⨎
T     A
T     A
G     C
A     T
C     G
      ⌣
```

Secondly, palindromic sequences are the particular sites at which specific *restriction endonucleases cut DNA, although not necessarily through the axis of symmetry. Palindromic sequences also reassociate very rapidly in Cot curve experiments (*see* Cot value); they are then known as *foldback DNA.

palisade mesophyll (palisade layer). *See* mesophyll.

pallium. *See* cerebral cortex.

palmella. A phase produced by some unicellular, colonial, or filamentous algae in response to dry conditions, in which the cells mass together, their flagella are withdrawn, and their cell walls gelatinize to produce an irregular mass of nonmotile cells embedded in a gelatinous matrix.

palmitic acid. *See* fatty acid.

palp. An appendage of many invertebrates, situated near the mouth. For example, a pair of tactile palps is present on the head of polychaete worms; the palps of crustaceans and insects are associated with the mouthparts.

palynology (pollen analysis). The method of studying life in the past by observation of the detailed structure of pollen grains and other spores. Different genera, and sometimes even species, of pollen are very distinctive in size, shape, and markings on the coat; therefore study of these pollen grains can indicate the nature of the dominant flora, and hence the climate, in past geological ages. Because the outer coat of a pollen grain (*see* perispore) is extremely resistant, pollen grains are well preserved in a number of rocks and are especially prolific in peat. Palynology is useful to the applied geologist in suggesting relationships between beds in which oil may be found.

pancreas. An elongated gland, lying alongside the lower side of the vertebrate stomach between the spleen and duodenum, that consists of both exocrine and endocrine tissues (*see* islets of Langerhans). The exocrine region forms the main bulk of the gland and is composed of groups of cells (*acini*) that produce a variety of digestive enzymes (mainly trypsinogen, lipase, amylase, and maltase). These are released via a system of branching ducts into the common pancreatic duct and from here alkaline pancreatic juice containing the enzymes is secreted into the duodenum under the stimulation of secretin, cholecystokinin-pancreozymin, or the vagus nerve.

pancreozymin. *See* cholecystokinin-pancreozymin.

Pangaea. An ancient crescent-shaped supercontinent comprising all the present-day continents joined together to form one continuous land mass. The subsequent fragmentation of Pangaea has been elucidated in relation to the theory of *continental drift.

pangenesis. The theory of heredity postulating that germs, humours, or essences migrate from individual body cells to the sex organs and contribute to the gametes. This theory gives a mechanism for the inheritance of acquired characteristics (*see* Lamarckism) but is not generally accepted today.

pangolin. *See* Pholidota.

panicle. A type of inflorescence that is basically a branched raceme, with each branch itself bearing a raceme of flowers, as in the oat. However the term is widely used for any complex branched racemose inflorescence, e.g. the horse chestnut, which is in fact a raceme whose branches are cymes.

$$HO-CH_2-\underset{\underset{CH_3}{|}}{\overset{\overset{CH_3}{|}}{C}}-\underset{\overset{OH}{|}}{CH}-\overset{\overset{O}{\|}}{C}-NH-CH_2-CH_2-COOH$$

Pantothenic acid

pantothenic acid. A water-soluble vitamin of the B complex (see formula), required in the diet of man and other vertebrates and occurring in yeast, liver, peas, etc. It functions as the precursor of *coenzyme A.

Pantotheria. An extinct order of Jurassic mammals, probably small carnivores or omnivores, e.g. *Amphitherium*. Pantotheres had long slender jaws with triangular premolars and molars. They are believed to have been ancestral to primitive marsupials and placental mammals.

papilla. 1. A projection occurring in various animal tissues and organs. Examples include *basilar papillae*, which bear the sense cells of the vertebrate ear; the *dermal papillae* of the vertebrate skin, which project from the dermis into the epidermis and give rise to the ridge pattern of fingerprints and to the teeth; *rectal papillae* in the hindgut of insects, which reabsorb water from the faeces; and *tongue papillae*, which bear the taste buds.
2. A small blunt-tipped hair in plants.

papillomavirus. A member of a class of papovaviruses. *See* virus.

papovavirus. *See* virus.

pappus. A ring of hairs that replaces the sepals in flowers of the family Compositae. The pappus is retained on the fruit and acts as a parachute to aid seed dispersal.

parabiosis. The surgical joining together of two animals in such a way that functional connections are formed between them. Each member of the pair is called a *parabiont*, and the pair are known as *parabiotic twins*. The operation is often performed between two insects so that any chemicals under study in the blood of one may pass into the other and their effects observed.

parallel evolution. The existence of similar adaptations in groups of animals and plants that are not closely related but have come to fill the same ecological niche. For example, marsupials in Australia and placentals elsewhere have undergone parallel evolution.

paramorph. A unit used in *classification below the species level for any variant within the species whose taxonomic status cannot be determined.

Paranthropus. See *Australopithecus.*

paraphysis. One of many sterile uniseriate hairs (i.e. composed of a single column of cells) found between the sex organs of certain plants, for example among the oogonia in the conceptacles of the Fucales (brown algae) and between the antheridia and archegonia on the bryophyte receptacle. Their function is protective and occasionally nutritive.

parapodium. One of a pair of lateral projections of the body wall arising from each segment of a polychaete worm. They typically bear a bundle of chaetae and are used in locomotion (both swimming and crawling) and, in some polychaetes, in respiration.

parasexual cycle (mitotic recombination). A cycle of reproduction occurring in the Fungi Imperfecti that involves genetic recombination without meiosis or the fusion of gametes, processes associated with conventional sexual reproduction. It starts with a heterokaryotic mycelium (*see* heterokaryosis) with coexisting haploid nuclei, formed by hyphal fusion. Rare nuclear fusions yield stable heterozygous nuclei, dividing at the same rate as the more numerous haploid nuclei. During mitosis, recombination in the heterozygous diploid nuclei occurs at a low rate. Diploid daughter cells with different properties result; some of these cells undergo *haploidization*, in which the chromosomes are reassorted without crossing over taking place, giving rise to recombinants of the parental nuclei.

parasite. An organism that lives in or on another living organism (the *host), from which it obtains food, shelter, and other requirements. The host may or may not suffer injurious effects by this relationship. Parasite and host are usually of different species. Some parasites, e.g. the rust fungi and the sporozoan Protozoa, have complex life cycles involving several generations and more than one host. A *facultative parasite* is an organism that usually lives as a saprophyte but can become parasitic under certain conditions; *obligate parasites* must always live parasitically. A *partial parasite* is a plant, such as mistletoe, that can carry out photosynthesis but obtains nutrient salts from its host. Parasites that live on the external surface of the host are called *ectoparasites*, e.g. fleas; those that live within the body of the host are *endoparasites*, e.g. *Plasmodium* (malaria parasite) and tapeworms. In metazoan endoparasites the alimentary canal is reduced or absent, food from the host being absorbed through the body surface. *See also* symbiosis.

parasitoid. An insect (usually a hymenopteran or dipteran) that is parasitic on another invertebrate and eventually kills its host, unlike a true parasite, which usually does not do so.

parastichy. The helix along which spirally arranged leaves are formed in the apex of a shoot. The degree of steepness of the helix varies according to the species. *See also* phyllotaxis.

parasympathetic nervous system. The part of the vertebrate *autonomic nervous system that has cholinergic peripheral nerve endings.

parathyroid glands. One or two pairs of endocrine glands of tetrapod vertebrates lying near or within the thyroid glands and developing from the posterior gill pouches. They were first named and described in 1880, by Sandström, and their secretion of parathyroid hormone and calcitonin in the regulation of calcium and phosphate metabolism became evident during the 1920s and 1960s respectively. Parathyroid secretory activity is regulated not by the pituitary gland but directly by the concentration of calcium in the blood.

parathyroid hormone (PTH). A single-chain polypeptide hormone that raises blood-calcium levels and is secreted by the parathyroid glands of tetrapod vertebrates in response to low blood-calcium levels (hypocalcaemia). In 1910, MacCallum first showed that the tetanic convulsions of animals with their parathyroids removed could be relieved with injections of calcium salts. PTH was isolated in 1925 and was shown in 1965 to be a polypeptide of about 75 amino acid residues. A precursor molecule of 84 residues has subsequently been isolated. PTH acts by stimulating bone resorption (which releases calcium salts), kidney reabsorption of calcium salts (associated with phosphate excretion), and intestinal absorption of calcium ions from the diet (which requires vitamin D).

paratonic movements. Movements of plants induced by external stimuli. They include taxes, tropisms, nastic movements, and some movements caused by pulvini of 'sensitive plants' (*see* phyllopodium). *Compare* autonomic movements.

paratype. *See* holotype.

Parazoa. A subkingdom of invertebrates containing the phylum *Porifera (sponges). *Compare* Protozoa, Metazoa.

parenchyma. 1. A plant tissue composed of thin-walled living cells that is concerned with vegetative functions and forms the *ground tissues of the plant. Parenchyma cells are the least modified of all plant cells and most closely resemble meristematic cells: they are regarded as the basic cell from which all other cell types have evolved. *Collenchyma and *sclerenchyma evolved by progressive thickening and lignification, respectively, of the cell wall.
Parenchyma cells occur in vascular tissue, in which they play an important role in the movement of water and food products in the xylem and phloem, respectively. In the secondary vascular tissue the parenchyma forms two major

systems: the horizontal system of *medullary rays, which provide radial transport, and the vertical system of *axial parenchyma*, which provides a link between the rays and also acts as a storage tissue for reserves such as oil and starch.
2. A loose spongy connective tissue of some invertebrates, e.g. the Platyhelminthes, consisting of cells lying in a matrix of fluid or gelatinous material.
3. The specific tissue of an organ, as distinct from the connective tissue, blood vessels, etc.

parichnos strands. Channels of thin-walled loosely arranged parenchyma cells occurring in some fossil Lepidodendrales. The function of this tissue is not known but it may have provided aeration for the underground organs.

parietal eye. *See* median eye.

parthenocarpy. The formation of fruits without the process of fertilization and therefore without the production of seeds. The ovary wall develops to form fruits that appear normal, e.g. seedless oranges and cultivated bananas. Parthenocarpy can be induced artificially by spraying the flowers with auxins; apples, tomatoes, and pears are often produced commercially in this way.

parthenogenesis. Reproduction in which eggs develop normally without being fertilized by a male gamete, producing an individual usually genetically identical to the parent. The main advantage of parthenogenesis is the acceleration of the reproductive rate and it occurs widely in plants. In animals, it is common in the Rotifera (males are unknown in one order) and in the Arthropoda. In some animals, e.g. aphids, several parthenogenetic generations alternate with a generation that reproduces normally (providing genetic recombination). In many cases *artificial parthenogenesis* can be initiated by chemical or physical stimuli.

parturition. Expulsion of the foetus at the termination of pregnancy in mammals. The process is initiated by complex mechanisms not fully understood. Increased production of cortisol by the foetus has been suggested as the primary signal in sheep, but the premature removal of the foetus in other species does not prevent the placenta and empty membranes from being carried to term and delivered at the normal time.

passage cells. Cells in the *endodermis, opposite to the protoxylem groups, that do not undergo secondary wall thickening but do possess Casparian strips and are thus assumed to allow the passage of solutes between the xylem and the cortex. Their occurrence may vary in a single axis; some parts possess passage cells, others have an endodermis composed entirely of thick-walled cells forming an impervious ring.

pasteurization. A process of heat treatment that kills pathogenic microorganisms in foods and drinks. For example, milk is maintained at a temperature of about 62°C for 30 minutes, which kills any pathogens but does not destroy harmless bacteria or affect taste. The process was orginally devised by Louis Pasteur (1822–95) to kill the spoilage microorganisms of wines and beers.

patella. A sesamoid bone in the tendon of the main extensor muscle of the mammalian hind limb, at the region where the tendon passes over the knee joint. It forms the kneecap in man.

pathogen. Any microorganism that causes disease or a toxic response. Such organisms are described as *pathogenic*.

patristic. Designating a similarity between types of plants resulting from common ancestry.

peat. The plant remains of bog and fen vegetation. The wetness of the substrate leads to anaerobic acid conditions, which inhibits the microorganisms of decay and leads to an accumulation of vegetable remains in the substrate – the peat. Several types of peat are recognized: (1) *basin peat* (or *topogenous*

peat), from bog vegetation, found in base-poor valley bottoms or ill-drained hollows; (2) *ombrogenous peat*, from raised or blanket bogs, in which the surface of the substrate is above the water table so that the major source of water is rain; (3) *blanket peat*, a type of ombrogenous peat, developed from blanket bog; (4) *topographic peat*, small areas of ombrogenous peat, similar to blanket bog but very localized; (5) *fen peat*, developed in base-rich fen conditions.

peck order (dominance hierarchy). The social hierarchy occurring in many animals that live together in groups; it is particularly well developed in birds. The top animal in the group, known as the *dominant* animal, behaves aggressively to all other members of the group. Each animal below the dominant member has its place in the order and is usually aggressive to all those inferior to it but is submissive to those above it in the order. The aggressive behaviour in birds usually takes the form of pecking.

pectic substances. Heterogeneous collections of acid polysaccharides found mainly in the primary *cell wall matrix. They are typically long-chain molecules (branched or straight) built up from arabinose, galactose, galacturonic acid, and methanol. The soluble pectic substances are the *pectic acids*, straight chains of galacturonic acid residues precipitated as calcium and magnesium pectates to form the middle lamellae between plant cell walls, and *pectinic acids* (pectic acids plus methanol). Pectinic acids with a high degree of methylation and with the addition of sugars and acids form *pectins*. Polymers of pectin form the insoluble pectic substances, the large and complex *protopectins* that comprise the major pectic component of primary cell walls. In ripening fruits protopectin is converted to pectins. These form gels at low concentrations (when sugar is added) and are therefore used commercially as gelling agents.

pectin. See pectic substances.

pectoral fin. *See* fins.

pectoral girdle (shoulder girdle). The skeletal structure in the trunk of vertebrates to which the forelimbs or pectoral fins are attached. It consists primitively of a cartilaginous hoop with lateral articulations for the fin bones. In the Osteichthyes and tetrapods it is a complex of dorsal cartilage bones (*scapula and *coracoid) and ventral bracing membrane bones, primitively the *cleithrum* and *clavicle, either or both of which may be lost in some groups. The scapula and coracoid provide the main attachment site for muscles of the forelimbs and form the glenoid cavity, in which the limb bone articulates. In fish the pectoral girdle is attached to the skull.

pedicel. A flower stalk. *Compare* peduncle.

pedipalp. One of a pair of appendages on the cephalothorax (*opisthosoma*) of the Arachnida. They are often leglike and usually sensory but are sometimes pincer-like and assist in eating, as in scorpions, while in male spiders (order Araneae) they are modified as accessory sex organs.

peduncle. An inflorescence stalk. *Compare* pedicel.

Peking man. *See Homo.*

pelagic. Living in the open waters of a sea or lake, as distinct from on the bottom. Pelagic plants and animals include the plankton and the nekton.

Pelecypoda. *See* Bivalvia.

pellicle. A protective proteinaceous layer surrounding many unicellular organisms, notably ciliate protozoans and euglenoid algae. It is flexible, allowing free movement while conferring definite shape.

pelvic fin. *See* fins.

pelvic girdle (hip girdle). The skeletal structure in the trunk of vertebrates to which the hind limbs or pelvic fins are attached. In fish it consists of a pair of cartilaginous or bony plates, fused medially and articulating laterally with the fins. In tetrapods the primitive cartilaginous girdle ossifies at three centres forming the *ilium, *ischium and *pubis. The ilium articulates with the ribs of the sacral vertebrae, thus uniting the girdle to the axial skeleton and transmitting the thrust of the rear limbs to the body. All the bones bear muscle attachments and contribute to the acetabulum, the site of articulation with the femur of the hind limb. In some vertebrates the pubes are fused ventrally at the *pubic symphysis.

pelvis. 1. The region of the lower abdomen bounded by the pelvic girdle.
2. The pelvic girdle.
3. *renal pelvis.* The expanded proximal end of the mammalian ureter, into which the collecting ducts of the kidney drain.

Pelycosauria. An order of the Synapsida containing the earliest and most primitive mammal-like reptiles, common in the Upper Carboniferous and Lower Permian. The suborder Sphenacodonta, from which the Therapsida and the mammals evolved, contained large aggressive terrestrial carnivores such as *Dimetrodon.*

penetrance (expressivity). The extent to which the effects of a gene are shown in the organism possessing it. It is expressed as the percentage of organisms showing the effect of a gene out of the total number known to possess it. Penetrance can vary considerably with different genes and with different organisms possessing the same gene. In Mendelian genetics, penetrance is assumed to be 100%. Variations in penetrance are thought to be due to the modifying action of other genes present and to the effects of the environment.

penicillins. A class of antibiotics that act by disrupting cell-wall synthesis in Gram-negative bacteria. They have the general formula shown, in which R is a variable side chain. Penicillin itself (i.e.

$$R - \overset{\overset{\displaystyle O}{\|}}{C} - NH - CH - CH \overset{S}{\underset{\displaystyle O = C - N - CH - COOH}{\diagdown}} C \overset{CH_3}{\underset{CH_3}{\diagup}}$$

General formula of penicillins

penicillin G, in which $R = C_6H_5CH_2$) is produced by the mould *Penicillium notatum*; various chemical substitutions of the side chain R produce penicillins with different properties.

penis. The unpaired erectile *intromittent organ of all male mammals, some reptiles (chelonians and crocodilians), and a few birds. In mammals the terminal part of the urethra lies within the penis. *Compare* clitoris.

Pennsylvanian. A subdivision of the *Carboniferous period in America that is equivalent to the Upper Carboniferous in Britain and continental countries.

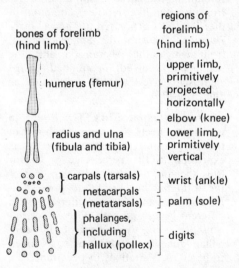

bones of forelimb (hind limb)	regions of forelimb (hind limb)
humerus (femur)	upper limb, primitively projected horizontally
	elbow (knee)
radius and ulna (fibula and tibia)	lower limb, primitively vertical
carpals (tarsals)	wrist (ankle)
metacarpals (metatarsals)	palm (sole)
phalanges, including hallux (pollex)	digits

Pentadactyl limb

pentadactyl limb. The type of limb that is characteristic of tetrapod vertebrates, basically having five terminal digits. It evolved from the paired fins of crossopterygian fish as an adaptation to walking on land. The basic plan of the

bones (see illustration) is often greatly modified by loss and fusion of the elements, particularly in the distal units. The different joint structure in the fore and hind limbs reflects the different changes in angle needed to turn pectoral and pelvic fins into limbs, the propulsive function of the hind limb, and the mode of walking of the species.

pentose. A *monosaccharide with five carbon atoms, e.g. ribose.

pentose phosphate pathway (hexose monophosphate shunt). A pathway of glucose oxidation occurring in the cytoplasm of cells. The pathway requires NADP as an electron acceptor and the NADPH generated provides the reducing power for many biosynthetic reactions, e.g. the synthesis of fats. In animals the pathway occurs mainly in the liver, adipose tissue, mammary glands, and adrenal cortex, where fatty acids and steroids are synthesized (as much as a third of the glucose oxidized in these tissues may be via the pentose phosphate pathway). Other important products include glyceraldehyde-3-phosphate (which can participate in glycolysis), ribose-5-phosphate (which is used for the synthesis of nucleotides and nucleic acids), and ribulose-5-phosphate (which, in photosynthetic organisms, combines with carbon dioxide to form sugars).

pepo. A unilocular many-seeded succulent berry-like *fruit that is derived from an inferior ovary and has a hard outer layer.

pepsin. A proteolytic enzyme, secreted by glands of the vertebrate stomach, that acts as an endopeptidase in the presence of hydrochloric acid in the gastric juice. *See* proteolysis.

peptidase. One of a group of enzymes that hydrolyse peptides into their constituent amino acids. *See* proteolysis.

peptide. One of a group of compounds consisting of two or more amino acids linked by covalent bonds between the amino group of one and the carboxyl group of the next. This type of bond is known as a *peptide bond* and peptides of three or more amino acids are called *polypeptides*. Polypeptides made up of only a few amino acids are called *oligopeptides*. *See* protein.

peptidoglycan. *See* mucopeptide.

peptone. A large protein fragment produced by enzyme action in the initial stages of protein digestion.

perennation. Any method of overwintering that occurs in plants. Annuals perennate by means of seeds resting in the ground, and biennials by storing food in underground storage organs such as tap roots. Herbaceous perennials perennate by means of underground storage organs such as bulbs, corms, rhizomes, or tubers; these perennating organs often also serve as organs of vegetative propagation. Woody perennials survive the winter either by leaf loss and therefore complete cessation of photosynthesis, as in deciduous trees and shrubs, or by reducing their metabolic activity, as in evergreens.

perennial. A plant that continues to grow from year to year, sometimes producing seed in the first year, sometimes undergoing several years growth before seeds are produced. *Herbaceous perennials* are not woody and their aerial parts die down each year. These plants pass the winter in the form of underground organs (*perennating organs*), which store food; new shoots grow from buds on the perennating organs the following year. *Woody perennials* – trees and shrubs – do not die down in autumn but have woody stems, which survive the winter above ground; growth continues in the following spring from buds at the end of the twigs. *Compare* annual, biennial, ephemeral.

perforation plate. A special area between two adjacent xylem vessel elements in which the wall material has been removed to allow free passage of sap. The presence of perforation plates is the sole feature that distinguishes vessel elements from tracheids (from which they are absent). Perforation plates may be *simple* (with a single perforation) or *multiple* (with several perforations).

perianth. The structure in a flower that surrounds the androecium and gynoecium, usually consisting of two whorls of leaflike parts. In monocotyledons these two whorls are usually similar; they may be brightly coloured and petalloid in insect-pollinated flowers or absent or scalelike in wind-pollinated ones. In dicotyledons the two whorls are not usually similar; the outer whorl consists of sepals and is known as the *calyx* and the inner whorl, the *corolla*, is made up of petals. In insect-pollinated flowers the corolla and sometimes also the calyx are brightly coloured to attract insects; in wind-pollinated flowers the corolla and calyx are usually reduced or absent.

periblem. The part of the apical meristem that gives rise to the cortex. *See* histogen theory.

pericardial cavity. The space enclosing the heart. In vertebrates it is a coelomic space bounded by a fibrous sac, the *pericardium*; in arthropods and molluscs it is part of the haemocoel.

pericarp (fruit wall). The structure formed from the ovary wall during fruit development. The pericarp may become compact and hard, as in achenes, or variously swollen; e.g. dry and fibrous, as in *Cocos nucifera* (coconut), or succulent, as in berries. The swollen pericarp usually has three distinct layers: the outer *exocarp* (or *epicarp*), forming a tough skin; the middle *mesocarp*, in which most expansion occurs; and the inner *endocarp*, which may be indistinguishable from the mesocarp (as in berries), leathery (as in citrus fruits), or stony (as in drupes). In flowers with inferior ovaries or extreme perigyny the ovary wall usually fuses with the accessory parts of the fruit, e.g. with the receptacle in pomes (extreme perigyny).

periclinal (in botany). Designating the plane parallel to the surface of an organ, e.g. one of the planes of cell division in meristematic tissue. *Compare* anticlinal.

pericycle. A layer of parenchymatous tissue, one to several cells thick, between the stele and the endodermis. It is present in most roots, in which it develops from the procambium and retains its meristematic capacity, forming the meristem that produces lateral roots and contributing to the root vascular cambium and phellogen at the onset of secondary growth. In stems its form and function are less clear. There is usually no distinct layer between the vascular tissues and cortex: the pericycle consists of fibres, either in the form of a cylinder or as caps to the phloem. It is likely that most structures termed pericyclic in the stems of seed plants derive from the outermost parts of the phloem tissues.

periderm. The outer protective secondary tissue of the roots and stems of woody gymnosperms and angiosperms, which replaces the axial epidermis when it is destroyed by secondary growth.
It comprises three layers. The outermost layer is the *phellem* (*cork*), which is produced to the outside of the phellogen and forms the true protective layer of the periderm. It consists of tightly packed prismatic cells, which in the mature state have suberized walls and have lost their living contents. The surface of the phellem is interrupted at intervals by *lenticels, which provide aeration passages in this otherwise impervious layer. The innermost layer is the *phelloderm*, which is produced to the inside of the phellogen and consists of living cells that resemble cortical cells in wall structure and contents. Between these layers lies the *phellogen* (or *cork cambium*). This is the lateral secondary meristem that produces the other two layers by periclinal divisions on both its inner and outer surfaces. It usually arises in the subepidermal layer, but it may arise (according to species) anywhere between the epidermis and the phloem (and occasionally in the xylem,

forming anomalous secondary thickening).

peridiole. A seminal particle containing basidiospores, formed by fungi of the order Nidulariales (bird's-nest fungi). It is formed from a single glebal chamber (*see* gleba).

peridium. The outer wall of the spore-producing body of the fungi. It is often simple, as in the Myxomycetes (in which it is a single layer), but it can be very complex, as in many Gasteromycetes (earth stars, puffballs, etc.), in which it is a multilayered structure.

perigyny. The condition of angiosperm flowers of having a flattened or cup-shaped receptacle with the gynoecium at the centre and the other flower parts inserted at the rim. The receptacle never fuses with the gynoecium, even in cases of extreme perigyny, when the receptacle is flask-shaped (e.g. in pomes); hence all perigynous flowers are regarded as having a superior gynoecium. *Compare* epigyny, hypogyny.

perikaryon. The cell body of a *neurone.

perilymph. A viscous fluid, resembling cerebrospinal fluid, that fills the space between the structures of the inner ear and the bones of the auditory cavity of vertebrates. The perilymph of the *cochlea acts as a conduction system for sound in amniotes.

periodontal membrane. The connective tissue membrane that connects the roots of teeth to their cavities in the jaw bones (*alveolar cavities*). While possessing similarities to the periosteum, it contains no elastic fibres and is composed mainly of collagenous bundles.

periosteum. The connective tissue membrane that ensheathes bones and provides attachment for tendons and muscles. The outer membrane is composed mainly of white fibrous tissue and elastic fibres, beneath which is a looser highly vascular layer in which osteoblasts are formed.

Peripatus. See Onychophora.

peripheral nervous system. All parts of the nervous system that are not included in the central nervous system. It is made up of nerves that serve as relay channels between the receptors and effectors and the integrative centres of the central nervous system. In vertebrates the cranial and spinal nerves constitute the peripheral nervous system. *See also* autonomic nervous system.

periphloic. *See* amphiphloic.

perisperm. A storage tissue in the seeds of certain angiosperms that develops from the *nucellus.

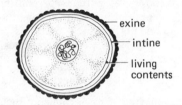

Fig.1: Perispore layers in a typical spore

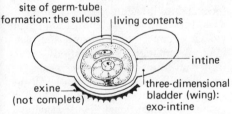

Fig. 2: Section through *Pinus* sp. pollen grain

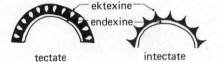

Fig. 3: Structure of the exine

Perispore structure

perispore (sporoderm). The outer durable protective layer of a spore. Due to *palynology, much attention has been directed to the structure of the microspores and megaspores of pteridophytes and the pollen grains of gymnosperms

and angiosperms. These possess an inner cellulose coat, the *intine*, which is easily destroyed, and an outer durable layer, the *exine* (Fig. 1). The durable nature of the exine is due to the presence of *sporopollenin. A third layer, the *exointine* (or *medine*), may be present in some spores between the intine and the extine, as in *Pinus* pollen (Fig. 2). The exine is the most complex layer and possesses great diversity in chemical composition and morphology. It comprises two layers, the *endexine* (or *mexine*), a continuous homogeneous membrane, and the *ektexine* (or *sexine*), a highly variable layer (Fig. 3).

Perissodactyla. The order of the Eutheria that contains the odd-toed ungulates: large herbivorous hoofed mammals in which the weight of the body is supported on the middle digit of the feet. The order includes the fast-moving horses (*Equus*), with a single toe; the primitive tapirs (*Tapirus*), with four-toed front feet and three-toed hind feet; and the armoured rhinoceroses (e.g. *Rhinoceros*), with three toes. *Compare* Artiodactyla.

peristalsis. Waves of muscular contraction passing along tubular organs, particularly the intestines, caused by sequential contraction of circular muscles.

peristome. **1.** (in botany). A single or double row of teeth (usually hygroscopic) at the apex of most moss capsules, through which the spores are shed.
2. (in zoology). The structure, sometimes involved in food collecting, that surrounds the mouth of many invertebrates, such as the ciliated funnel-shaped groove around the mouth of *Stentor*, *Vorticella*, and some other ciliate Protozoa.

perithecium (pyrenocarp). A flask-shaped *ascocarp whose inner surface is lined with a hymenium that produces the asci. At maturity the ascospores are ejected through the apical ostiole by the bursting of the asci. *See also* apothecium, cleistothecium.

peritoneum. The coelomic epithelium that lines the posterior coelomic cavity (*peritoneal cavity*) of vertebrates and therefore surrounds the gut.

peritrichous. Designating flagella of a bacterium that are distributed over the entire surface of the cell, or the bacteria that possess such flagella.

perixylic. *See* amphixylic.

permanent teeth. The second and final set of teeth occurring in most mammals, which replace the *deciduous teeth.

Permian. The sixth and last period of the Palaeozoic era, extending from 270 to 225 million years ago. It is named from Perm, on the River Volga in Russia, where rocks of the period were first recognized. In some places the Permian system grades into the Triassic and the two can be considered as a single system, the *Permo-Triassic* (or *Permo-Trias*). In many regions Permian fossils are scarce; they consist of land-living animals such as lungfish and labyrinthodont amphibians and xerophytic plants, indicating an increasingly dry climate. Marine fossils of the Permian include foraminiferans, ammonites, brachiopods, corals, and sponges. At the end of the Permian many marine groups died out, including the trilobites, many Palaeozoic crinoids, and some corals. *See also* geological time scale.

peroxisome. *See* microbody.

petal. One of the structures in a flower that form the inner whorl of the *perianth. Petals are thought to be modified leaves (sterile sporophylls) and are known collectively as the *corolla*. They are often large, flat, and brightly coloured, which attracts the insects that cause pollination. In wind-pollinated flowers, petals are small or nonexistent.

petiole. The stalk of a *leaf, which bears the leaf lamina and is attached to the

plant stem by means of a *phyllopodium.

petri dish. A shallow flat lidded container made of glass or clear plastic in which bacteria, moulds, or tissue cultures can be grown in a nutrient medium or on a nutrient agar.

pH. A measure of the concentration of hydrogen ions in a solution. It is defined as $-\log$ [H$^+$], where [H$^+$] is the concentration of hydrogen ions. Pure water at normal temperatures dissociates only very slightly into hydrogen ions and hydroxyl ions, the concentration of each type of ion being 10^{-7} mole per cubic decimetre. The pH of pure water is therefore $-\log 10^{-7} = 7$ and this figure represents neutrality on the pH scale. A pH below 7 indicates acidity and a pH in excess of 7 indicates alkalinity.

PHA. *See* phytohaemagglutinin.

Phaeophyta. Brown algae, including *Fucus* (wracks) and *Laminaria* (kelps). They are filamentous or pseudoparenchymatous chromophytes possessing fucoxanthin in addition to chlorophylls a and b and β-carotene. Their main storage products are laminarin and mannitol. Alternation of generations occurs in some forms and is the means by which the three subgroups can be distinguished: Isogeneratae (isomorphic alternation of generations); Heterogeneratae (heteromorphic alternation of generations); Cyclosporae (absence of alternation of generations). Sexual reproduction varies from isogamy to oogamy, with at least one biflagellate gamete.

phage. *See* bacteriophage.

phagocyte. A cell that has the ability to ingest extracellular particles by engulfing them with its own cytoplasm, a process known as *phagocytosis* (*see* endocytosis). Although many protozoans are phagocytic the word is more commonly applied to those cells that occur throughout vertebrate tissues and are responsible for the ingestion of bacteria and foreign particles, i.e. *polymorphs and *macrophages.

phagocytosis. *See* endocytosis.

phalange (phalanx). One of the rod-shaped bones of the digits of the tetrapod *pentadactyl limb. The most proximal phalanges articulate with the metacarpals or metatarsals. Except in aquatic mammals, there is a maximum of five phalanges per digit, the inner digit usually being shorter than the rest. *See also* hallux, pollex.

phanerogam (in former plant classification schemes). A spermatophyte, so called because the sexual reproductive organs are clearly visible in cones or flowers. *Compare* cryptogam.

phanerophyte (in *Raunkiaer's classification). A plant that bears its winter buds well exposed to the air. Many trees and shrubs are phanerophytes. *Megaphanerophytes* and *mesophanerophytes* are trees whose winter buds are over 8 metres above the level of the soil, the former typically being taller than the latter; a *microphanerophyte* is a tree or shrub whose buds are between 2 and 8 metres above the soil surface; a *nanophanerophyte* is a shrub with its buds between 0.25 and 2 metres above the soil.

pharyngeal pouch and cleft. *See* gill pouch.

pharynx. 1. An endodermal region of the vertebrate alimentary canal lying between the buccal cavity and the oesophagus. Stimulation of the pharynx by food initiates reflex muscular activity causing swallowing (*see* deglutition). In fish and aquatic amphibians the pharynx is pierced laterally by the gill slits; in other vertebrates it contains the paired openings of the Eustachian tubes (representing the openings of the spiracular gill slit). The swim bladder and lungs are homologous derivatives of the pharynx. The swim bladder may open from the pharynx dorsally or ventrally; the lungs open ventrally through the glottis. Other derivatives of the pharynx

are the thyroid, thymus, and parathyroid glands.
2. The corresponding region of invertebrates, especially protochordates, in which it contains the endostyle and is perforated by gill slits.

Phasmida. The order of herbivorous exopterygote insects that contains the stick and leaf insects, found in the warmer parts of the world. The body is either cylindrical and elongated (stick insects) or flattened and leaflike (leaf insects) and provides efficient camouflage among the twigs and foliage in which they live. Some phasmids have wings, which they use in a gliding flight; others are wingless. Parthenogenesis is very common.

phellem. *See* cork, periderm.

phelloderm. The inner layer of *periderm, consisting of cells resembling cortical parenchyma.

phellogen (cork cambium). The lateral meristem producing the *periderm.

phenetic. Designating a classification based on observed similarities and differences in appearance, as opposed to one based on evolutionary descent. *Compare* phylogenetic.

phenocopy. An environmentally produced change in an organism, induced early in development, that is very similar to a gene mutation but is not inherited. For example, irradiation of mammalian embryos at sensitive stages of their development in the uterus produces abnormalities that are phenocopies of mutations.

phenotype. The physical characteristics, collectively, of an organism, determined by the *genotype and the environment. Organisms with the same genotype may have different phenotypes in different environments. For example, two plants may be genotypically short, but if one is grown under conditions of poor light, it will become etiolated and hence taller than the other. Organisms with the same genotype may also show different phenotypes if the *penetrance of the gene differs. On the other hand, organisms with different genotypes may have the same phenotype if each contains a dominant gene: in the same environment the homozygous organism *AA* is phenotypically identical to the heterozygous *Aa* in respect of gene *A*.

phenylalanine (phe). An amino acid, $C_6H_5CH_2CH(NH_2)COOH$, one of the 20 common amino acids occurring in proteins and an *essential amino acid for man.

phenylketonuria. A hereditary disorder, carried as a single recessive gene, in which the amino acid phenylalanine fails to be metabolized to tyrosine. The disorder results in excretion of phenylpyruvic acid (a precursor of phenylalanine) in the urine and, usually, severe mental retardation.
Phenylketonuria can be detected soon after birth and a diet low in phenylalanine minimizes the symptoms.

pheromone. A substance excreted by an animal in small amounts that causes specific reproductive, developmental, or behavioural responses in neighbouring members of the same species. The earliest and best studied pheromones are the sex attractants produced by Lepidoptera and the queen-bee substance excreted by the queen of a hive. Characterized as 9-ketodecanoic acid, queen-bee substance is eaten by the workers, in which it inhibits the development of the ovaries (thus making them sterile) and prevents their manufacture of queen-bee cells in the hive. *See also* kairomone.

phloem. The principal food-conducting tissue of vascular plants, which together with the xylem forms the *vascular tissue. The first phloem to be formed is the *primary phloem*, which develops from the procambium of a primary meristem and consists of *protophloem and *metaphloem. *Secondary phloem* is found in plants with secondary thickening and is formed from the vascular cambium. Phloem is a composite tissue composed of several cell types. The *sieve elements (the conducting cells), *companion cells, and phloem parenchyma all have thin cellulose walls and are usually disorganized and crushed at the end of their functional life. However, phloem is often associated with the development of *fibres, which arise either within the phloem itself or as caps or sheaths around it. These fibres are always thick-walled but are not always lignified. Occasionally there may be other sclerenchymatous cells in the phloem.

phloroglucin. *See* staining.

Pholidota. An order of the Eutheria containing a single genus, *Manis* (pangolin or scaly anteater), a nocturnal insectivorous often arboreal mammal of Asia and Africa. *Manis* has a long toothless snout and a long thin tongue for collecting ants and termites, clawed feet for digging, and a prehensile tail for climbing. The body is covered with overlapping horny scales and the animal can roll into a ball for defence.

Phoronida (Phoronidea). A small phylum of marine wormlike invertebrates living in self-secreted chitinous tubes attached to rocks. The food-catching organ is a *lophophore and the gut is U-shaped. Phoronids have a closed blood vascular system, with haemoglobin as the respiratory pigment.

phosphagen (phosphocreatine). *See* creatine.

phosphatides. *See* phospholipids.

phosphatidic acid. A simple phosphoglyceride with two fatty-acid residues esterified to carbons 1 and 2 of glycerol phosphate. It is formed in the biosynthesis of the more abundant phosphoglycerides (*see* phospholipids).

phosphocreatine (phosphagen). *See* creatine.

phosphoglyceride. *See* phospholipids.

phospholipids (phosphatides). Polar lipids that are important components of cell membranes. Phospholipids can be divided into two groups: the phospho-glycerides and the sphingomyelins.

Phosphoglycerides are fatty-acid esters of glycerol phosphate with an alcohol group (e.g. ethanolamine, choline, serine, inositol) esterified to the phosphate. The most important phosphoglycerides are *phosphatidyl ethanolamine* (*cephalin*) and *phosphatidyl choline* (*lecithin*), the former being particularly abundant in the brain. Also belonging to this group are the *plasmalogens*, in which an α,β-unsaturated fatty aldehyde and a carboxylic acid are esterified to the glycerol and a base (e.g. ethanolamine) is often esterified to the phosphoric acid. Plasmalogens are concentrated in the brain and heart.

Sphingomyelins are derivatives of sphingosine with a fatty acid in amide linkage to the amino group of sphingosine phosphate and a base, usually choline, esterified to the phosphate. They are abundant in the brain.

Phospholipid molecules are *amphipathic, containing a polar head of the negative phosphate group and the positive alcohol group and a hydrophobic tail of the fatty-acid chains.

phosphoprotein. One of a group of conjugated proteins in which phosphoric acid is bound to the protein portion of the molecule. The group includes *casein.

photic zone. The surface waters of a sea or lake, into which sufficient light penetrates for photosynthesis.

photoautotrophic. *See* autotrophic.

photoheterotrophic. *See* heterotrophic, phototrophic.

photonasty. Nastic movement in response to light. *See* nyctinastic movements.

photoperiodism. The response by an organism to length of day (*photoperiod*). Flowering of most plants and certain other plant responses (such as tuber and bulb formation, leaf fall, bud dormancy) can be controlled by photoperiod. Plants

may flower in response to short or long days and are called *short-day* and *long-day plants* respectively. Examples of the former include chrysanthemum and cocklebur, and of the latter spinach and certain cereals. The critical factor is, in fact, the length of the dark period. For instance, a brief flash of white or red light during a long night will inhibit flowering of a short-day plant but stimulate flowering of a long-day plant. The red flash effect can be reversed by a far-red flash, indicating that *phytochrome is the photoreceptive pigment. The leaves are the sensitive organs and the stimulus is transmitted from them to the terminal bud (*see* florigen, gibberellin). Some plants, e.g. tomato, flower independently of day length: they are known as *day-neutral plants*. The breeding season of many animals and many other seasonal activities, such as *migration (in birds) are determined by photoperiod. *See also* circadian rhythm.

photophosphorylation (photosynthetic phosphorylation). The synthesis of ATP from phosphate and ADP during photosynthesis, using light energy. There are two types: *cyclic photophosphorylation*, coupled to cyclic electron flow, in which ATP is the only product; and *noncyclic photophosphorylation*, which is coupled to noncyclic electron flow, the electrons being used to reduce $NADP^+$ as well as to make ATP. *See* photosynthesis.

photoreactivation. *DNA repair that requires the presence of light. One type of mutation incurred by DNA, especially by irradiation with ultraviolet light, is the formation of thymine dimers between two adjacent thymine bases in the same DNA strand. Such dimers are cleaved by enzymes in the presence of visible light of wavelength 300–400 nm. *See also* dark repair.

photoreceptor. A sense organ responding to light. *See* eye.

photorespiration. A light-dependent type of respiration that occurs in most photosynthetic plants and differs from normal (or dark) respiration. Glycollate, produced in chloroplasts by oxidation (using oxygen) of a Calvin cycle carbohydrate, is the substrate. It is oxidized to glyoxylate in peroxisomes (*see* microbody) and recycled to form a Calvin cycle carbohydrate via intermediates including the amino acids glycine and serine. The wasteful loss of carbon dioxide and energy in the form of ATP and $NADPH_2$ that this entails reduces the efficiency of photosynthesis. Some plants, characterized by very low carbon dioxide *compensation points, have very low rates of photorespiration. These are mostly C_4 plants (*see* photosynthesis), whose special type of carbon dioxide fixation apparently reduces glycollate production and hence increases photosynthetic efficiency.

photosynthesis. The synthesis of organic compounds by reduction of carbon dioxide using light energy absorbed by chlorophyll. In green plants, in which water is the hydrogen donor and source of released oxygen, it can be represented by an empirical equation:

$$CO_2 + 2H_2O \xrightarrow[\text{light}]{\text{chlorophyll}} [CH_2O] + H_2O + O_2$$

The evolution of photosynthesis was responsible for the switch from an anaerobic to the present aerobic atmosphere of the earth (*see* origin of life). Photosynthesis serves directly or indirectly as the source of carbon and energy for all forms of life except chemosynthetic organisms. In eukaryotes it takes place in chloroplasts.

Photosynthesis comprises *light* and *dark reactions*. The light-dependent reactions take place on thylakoid membranes and produce the ATP and $NADPH_2$ used in the subsequent dark reactions. The light-absorbing pigments are distributed in two systems, *Photosystems* or *Pigment Systems I* and *II* (*PSI* and *PSII*), prob-

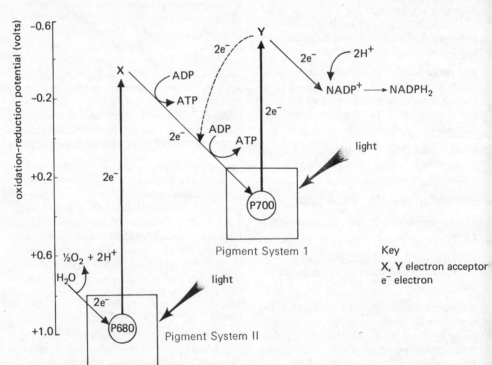

The main photosynthetic pigments

ably in *photosynthetic units. Each system contains chlorophyll a and accessory pigments, the latter mainly in PSII. Each also has photoreactive centres, or traps, containing one molecule of *P700* (PSI) or *P680* (PSII) (see diagram). These are probably modified chlorophyll a molecules; they collect energy absorbed by the other pigments, become excited, and emit high-energy electrons that are accepted by electron carriers (X and Y in diagram). Electrons from PSII flow down an electron transport chain between the two systems; their energy is used to generate ATP (*noncyclic photophosphorylation*) and finally they replace electrons lost from PSI. Electrons from PSI flow down a second chain, either reducing NADP$^+$ or recycling to PSI causing *cyclic photophosphorylation* (*see* photophosphorylation). The electrons (and hydrogen) used to reduce NADP$^+$ are derived ultimately from water (since water supplies electrons to replenish PSII), with the evolution of oxygen. Photosynthetic bacteria, which may lack PSII, use other electron donors to PSI and therefore do not evolve oxygen. For example, green and purple sulphur bacteria use hydrogen sulphide and release sulphur; purple nonsulphur bacteria use an organic molecule.

The dark (light-independent) reactions of photosynthesis use the energy (ATP) and reducing power (NADPH$_2$) produced in the light reactions to reduce carbon dioxide (CO_2). In eukaryotes it takes place in the chloroplast stroma. There are two possible routes. In some plants, the C_3 *plants*, the first product is a 3-carbon (C_3) compound, phosphoglyceric acid (PGA), two molecules of which are formed when CO_2 combines with a C_5 sugar, ribulose diphosphate. PGA may be used for fatty acid or amino acid synthesis, but is usually reduced (using NADPH$_2$ and ATP) to phosphoglyceraldehyde, a triose phosphate. This feeds a complex cycle, the Calvin cycle (or *Benson-Calvin-Bassham cycle*), that produces hexoses (e.g. glucose and fructose) and regenerates

ribulose diphosphate. Similar cycles probably operate in photosynthetic bacteria and in chemosynthetic organisms, in which oxidative metabolism supplies ATP and NADPH$_2$. C_3 plants also produce glycollate in varying amounts, as well as PGA, as a result of *photorespiration.

The second route is typical of tropical grasses and certain other plants. These are called C_4 *plants* because the first products are C_4-dicarboxylic acids. Oxaloacetate, the first, is made by combination of CO_2 with the C_3 compound phosphoenolpyruvate (PEP) in mesophyll chloroplasts. The enzyme involved has a very high affinity for CO_2, resulting in low CO_2 *compensation points in C_4 plants, and a greater efficiency of CO_2 fixation. Oxaloacetate is rapidly converted to the C_4 acids malate and aspartate, which are transported to specialized chloroplasts (longer and with reduced grana) of the large cells surrounding the vascular bundles (*bundle-sheath cells*) typical of C_4 plants. Here they release CO_2, which is refixed as in C_3 plants. Thus a carbon dioxide pump operates between mesophyll and bundle sheath chloroplasts. This modified pathway is known as the C_4-*dicarboxylic acid pathway* (or *Hatch-Slack pathway*). The concentrations of CO_2 built up in the bundle sheaths are high enough to inhibit photorespiration; C_4 plants are therefore photosynthetically more efficient than C_3 plants (in which photorespiration largely wastes CO_2 and energy) and are capable of more rapid growth. Optimum growth in these plants occurs at higher light intensities and temperatures than in C_3 plants and they use only half the water per unit increase in dry weight. C_4 plants are therefore well adapted to tropical climates.

photosynthetic pigments. The light-absorbing pigments of photosynthesis, located on *thylakoid membranes. Several classes exist; some are *accessory pigments*, whose function is to collect light energy and pass it to a *principal pigment* (see table). The pigments are distributed

class of pigment	name	location
CHLOROPHYLL (Chl)	†Chl a	all photosynthetic plants except bacteria
	*Chl b	higher plants, green algae
	*Chl c	brown algae, diatoms, dinoflagellates
	*Chl d	some red algae
	†Bacteriochlorophyll	purple and green bacteria
	†Chlorobium chlorophyll (Bacterioviridin)	green bacteria
CAROTENOID	*Carotenes *Xanthophylls }	all photosynthetic plants
PHYCOBILIN	*Phycoerythrin	main phycobilin in red algae; also blue-green algae
	*Phycocyanin	main phycobilin in blue-green algae; also red algae

*accessory pigments   †principal pigments

Postulated light reactions of photosynthesis

in two systems, Pigment Systems I and II (*see* photosynthesis).

All photosynthetic organisms contain chlorophylls and carotenoids. *Chlorophylls* absorb mainly red and blue-violet light, reflecting green light, and therefore (unless masked by other pigments) impart a green colour to the organism. Structurally, the chlorophyll molecule has a roughly square head (porphin (or tetrapyrrole) ring; *see* porphyrin) with magnesium at its centre and a long tail (a long chain alcohol, phytol). Different chlorophylls have different side-chains. *Chlorophyll a* (and its bacterial equivalents), the most important pigment, has various forms with different absorption peaks, e.g. Chl a 670, 695, 700, 680. The latter two form the energy traps of Pigment Systems I and II respectively.

Carotenoids are yellow, orange, red, or brown pigments that absorb strongly in the blue-violet range. They are usually masked by chlorophylls, which they may protect from oxidation by molecular oxygen. With anthocyanins they contribute to autumn foliage shades when chlorophyll is lost. They are also widely distributed in nonphotosynthetic tissues, usually in plastids. Thus they form the bright yellows and oranges of many flowers and some fruits, e.g. tomato.

There are two types: the *carotenes*, which are hydrocarbons (tetraterpenes), and the *xanthophylls*, which are similar but contain oxygen. β-carotene is the most widely distributed carotene (well known as the orange pigment of carrots); it is converted to vitamin A by vertebrates. The major xanthophylls of higher plant leaves are *lutein*, *violaxanthin*, and *neoxanthin*. Another xanthophyll, *fucoxanthin*, which has an especially broad absorption spectrum, is responsible for the brown colour of diatoms and brown algae.

Phycobilins are related to bile pigments. They are tetrapyrroles, like the chlorophylls, but with an open-chain structure and lacking magnesium. They are bound to water-soluble proteins in small particles called *phycobilisomes* and make efficient use of the middle regions of the visible light spectrum. *Phycocyanin* absorbs orange and red light, appearing blue. With chlorophyll a, it is responsible for the colour of blue-green algae. Red algae contain a high proportion of the red *phycoerythrin*, which absorbs green light efficiently.

photosynthetic unit. A hypothetical light-harvesting unit of photosynthesis, comprising in green plants about 300 light-absorbing chlorophyll a molecules plus associated molecules that supply excitation energy (excitons) to a reaction centre, or trap, consisting of a modified chlorophyll a molecule (either *P700 or *P680). Two types of unit of different sizes may exist, containing pigments of either Pigment System I (P700 trap) or Pigment System II (P680 trap). Photosynthetic units may correspond to the structural units called *quantasomes. The units of bacteria are thought to contain about 50 bacteriochlorophyll molecules.

Photosystems I and II. See photosynthesis.

phototaxis. See taxis.

phototrophic (photosynthetic). Designating organisms (phototrophs) that use light energy to synthesize their organic requirements, either from inorganic precursors (photoautotrophic organisms) or from organic precursors obtained from the environment (photoheterotrophic organisms). Most phototrophs are photoautotrophic and include all green plants. See also autotrophic (for classification).

phototropism (heliotropism). Tropic movement in response to light (see tropism). Coleoptiles and most stems are positively phototropic, i.e. they grow towards light; since leaves are usually plagiotropic to light, the combined effect is to ensure the optimum arrangement of leaves to trap light energy for photosynthesis. The tip of the stem or coleoptile is photosensitive; auxin accumulates on its shaded side and moves down the organ causing faster growth on that side, and hence bending towards the light. Most roots are insensitive to light; others are negatively phototropic, e.g. sunflower.

phragmoplast. The region between the daughter nuclei of a dividing plant cell. It consists initially of spindle fibres (microtubules) only, which proliferate rapidly to form a barrel-shaped birefringent structure containing ribosomes, Golgi apparatus, microtubules, and endoplasmic reticulum. It contains the cell plate and functions in *cytokinesis; the microtubules may serve to guide Golgi vesicles to the plate during its formation.

phycobilin. See photosynthetic pigments.

phycobilisome. One of many particles, about 35 nm in diameter, that contain phycobilins and cover the photosynthetic lamellae of red and blue-green algae. See also photosynthetic pigments.

phycobiont. The algal constituent of a lichen. Compare mycobiont.

phycocyanin. A blue phycobilin pigment. See photosynthetic pigments.

phycoerythrin. A red phycobilin pigment. See photosynthetic pigments.

Phycomycetes. A group of mycelial fungi (Eumycophyta) whose hyphae are coenocytic or septate and whose sexual reproduction results in the formation of a zygospore (from two equal gametangia) or an oospore (from two unequal gametangia). The sex organs are rarely produced in a fruiting body and under certain conditions flagellate zoospores may be produced. The group includes many important parasites, including the damping-off and downy mildew fungi.

phylloclade. A cladode, particularly the swollen cladode of a succulent plant, such as a cactus.

phyllode. A petiole that is expanded to resemble a leaf and provide a surface area for photosynthesis. The lamina itself is undeveloped. Phyllodes occur in some species of Acacia and in Lathyrus nissolia (grass vetch).

phyllopodium. 1. (in botany). The base of a leaf stalk, which acts as a joint between the leaf and the stem. All or part of the phyllopodium may become expanded to form a cushion, the pulvinus. Changes in turgor pressure of the cells of the pulvinus bring about alterations in the position of the leaf. In both monocotyledons and dicotyledons the phyllopodium may form a leaf sheath, as in grasses and *Heracleum sphondylium* (hogweed); it may also produce stipules. **2.** (in zoology). The type of flattened appendage characteristic of crustaceans of the subclass Branchiopoda. *See also* biramous appendage.

phyllotaxis (phyllotaxy). The distribution of leaves around a stem. It is frequently expressed as a fraction in which the numerator denotes the number of circuits of the stem between one leaf and the first leaf that occurs directly above it and the denominator denotes the number of leaves involved in these circuits; for example, 2/5 represents two circuits of the stem involving five leaves (the sixth leaf would be directly above the first). The most common leaf arrangements are expressed in the fractional sequence known as the *Fibonacci series* (or *Fibonacci summation*), in which the value of each denominator and numerator is the sum of the corresponding values of the previous two fractions (1/2, 1/3, 2/5, 3/8, 5/13, 8/21, etc.). The series culminates in a value that would correspond to an angle of divergence between leaf primordia of 137° 30′ 2″ (the *ideal Fibonacci angle*), which, if achieved in a plant, would mean that no leaf overshadowed another and would thus produce the ideal leaf mosaic. *See also* leaf.

phylogenetic. Designating a classification based on phylogeny, i.e. on evolutionary descent. *Compare* phenetic.

phylogeny. The history of the evolution of a species, genus, phylum, etc. *Compare* ontogeny. *See* recapitulation.

phylum (*pl.* **phyla**). A unit used in the *classification of animals. A phylum consists of a number of classes, or occasionally of only one class, with certain important characteristics in common, implying that all members are descended from a common ancestor. For example the phylum Protozoa consists of unicellular organisms; the phylum Arthropoda contains invertebrates with exoskeletons and jointed appendages.

Large phyla are divided into *subphyla*; for example the phylum Chordata is divided into the subphyla Urochordata, Cephalochordata, and Vertebrata. Subphyla are then divided into classes. The corresponding unit in plant classification is the division (although the phylum is used in some plant classification schemes).

Physarum. *See* slime fungus.

physiological saline. *See* Ringer's solution.

physiological specialization. *See* specialization.

physiology. The study of the functioning of organisms and their parts. *Compare* morphology.

phytane. *See* chemical fossils.

phytoalexin. A nonspecific antibiotic produced by a plant in response either to infection by a microorganism (usually a fungus) or occasionally to chemical or environmental factors or injury. Phytoalexins are produced in appreciable amounts and contribute to disease resistance. Many phytoalexins are phenolic compounds; more than twenty have been chemically identified.

phytochrome. A blue-green proteinaceous pigment found in low concentrations in nearly all parts of higher plants. There are two forms, one (P_R or P_{660}) absorbing red and the other (P_{FR} or P_{730}) far-red light; these forms interchange rapidly and reversibly as shown in the diagram.

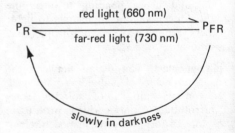

Interchangeable forms of phytochrome

The physiologically active P_{FR} form mediates a range of important morphogenetic responses to light, being formed in red (and hence white) light, even of very low intensity and short duration. Processes controlled include *photoperiodism (and hence floral initiation); greening and expansion of young or etiolated leaves and cotyledons; inhibition of etiolation; breaking of dormancy of certain seeds; and anthocyanin formation.

phytogeography. *See* plant geography.

phytohaemagglutinin (PHA). A *lectin that is bound by the glycoproteins at the cell surface and thereby stimulates some cells to divide. PHA is commonly used to stimulate *in vitro* division of circulating lymphocytes.

phytohormone. A plant hormone. *See* growth substance.

phytokinin (cytokinin). A naturally occurring plant *kinin.

phytoplankton. Plant members of the *plankton.

pia mater. The innermost of the three *meninges investing the tetrapod brain and spinal cord: it is soft and vascular. *See also* subarachnoid space.

picornavirus. *See* virus.

picro-carmine. *See* staining.

Pigment Systems I and II. *See* photosynthesis.

pikas. *See* Lagomorpha.

pileus. The cap or upper part of the fruiting body of certain fungi, especially the Agaricales, on or under which the spore-producing tissues are developed.

pili (fimbriae). Fine straight processes exclusive to certain bacteria, projecting from the cell wall in great numbers. Composed of identical protein subunits helically arranged around a central hollow core, they are involved in DNA exchange during *conjugation.

piliferous layer. The epidermal region of a *root on which the root hairs are produced.

Piltdown man. A fraudulent fossil man that was found at Piltdown, Sussex, and given the name *Eoanthropus*. Skull fragments were first found by Charles Dawson (1864–1916), in 1911, and subsequent discoveries led to the reconstruction of part of a skull. Chemical tests on the skull from 1949 to 1953 showed that the jaw bone was that of a modern ape and that the braincase was Pleistocene, but its origin unknown. The skull had been artificially coloured and the teeth artificially ground down, indicating that the skull fragments had been deliberately planted. Despite much speculation and circumstantial evidence, the perpetrator of the hoax has never been positively identified.

pineal eye. *See* median eye.

pineal gland. A small cone-shaped outgrowth of the posterior part of the vertebrate forebrain that is innervated by the sympathetic nervous system and may have an endocrine function. In some lower vertebrates it is externally visible as the pineal eye (*see* median eye). In higher vertebrates the gland is deeply embedded in surrounding neural tissue although it may still be responsive to light that penetrates the skull. The pineal gland secretes melatonin and vasotocin; a number of other proteins and peptides extracted from the pineal gland may also prove to have hormonal function.

pinna. The outermost part of the outer ear, present in some mammals. It consists of a flap of skin and cartilage around the external opening of the ear that aids the collection of sound waves.

Pinnipedia. An order of the Eutheria containing the seals (e.g. *Phoca*), sea-lions (e.g. *Eumetopias*), and the walrus (*Odobenus*): marine carnivorous mammals with a streamlined body covered with thick fur and limbs modified as flippers. Pinnipeds have reduced and simplified teeth, often with cusps for holding fish. *Odobenus* eats molluscs dug up with the tusklike canines. Pinnipeds breed on land.

pinocytosis. *See* endocytosis.

pistil. The seed-bearing organ of angiosperms, consisting of the *stigma, *style and *ovary. It is formed of a single carpel in apocarpous gynoecia (see illustration at *ovule) and of two or more united carpels in syncarpous gynoecia.

Pithecanthropus. See Homo.

pith (medulla). The part of the *ground tissues of a plant that is internal to the primary vascular tissue when this is in the form of a ring (either complete or as a ring of vascular bundles; *see* stele). Occasionally, additional strands of fibres, xylem, or phloem or complete vascular strands may occur within the pith: these are termed *medullary bundles*. Although the pith is usually parenchymatous, it may be partly or entirely sclerenchymatous and often contains such structures as laticifers and resin canals. In some plants it is hollow except for horizontal plates of tissue, usually at the nodes (*diaphragmed pith*). The plates of

parenchymatous tissue extending from the pith to the cortex between the vascular bundles (when the primary vascular tissue is in the form of a ring of bundles) are termed *primary medullary rays* (or *pith rays*). *See* medullary ray.

pit organ. A receptor of snakes of the family Crotalidae (e.g. rattlesnakes) and of some snakes of the family Boidae (e.g. pythons) that is sensitive to small changes in heat and is therefore used for the detection of live prey. The organ consists of an innervated membrane stretched across a pit located between the eye and nostril.

pitressin. *See* vasopressin.

pits. Depressions or cavities on the secondary wall of a plant cell that allow freer movement of substances between adjacent cells. Similar areas in the primary cell wall (which have abundant plasmodesmata in living cells) are termed *primary pit fields* and pit development usually occurs at these areas. A pit consists basically of the *pit membrane*, which is composed of the middle lamella plus primary wall and may have a *torus, and the *pit cavity*, the disconti-

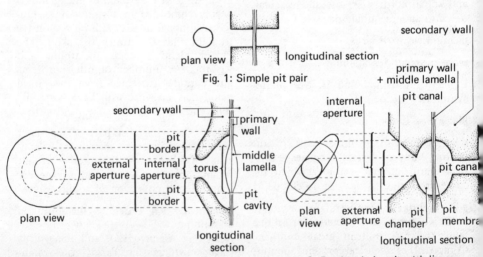

Fig. 1: Simple pit pair

Fig. 2: Bordered pit pair with round internal aperture

Fig. 3: Bordered pit pair with linear internal aperture

Pit structure

nuity in the secondary wall. The delimitation of the pit on the pit-membrane side is termed the *external aperture*, and on the cell-lumen side, the *internal aperture*. Pits with straight-sided cavities are termed *simple* (Fig. 1); those in which the secondary wall arches over the cavity are known as *bordered* (Figs. 2 and 3). Pits usually occur in pairs (termed *pit pairs*) on either side of the middle lamella between two abutting cells. A single pit is termed a *blind pit*. The internal aperture varies in shape from round (Fig. 2) to linear (slitlike) (Fig. 3). When the secondary wall is very thick the cavity may consist of a *pit chamber* connected by a narrow tube, the *pit canal*, to the cell lumen (Fig. 3). Different types of pits are formed between cells of different types, and the pitting between vertical elements of xylem and the ray parenchyma is often characteristic of particular plants. The pits on the vertical walls of tracheary elements are arranged in one of three ways (*see* pitted thickening).

pitted thickening. A type of secondary wall formation in xylem vessels and tracheids in which the wall material forms a continuous layer over the primary wall except for special areas termed *pits. The pits may be simple or bordered and their arrangement varies: they may be grouped in horizontal pairs or rows (*opposite pitting*) or in diagonal rows (*alternate pitting*) across the vessel or tracheid wall or they may be scalariform (*see* scalariform thickening). In gymnosperms the pits may possess a *torus. Pitted secondary walls occur in the last-formed metaxylem elements of the primary xylem and in the secondary xylem elements. *Compare* annular, spiral, and reticulate thickenings.

pituitary gland (hypophysis). A major endocrine gland of vertebrates that occurs within the skull and is attached by a short stalk to the hypothalamus. It secretes a number of important protein and glycoprotein hormones and consists of two separately derived components.

The *adenohypophysis* is derived from an invagination of the embryonic mouth and consists of the *pars distalis*, *pars tuberalis*, and *pars intermedia*. The *neurohypophysis* develops from an outgrowth of the posterior part of the forebrain and consists of the *pars nervosa* and the *infundibulum* (neural stalk), which forms the infundibular stem and median eminence. The pars distalis and pars tuberalis constitute the anterior lobe; the pars intermedia and pars nervosa the posterior lobe.

The pars distalis secretes at least seven hormones (*see* growth hormone, ACTH, lipotrophin, thyrotrophin, luteinizing hormone, follicle-stimulating hormone, prolactin). The pars intermedia secretes *melanocyte-stimulating hormone. The secretion of these hormones is regulated by factors (or hormones) synthesized by the hypothalamus and released into the portal blood vessels of the median eminence (*see* neuroendocrine systems).

The pars nervosa secretes *oxytocin and *vasopressin. These hormones are formed in specific groups of neurones in paired supraoptic and paraventricular nuclei within the hypothalamus; they are transported in granules down the axons of the infundibular stem and stored in the pars nervosa. The endocrine role of the pituitary gland has been known for more than a century but was only fully established in the 1920s, by studies of the deficiency syndromes resulting from hypophysectomy.

placenta. **1.** A temporary flat organ within the uterus of mammals and other viviparous animals that establishes a close association between the foetal and maternal blood circulations. It consists of both embryonic and maternal tissues and enables the foetus to depend entirely on maternal systems for obtaining oxygen and nutrients as well as for the removal of metabolic waste products. The degree of union of the tissues (*placentation*) varies between mammalian types: in ungulates the outer chorionic tissues of the embryo are merely closely applied to the maternal endometrium. In many groups, however, maternal tissue is eroded in such a way that direct contact is made with the maternal blood vessels. In primates (including humans) foetal tissue is directly bathed in maternal blood, whereas in rodents the foetal capillaries are directly bathed in maternal blood. The placenta also produces hormones (gonadotrophins, oestrogens, and progesterone) and in some species takes over the reproductive endocrine roles of the pituitary and ovaries during pregnancy. Soon after parturition the placenta is delivered as the *afterbirth*.

2. The part of a plant ovary to which the ovules are attached, which often corresponds to the line of fusion of the carpel edges. There are typically two placentae per carpel (one on each lateral margin) but the various types of infolding and fusion of the carpels in ovary formation have led to a variety of *placentations.

3. The tissue to which sporangia or spores are attached.

Placentalia. The placental mammals (*see* Eutheria).

placentation. **1.** The arrangement of placentae in a plant ovary. The principal placentations are (1) *marginal*: along the suture formed by the carpel edges in monocarpellary (simple) ovaries; (2) *parietal*: along the suture lines formed by the fusion of the carpel edges in polycarpellary (compound) unilocular ovaries; (3) *axile*: around a central column of tissue that is connected to the ovary wall by septa in polycarpellary multilocular ovaries; (4) *free central*: around a central column of tissue in polycarpellary ovaries in which the septa between the carpels have disappeared to produce a single loculus; (5) *superficial*: over the entire inner surface of the ovary wall; (6) *basal*: at the base of the ovary; and (7) *apical*: at the top of the ovary.

2. The type of union between foetal and maternal tissues in the mammalian *placenta.

Placodermi. A class of extinct fishes common in the Devonian. They had a heavy bony armour over the head and front part of the body, an endoskeleton of bone, autostylic jaw suspension, paired fins, and a heterocercal tail. The first gill slit was not modified as a spiracle, as in other fishes. Placoderms were probably more closely related to the Chondrichthyes than to the Osteichthyes. There are several orders, including the Antiarchi and Arthrodira.

Placodontia. A suborder of the Sauropterygia containing large extinct Triassic reptiles, e.g. *Placodus*, specialized for life in shallow coastal waters. Placodonts had long limbs with flattened paddle-like feet with which they rowed themselves through the water.

placoid scale (denticle). A toothlike scale, characteristic of the Chondrichthyes, consisting of a basal plate embedded in the skin with a pointed spine projecting from the epidermis. It is composed of dentine penetrated by numerous fine canals with a pulp cavity in the centre containing blood vessels, nerves, and odontoblasts. The spine is covered with a layer of enamel. Modified placoid scales in the mouth function as teeth. *Compare* ganoid scale, cosmoid scale.

plagioclimax. The steady state (*climax) established in an area in which the natural succession of plants has been changed or deflected by the influence of one or more environmental factors. For example, the chalk grasslands of England have been maintained in their condition as a result of continual grazing by sheep and rabbits and by cultivation. If these influences were removed, the natural succession would result in the establishment of chalkland scrub.

plagiogeotropism. Plagiotropic response to gravity. *See* geotropism.

plagiotropic. *See* tropism.

planarians. *See* Turbellaria.

planation. The restriction of branching in part (or all) of an organism to a single plane. Planation is thought to have played a role in the evolution of megaphylls (*see* telome theory).

plankton. Minute plants (*phytoplankton*) and animals (*zooplankton*) that float in the surface waters of a sea or lake; they are of great economic and ecological importance. The chief constituents of phytoplankton are unicellular algae, which carry out photosynthesis and form the basis of the food chains that support all aquatic life. The zooplankton, typically consisting of animals with weak locomotory powers, includes protozoans, small crustaceans, and various invertebrate larvae.

plant geography (phytogeography). The study of the distribution of plant species over the surface of the earth. *Compare* zoogeography.

plantigrade. Designating a gait of mammals in which the entire foot, i.e. digits and metacarpals (or metatarsals), remains flat on the ground. This is the most primitive gait and is characteristic of primates, insectivores, bears, etc. *Compare* digitigrade, unguligrade.

planula. The free-swimming ciliated larva of many Cnidaria (Hydrozoa and Scyphozoa), which has an outer layer of ectoderm and an inner layer of endoderm but no body cavity. On attaching to a hard substrate it develops an internal cavity, mouth, tentacles, etc.

plaque. 1. A transparent zone of lysed cells in an opaque film of susceptible bacteria grown on an agar medium, produced by bacteriophage activity. The plaque is formed by localized cycles of bacteriophage infection, growth, and lysis of the host bacteria, starting from a single bacteriophage particle or infected cell in the bacterial culture. Similar plaques are formed in tissue cultures of animal cells infected with a virus.
2. A deposit of mucus, bacteria, etc., that forms on the surface of the teeth and may contribute to the development of caries.

plasma. *See* blood plasma.

plasma cells. Connective tissue cells usually found in large numbers in areas of inflammation associated with chronic infection. They are thought to be derived from lymphocytes or lymphocyte precursor cells (*lymphoblasts*) and are responsible for the production of antibodies.

plasmagel. The gel-like state of protoplasm, which may be reversibly transformed to *plasmasol. Ectoplasm is typically a plasmagel.

plasmagene. A self-duplicating cytoplasmic entity containing its own set of genes independent of the nucleus. Its inheritance is therefore non-Mendelian since it does not involve fusion of nuclei (gametes). *See* cytoplasmic inheritance.

plasmalemma. *See* plasma membrane.

plasmalogens. *See* phospholipids.

plasma membrane (plasmalemma). The *membrane that surrounds the protoplasm of a cell.

plasmasol. The sol-like (fluid) state of protoplasm, which may be reversibly transformed to *plasmagel. Endoplasm is usually in a plasmasol condition.

plasmid. A genetic element, often found in bacterial cells, that is separate from the genomic DNA and replicates independently of it. At one time plasmids capable of integration into the genome were called *episomes, but the term plasmid is now generally used for all independent DNA factors. Plasmids include some bacteriophages and the factors bearing genes for *bacteriocins (Col factors), drug resistance (R factors), and bacterial sex (*F factors). All consist of circles of double-stranded DNA. *Chimaeric factors* contain sequences of eukaryotic genes; they are produced by modern techniques of gene manipulation and are widely used as a means of cloning genes in bacterial hosts.

plasmin. A nonspecific enzyme that is responsible for the dissolution of blood clots (*fibrinolysis). It exists in normal blood as the inactive precursor *plasminogen*, which is converted into active plasmin by several proteolytic factors, e.g. trypsin.

plasmodesma (*pl.* **plasmodesmata).** A narrow tube traversing the plant cell wall through which the protoplasm of adjacent cells is continuous (*see* symplast). The tube is lined by the plasma membrane and contains a central, possibly tubular, core normally associated at either end with endoplasmic reticulum. The number per cell varies; they are sometimes concentrated in primary pit fields (*see* pits). Sieve plate pores are derived from plasmodesmata.

Plasmodiophorales (Plasmodiophoromycetes). A group of endoparasitic fungi whose plant body consists of a plasmodium (within a host cell). They are sometimes placed in the Myxomycophyta but are more usually included in the *Eumycophyta, as they will produce flagellate zoospores under certain conditions.

plasmodium. An acellular multinucleate amoeboid protoplasmic mass bounded by a plasma membrane, such as forms the vegetative phase of the Myxomycetes (slime fungi). Growth by plasmogamy may occur between plasmodia of the same species. In the Acrasiales (cellular slime fungi) the constituent amoebae retain their individuality within the protoplasmic mass, which is then termed a *pseudoplasmodium. Compare* cell, coenocyte, syncytium.

Plasmodium. See Sporozoa.

plasmogamy. The union of two or more protoplasts, which occurs in the formation of a heterokaryon or precedes karyogamy in sexual reproduction.

plasmolysis. The loss of water from a plant or prokaryote cell to the point at which the protoplast shrinks away from the cell wall. It occurs when the cell is in contact with a hypertonic solution. As the cell loses water, its volume, and hence also its turgor pressure, decreases. Eventually no further decrease in volume is possible owing to the relative rigidity of the cell wall. At this point, known as *incipient plasmolysis,* turgor pressure is zero. As the protoplast shrinks further it pulls away from the cell wall around all or some of its surface.

plastid. An organelle present in all plants except bacteria, blue-green algae, and fungi; it is enclosed by two membranes (the envelope) and has various functions. Plastids are classified according to their pigmentation. *Chloroplasts contain photosynthetic pigments, including chlorophyll, and carry out photosynthesis. In *chromoplasts*, the pigments are predominantly or exclusively carotenoids, whose red or yellow colour masks any chlorophyll that may be present. Chromoplasts are usually derived from chloroplasts or leucoplasts and are found particularly in fruits and flowers of higher plants, in which their bright colours may serve to attract animals for pollination and seed dispersal. *Leucoplasts* are colourless plastids, lacking pigments, and are often modified for the storage of food, particularly starch (*see* amyloplast). They occur in a variety of tissues, including the epidermis, root parenchyma, and young leaves. Interconversion between all three plastid types can occur. Plastids may be modified for storage of food reserves and can alternatively be classified according to the storage product: *amyloplasts* store starch; *elaioplasts* (*oleoplasts* or *lipidoplasts*) store lipids in the form of fats or oils; *proteoplasts* store protein in various forms, for example as aleurone grains (*aleuroplasts*).

Continuity of plastids from one generation to the next is maintained either by the synchronization of plastid division with cell division (primitive algae, bryophytes, and pteridophytes) or by differentiation of new plastids from much smaller bodies called *proplastids*, located principally in the meristematic regions.

plastochron. The period of time between the initiation of one leaf and the next in the shoot apex, i.e. the time between the initiation of nodes. The leaves develop either singly, in pairs, or in whorls, according to phyllotaxis. The term may also be used for the time interval between the initiation of other organs or structures that develop in a sequence.

plastocyanin. A blue copper-containing protein that is an electron carrier of chloroplasts.

plastogene. A self-duplicating plastid containing a set of non-nuclear genes whose inheritance is therefore non-Mendelian (not determined by fusion of nuclei). It is a type of *plasmagene.

plastoglobuli (osmiophilic globules). Spherical globules of variable size found in the stroma of chloroplasts, often enmeshed between the lamellar membranes. They are composed largely of lipid and are therefore osmiophilic, i.e. they stain conspicuously with osmium tetroxide. During chloroplast ageing and during the transition of chloroplasts to chromoplasts in certain tissues, the globules become very large and accumulate carotenoid pigments.

plastoquinone. A quinone, closely resembling *coenzyme Q (ubiquinone) of mitochondria, that is an electron carrier of chloroplasts.

plastron. The flat ventral section of the shell of chelonians. It is derived from the expanded membrane bones of the pectoral girdle and other bony elements and is overlaid with horny epidermal plates (tortoiseshell). *Compare* carapace.

platelet. A minute cytoplasmic particle, about 2 μm in diameter, that is found in mammalian blood and is derived from giant cells of the bone marrow. Platelets play an essential role in the mechanism of blood clotting, providing a factor necessary for the activation of *thromboplastin, and they also contain a number of pharmacologically active compounds, i.e. histamine, serotonin, and ATP, which have important physiological effects in injury.

Platyhelminthes. A phylum of acoelomate triploblastic invertebrates, the flatworms. The body is bilaterally symmetrical, unsegmented, and flattened dorsoventrally, providing a large surface area for respiration. There is no blood vascular system. The gut (when present) is often branched and has only one opening, the mouth, with a sucking pharynx. Excretion is effected by protonephridia and reproduction by a complex hermaphrodite system. The phylum includes the classes *Turbellaria (planarians), *Trematoda (flukes), and *Cestoda (tapeworms).

platypus (duck-billed platypus). *See* Monotremata.

pleated sheet. *See* beta-pleated sheet.

Plecoptera. An order of exopterygote insects, the stoneflies, in existence since Permian times. The adults have a flattened body with long antennae and two pairs of membranous wings (the hind wings are larger), which are folded flat over the body at rest. Stoneflies are found among the stones and vegetation at the edge of streams, ponds, etc.; they are short-lived and have weak biting mouthparts and many species do not feed. The aquatic nymphs are found mostly in running water.

plectenchyma. A tissue composed of closely woven filaments or hyphae that forms the thallus in some algae, such as the larger Phaeophyta, and certain fungal structures, such as stromata and sclerotia. It may be a *prosenchyma or a *pseudoparenchyma.

plectostele. *See* stele.

pleiomorphism. A type of polymorphism in which there are several different stages in the life history of an organism. It is seen in the life history of insects, which have larval, pupal, and adult stages, and in that of some fungi, which develop in different spore stages.

pleiotropy. A situation in which a single gene affects two or more apparently unrelated aspects of the phenotype of an organism. Genes that code for protein with important roles in early development often display pleiotropy.

Pleistocene. The first epoch of the Quaternary period, in which the Ice Ages occurred. These consisted of several glacials and interglacials, during which the climate varied from very cold, with a tundra vegetation, to warm temperate, with temperate forests. These climatic changes are indicated by the changes in the vegetation. The vertebrate fossils of the Pleistocene include new mammal genera such as *Elephas*, *Bos*, and *Equus*. At the end of the Pleistocene many large mammals became extinct, including the cave bear, Irish elk, mammoth, and giant sloth. During this epoch man evolved from the australopithecines to *Homo neaderthalensis* and *H. sapiens* and the *Palaeolithic cultures were established. *See also* geological time scale.

plerome. The part of the apical meristem that gives rise to the tissues internal to the cortex. *See* histogen theory.

Plesiosauria. An extinct suborder of the Sauropterygia containing marine reptiles that evolved from the Nothosauria in the Triassic and were common in the Jurassic and Cretaceous. They were large (up to 12 metres long), with a short broad flat body, and they used their limbs, which were modified as large strong fairly rigid paddles, to row themselves through the water. Some plesiosaurs, e.g. *Plesiosaurus*, had a very long flexible neck and a small head with long sharp teeth for feeding on fish. Others, e.g. *Pliosaurus*, were more powerful swimmers with longer paddles, a shorter neck, and a very large skull with long jaws and large blunt teeth for crushing molluscs.

pleura. A closed sac of serous membrane in mammals that covers each of the lungs (*pulmonary pleura*) and lines the wall of the chest cavity and the upper surface of the diaphagm (*parietal pleura*). Each pleura encloses a coelomic space, the *pleural cavity*.

pleurocarp. A moss with a prostrate and freely branching growth habit and laterally borne sex organs. *Compare* acrocarp.

pleuropneumonia-like organisms (PPLO). *See* mycoplasmas.

plexus. A diffuse network of neurones. For example, the *brachial plexus* is formed from interconnecting branches of the spinal nerves that supply the forelimbs or fins of vertebrates.

Pliocene. An epoch of the *Tertiary period.

ploidy. The number of complete chromosome sets represented in the nucleus of a cell, e.g. haploidy (1), diploidy (2), triploidy (3), tetraploidy (4).

plumule. 1. The apical bud of a seedling, which appears above the node of the cotyledon (*see* epicotyl).
2. A down feather (*see* feathers).

pluteus. A larva of the Echinoidea and Ophiuroidea, in which a ciliated band for locomotion extends onto projecting arms. *See* dipleurula.

pneumatophore. A specialized negatively geotropic *root.

pod. *See* legume.

Pogonophora. A phylum of marine wormlike invertebrates, the beard worms, living in chitinous tubes projecting from the mud on the ocean floor. The body and coelom are divided into three parts, the anterior section bearing between one and many tentacles. There are no respiratory or alimentary systems and the tentacles are thought to function in gaseous exchange, food capture, and extracellular digestion.

poikilothermy. The condition of being unable to regulate the body temperature, which therefore fluctuates with the temperature of the external environment. Most animals except birds and mammals are poikilothermic (or *cold-blooded*). *Compare* homoiothermy.

polar body (polocyte). *See* oocyte.

pollen. The mature microspores of gymnosperms and angiosperms (*see* microsporangium). *See also* perispore.

pollen analysis. *See* palynology.

pollen chamber. A small cavity inside the micropyle of the ovules of certain gymnosperms, including many cycads, within which the pollen grains are trapped.

pollen droplet (pollination drop). A small drop of liquid exuded from the micropyle of some gymnosperm ovules in which the pollen grains are trapped. In some gymnosperms, e.g. the Taxodiaceae, the drop is actively resorbed when pollen grains of the right species are trapped, drawing the pollen into the micropyle. In gymnosperms with saccate (sac-bearing) pollen, e.g. the Pinaceae, the sacs act as flotation devices and the grain floats up through the pollen droplet to the ovum. Both methods are termed *drop mechanisms*.

pollen sacs. The microsporangia of gymnosperms and angiosperms. In most stamens, they constitute the anthers, each loculus of the anther being equivalent to one pollen sac.

pollen tube. A filamentous extension from the microspore (i.e. pollen grain) of gymnosperms and angiosperms, produced after pollination and usually serving to bring the male gametic nucleus into close proximity with the female nucleus. In gymnosperms other than those with flagellate sperms, the pollen grain is deposited at the micropyle and the pollen tube grows through the nucellus to the egg cell. In gymnosperms with flagellate sperms (Cycadales, Ginkgoales) the pollen tube is a hausto-

rial structure obtaining nourishment from the nucellus. The sperms are released from a branch of the pollen tube outside the nucellus into the liquid in the pollen chamber; they then swim to the egg cell to fertilize it. In angiosperms the pollen grain is deposited on the stigmatic surface of the pistil and the pollen tube grows down between the cells of the style into the loculus of the ovary. It enters the ovule either through the chalazal end (*chalazogamy*) or through the micropyle (*porogamy*).

A pollen tube usually possesses three nuclei: a *tube nucleus* (or *vegetative nucleus*) and two *generative nuclei* (male gametic nuclei). In gymnosperms and angiosperms one generative nucleus fuses with the egg cell to form a zygote. In gymnosperms and some angiosperms the other nuclei disintegrate, but in certain angiosperms the second generative nucleus fuses with a polar nucleus to form the *primary endosperm nucleus*, which gives rise to the endosperm tissue (when this is present in the seed); this is termed *double fertilization*. *See also* embryo sac.

pollex. The digit on the inner side of the tetrapod forelimb. It is often shorter than the other digits and in many terrestrial mammals it is absent. In man and arboreal mammals it is opposable and in flying vertebrates it is specialized as a clutching organ (in bats) or as an aerodynamic device (in birds). *Compare* hallux.

pollination. The transfer of pollen from anther to stigma in angiosperms and from male cone to female cone in gymnosperms. *Self-pollination* is the transfer of pollen from the anther to the stigma of the same flower: it reduces variation and is a type of inbreeding. *Cross-pollination* is the transfer of pollen from the anther of one plant to the stigma of a flower of a different plant: it encourages variation and is a type of outbreeding. However, it is more hazardous than self-pollination as an agent (*vector*) is necessary to transfer the pollen; if the vector fails to cause pollination no seed will be set. Therefore many plants balance the advantages of cross-pollination with those of selfing by having a mechanism such as monoecism, *dichogamy, or *cleistogamy, which encourages crossing but allows selfing to occur if crossing fails. Some plants have only cross-pollination, with an *incompatibility mechanism or dioecism to make selfing absolutely impossible; others habitually self-pollinate, often in the bud before the flower opens. The vector carrying pollen from the anther to the stigma may be an insect (*see* entomophily), wind (*see* anemophily), or more rarely water (*see* hydrophily).

pollution. The presence in the environment of significant amounts of unnatural substances or abnormally high concentrations of natural constituents at a level that causes undesirable effects, such as bronchial irritation, corrosion, or ecological change.
Water pollution.
1. Rivers and lakes. Man requires water containing no toxic or distasteful substances and no pathogenic organisms; aquatic plants and animals require water containing sufficient oxygen for respiration. Although the situation is improving, there are still about 5000 miles of polluted rivers in Great Britain; even after purification some inland waters are too polluted to be used by man.

Pollution caused by organic wastes, such as untreated or badly purified sewage, is harmful to man and depletes the oxygen supply. The organic matter is decomposed by bacteria, which require oxygen for respiration. The amount of oxygen they use is known as the *Biochemical Oxygen Demand (BOD) and the organic pollution in a river can be estimated by measuring the BOD; the higher the BOD, the greater the pollution. A badly polluted river is characterized by the presence of sewage fungus, worms (Tubificidae), and red midge larvae (Chironomidae), which replace the algae, snails, leeches, fish, etc., that inhabit unpolluted waters.

Inland waters can be polluted by excess nutrients. These are derived from sewage effluent and also from agricultural fertilizers, rich in nitrogen and phosphorus, that are carried by rain water or ground water seepage into lakes and rivers. The nutrients cause artificial eutrophication of the water (*see* eutrophic), with the resultant prolific growth (bloom) of certain algae, especially *Cladophora*. The algal bloom not only clogs water-purifying plants but also deoxygenates the water (by respiration when alive and by bacterial decay when dead) and crowds out other organisms.

Chlorinated hydrocarbon pesticides, notably DDT, that reach rivers and lakes either poison aquatic organisms or accumulate in their tissues. At each stage of a food chain there may be a factor of concentration of from two to seven times. Some industrial effluents contain undesirable quantities of metals and their salts, such as lead, copper, and zinc, which are not removed by the normal treatment processes. Hard nonbiodegradable detergents (i.e. detergents not susceptible to bacterial decay), which used to cause foaming and other undesirable effects on reaching rivers, have now been replaced by soft detergents, which are broken down during sewage treatment.

Heat is also classed as a form of pollution (*thermal pollution*). Aquatic life is sensitive to temperature change; trout can be killed by temperatures above 25°C and the coarse fish that survive become fewer as the temperature reaches and exceeds 30°C. However, the efficient use of cooling towers, which also aerate the water, reduces the damage caused by cooling water returned to rivers from power stations and factories.
2. Oceans and seashores. The most damaging pollution is caused by oil spillage from tankers, the most serious of which was the Torrey Canyon disaster of 1967, when 60 000 tonnes of oil were released. Oil is particularly injurious to sea birds, especially to small populations of rarer species such as guillemots and auks. Oil

also produces widespread contamination of beaches.

The accumulation of nonbiodegradable plastics rubbish that is discharged into the sea is creating a growing problem.

Sewage and industrial effluents are unhygienic for bathers but, as the volume of diluting water is greater, they affect oceans to a lesser extent than rivers and lakes.

Air pollution.

Most air pollutants are particles or gases that have entered the atmosphere from the burning of carbonaceous fuels, from industrial processes, and from car exhausts. Large quantities of dust, grit, etc., are produced by the burning of domestic and industrial carbonaceous fuels; as much as one tonne of dust per square mile per day may settle in heavy industrial areas. The smaller particles (smoke) can be drawn into the lungs, causing blackening of the tissues. The presence of smoke in the atmosphere reduces the light intensity and therefore the rate of photosynthesis in plants. Smog (smoke + fog) imposes heart strain on people suffering from bronchitis and other respiratory diseases; about 4000 people died during the London smog of 1952. However, since the establishment of urban smoke control areas (smokeless zones) under the Clean Air Acts of 1956 and 1968, smog has almost disappeared in Britain. Smog now usually refers to the eye-irritating haze produced by the action of sunlight on a mixture of nitrogen oxides and hydrocarbons from car exhausts (photochemical smog), which is a growing problem in the United States.

Much attention has been given in recent years to the oxides of sulphur and nitrogen as air pollutants. Nearly all fuels contain sulphur. Nitrogen oxides are produced industrially by combustion at very high temperatures. At the concentrations created by well-dispersed emissions away from urban areas they may be of some benefit: sulphur dioxide acts as a fungicide to crop plants and the deposition of sulphur into the soil from the atmosphere has been reported to increase crop yields, especially of grasses (sulphur and nitrogen are essential plant nutrients). At concentrations that can be reached in cities, both sulphur and nitrogen are potentially damaging to plants and to people with lung diseases; they are definitely injurious at more than 5 ppm.

Carbon monoxide and lead are dangerous pollutants emitted by petrol engines. Carbon monoxide combines with haemoglobin in the blood and thus interferes with oxygen uptake; tunnels and underground car parks must therefore have adequate ventilation. The carbon monoxide produced by heavy traffic in busy streets does not approach toxic levels but its effects on driving performance are uncertain. Vegetation near busy roads contains a high proportion of lead but the amount of lead in the blood of city dwellers has not yet reached the clinical poisoning level. However, in some countries steps are being taken to reduce the lead content of petrol.

Carbon dioxide, produced by traffic and burning fuel, is slowly building up in the atmosphere (290 ppm 100 years ago; 330 ppm now). The long-term effects of this are not yet certain, but it is thought that carbon dioxide could act as a blanket preventing heat loss from the atmosphere, which would result in an overall increase in the temperature of the earth (*see* greenhouse effect).

polocyte (polar body). *See* oocyte.

polyacrylamide gel. An inert medium widely used for *electrophoresis, especially of proteins and nucleic acids. The acrylamide is prepared as a liquid in a suitable electrophoretic buffer and added to an activator or hardener in the tubes or plates to be used in the separation. Setting of the gel follows within minutes, after which it is cooled, the samples applied, and the current switched on to separate the components.

polyamines. Compounds that contain two or more amino groups. Examples are *putrescine*, $NH_2(CH_2)_4NH_2$, *cadaverine*, $NH_2(CH_2)_5NH_2$, and *spermine*,

$NH_2(CH_2)_3NH(CH_2)_4NH(CH_2)_3NH_2$. At physiological pH these compounds are multivalent cations and are found associated with the anionic sites (i.e. phosphate groups) of DNA helices in some viruses and bacteria. This neutralizing effect is analogous to the action of histones in eukaryotic cells and gives the DNA molecule greater flexibility.

Polychaeta. A class of mostly marine worms, the bristle worms, of the phylum Annelida. Each segment of the body has a pair of limblike parapodia bearing numerous chaetae. The head is well-defined and bears sense organs. Many polychaetes, e.g. *Eulalia*, are active carnivorous crawlers. Some, e.g. *Nereis* (ragworm) and *Arenicola* (lugworm), burrow in sand or mud; others, e.g. *Sabella*, build tubes of sand, mucus, or shell fragments in which they live. These polychaetes have various feeding methods.

polyembryony. The formation of more than one *embryo from a single zygote. It occurs in seed plants, in which several embryos are found in one ovule, and in many group of animals, e.g. the Platyhelminthes. *Identical twins are produced by polyembryony.

polygene. One of a number of genes that together bring about continuous *variation in a characteristic.

polymerase. An enzyme responsible for synthesizing a polymer. Two classes of such enzymes are the *DNA polymerases* and the *RNA polymerases* (or *transcriptases*). In eukaryotic cells there are a number of DNA polymerases, only one of which is responsible for general DNA replication; the others are *DNA repair enzymes. There are four main types of RNA polymerase in eukaryotic cells: Types I to IV. Type I is responsible for transcription of ribosomal RNA genes (except 5S RNA genes), Type II for messenger RNA transcription, Type III for transfer RNA and 5S ribosomal RNA transcription, and Type IV for transcription from the mitochondrial DNA. Bacteria possess a single type of RNA polymerase; they also have repair polymerases in addition to the general DNA polymerase involved in DNA replication. Some special polymerases are associated with viral replication, notably *reverse transcriptase (RNA-dependent DNA polymerase), which synthesizes DNA from an RNA template. It occurs in the replication cycle of some oncogenic viruses.

polymorph (polymorphonuclear leucocyte). One of a group of white blood cells, about 10–12 μm in diameter, having lobulated nuclei and distinct cytoplasmic granules. This name is commonly applied to the three principal granulocytic white cells in blood: *neutrophils, *basophils, and *eosinophils, which usually represent about 60–65% of the white cells of human blood. All polymorphs are phagocytic and migrate freely from the blood vessels into tissues during inflammation.

polymorphism. The existence of two or more different forms (*morphs*) of individuals in the same species. There are two basic types of polymorphism. *Balanced polymorphism* is characterized by the coexistence of the different morphs all the time in the same population. It is seen in animal populations in which the two sexes differ in appearance or where a *caste system exists and in plant populations of pin- and thrum-eyed forms of primroses. (*See also* apostatic selection.) In *transient polymorphism*, the two morphs exist in the population together for only a short time, while one form is replacing the other. This occurs in moths undergoing the process of *industrial melanism. *See also* pleiomorphism.

polynucleotide. *See* nucleotide.

polyomavirus. A member of a class of papovaviruses. *See* virus.

polyp (hydranth). The sedentary form of the Cnidaria, which has a cylindrical stalklike body attached at the base to a firm substrate with a mouth, surrounded by tentacles, at the top. Polyps occur in the classes Hydrozoa and Anthozoa (sea anemones and corals) and may be single, as in *Hydra*, or colonial, as in *Obelia* and the corals. Hydrozoan polyps reproduce asexually by budding, giving rise to new polyps or to medusae; other polyps, e.g. *Anemonia* (sea anemone), reproduce sexually. In the class Scyphozoa (jellyfish) the polyp is reduced or absent and only medusae occur. *Compare* medusa.

polypeptide. *See* peptide, protein.

polyphyletic. Designating a number of species, genera, etc., that, although grouped together, are derived from several ancestral forms. Such species do not form natural groups and should be subdivided in classification into smaller natural groups. *Compare* monophyletic.

polyphyodont. *See* dentition.

polypide. The polyp-like individual of a colony of *Ectoprocta or Entoprocta.

polyploidy. The condition in which the basic (haploid) number of chromosomes in an organism is multiplied by three, four, five, or more. If the haploid number is n, and the diploid $2n$, a polyploid may be $3n$ (triploid), $4n$ (tetraploid), $5n$ (pentaploid), and so on. Polyploidy occurs in both animals and plants but is more common in the latter; it may arise naturally but can be induced by treating cells with colchicine or similar chemicals.
There are two types of polyploidy. *Autopolyploidy* occurs when the chromosome number of an otherwise normal organism becomes multiplied. It has been used commercially in breeding crop plants (including sugar beet, tomatoes, and tobacco plants) to produce a more vigorous or sturdy growth. The main disadvantage of these autopolyploids is that they are usually less fertile than diploids. Although animals are probably never entirely autopolyploid, many have some polyploid cells, produced by *endomitosis.

Allopolyploidy occurs when the chromosome number in a sterile hybrid becomes doubled. It results in the new organism increasing its fertility and becoming a new species that is fertile with polyploids like itself but infertile with its diploid parental species. Many species of flowering plants are thought to have originated by allopolyploidy and can be recognized by the fact that their chromosome number is the sum of those of the parents. For example the cross between *Triticum* (wheat) ($2n = 42$) and *Secale* (rye) ($2n = 14$) gave a sterile hybrid with $2n = 28$. This then doubled its chromosome number to give a fertile allotetraploid, *Triticale*, with $2n = 56$. Bread wheat itself is a hexaploid ($6n$) that has been produced in cultivation during the last 3000 years. Animals rarely, if ever, form new species by allopolyploidy. *Compare* aneuploidy.

polyribosome. *See* ribosome.

polysaccharides (glycans). A group of carbohydrates consisting of many monosaccharide units joined by glycosidic linkages (*see* glycoside). Polysaccharides may be distinguished from sugars by being insoluble (or nearly so) in water and by not having a sweet taste. The group contains the storage carbohydrates, e.g. *glycogen in animals and *starch in plants; it also includes important structural compounds, e.g. *cellulose in plants, *chitin in plants and animals, and *mucopolysaccharides in animals.

polysome (polyribosome, ergosome). *See* ribosome.

polysomy. The condition in which one or more chromosomes are represented more than twice in a nucleus, cell, or organism so that the diploid chromosome complement is $2n + x$, where n is the haploid number. *See also* aneuploidy.

polyspermy (in zoology). Entry of more than one sperm into an ovum at *fertilization.

polystele. *See* stele.

polytene. Designating a chromosome, or sometimes a nucleus or cell, in which the chromatids have duplicated but not separated, so that they come to lie side by side in many parallel strands. This produces a very large chromosome, known as a *giant chromosome*, having conspicuous transverse bands, which stain with basic dyes, interspersed with unstained regions. The bands are thought to indicate the arrangement of genes along the chromosomes. Polytene chromosomes are found in certain cells of some dipterans, especially in the salivary glands of *Drosophila*, where they have been used to study gene activity. They can be used, together with crossover values, to make a *genetic map.

polythetic. Designating a method of classification in which organisms belonging to any taxon must possess a large number of characteristics in common.

polytopic. Designating organisms of a taxonomic group that occur in more than one region.

Polyzoa (Bryozoa). *See* Ectoprocta, Entoprocta.

pome. A succulent *fruit characteristic of certain Rosaceae whose flowers show extreme perigyny. The flesh of the fruit is formed from the hollow receptacle, which encloses the carpels.

population (in ecology). A group of individuals of the same type, particularly of the same species, within a *community. Populations have certain characteristics not shown by individual organisms or the community as a whole, and the study of these can elucidate the ecology of the species and of the community. Characteristics of a population include density (size in relation to unit space), birth and death rates (natality and mortality, respectively), age distribution, sex ratio, dispersion (distribution of the individuals within the area), and growth rate.

P:O ratio. *See* oxidative phosphorylation.

pore complex. The structure that makes up a nuclear pore in the eukaryotic nuclear envelope (*see* nucleus). There may be hundreds or thousands of nuclear pores per nucleus and they tend to be concentrated in patches on the envelope. The pores are not simply holes: each is largely filled by an annulus, fitting like a grommet in a pipe. Although some of the sieving effect of the pores may operate simply on particle or molecule size, other effects are similar to active transport and involve the expenditure of ATP.

poricidal. *See* dehiscence.

Porifera. A phylum of primitive multicellular animals, the sponges, representing a separate evolutionary line from the Metazoa and therefore placed in a separate subkingdom, the Parazoa. The body of a sponge is basically a loose aggregation of cells forming a hollow vaselike structure but lacking intercellular nervous coordination. It is lined by *choanocytes, which cause currents of water to flow in through apertures (*ostia*) in the body wall and out through one or more openings (*oscula*) at the top. Sponges have an internal skeleton of calcareous or siliceous spicules or protein fibres (as in the bath sponge). All sponges are sessile and all except one family are marine.

porogamy. *See* pollen tube.

porphyrin. One of a group of pigments, widely distributed in living organisms, that are derived from *porphin*, a ring structure of four pyrrole nuclei linked by carbon atoms. The most common porphyrin is *protoporphyrin IX* (see formulae). The nitrogen atoms of porphyrins are often coordinated to metal ions (e.g. iron, magnesium) to form chelates, of which *haem (protoporphyrin combined with FeII) is the most important. *See also* chemical fossils.

Porphyrin

portal vein. Any blood vessel connecting two capillary beds, as in the *renal portal system and *hepatic portal system.

position effect. The phenomenon of the expression of a gene being changed when its position on the chromosome is altered, for example by translocation, inversion, or crossing over.

postcaval vein. *See* vena cava.

posterior. 1. Designating the part of an animal that is furthest away from the head region or front part. In bipedal animals, including man, the posterior surface corresponds with the dorsal surface.
2. Designating the part of a lateral bud or flower that is nearest the main axis. *Compare* anterior.

potentiation. *See* synergism.

poxvirus. *See* virus.

PPLO (pleuropneumonia-like organisms). *See* mycoplasmas.

Pre-Cambrian. The unit of geological time that preceded the Cambrian period, i.e. the time before 600 million years

ago. Pre-Cambrian rocks contain no definite (i.e. structural) fossils, but some structures found in these rocks may be the remains of the precursors or products of organisms (*see* chemical fossils). In some Pre-Cambrian limestone rocks of Australia, Siberia, and parts of the USA there are structures known as *stromatolites, which may have been formed by blue-green algae. Frond- and disclike impressions of a supposed plant (*Charnia*) have also been found. Amino acids have been identified from Pre-Cambrian rocks dated at 1700 million years old. *See also* geological time scale.

precaval vein. *See* vena cava.

precipitin. An antibody that combines specifically with and precipitates soluble antigen. This activity is utilized in the *precipitin reaction*, which detects and identifies antigens.

preformation. The theory that a whole miniature adult organism (*homunculus*) exists inside an egg or sperm and that development consists merely of the expansion of this miniature. Some 17th-century theorists considered that the homunculus existed inside the egg (*ovist theory*) and that the sperm merely triggered development; others that it was found inside the sperm (*spermatist (spermist) theory*) and that the egg was merely an aid to development. The theories of preformation culminated in the *box theory*, which stated that the egg or sperm of the homunculus must contain the homunculus for the next generation, and so on for all succeeding generations. *Compare* epigenesis.

premaxilla. An anterior tooth-bearing membrane bone of the upper jaw of most vertebrates. It bears the incisor teeth in mammals and forms the bulk of the upper beak in birds.

premolar. A ridged multiple-rooted tooth of mammals, two or more of which are situated between the canine teeth (or incisors) and the molars and are used for grinding and pounding food. While having structural similarities to the molars, they differ in being the only grinding teeth (cheek teeth) represented in the deciduous teeth.

presumptive. Designating a cell or cells in the early animal embryo that can normally be presumed to develop into a particular adult tissue or organ even before the cells have become *determined.

Pribnow box. *See* TATA box.

prickle. A massive woody *trichome (as such, entirely epidermal in origin). *Compare* spine, thorn.

primary growth. Growth that gives rise to the primary plant body.

primary plant body. A plant or the parts of a plant consisting of primary tissues, i.e. those that have been laid down in the formation of the embryo and are thereafter formed by the activity of the *apical meristems. *Compare* secondary plant body.

primary structure. That aspect of the structure of a *protein or polynucleotide that depends on covalent bonding, i.e. the linear sequence of amino acids in a polypeptide chain and any covalent bridging within it or of nucleotides in a single strand of DNA or RNA.

Primates. An order of the Eutheria containing basically arboreal mammals characterized by a very highly developed brain, quick reactions, and binocular vision (the eyes face forward and are separated from the temporal fossa by a bony plate or ring). The skeleton is unspecialized; the thumb and usually the big toe are opposable for grasping and the digits have sensory pads and nails replacing claws. Only a few young are produced at one birth, and these undergo a long period of growth and development, allowing learning. The most primitive group is the Prosimii (Lemuroidea), e.g. *Galago* (bushbaby) and *Lemur* (lemurs). The Anthropoidea contains the New World monkeys, e.g. *Alouatta* (howler), which have prehensile

tails, and the Old World Monkeys, e.g. *Macaca* (rhesus monkey, Barbary ape), which never have a prehensile tail. The Hominoidea includes the great apes, e.g. *Pongo* (orang-utan), and man and his precursors (*see* hominid): tailless primates with brachiating arms.

primitive streak. A longitudinal band of embryonic mesodermal cells that develops within a dorsal groove along the length of the gastrula of mammals and birds.

primordium. A group of cells that gives rise to a tissue, an organ, or a group of associated organs (such as a flower), or an immature cell before it has differentiated into a specific type. Examples are xylem-vessel and sclereid primordia.

prisere (primary sere). *See* sere.

pristane. *See* chemical fossils.

probe DNA. A DNA molecule radioactively labelled (most frequently with ^{32}P) and used to detect nucleic acid molecules of complementary sequence by molecular hybridization (*see in situ* hybridization). *Autoradiography is often used to reveal the presence of the probe DNA and thus to localize the complementary hybridizing sequences. *See also* nick translation.

Proboscidea. The order of the Eutheria that contains the modern elephants, *Loxodonta* (African elephant) and *Elephas* (Indian elephant), as well as numerous extinct forms, including the mammoths. Modern proboscideans, the largest terrestrial mammals, are characterized by a prehensile proboscis (trunk) formed from the elongated nose and upper lip and used for bathing, drinking, and collecting vegetation. Lower incisors, canines, and premolars are absent; the two upper incisors form the tusks, which assist in food collection and defence. The huge molars have sharp grinding transverse ridges and only two pairs are used at a time, being replaced when worn down.

procambium (provascular tissue). The meristematic tissue of an *apical meristem that gives rise to the primary vascular tissues.

procaryote. *See* prokaryote.

Proconsul. *See* Dryopithecus.

proctodaeum. A posterior invagination of the ectoderm of the embryo that opens into the archenteron. It gives rise to the terminal regions of the alimentary canal, e.g. the hindgut of insects and the rectum, cloaca, and anus of vertebrates.

producer. An autotrophic organism in an *ecosystem, which synthesizes complex organic substances from simple inorganic materials, as by photosynthesis (green plants) or chemosynthesis (some bacteria). *See also* food chain.

productivity (production) (in ecology). The total mass of organic food manufactured in an ecosystem in a certain period of time. It is the net yield of the producers and consumers and determines the amount of living matter in an ecosystem. *Primary productivity* (or *production*) is the total amount of organic matter synthesized by the producers (by photosynthesis or chemosynthesis); net primary production is the food stored in plant tissues, which is potentially available to the consumers, i.e. food in excess of that used by the producers during respiration.

proembryo. *See* embryo.

profundal. Designating the deepest part of a lake, below a depth of 10 metres. The profundal zone contains only heterotrophic organisms. *Compare* littoral, sublittoral.

progesterone. A steroid hormone produced chiefly by the corpus luteum of the mammalian ovary but also by the testis, adrenal cortex, and placenta (see formula). Its most important role in the female is to prepare the reproductive organs for pregnancy (*see* oestrous cycle) and to maintain the uterus throughout gestation, but progesterone is also an

Progesterone

intermediate in the biosynthesis of all steroid hormones. It was first isolated from pig ovaries in 1934.

progestogen. Any of a group of substances that show progesterone-like effects on the female mammalian reproductive organs.

proglottis. One of the numerous segments of the body of a tapeworm (*see* Cestoda), which are budded off from the scolex (head). Each contains male and female reproductive organs; the male organs mature first so that the anterior proglottides contain only functional male organs, those in the middle have both male and female organs, and each of the posterior proglottides is filled by a large uterus containing fertilized eggs. The posterior segments break off from the parent and are passed out with the host's excreta.

prohormone. A large precursor protein from which polypeptide hormones are produced by enzymic cleavage. The first to be established was *proinsulin* (*see* insulin) in 1967.

prokaryote (procaryote). An organism whose genetic material is not contained within a true nucleus but lies free in a special region of the cytoplasm called the *nucleoid*. Prokaryotic organisms comprise mainly the bacteria and blue-green algae. *Compare* eukaryote. *See* cell.

prolactin (lactogenic hormone, luteotrop(h)ic hormone, LTH). A protein hormone secreted by the pars distalis of the pituitary gland in mammals and by corresponding tissue in all other vertebrates. In mammals it stimulates and maintains lactation and (in some) the secretion of progesterone from the corpus luteum. In birds it promotes secretion of 'milk' from the crop glands – an ability utilized in bioassays of the hormone before the more sensitive *radioimmunoassays were available. The association of the pituitary with lactation was first demonstrated in 1928; prolactin was isolated in 1937 and its structure determined in 1969. It consists of a single chain of 198 amino acid residues with three disulphide linkages and is structurally similar to growth hormone. In lower vertebrates prolactin shows a wide range of effects on activities such as osmoregulation, reproduction, growth, catabolism, and associated behaviour responses and its functional adaptability may have contributed to the diversification of the vertebrates. *See also* gonadotrophin.

prolamellar body. *See* etioplast.

prolamine. One of a group of simple plant proteins that are soluble only in aqueous alcohol. The group includes *gliadin*, a constituent of *gluten.

$$H_2C \text{---} CH_2$$
$$H_2C \diagdown \quad HC \text{---} COOH$$
$$\underset{\underset{H}{N}}{}$$

Proline

proline (pro). An amino acid (see formula), one of the 20 common *amino acids found in proteins. Due to its cyclic nature, proline gives rise to a bend whenever it occurs in a polypeptide chain and so contributes to the secondary structure of proteins. Its 4-hydroxy derivative (*hydroxyproline*) is also found in proteins.

promeristem. *See* apical meristem.

promoter. The DNA sequence that promotes transcription of a gene. It is normally assumed to be an attachment site for RNA polymerase. In the *lac operon the promoter sequence lies between the coding gene for the repressor protein and the operator sequence. *See also* TATA box.

pronation and supination. The movement of a forefoot or hand with respect to the elbow through 90° in either direction. In man movement of the hand from the vertical position (i.e. ulna and radius parallel) through 90° so that the palm is pointing downwards (i.e. ulna and radius crossed) is *pronation*; movement in the opposite direction, so that the palm is pointing upwards, is *supination*.

prone development (in botany). *See* embryo.

pronephros. The first (anterior) part of the *kidney to appear in the embryonic development of vertebrates. It is functional in larval fishes and amphibians but in amniotes it is transient and never functional. It is drained by the Wolffian duct. *Compare* mesonephros, metanephros.

pro-oestrus. *See* oestrous cycle.

prophage. *See* lysogeny.

prophase. The first stage of *mitosis and *meiosis. In meiosis prophase I is subdivided into leptotene, zygotene, pachytene, diplotene, and diakinesis.

proplastid. A small body of obscure origin, about $0.5-1$ μm in diameter, that multiplies and differentiates into a *plastid. Proplastids are usually found in meristematic regions of plants.

proprioceptor. A *receptor that is sensitive to the position and movement of the body or parts of the body in relation to gravity. Proprioceptors include the maculae and cristae of the vertebrate inner ear and the statocysts of invertebrates.

prosencephalon. *See* forebrain.

prosenchyma. A tissue composed of elongated cells, usually with tapering ends, forming, for example, the conducting tissues of vascular plants. The term prosenchyma is also used for a loosely packed *plectenchyma in which the constituent filaments are still visible. *Compare* pseudoparenchyma.

Prostaglandin E_1

prostaglandin. One of a group of chemically related hormone-like substances that are formed from essential fatty acids and occur in most mammalian tissues, particularly in human seminal fluid. They were first discovered in human semen in the early 1930s and many varieties, including *prostaglandin E_1 (PGE$_1$)*, have now been isolated (see formula). Prostaglandins have a wide spectrum of pharmacological activity but are best known for their potent effects on smooth muscle, particularly in stimulating contraction and relaxation of the human uterus. Their main therapeutic use has been to induce abortion and labour in women. By their vasodilatation (or vasoconstriction) of blood vessels, they can regulate blood flow and have been shown to assist hormone secretion by increasing the blood flow through endocrine glands. Prostaglandins have also been implicated in various hormone effects because of their ability to modify cyclic AMP levels. They are known to be released during the inflammatory response of damaged tissue, and the analgesic effects of aspirin are thought to be due to an inhibition of prostaglandin synthesis.

prostate gland. A gland of male mammals that surrounds the neck of the bladder and urethra and, under the regulation of androgens, releases certain substances into the semen, including an antiagglutinating factor and a vitamin E derivative.

prosthetic group. A nonprotein molecule that is combined with a protein to form a complex molecule. For example, lipids and polysaccharides are the prosthetic groups of lipoproteins and glycoproteins, respectively (*see* conjugated protein), and certain enzymes require coenzymes as prosthetic groups.

protamine. One of a group of simple proteins of low molecular weight (about 5000) that are rich in basic amino acids. Many protamines are found associated with nucleic acids, as for example *salmine*, occurring in the sperm of salmon; others are associated with acidic proteins.

protandry. 1. *See* dichogamy.
2. The condition in hermaphrodite animals in which the spermatozoa are produced before the ova.

protease. A proteolytic enzyme. *See* proteolysis.

protein. One of a group of macromolecules that are fundamental to the structure and function of all living organisms. Proteins are made up of one or more chains of *amino acids; consecutive amino acids are linked covalently between the α-amino group of one and the α-carboxyl group of the next with the elimination of a molecule of water:

This linkage is called a *peptide bond*. Protein molecules containing three or more amino acids (some may contain several hundred) are known as *polypeptides*. About 20 amino acids are found in naturally occurring proteins and the specific sequence of amino acids in a polypeptide chain is genetically controlled by the cell in which it is made (*see* protein synthesis). Proteins such as *albumins, *globulins, and *protamines, consisting solely of amino acids, are known as *simple proteins*; those consisting of an amino-acid sequence with nonprotein prosthetic groups attached are *conjugated proteins.

There is great variety in the size and structure of proteins. Molecular weights range from a few thousand (for protein hormones, e.g. insulin) to several million (e.g. for enzyme complexes). The three-dimensional structure of a protein, i.e. its *conformation*, determines its specific biological properties. The variation in protein conformation enables a wide range of functions; for example, some proteins (e.g. collagen, keratin) are structural, others are enzymes, antibodies, or hormones. There are four levels of protein conformation. The *primary structure* is the specific amino-acid sequence in the polypeptide chain. The *secondary structure* is maintained by hydrogen bonds at regular intervals. Intramolecular hydrogen bonding produces a regular coiling, commonly in the form of an *alpha-helix, which is characteristic of fibrous proteins and also present in globular proteins. Intermolecular hydrogen bonding gives rise to the *beta-pleated sheet, found in silk. The *tertiary structure* is formed by the folding of the chain upon itself and is maintained by *disulphide* (S–S) *bridges* and noncovalent bonds such as *hydrophobic interactions. It results, for example, in the formation of active sites in enzymes. *Quaternary structure* is the arrangement of polypeptide chains in proteins, such as haemoglobin, that have more than one polypeptide per molecule. *See also* denaturation, proteolysis.

proteinase (endopeptidase). One of a group of proteolytic enzymes that split proteins into smaller peptide fractions. *See* proteolysis.

protein synthesis. The synthesis of protein molecules from their constituent amino acids takes place on the *ribosomes of cells. The information for determining the sequence of amino acids in a particular protein is encoded in the base sequence of *messenger RNA (mRNA), which is transcribed from DNA in the nucleus (*see* transcription): the sequence of nucleotides in the mRNA determines the sequence of amino acids in the protein (*see* genetic code), each nucleotide triplet (*codon) specifying a single amino acid. The mRNA migrates into the cytoplasm and becomes associated with the ribosomes, usually forming polysomes. It acts as a template for the synthesis of a particular protein, the sequence of base triplets in the mRNA determining the sequence of amino acids in the protein (*see* translation).

proteolysis. The hydrolysis of proteins into their constituent amino acids. The enzymes responsible are known as *proteolytic enzymes* (or *proteases*). Extracellular proteolysis is carried out by *peptidases; *endopeptidases* (or *proteinases*) split the whole protein into smaller peptide fractions, while *exopeptidases* split the terminal peptide bonds of the molecule. The amino acids thus released can pass into the cells. In vertebrates, extracellular proteolysis is carried out by endopeptidases, such as pepsin, in the stomach and by exopeptidases, including trypsin and chymotrypsin, in the intestines.

Intracellular proteolysis is catalysed by the *cathepsins.

proteolytic enzyme (protease). *See* proteolysis.

proteoplast. A *plastid that stores protein.

prothallus. A small flattened free-living thalloid structure that bears sex organs and forms the gametophyte generation of pteridophytes. In homosporous plants only one type of prothallus is formed and it bears both the sex organs, but in heterosporous plants the smaller microspores give rise to small male prothalli, which develop antheridia, and the larger megaspores form the female prothalli, which develop archegonia. In seed plants the products of the pollen grains represent the male gametophyte prothallus, and the embryo sac the female gametophyte prothallus.

prothoracic gland. One of a pair of many-branched organs in the thoracic region of insects that is the source of moulting hormone (*see* ecdysone) or of the enzymes required for its synthesis. It has been well studied in certain Lepidoptera, in which it is associated with the tracheal system of the head and prothorax, and its role in moulting was first demonstrated in silkworm larvae in 1940.

prothrombin. The enzymically inactive precursor of *thrombin, which is present in normal blood plasma. It is a glycoprotein containing 4–5% carbohydrate and consists of two peptide chains.

Protista. A third kingdom of organisms, distinct from plants and animals, proposed by Haeckel in 1866. Originally it included all bacteria, protozoans, algae, and fungi, i.e. organisms mostly showing little differentiation into separate cell types and tissues. The grouping can now be seen as artificial in terms of taxonomic and other criteria. However, the term is still used, though sometimes in a narrower sense; for example it has been suggested that the Protista (protists) should include only one-celled organisms (bacteria, unicellular and colonial algae, protozoans, and some fungi).

Protochordata. A subdivision of the Chordata that includes the *Urochordata and *Cephalochordata, i.e. all invertebrate chordates.

protoderm. The meristematic tissue of an apical meristem that gives rise to the epidermal structures.

protogyny. 1. *See* dichogamy.
2. The condition in hermaphrodite animals in which the ova are produced before the spermatozoa.

protomeristem (metrameristem). *See* apical meristem.

protonema. The first structure produced from a germinating spore. The term is usually restricted to the structure developed from bryophyte spores, which is usually filamentous (though it may be thalloid, as in the genus *Sphagnum*) and produces numerous leafy buds that grow into the gametophyte plants. A similar protonema is produced by germinating bryophyte gemmae.

protonephridium. *See* nephridium.

protophloem. The part of the primary phloem formed before the axis or structure in which it occurs has finished elongating. Protophloem elements are short-lived and soon crushed since they lose their nucleus during formation and so cannot keep pace with the growth and extension of the surrounding tissues. *Compare* metaphloem.

protoplasm. The living contents of a cell, comprising the cytoplasm (including the plasma membrane) and the nucleus (or nucleoid).

protoplast. The total protoplasm of a cell, excluding material outside the plasma membrane. Protoplasts of plant cells and some prokaryotes can be prepared by enzymic digestion of the cell walls, using cellulase or lysozyme respectively. *See also* spheroplast.

protopodite. *See* biramous appendage.

protostele. *See* stele.

Prototheria. The subclass of the Mammalia that contains the most primitive living mammals, included in a single order, the *Monotremata. Monotremes probably evolved from the ancestral synapsid reptiles independently of other mammals. The skeleton and body organs retain many reptilian features, including a primitive pectoral girdle and a cloaca. The young hatch from large yolky eggs and are nourished by milk secreted by primitive mammary glands that lack nipples. Temperature control is poor, but the body hair, heart, and diaphragm are typically mammalian. Teeth are absent in adults. *Compare* Eutheria, Metatheria.

prototrophic. Designating microorganisms that are able to grow without addition of complex compounds to their growth media. For example, a mutant may require a particular amino acid for growth while the wild type is prototrophic. *Compare* auxotrophic.

protoxylem. The part of the primary xylem formed before the axis or structure in which it occurs has finished elongating. Protoxylem elements are short-lived and soon crushed since they lose their living contents during formation and so cannot keep up with the growth and extension of the surrounding tissues. *Compare* metaxylem.

Protozoa. A phylum or subkingdom of minute acellular organisms whose members range from plantlike forms to types that feed and behave as animals. Parts of the body may be specialized as organelles, e.g. cilia and flagella, but there is no fundamental type of body form. Some protozoans are colonial. The basic method of reproduction is binary fission, but multiple fission and conjugation also occur in some species. Protozoans are cosmopolitan, inhabiting marine, freshwater, and damp terrestrial environments, and many are parasites. The phylum is divided into the classes *Mastigophora, *Sarcodina, *Sporozoa, and *Ciliata.

Protura. An order of minute wingless insects of the subclass Apterygota. These colourless insects lack eyes and antennae and use their front legs, which are held forward, as sensory organs. They have piercing mouthparts and live in the soil, under stones, etc., feeding on decaying organic matter.

provascular tissue. *See* procambium.

proventriculus. The soft anterior part of the stomach of birds, which secretes gastric juice. The pyloric region of the stomach is modified as the gizzard.
The term is also used as a synonym for the gizzard of insects and crustaceans.

provirus. A latent virus genome present but unexpressed in a host chromosome. *See* reverse transcriptase.

proximal. Designating the part of a tissue, organ, limb, etc., that is nearest to the point of attachment or origin. For example, the humerus is the proximal part of the forelimb. *Compare* distal.

psalterium. *See* omasum.

pseudoallele. A gene that appears to behave as a single allele but within which crossing over can occur.

pseudocarp (false fruit). A *fruit that incorporates structures other than the ovary. All composite fruits are pseudocarps.

pseudocoelomate. Designating any invertebrate whose body cavity is not a true coelom but is thought to be a persistent blastocoel. Pseudocoelomate phyla include the *Aschelminthes, *Acanthocephala, and *Entoprocta.

pseudogene. A DNA sequence that is largely homologous to a structural gene sequence but is apparently never transcribed. Pseudogenes have been discovered by genetic engineering techniques and some (e.g. globin pseudogenes) are situated close to the locus of the active structural gene. The function of pseudogenes is unknown but they are commonly believed to represent redundant DNA and may be a by-product of the evolution of the genome.

Pseudomonas. A genus of strictly aerobic bacteria widely distributed in soil and water. The cells are rod-shaped and usually motile. A few species are pathogenic to man, including *P. aeruginosa*, which can cause septicaemia, abscesses, and urinary-tract infections.

pseudoparenchyma. A *plectenchyma in which the filaments or hyphae have lost their individuality, their cells separating and becoming isodiametric. It becomes indistinguishable from parenchyma in its mature state while differing from it in ontogeny. *Compare* prosenchyma.

pseudoplasmodium. *See* plasmodium.

pseudopodium. A temporary projection from the cell of some Protozoa, especially the Sarcodina (e.g. *Amoeba*), used for locomotion and food capture. Pseudopodia, which are thought to be formed by changes in the consistency of the cytoplasm, may be in the form of fine threads (*filopodia*), blunt projections (*lobopodia*), or a branching network (*rhizopodia*); some (*axopodia*) have an internal supporting rod. Pseudopodia are also formed by macrophages.

pseudopregnancy. A state resembling pregnancy in certain mammals, including rodents, without the formation of embryos. *See* oestrous cycle.

Pseudoscorpiones. The order of the Arachnida that contains the pseudoscorpions (e.g. *Chelifer*): small arachnids that resemble true scorpions, having large pincer-like pedipalps but lacking a tail and sting. The small chelicerae have poison glands and apertures for the secretion of silk, which is used to construct small cells in which the animals moult and rear their young. Pseudoscorpions are widespread but secretive, usually living under stones.

Psilophytopsida. *See* Psilopsida.

Psilopsida (Psilophyta). A group of homosporous rootless pteridophytes with dichotomously branching rhizomes and aerial branches; the latter are either naked or have spirally arranged scalelike or leaflike *microphylls. Sporangia are thick-walled and terminal on main (or occasionally lateral) branches. There are two major subgroups: Psilotales and Psilophytales. The former contains the extant members (two genera, *Psilotum* and *Tmesipteris*); the latter contains the fossil members, a very ancient and heterogeneous group that includes the earliest vascular plants (from the late Silurian of Czechoslovakia, 4.8×10^8 years old). These two subgroups are sometimes raised to the rank of Psilotopsida and Psilophytopsida, respectively, due to the controversy over whether *Psilotum*

and *Tmesipteris* are primitively or secondarily reduced simple plants.

Psilotopsida. *See* Psilopsida.

Psocoptera. An order of tiny exopterygote insects, the book-lice. Most species are found in warm regions and are winged, living in trees, under bark, etc., and feeding on decaying organic matter. Domestic forms, e.g. *Liposcelis*, are wingless and feed on moulds in damp wallpaper, old books, etc.

psychrophilic. Designating microorganisms that can grow at temperatures below 20°C. *Obligate psychrophiles* require an optimum temperature of 15–18°C (they are killed at 20°C); *facultative psychrophiles* have an optimum similar to that of mesophiles (i.e. 30–45°C) but can grow, although more slowly, at 20°C or lower. *Compare* mesophilic, thermophilic.

Pteraspida. *See* Heterostraci.

Pteridophyta. A group of vascular plants typically having a small free-living gametophyte generation, which produces the archegonia and antheridia. The megasporangium never forms an ovule since it lacks true integuments (though analogous structures such as megasporophyll flanges may be produced). There are four groups of pteridophytes: the *Lycopsida, *Sphenopsida, *Psilopsida (sometimes split into Psilotopsida and Psilophytopsida), and *Pteropsida (in its restricted sense).

Pteridospermae. *See* Cycadopsida.

pterodactyls. *See* Pterosauria.

Pteropsida (in most plant classification schemes). A group of homosporous or heterosporous pteridophytes comprising the ferns. The plant body is differentiated into roots, stems, and leaves; the latter are spirally arranged *megaphylls (fronds), although some early fossil members show little distinction between stem and leaf. Secondary thickening occurs only very rarely and to a limited extent. The sporangia may be thin- or thick-walled (*see* leptosporangiate, eusporangiate) and may either terminate a branch or be borne on a frond (at the margin or on the abaxial surface).

Some botanists enlarge this group to include the gymnosperms and angiosperms as well as the ferns (which are then included in the subgroup Pterophyta or Filicinae), on the supposition that the three groups are related.

Pterosauria. An extinct order of the Archosauria containing the flying reptiles (pterodactyls) of the Jurassic and Cretaceous. They were characterized by long arms terminating in three small claws and a very long fourth finger, which, with the pteroid bone on the wrist, supported the leathery wing membrane. The wing was probably also attached to the short weak hind legs. The more primitive pterosaurs, e.g. *Rhamphorhynchus*, had a long beak with pointed teeth projecting forwards and a long tail terminating in a membrane that acted as a rudder. Tail and teeth were absent in more advanced forms such as *Pteranodon*, which had a wingspan of nearly 8 metres.

Pterygota (Metabola). A subclass of insects that are typically winged, although the wings have been secondarily lost in some species. The subclass is divided into the *Exopterygota and *Endopterygota.

ptyalin. An amylase found in the saliva of some mammals.

ptyxis. The way in which young leaves are folded in the buds of vascular plants, which involves rolling, folding, or pleating or any combination of these. *See also* vernation, aestivation.

pubic symphysis. A ventral articulation between the pubic bones of the pelvic girdle that occurs in mammals, many reptiles, and *Archaeopteryx*. It gives support to the soft organs of the abdomen and in mammals it loosens during parturition to ease birth. It is absent in birds as egg laying requires a large pelvic outlet.

pubis. A paired cartilage bone forming the anterior ventral element of the tetrapod *pelvic girdle. In mammals and many reptiles the two pubes are united ventrally by the pubic symphysis.

puff (Balbiani ring). A swelling that appears in the giant polytene chromosomes of the salivary glands of certain dipterans. Puffs always appear in the same place on the chromosome at the same time in the development of the insect and can be correlated with developmental events such as ecdysis (*see* ecdysone). RNA is found in the region of the puff, which is therefore thought to indicate the site of messenger RNA synthesis by the gene.

pulmonary artery. A paired blood vessel that branches from the sixth (pulmonary) aortic arch and passes deoxygenated blood to the lungs from the single ventricle in lungfish and amphibians and from the right ventricle in amniotes.

pulmonary vein. A paired blood vessel passing oxygenated blood from the lungs to the left atrium of the heart in lungfish and tetrapods.

pulp cavity. The internal cavity of a tooth, which contains the *tooth pulp* – a connective tissue matrix containing collagen fibrils, blood vessels, nerve fibres, and white cells. Its periphery is lined with *odontoblasts and the whole cavity is encased in *dentine except for a small canal at the base through which nerve fibres and blood vessels pass from the gum.

pulse. A series of intermittent waves of *vasodilatation that spread outward from the heart along the main arteries. It is a combination of two factors: (1) the ejection of blood into the aorta from the left ventricle of the heart at systole and (2) the resistance to blood flow of the capillary bed. The pulse is independent of blood flow and travels at a much higher velocity (about 7 metres per second in man).

pulvinus. A padlike structure formed from the *phyllopodium.

punctuated equilibrium. The theory that species usually arise relatively quickly in geological time rather than through a long process of gradual change. This is opposed to the traditional neo-Darwinian theory of evolution. *See* cladistics.

pupa. The nonfeeding immobile form of an endopterygote insect, in which the transformation from larva to adult (metamorphosis) occurs. Pupae are usually *exarate*, with movable wings and limbs, but the chrysalids of the Lepidoptera (butterflies and moths) are *obtect*, with wings and limbs fused to the body, and the pupae of some Diptera (flies) are *coarctate*, with a hard barrel-shaped *puparium* protecting the exarate pupa.

pupil. The opening in the iris of vertebrates and cephalopods through which light enters the eye. Nocturnal animals have a slitlike pupil, which can be more completely closed by the muscles of the iris to exclude bright light.

pure line. A continuous series of generations of an organism that are consistently homozygous for one or more characters or genes. A pure line is produced by crossing two organisms homozygous for the genes. In practice this is best achieved by self-fertilization in plants and by inbreeding animals. Organisms of a pure line are said to *breed true* for the character(s) under consideration.

Purine

purine. One of a group of nitrogenous bases whose parent compound has the formula shown. The two most abundant purines are *adenine and *guanine, which are constituents of nucleic acids and coenzymes (*see* nucleotide); *uric

acid is the end product of purine metabolism and the main nitrogenous excretory product of some animals.

Purkinje fibres. Large atypical muscle fibres that are found in the ventricular walls of the hearts of certain mammals and are involved in conducting waves of contraction throughout the ventricular muscle.

putrescine. *See* polyamines.

pycnidium. A hollow sorus of some Fungi Imperfecti containing sporogenous hyphae that produce *pycnospores* by abstriction at the tips of conidia. Formerly the term was also used for the *spermogonium of the rusts, before this was recognized as having a sexual function.

pycnium. A former name for the *spermogonium of rusts.

Pycnogonida. A marine class of Arthropoda that contains the sea spiders, e.g. *Nymphon*. The abdomen is greatly reduced and bears four, five, or six pairs of legs, which are often very long and contain extensions of the gut and gonads. The mouth is at the tip of a proboscis, which is inserted into the prey. Chelicerae and pedipalps may be present.

pycnoxylic. Designating gymnosperm wood, such as that produced by the Coniferopsida, that has narrow parenchyma rays and is therefore hard and compact. *Compare* manoxylic.

pylorus. A valve in the alimentary canal of vertebrates, primitively separating the anterior (collecting and storage) regions from the posterior (digestive) regions. In many animals it is specialized with a muscular sphincter, which regulates the passage of food from the stomach to the intestine.

pyramid of biomass. A diagrammatic representation of the total biomass at all trophic levels in a *food chain. The biomass decreases slightly at each successive level up the food chain (*compare* pyramid of numbers).

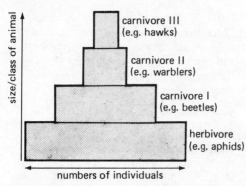

Pyramid of numbers

pyramid of numbers. A diagrammatic representation of the numbers of animals at all trophic levels in a *food chain (see illustration). A decrease occurs at each successive level, which is more noticeable than the decrease in biomass (*see* pyramid of biomass) because animals at the end of a food chain tend to be fewer, although larger, than those at the lower levels.

pyranose. A monosaccharide that exists in the form of a six-membered ring of five carbon atoms and one oxygen atom. An example is α-D-*glucopyranose,* one form of *glucose. *Compare* furanose.

pyrenocarp. 1. *See* perithecium.
2. *See* drupe.

pyrenoid. A small protein body of variable shape found in the chloroplasts of most algae. Pyrenoids are associated with the storage of polysaccharide reserves, either within the chloroplast (e.g. starch sheaths surround the pyrenoids of many green algae) or in the cytoplasm, where the reserves often occupy a zone close to the chloroplast.

pyridoxal phosphate. A coenzyme that is derived from pyridoxine and participates in all transaminase reactions (*see* transamination) and also in other reactions of α-amino acids, such as serine-threonine deamination and tyrosine decarboxylation.

Pyridoxine

pyridoxine (vitamin B$_6$). A water-soluble vitamin of the B complex (see formula) that is required in the diet of many animals and microorganisms, functioning as the precursor of the coenzyme pyridoxal phosphate. A deficiency of this vitamin can cause anaemia and dermatitis in rats.

Pyrimidine

pyrimidine. One of a group of nitrogenous bases whose parent compound has the formula shown. The three most abundant pyrimidines are *cytosine, *thymine, and *uracil, which are constituents of nucleic acids (*see* nucleotide).

Pyrrophyta. A group of unicellular chromophyte algae characterized by cellulose walls (not silicified), often in two valves; the presence of chlorophylls a and c and β-carotene; and the formation of starch as a storage product. There are two subgroups: *Cryptophyceae and *Dinophyceae.

pyxidium. A type of capsular *fruit that dehisces by means of a circular lid.

Q

Q$_{10}$. *See* temperature coefficient.

Q$_{O_2}$. *See* oxygen quotient.

quadrat. A square of ground, usually 1 or 0.5 metres square, that is marked out to study the distribution of species in an area.

quadrate. A bone of the upper jaw of all bony vertebrates except mammals, derived from the palatoquadrate bar. It hinges with the articular bone of the lower jaw and connects the jaws to the cranium either directly (*autostylic or *autodiastylic jaw suspension), through the hyomandibular (*hyostylic jaw suspension), or by both these articulations (*amphistylic jaw suspension). In mammals it is represented by the *incus.

qualitative inheritance (discontinuous variation). *See* variation.

quantasome. One of many small regularly arranged particles, about 18 × 16 × 10 nm, located on or in chloroplast thylakoid membranes, visible with the aid of electron microscopy and isolated by suitable fragmentation techniques. They are thought to be either artefacts or structural units of photosynthesis, containing pigments and other molecules. They are just large enough to be the postulated *photosynthetic units.

quantitative inheritance (continuous variation). *See* variation.

quantum yield (quantum efficiency). The number of molecules of carbon dioxide fixed, or oxygen evolved, per light quantum absorbed in photosynthesis. It is the reciprocal of the *quantum requirement* (or *quantum number*), the number of light quanta required for the reduction of one carbon dioxide molecule. The theoretical minimum quantum requirement for photosynthesis is three, but in practice it is usually postulated to be eight (a quantum yield of $\frac{1}{2}$). The higher the quantum yield of a photochemical reaction, the higher its efficiency.

Quaternary. The second period of the Cenozoic era, extending from one million years ago to the present day. It consists of two epochs, the *Pleistocene and *Holocene. *See also* geological time scale.

quaternary structure. The arrangement of polypeptide chains in a *protein molecule that is made up of more than one polypeptide.

quiescent centre. A group of cells at the very tip of an apical meristem that differ physiologically from the surrounding cells of the apex. It appears to be common to most root apices but has also been demonstrated in some shoot apices. Its principal feature is a much lower rate of mitosis than the surrounding tissue. However, its size appears to fluctuate and occasionally it may become indistinguishable from the rest of the apex, suggesting that it may be intermittently quiescent. The quiescent centre may be a site of auxin formation and seems to be the source of the active initials in the meristem by its (infrequent) mitoses. It also provides a reservoir of cells whose inactivity makes them less prone to damage such as chromosomal aberrations.

quillworts. *See* Lycopsida.

R

rabbits. *See* Lagomorpha.

raceme. A type of racemose inflorescence in which stalked flowers are borne on one main axis with the oldest flowers at the base of the inflorescence and the youngest at the top, as in antirrhinum and lupin (see illustration).

racemose inflorescence. A type of inflorescence in which growth is monopodial (or indefinite), i.e. the main axis contin-

Raceme

ues to grow at the tip and the flowers arise below it. The flowers open in succession with the oldest towards the bottom of the inflorescence and the youngest towards the top. In a flattened inflorescence the oldest flowers are to the outside and the youngest towards the centre. The types of racemose inflorescences are *raceme, *panicle, *corymb, *umbel, *spike, *catkin, *spadix, and *capitulum. *Compare* cymose inflorescence.

rachis (rhachis). A shaft or axis. In botany it refers to (1) the axis of an inflorescence, e.g. the stem of a grass flower to which the spikelets are attached (the axes of the spikelets are called *rachillas*); (2) the part of the axis of a compound leaf that bears the leaflets or pinnae. In zoology, it is usually applied to the shaft of a contour feather.

radial symmetry. The arrangement of the parts of an animal around a central axis so that any two planes are approximately mirror images of each other. It is characteristic of many animals that are basically sedentary, such as the Coelenterata and Echinodermata.
Plants or plant organs (particularly flowers) showing this type of symmetry are termed *actinomorphic*. *Compare* bilateral symmetry.

radicle. The embryonic root of angiosperms and gymnosperms, which is continuous with the hypocotyl. It is the first structure to appear in the germinat-

ing seedling, often emerging via the micropyle.

radioactive dating. Any of various *dating techniques that give the absolute age of a sediment or fossil. All methods depend on the fact that naturally occurring radioactive isotopes (radioactive forms of an element) decay at a known rate. By calculating the amount of isotope left in a sediment or fossil, and by knowing the amount present when it was first laid down and the rate of decay, it is possible to work out the age of the specimen. This method depends on several assumptions, the most important being the known proportion of radioactive to nonradioactive isotopes at the time the fossil or sediment was laid down. The radioactive isotopes most often used are carbon (carbon-14), potassium-argon, and uranium.
The carbon-14 method (*radiocarbon dating*) can be used to date organic material directly, up to an age of 7000 years, since carbon-14 has a half life of 5730 years, i.e. the radioactivity decreases to half in this time. Carbon-14 is produced in the upper atmosphere by the action of cosmic radiation on nitrogen and becomes incorporated into atmospheric carbon dioxide in a known proportion to nonradioactive carbon. The carbon dioxide is absorbed by plants during photosynthesis and becomes incorporated into the animals that eat them. When a plant or animal dies, the carbon-14 present begins to decay. The amount of residual radioactivity can be measured, enabling the absolute age to be calculated.
Potassium-argon dating utilizes the fact that naturally occurring potassium contains the radioisotope potassium-40, which decays to the gas argon-40; this becomes trapped in minerals containing potassium. The decay is much slower than that of carbon-14 (potassium-40 has a half life of 1300 million years), which considerably extends the range of absolute dating.

radioactive labelling. The incorporation of radioactive isotopes (e.g. ^{14}C, ^{3}H, ^{32}P), or *tracers*, into chemical compounds. The technique is widely used to study biological processes, in which labelled molecules can be traced during such experimental procedures as *chromatography and *electrophoresis. Using labelled precursors, the fate of radioactive molecules within cells can also be studied and metabolic pathways worked out. Radioactively labelled compounds can be detected and quantified by such means as *autoradiography and liquid scintillation counting.

radioimmunoassay. The most widely used technique for measuring polypeptide hormones in biological tissues and fluids. It is based on the ability of an unlabelled hormone to inhibit competitively the binding of labelled hormone by specific antibodies. The hormone concentration of the unknown sample is determined by comparing the degree of inhibition with that produced by a series of standards containing known amounts of the hormone. This technique has outstanding advantages in sensitivity, specificity, practicability, and precision over other procedures and can measure normal circulating levels of hormones (in the range 10^{-8} to 10^{-4} kg/m^3) with reasonable reliability. The method was first described by Berson and Yalow in 1960 for the measurement of plasma insulin in man. It has also been used to assay nonpeptide substances, such as steroids, prostaglandins, and nucleotides.

Radiolaria. An order of marine Protozoa of the class Sarcodina characterized by a chitinous capsule, separating the protoplasm into outer and inner parts, and a siliceous internal skeleton strengthening the pseudopodia. The order has been in existence since Pre-Cambrian times; the siliceous parts of radiolarians are constituents of deposits (oozes) on the ocean floor and of rocks, notably flint.

radius. One of the two long bones of the lower region of the tetrapod forelimb (*compare* ulna). In the primitive condition it lies on the inner side and is the main supporting element of the limb. *See* pentadactyl limb.

radula. A tooth-bearing ribbon borne on the muscular tongue of most molluscs, used for rasping food from the substratum. It is continuously replaced as it becomes worn out. The radula is secondarily modified in some species for other methods of food gathering, e.g. scraping, boring, and slicing flesh.

Ramapithecus. A genus of manlike fossil apes of the Miocene or early Pliocene, dated 12 to 14 million years ago. They show hominid dental features and may be the ancestors of true hominids. *See also Kenyapithecus.*

ramentum (*pl.* **ramenta).** A multicellular *trichome consisting of a plate of cells attached laterally to a stem or rachis, particularly one of the brown scaly structures on the rachis of a fern frond.

raphe. 1. The narrow slit on the valve face of a diatom *frustule.
2. The line of fusion between the funicle and integument of an inverted ovule.
3. Any line of suture (junction) in organs, such as the junction between the two halves of the vertebrate brain.

raphide. A fine needle-shaped crystal of calcium oxalate occurring in certain plant cells, usually in bundles.

Ratitae. *See* Palaeognathae.

Raunkiaer's classification. A system for classifying plants according to the position of their perennating buds (winter buds). *See* chamaephyte, geophyte, helophyte, hemicryptophyte, hydrophyte, phanerophyte, therophyte.

rays (the fish). *See* Batoidea.

reaction time. *See* latent period.

recapitulation. A theory put forward by Ernst Haeckel (1834–1919) in the 19th century that ontogeny repeats phylogeny, i.e. that each organism in its development from zygote to adult climbs its own family tree. For example, a mammal starts life as a single cell, resembling its protozoan ancestors, then becomes a two-layered embryo, resembling a coelenterate ancestor, and later goes through a stage of having gill slits, similar to its fish ancestors. This theory has been largely discredited; the evidence indicates only that there is a closer resemblance between embryos of related animals than between the adults themselves.

Recent. *See* Holocene.

receptacle (torus, thalamus). The upper end of the flower stalk in an angiosperm, from which the perianth, androecium, and gynoecium arise.

receptor. A cell or part of a cell that is specialized to respond to a stimulus from the internal or external environment of an animal and to convert it into a local graded membrane potential. In a sensory neurone, this *receptor* (or *generator*) *potential* triggers a burst of propagated impulses whose frequency reflects the stimulus strength (*see* adaptation). In a primary sense cell, such as a skin mechanoreceptor, transduction and impulse initiation occur in the same cell; in a secondary sense cell, such as a vertebrate taste receptor, the receptor potential triggers impulses in a succeeding neurone. Most receptors are associated with accessory structures, which restrict the range of effective stimuli to one or two qualities of a single class of stimulus and increase sensitivity to these qualities (*compare* crista, macula). Receptors may be classified according to their site (*see* interoceptor, exteroceptor) or according to the nature of the effective stimulus (*see* chemoreceptor, photoreceptor, mechanoreceptor). *See also* sense organ.

receptor potential (generator potential). The graded depolarization evoked in a *receptor cell by an environmental stimulus.

recessive. (Designating) the member of a pair of alleles that does not show its effect in the presence of any other alle-

lic partner. Therefore a recessive shows up in the phenotype only when it is homozygous in the genotype; it is then known as a *double recessive*. If a dominant gene *A* has a recessive allele *a*, the phenotype of the recessive shows only in the homozygous double recessive *aa*. Recessives arise from dominant genes by mutation and are frequently deleterious. There is sometimes more than one recessive corresponding to a dominant. *Compare* dominant.

recipient. A person or animal that receives organs, tissues, or blood derived from another individual of the same or of a different species. *See* graft.

reciprocal cross. A pair of matings in which the genotypes of the male and female gametes are reversed in the second cross. For example, if a male *AA* is crossed with a female *aa* in the first cross, a male *aa* is mated with a female *AA* in the second. It is used to determine whether the sex has any influence on the result of the cross.

recombinant DNA. DNA formed when single strands combine by complementary base pairing to yield double helices. Such reactions occur in nature during *crossing over in meiosis and between sister chromatids during normal cell division. Recombination also occurs in bacterial *conjugation and *transformation and it is widely used *in vitro* in *genetic engineering (*recombinant DNA technology*).

recombination. The formation of a zygote containing combinations of genes that are different from the combinations in either parent. For example, if a parent *AAbb* is crossed with *aaBB*, it is possible to produce an individual containing *AaBb*, which is both phenotypically and genotypically different from the parents. Recombination results from the process of *crossing over during meiosis in eukaryotes or from simple DNA exchange in prokaryotes. Some recombination events, however, appear to involve the addition of a new sequence to an existing DNA molecule, without exchange (*see* additive recombination). Recombination is an important means of producing variation, upon which natural selection can act to bring about evolutionary change.

recon. The unit of genetic recombination, now known to be an individual base pair in a DNA molecule. Although recombination of only one nucleotide length is unlikely to occur, there is no larger sequence that cannot be broken and in which recombination cannot occur.

rectum. The terminal ectodermal section of the alimentary canal, in which faeces are stored; it is closed in mammals by sphincters at either end. In insects it is specialized for the reabsorption of water.

red algae. *See* Rhodophyta.

red blood cell (red blood corpuscle, erythrocyte). The principal type of cell of vertebrate blood, responsible for the transport of oxygen from the lungs to the tissues and of carbon dioxide from the tissues to the lungs. In mammals red cells are flattened non-nucleate biconcave discs; in all other vertebrates the nucleus is retained and the cells tend to be oval and larger. Their size varies considerably in different mammals; in man they are 7–8 μm in diameter. There are about 5 000 000 red blood cells in one cubic millimetre of human blood, each having a lifespan of about 120 days. Each red cell has a colloidal matrix containing a solution of the respiratory pigment *haemoglobin, which is responsible for binding oxygen and carbon dioxide.

redia. A larval stage of endoparasitic flukes (*see* Trematoda) that develops asexually in a *sporocyst in the secondary host, a snail, and has an elongated body with a mouth, suctorial pharynx, and a simple gut. It usually migrates to the digestive gland of the snail, where it produces more rediae or *cercaria larvae asexually. *See also* miracidium.

reduction division. *See* meiosis.

reflex. An innate stereotyped response to a stimulus, e.g. the rapid and involuntary withdrawal of a limb following a pain stimulus. Simple reflex actions are mediated by a *reflex arc*, in which the receptor and effector are linked directly (*see* effector (independent)), or through a monosynaptic pathway involving only afferent sensory and efferent motor neurones. Forms of behaviour based on reflexes occur in all Metazoa, but in animals with a well-developed central nervous system, excitatory and inhibitory *interneurones are interpolated between the afferent and efferent pathways. This enables complex integrative interactions, such as simultaneous reflex contraction in an effector muscle. The brain may also be involved (*see* conditioned reflex). Reflexes control posture (*see* muscle spindle) and pupil size (*see* iris) in vertebrates.

refractory period. The recovery period of a neurone membrane following the passage of a nervous impulse. The *absolute refractory period* is the first phase of recovery, during which no stimulus, however large, can elicit a further impulse. This is followed by a *relative refractory period*, during which only an abnormally large stimulus can elicit an impulse.

refugium. A small isolated region where extensive climatic change, which has affected surrounding regions, has not taken place. Such a region is usually a *nunatak*, i.e. a mountain that escaped the Pleistocene glaciation affecting neighbouring lower-lying regions and that therefore provided an isolated and protected habitat for a small group of animals and plants throughout the Ice Age. *See also* relic(t).

regeneration. The regrowth of parts of an organism lost through injury, *autotomy, or other means. Regeneration is very common in plants, occurring for example from stem and leaf cuttings and by other means of vegetative propagation and from *calluses. Lower animals have greater powers of regeneration than those higher in the evolutionary scale. Many invertebrates, including coelenterates, planarians, and nemertines, can undergo dedifferentiation in adverse conditions, e.g. starvation, and regenerate when conditions improve. The planarian *Dugesia* is well known for its power of regenerating complete new organisms from small pieces cut from the original. Crustaceans (e.g. crabs) and echinoderms (e.g. starfish and brittle stars) can regenerate new limbs and arms, respectively; amphibians can regenerate tails and limbs and lizards can replace tails shed by autotomy. Regeneration in mammals is restricted to wound healing and regrowth of peripheral nerve fibres. If a large part of an organ, such as the liver or pancreas, is removed the remaining part will increase to the size of the whole organ without regenerating the part lost; this is known as *compensatory hypertrophy*.

Regeneration in both invertebrates and vertebrates involves the aggregation of a mass of undifferentiated cells (*blastema*) at the site of the injury. These cells grow and differentiate to form the new tissue. Plants and some invertebrates (e.g. coelenterates) can also regenerate by *morphallaxis*, in which the missing parts are replaced by reorganization of pre-existing neighbouring tissues.

regma. A type of schizocarpic *fruit that breaks up into one-seeded dehiscent fragments.

regulation egg. A fertilized ovum in which the direction of development of the cells of the embryo is not determined until cleavage is well advanced. Regulation eggs can recover from early damage or disturbance to complete normal development. *Compare* mosaic egg.

regulator gene. *See* operon.

reinforcement (in animal learning behaviour). An event that alters the rate of intensity of an animal's response to a stimulus. *Positive reinforcement* (reward),

given after an animal has made a response, increases the rate or activity of the response; *negative reinforcement* (punishment) decreases it.

relaxin. Any of a group of mammalian polypeptide hormones secreted by either the ovaries, placenta, or uterine tissue (depending on the species) during the later stages of pregnancy. Relaxin in the blood reaches high levels during the terminal stages of human pregnancy and disappears within 24 hours after delivery. Although its precise function remains to be established, relaxin is known to break down cartilage and collagen fibre, thus causing relaxation of the pelvic ligaments and facilitating parturition. It was first demonstrated in guinea pigs by Hisaw in 1926.

releaser. Any stimulus that causes an instinctive pattern of behaviour in an animal. A *social releaser* is a ritualized activity that acts as a stimulus to produce a response in another member of the species. The term was first coined by Konrad Lorenz, who also postulated a special neurosensory mechanism, an *innate releasing mechanism*, in the animal receiving the stimulus, which would enable it to respond in the correct way. In the course of evolution releasers have become incorporated into the courtship and threat displays of many species.

relic(t). (Designating) a group of organisms that are the remains of a formerly more widely distributed group. A relic(t) distribution of fauna and flora is typical of a *refugium.

renal portal system. An arrangement in amphibians and some fish and reptiles of paired veins, derived from the posterior cardinal veins, taking blood from the capillary beds of the hind limbs and tail to a capillary bed in the kidneys. The blood is then returned to the heart by the posterior cardinal veins. In amniotes, the renal portal veins become part of the posterior vena cava.

renaturation. *See* denaturation.

renin. An enzyme released from the kidneys of people with high blood pressure that stimulates the formation of *angiotensin from a liver globulin.

rennin. An enzyme, secreted by the stomach of young mammals, that coagulates the casein protein of milk.

repetitious DNA. A fraction of DNA comprising nucleotide sequences that are repeated many times in the genome of any one cell. It can be subdivided into *highly repetitious DNA* and *moderately repetitious DNA* (*intermediate repetitive DNA*). Highly repetitious DNA consists of sequences represented more than 1000 times per genome; many of these sequences are very short, consisting of less than 100 base pairs. Such material is concentrated in *heterochromatin and, in chromosomes, is largely located at and around the *centromere. Moderately repetitious DNA consists of sequences that are repeated between 10 and 1000 times per genome. This fraction of DNA reassociates at intermediate *Cot values and can be isolated by DNA reassociation experiments. It consists

mainly of relatively long sequences (between 1000 and 3000 bases) and there is evidence to indicate that many of these are interspersed with the so-called *single-copy* (or *unique*) *sequences*. Moderately repetitious DNA accounts for between 10% and 20% of the genome of an average eukaryotic organism; it includes the genes for ribosomal and transfer RNA, structural genes for histone, and a large remaining fraction, often assumed to have a regulatory function.

replacing bone. *See* cartilage bone.

replicase. An enzyme that catalyses the replication of a macromolecule (especially DNA or RNA). Examples are DNA and RNA *polymerases.

replication. The process by which two molecules of DNA are formed from a parent molecule in such a way that each of the daughter molecules is identical to the parent. It involves the splitting of the double-stranded parent molecule into two single strands, each of which controls the synthesis of a new strand complementary to itself. The enzyme responsible for the synthesis of the com-

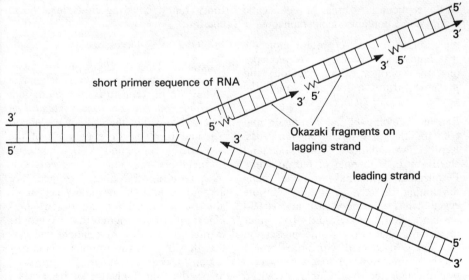

Replication of DNA

plementary strand (a DNA *polymerase) uses deoxyribonucleoside triphosphates as substrates. Because of the specificity of base pairing, the new double-stranded molecules are exact duplicates of the old. One half of the parental DNA goes to make up half of each of the daughter strands, i.e. the replication is *semiconservative*.

Since each newly synthesized strand of DNA has an orientated sequence of nucleotides running from a 5' end to a 3' end, and since the DNA polymerase can only utilize the template strand running from 3' to 5', it follows that one of the parent strands cannot be copied in a straightforward fashion. For this template, the polymerase molecule synthesizes short pieces of DNA termed *Okazaki fragments, which are later spliced to form a continuous strand. Each new DNA sequence, including each Okazaki fragment, is primed by a very short sequence of newly synthesized RNA. This RNA is later cleaved out and the space filled in with DNA. (See illustration.)

replicon. A length of DNA that is replicated as a unit from a single initiation site (origin of replication). A bacterial chromosome and a plasmid are both single replicons, whereas a eukaryotic chromosome contains many replicons.

repressor molecule. A protein molecule that binds to a specific DNA sequence (e.g. the operator of an *operon) and prevents transcription of adjoining genes.

Reptilia. The class of the Vertebrata that contains the first terrestrial tetrapods. Reptiles are adapted to life on land chiefly by their manner of reproduction. Fertilization is internal, with the young developing directly from an *amniote egg that has a leathery shell and is laid on land, i.e. it is *cleidoic*. The other important adaptation is the possession of a dry skin covered with horny scales, which minimizes water loss by evaporation through the skin. Other advanced features include clawed digits and a

metanephric kidney *(see* metanephros). Like amphibians, but unlike birds and mammals, reptiles are poikilothermic. Reptiles evolved from labyrinthodont amphibians to become the dominant tetrapods of the Mesozoic, when they underwent adaptive radiation into aerial, terrestrial, and aquatic forms. Some groups gave rise to the birds and mammals. There are six subclasses: *Anapsida (cotylosaurs and chelonians), *Lepidosauria (lizards, snakes, etc.), *Archosauria (crocodiles, pterosaurs, and dinosaurs), *Ichthyopterygia (ichthyosaurs), *Synaptosauria (plesiosaurs, etc.), and *Synapsida (mammal-like reptiles).

resin. One of a group of acidic substances produced by many trees and shrubs, especially conifers. Some resins are phenol derivatives, others are terpene derivatives. They occur as solids or dissolved in essential oils forming balsams, e.g. turpentine. In conifers they are usually found in resin ducts: schizogenous canals lined with resin-secreting cells. The formation of similar canals, and high flows of resin, can be induced by injury or infection; blocking of vascular elements may prevent the spread of infection. Resins are sometimes found covering buds, e.g. horse chestnut.

resolution. *See* microscope.

respiration. One or all of the processes involved in the extraction of chemical energy from foodstuffs by oxidation. *Internal* (*cellular* or *tissue*) *respiration* takes place within the cells of the organism and involves the generation of the high-energy compound ATP by a series of metabolic reactions. These reactions may require atmospheric oxygen (*see* aerobic respiration) or take place in its absence (*see* anaerobic respiration). Aerobic respiration requires that oxygen be extracted from the environment and carbon dioxide, a waste product of the oxidation, discharged into it. The processes involved in the exchange of these gases between the organism and the environment are termed *external respiration*. Gas exchange is often facilitated by use of a *respiratory organ, which is ventilated or irrigated by organized *respiratory movements, and is often coupled with a *respiratory pigment in the circulatory system.

respiratory chain. *See* electron transport chain.

respiratory movement. The movement made by animals that effects the active passage of air or water across the respiratory surface and so promotes the rapid and efficient exchange of oxygen and carbon dioxide. The movements used vary greatly with the nature of the respiratory organs. Breathing in mammals involves the lowering of the diaphragm and expansion of the rib cage to draw in oxygen and their return to their normal positions to expel carbon dioxide.

respiratory organ. An animal organ specialized to provide a surface for the efficient exchange of respiratory gases between the organism and the environment, e.g. *lung (tetrapods), *gill (aquatic animals), and *trachea (insects).

respiratory pigment. A coloured substance that increases the oxygen-transport capacity of the circulatory system by combining reversibly with oxygen. The pigment may occur free in the plasma or be confined to corpuscles. The term is sometimes used to include the pigments involved in cellular respiration, i.e. the flavoproteins. *See also* haemoglobin, haemerythrin, chlorocruorin, haemocyanin.

respiratory quotient (RQ). The ratio of the volume of carbon dioxide produced by an organism during respiration to the volume of oxygen consumed. Theoretical calculation of RQs involved in the complete oxidation of different foodstuffs predicts a value of 1 for carbohydrate, approximately 0.8 for protein, and approximately 0.7 for fats. The RQ is simple to estimate *in vivo* and, if nitrogen excretion is also measured, gives information about the foodstuffs utilized

by organisms. However, the results are rendered ambiguous by certain metabolic states, e.g. the interconversion of foodstuffs (especially carbohydrates to fats, which produces an abnormally high RQ) and the creation and discharge of an *oxygen debt.

response. The change in a cell, tissue, or organism that constitutes a reaction to a stimulus. *See* irritability, nervous system.

resting nucleus and cell. *See* interphase.

resting potential. The steady-state potential difference that exists across the membrane of a cell when it is not excited by a stimulus or spontaneous activity. A resting potential exists because the cell membrane is semipermeable, which enables the unequal distribution of ions between the extracellular and intracellular media. A *neurone typically exhibits a resting potential of − 70 mV (inside negative). The extracellular medium contains a high concentration of potassium ions, balanced by protein anions. The membrane is almost impermeable to sodium ions, which are therefore excluded from the cell. The membrane is permeable to potassium ions, which tend to diffuse down their concentration gradient, carrying positive charges outwards. When the potential difference thus produced is equal and opposite in effect to the concentration gradient, net diffusion in either direction ceases and a steady state is reached. The resting potential is thus the potential gradient across the membrane that offsets the concentration gradient due to the imbalance of potassium ions at equilibrium. The movement of ions needed to produce a resting potential of −70 mV is insufficient to affect the neutrality of either the intracellular or the extracellular medium. The membrane is not perfectly impermeable to sodium ions, which leak slowly and continuously into the cell and are removed by the *sodium pump. The imbalance of sodium ions, which is necessary for the maintenance of the resting potential, is therefore dependent on the metabolic

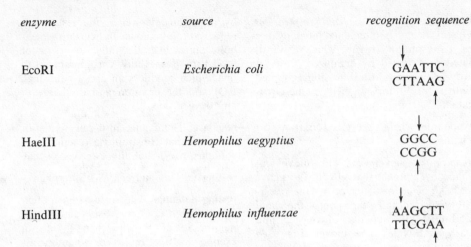

enzyme	source	recognition sequence
EcoRI	*Escherichia coli*	↓ GAATTC CTTAAG ↑
HaeIII	*Hemophilus aegyptius*	↓ GGCC CCGG ↑
HindIII	*Hemophilus influenzae*	↓ AAGCTT TTCGAA ↑

Commonly used restriction endonucleases

energy that drives the sodium pump. *See also* impulse.

restriction endonuclease (restriction enzyme). An enzyme that cuts a DNA sequence internally at a particular site with a characteristic sequence of bases (*see* endonuclease). Most restriction endonucleases cut DNA at *palindromic sequences, although not necessarily through the axis of symmetry. They are produced by many bacteria as protection against the foreign DNA of invading viruses. Bacteria modify their genomic DNA by methylation to protect it from attack by the restriction enzymes. Viral DNA appearing in a bacterial cell is not methylated and is therefore degraded by the restriction endonuclease present. These enzymes are now important tools in *genetic engineering. A list of common restriction enzymes is given in the table.

reticular activating system (reticular formation). A system of interconnected nerve fibres within the brain that receives sensory stimuli from the peripheral sense organs and transmits them to all the higher centres of the brain. This results in *arousal of the higher centres, which leads to increased responsiveness of the animal to the stimuli.

reticular fibres (argentophil fibres, argyrophil fibres). Fine branching fibres, sparsely distributed in vertebrate connective tissue, that form a supporting network (*reticulum*) around muscle fibres, blood vessels, nerves, epithelial structures, and glandular organs. They are composed of the protein *reticulin* and are usually spatially continuous with and similar in structure to *collagen fibres. They differ from the latter in their staining properties and are thought to resemble an immature form of collagen.

reticulate thickening. A pattern of secondary wall formation in primary xylem vessels and tracheids in which the wall material is laid down in an irregular anastomosing network. It is usually the third type of thickening to appear and develops in the last-formed protoxylem and earliest metaxylem elements. *Compare* annular, spiral, scalariform, and pitted thickenings.

reticulin. The protein of *reticular fibres.

reticulocyte. An immature red blood cell that has just been formed from a red-cell precursor (*see* erythroblast). Reticulocytes have a reticular (netlike) cytoplasm, lack a nucleus, and stain with basic dyes such as methylene blue; they are found in large numbers in the blood after haemolysis and haemorrhage.

reticuloendothelial system. The system of macrophages in vertebrate tissues.

reticulum. The second chamber of the stomach of ruminants. *See* Ruminantia.

retina. The sensory innermost layer of the eyes of vertebrates and cephalopods. Except where it forms part of the iris and ciliary body, it consists of a layer of photosensitive cells (*see* rod, cone) linked to fibres of the *optic nerve by intermediate cells, which, with glia and blood vessels, constitute the *ganglion layer*. In cephalopods the retina is an ectodermal structure and light falls directly onto the photosensitive cells, the ganglion layer lying beneath them. In vertebrates the retina is a fused double layer of cells derived from a diverticulum of the brain and is therefore inverted: the photosensitive cells are in contact with the choroid and light must pass through the ganglion layer to reach them. *See also* blind spot, fovea, macula.

retinal (retinene). The aldehyde of vitamin A, which combines with the protein opsin in the rods of the retina to form the light-sensitive pigment *rhodopsin.

retinol. *See* vitamin A.

reverse transcriptase (RNA-dependent DNA polymerase). An enzyme that directs the synthesis of DNA from an RNA template (*reverse transcription*). It is found in certain RNA viruses, such as the Rous sarcoma virus, that replicate by means of a DNA intermediate called the *provirus*. This enzyme is widely used in *genetic engineering technology to produce complementary DNA (cDNA) from a purified preparation of a specific messenger RNA.

rhachis. *See* rachis.

rhesus system. *See* blood groups.

Rhipidistia. A suborder of the Crossopterygii containing the stock from which all land vertebrates evolved. These primarily freshwater fishes, e.g.

the early *Osteolepis* and the more advanced *Eusthenopteron*, first appeared in the late Devonian and were extinct by the end of the Palaeozoic. Resemblances to the Labyrinthodontia (early amphibians) included many details of the endoskeleton, particularly that of the paired fins (which closely resembled that of the tetrapod limb), and the internal structure of the teeth.

rhizoid. One of many uni- and multicellular filamentous outgrowths that are produced by some algae and by the gametophytes of bryophytes and pteridophytes and function as roots.

rhizome. An organ of vegetative propagation and sometimes also of perennation in vascular plants. It consists of a horizontal underground stem bearing leaves, shoots, and adventitious roots. In plants such as couch grass the rhizome is thin and used only for vegetative propagation; it produces shoots at intervals and the old parts rot away. In other plants, such as iris and Solomon's seal, the rhizome stores food in winter and thus acts as a perennating organ. In many species of iris, the rhizome lies on the surface of the soil. *Compare* stolon.

rhizomorph. A stout rootlike strand developed by some fungi. It is composed of vegetative hyphae forming a highly organized structure and serves for vegetative spread, as in *Armillaria mellea* (honey fungus), a parasite of trees.

rhizophore. An organ produced in certain pteridophytes (e.g. *Selaginella*) that bears the roots and appears to be intermediate between root and shoot in anatomy and morphology.

Rhizopoda. A subdivision of the protozoan class *Sarcodina.

Rhodesian man. *See Homo.*

Rhodophyta. Red algae: multicellular (very occasionally unicellular) algae that show alternation of generations and possess r-phycocyanin and r-phycoerythin as well as β-carotene and chlorophylls a and d. The storage product is *floridean* starch (a carbohydrate resembling starch). The chloroplasts, in contrast to those of the other eukaryotic algae, contain only single thylakoids (similar to the blue-green algal pigment membranes), and the red algae never produce a motile stage. They have sexual reproduction, which occurs by means of a *carpogonium and a *spermatium. See also Aconta.

rhodopsin (visual purple). The light-sensitive pigment of vertebrate *rod cells, composed of retinal, the aldehyde of vitamin A, attached to a protein, opsin. Light initiates a series of reactions leading to separation of retinal from opsin, which initiates nervous activity in the rod. The bleached pigment is reconstituted in the dark. Adaptation to low levels of illumination is aided by increase in the amount of pigment.

rhombencephalon. See hindbrain.

Rhynchocephalia. An order of the Lepidosauria that contains many extinct Triassic reptiles and a single living genus, Sphenodon (tuatara). The postcranial skeleton is primitive, the teeth are fused to the jaws (as opposed to being embedded in sockets), and the front of the skull is drawn out into a beak. Sphenodon, the most primitive living reptile, is confined to a group of islands off New Zealand. It has many primitive features, such as a pineal eye in the skull roof.

Rhynchocoela. See Nemertina.

rhytidome (outer bark). See bark.

rib. One of a series of curved membrane bones that articulate with the vertebrae. In fish they develop between the myotomes and transfer the muscular force of the myotomes to the vertebral column. In tetrapods the ribs form much of the skeleton of the thoracic region, articulating dorsally with the thoracic vertebrae and, except in amphibians, ventrally with the sternum. Thus they form a skeletal cage around the lungs and are involved in respiratory movements.

Many fish possess an additional ventral series of ribs, not articulating with the vertebrae, that support the viscera. See also vertebral column, carapace.

Riboflavin

riboflavin (vitamin B₂). An essential nutritional factor for mammals that forms part of the *vitamin B complex. It is obtained from green vegetables, yeast, milk, liver, etc. Riboflavin was first detected in 1879 by Blyth and its structure was determined by synthesis in 1935 by Kuhn, Karrer, and others (see formula). Riboflavin is essential for carbohydrate metabolism, functioning as a precursor of the coenzymes FMN and FAD.

ribonuclease. See RNase.

ribonucleic acid. See RNA.

ribose. A pentose sugar, $C_5H_{10}O_5$, whose dextrorotatory form (D-ribose) is a component of *RNA.

ribosomal RNA (rRNA). See ribosome, RNA.

ribosome. A particle consisting of roughly equal amounts of RNA and protein (i.e. a ribonucleoprotein particle), many of which (up to several million) occur in virtually all living cells and are the sites of *protein synthesis. Two types of ribosome are recognized, according to their S values (rate of sedimentation in a centrifuge; see Svedberg unit). Both types consist of two subunits. The prokaryote type is 70S (with 50S and 30S subunits) and about 18 nm in diameter. This type is also found in chloroplasts and mitochondria of eukaryotes. The eukaryote type is 80S (60S and 40S subunits) and about 22 nm in diameter. It is found in the cytoplasm, though its RNA is made in the nucleolus. The RNA molecules of ribosomes have characteristic sizes and base compositions and are called *ribosomal RNA (rRNA)*. During protein synthesis ribosomes associate with messenger RNA (mRNA), usually forming *polysomes* (*polyribosomes*). Each polysome is a single mRNA molecule in the process of *translation by a variable number of ribosomes arranged along its length like beads on a string. Polysomes occur either free in the cytoplasm or bound to the surface of the endoplasmic reticulum (ER) or outer membrane of the nucleus (usually adopting spiral forms in the latter case). Proteins from free ribosomes are released into the hyaloplasm but those from membrane-bound ribosomes are usually passed into the ER cisternae to be later secreted or otherwise transported.

rickettsiae. A group of obligate intracellular prokaryotic parasites of fleas, lice, ticks, and mites. They are similar in structure to bacteria (for example, their cell walls contain mucopeptide, a substance characteristic of bacterial cell walls), but they can multiply only within their arthropod hosts and are therefore considered to be intermediate between bacteria and viruses. In arthropods they produce no ill effects; however, if they are transmitted to mammals, including man, by a bite of the arthropod host they cause severe, sometimes fatal, disease. Rickettsial diseases of man include typhus, Rocky Mountain spotted fever, and Q fever.
The group takes its name from the principal genus, *Rickettsia*, which was named after H. T. Ricketts (1871–1910), an American pathologist who died of typhus while investigating the cause of the disease.

Ringer's solution. An aqueous solution of calcium, sodium, and potassium chlo-rides, used as a medium for living cells or tissues undergoing *in vitro* investigations. It is named after the 19th-century physiologist Sidney Ringer. Sometimes other salts are added, in order to mimic closely the natural surroundings of the cells *in vivo*. The solution must be isotonic with the cells and at the correct pH. To achieve this it must be buffered with bicarbonate or phosphate. The resulting solution is often also known as *physiological saline*. It is now known that virtually all tissues can be kept alive at least for a time in such a solution.

ring-porous. Designating wood with most of the vessels aggregated in the early wood. *See* growth ring.

ring species. Two or more species that do not interbreed where their ranges overlap but are connected by a ring of subspecies between which breeding can occur. For example, *Larus argentatus* (herring gull) and *L. fuscus* (lesser black-backed gull) behave as good species in western Europe where their ranges overlap. However there are subspecies of *L. argentatus* in North America and of *L. fuscus* in Siberia that interbreed with each other as well as with members of their own species. They thus form a circumpolar chain linking the two good species.

ritualization. The process, in the course of the evolution of animal behaviour, in which activities of one individual (often displacement activities) come to cause a certain response in another individual of the same species. It is particularly evident in courtship displays; for example, the courtship of the great crested grebe shows elements of nest-building beha-

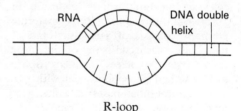

R-loop

viour, which have evolved by ritualization.

R-loop. A region in a DNA double helix where one DNA strand has become displaced and paired with a complementary RNA strand instead of its DNA partner (see illustration).

Section of RNA chain

RNA (ribonucleic acid). A nucleic acid that serves as the genetic material of some viruses and has many important roles as an intermediate molecule in *protein synthesis. An RNA molecule normally consists of a single strand of nucleotides, each consisting of the sugar ribose (which replaces the deoxyribose of DNA) and phosphoric acid with one of four nitrogenous bases: adenine, guanine, cytosine, or uracil. Uracil is the only base that occurs in RNA but not in DNA: in the sequence arrangement of RNA it is analogous to the thymine of DNA (see illustration).

Some forms of RNA can fold into double-stranded regions of complementary base pairs, but most RNA molecules are substantially single-stranded and are not base paired. The chief types of RNA found in cells are the heterogenous nuclear RNA (*HnRNA), which is the immediate transcription product of the structural genes; *messenger RNA, which is produced from HnRNA; *ribosomal RNA (rRNA)*, which, together with ribosomal protein, forms the *ribosomes; and *transfer RNA, which is responsible for carrying specific amino acid molecules to the messenger RNA on the ribosome during protein synthesis.

Although RNA is normally the product of transcription from the template molecule DNA, in some viruses DNA can be synthesized from an RNA template by the action of *reverse transcriptase.

RNA-dependent DNA polymerase. *See* reverse transcriptase.

RNA polymerase. *See* polymerase.

RNase (ribonuclease). Any of various enzymes that degrade RNA by hydrolysing the phosphodiester bonds in the sugar–phosphate backbone. Many attack only specific structures (e.g. RNase T attacks only the ends of hairpin loops, such as those in transfer RNA molecules) and so yield specific RNA fragments that can be used for *fingerprinting.

rod. A light-sensitive cell present in the *retina of most vertebrates. It consists of a photosensitive outer segment, in close contact with the choroid, linked by a neck containing a ciliary structure to a cell body, which synapses with the ganglion layer of the retina. The outer segment contains the visual pigment *rhodopsin, arrayed on membranous lamellae oriented at right angles to the incoming rays of light. Rods are responsible for vision in poor light and are the only visual cells of most nocturnal vertebrates. The sensitivity of the retina is increased, but the acuity decreased, by *summation in which many rods synapse with one fibre of the optic nerve. The retina of cephalopods contains analogous cells. *Compare* cone.

Rodentia. The largest order of the Eutheria, comprising herbivorous or omnivorous gnawing mammals with two large incisor teeth in each jaw that grow continuously and have enamel only on the front. The wearing down of the softer dentine behind produces a sharp cutting tool. There is a gap (*diastema*) between the gnawing incisors and the grinding molars. While gnawing wood or other inedible matter, the front part of the mouth can be shut off from the throat by drawing in folds of skin in the diastema region, which ensures that the material is not swallowed. There are three main groups: the sciuromorphs, e.g. *Sciurus* (squirrel), *Castor* (beaver); the myomorphs, e.g *Rattus* (rat), *Mus* (mouse); and the hystricomorphs, e.g. *Hystrix* (porcupine), *Cavia* (cavy).

rogue. *See* sport.

root. 1. The part of the axis of a vascular plant that is concerned with anchorage and the absorption of water and mineral ions. It is characterized by the absence of leaves, the presence of a protective *root cap* over the *apical meristem, lateral branches that are endogenous in origin, i.e. arising from the deep tissues of the axis (*see* pericycle), and are borne in a random fashion, primary vascular tissues (xylem and phloem) that are on different radii, and the presence of *root hairs* (or *pili*). These are produced on a region of epidermis just behind the apical meristem known as the *piliferous layer*. Formed as tubelike protrusions from single epidermal cells, root hairs are delicate and short-lived and carry out the absorptive functions of the root.

The first root formed in a plant is the *radicle. Roots derived from the radicle are termed *primary*; all other roots are adventitious. When the radicle forms a large main root with small lateral branches a *tap-root system* is produced; when the radicle and its branches are of similar size a *fibrous-root system* is developed.

Roots may become modified in various ways. Storage roots are those that become swollen with tissue (normally parenchymatous) containing food reserves. They may be formed from a tap root plus part of the hypocotyl, as in root crops such as turnips and sugar beet, or as *root tubers*, formed only from root tissue of fibrous roots or adventitious roots. Supporting roots include *buttress roots*, produced by an asymmetrical vertical thickening on the main roots at the base of tropical trees; *prop roots*, which grow vertically downwards from the main branches of trees; *stilt roots*, produced from the main axis of a plant, e.g. from the nodes of *Zea mays* (maize); and *clasping roots*, which are haptotropic. Other modifications include *haustoria in some parasitic plants; *pneumatophores*, which are negatively geotropic roots that emerge above ground level to act as organs of gaseous exchange, produced by many swamp plants growing in water-logged mud; and *aerial roots*, which trail down from epiphytic plants to produce a normal root in the ground (the outer layer of the aerial portion forms a *velamen). Roots may become sclerified, as in palms, to form *root spines* or *root thorns*. Nutritionally important modifications arise from symbiotic relationships with fungi (*see* mycorrhiza) and bacteria. For example, nitrogen-fixing bacteria within the root tissue of leguminous plants cause localized stimulation of growth that results in swellings termed *root nodules* (*see* nitrogen fixation).

2. The point at which a vertebrate segmental nerve arises from the *central nervous system. Each spinal nerve has two roots: the *dorsal root* (posterior in man and other bipedal vertebrates) carries sensory fibres from the receptors and bears a ganglion containing the cell bodies; the *ventral* (*anterior*) *root*, carries both somatic motor fibres innervating the striated muscles and autonomic motor fibres innervating the smooth muscles and glands. The motor neurone bodies lie in the grey matter of the spinal cord. In all vertebrates except the cyclostomes, the roots fuse close to the cord to form mixed spinal nerves. Dorsal and ventral roots of the segmental *cranial nerves can also be distinguished, although these roots are functionally mixed and do not fuse.

rootstock. An upright underground stem, with its upper end flush to the surface of the soil, bearing leaves and buds at the upper end and roots at the lower end. It is most commonly found in plants with a basal rosette of leaves, such as dandelions and daisies, and can serve as an organ of vegetative propagation.

Rotifera. A widely distributed phylum of minute aquatic pseudocoelomate invertebrates, the wheel animalcules. These bilaterally symmetrical unsegmented animals are characterized by a ciliated crown (*corona*) on the head used in feeding and locomotion, which, when beating, resembles a rotating wheel. Rotifers have a muscular pharynx bearing well-developed jaws. Protonephridia are the excretory organs (*see* nephridium). The males are often degenerate and parthenogenesis is common. *See also* Aschelminthes.

roundworms. *See* Nematoda.

Rous sarcoma. A tumour occurring in the domestic chicken and caused by *Rous sarcoma virus* (*RSV*). This *oncogenic virus was discovered in 1911 by Peyton Rous and the tumour is a classic example of a virally induced cancer.

rumen. The first chamber of the stomach of ruminants. *See* Ruminantia.

Ruminantia. A suborder of the *Artiodactyla whose members have a compli-

cated digestive system, which allows food to be swallowed quickly and thoroughly digested later, away from predators. The most advanced ruminants, including the deer, giraffe, and bovids (antelopes, cattle, sheep, goats, etc.), have a four-chambered stomach. Food is partially digested in the first two chambers, the *rumen* and *reticulum*, and is regurgitated in small amounts to be thoroughly chewed (chewing the cud). It then passes to the third and fourth chambers, the *omasum* (or *psalterium*) and *abomasum*, where digestion is continued.

runner. *See* stolon.

rusts. A group of parasitic basidiomycete fungi belonging to the order Uredinales, many of which attack plants of agricultural importance, including the Gramineae (grasses). The life cycle is typically as follows. A basidiospore infects the secondary host, such as *Berberis vulgaris* (barberry) for *Puccinia graminis*, to produce a mycelium with one nucleus per cell. This produces *spermogonia, which results in the formation of a dikaryotic mycelium. This then produces aecidiospores (*see* aecidium), which infect the primary host, such as a grain crop, and form a dikaryotic mycelium in it. This mycelium produces uredospores (or *brand spores*) (*see* uredium), in the early part of the season, for dissemination, and later two-celled teleutospores (*see* teleutosorus). The latter act as the resting stage of the life cycle, germinating the following season to produce basidiospores.

S

sacculus. The ventral cavity of the vertebrate membranous labyrinth, from which the cochlea arises in amniotes. *See* inner ear.

sacral vertebrae. The bones of the lower back region of the *vertebral column that are involved in articulation with the tetrapod pelvic girdle. *See* sacrum.

sacrum. A unit of one (in amphibians) or more (in amniotes) sacral vertebrae and their ribs, fused to serve as a firm attachment site for the ilium of the pelvic girdle.

safranin. *See* staining.

salamanders. *See* Urodela.

saliva. The secretion of the salivary glands, basically consisting of mucus, which moistens and lubricates food. In some tetrapods and insects the saliva contains amylases, e.g. ptyalin in mammals, which initiate the digestion of starch. The saliva of blood-sucking animals, e.g. leeches, mosquitoes, contains an anticoagulant.

salivary glands. Ectodermal glands that are derived from the buccal cavity (vertebrates) or the foregut (invertebrates) and secrete saliva. The salivary glands may be specialized to produce poisons (some carnivores, e.g. lizards) or adhesive substances (birds, for building nests).

saltatory conduction. The mode of transmission of nervous impulses in myelinated nerves. The insulating power of the myelin sheath permits efficient passive transmission of the response by local currents along the fibre axis in the internode region; the signal is boosted at the nodes of Ranvier, where the absence of myelin allows the generation of an impulse. Saltatory conduction is much more rapid and energetically economical than continuous conduction. *See* impulse.

samara. A *fruit resembling an achene but with the pericarp extended to form a wing or membrane to aid dispersal.

saponification. The alkaline hydrolysis of glycerides to yield glycerol and a soap (a salt of a fatty acid). For example, the triglyceride palmitin reacts with caustic soda to give sodium palmitate and glycerol.

saprophyte. An organism that obtains its nourishment from dead or decaying organic matter. Enzymes produced by the saprophyte are secreted onto the organic matter, which is digested externally, absorbed, and assimilated. Many fungi and bacteria are saprophytes: they play an important part in the recycling of nutrients (*see* food chain).

saprozoic. Designating organisms that feed on solutions of organic material rather than on solid organic matter. Saprozoic organisms include the flagellate protozoan *Polytoma uvella* and many gut parasites.

sapwood (alburnum). *See* wood.

Sarcodina. A class of Protozoa characterized by *pseudopodia, used for locomotion and food capture. Most species are solitary and free-living and some secrete or construct an outer protective test or shell. The Rhizopoda, e.g. *Amoeba* and the *Foraminifera, have no internal skeleton, whereas the Actinopoda, which includes the Heliozoa and *Radiolaria, have stiff pseudopodia strengthened by a central internal filament.

sarcoma. Any tumour arising in connective tissue and normally constituting a solid mass of cells. Sarcomas are often highly malignant and represent one of the commonest forms of *cancer. *Compare* carcinoma.

sarcomere. A unit of the ultrastructure of *striated muscle.

sarcoplasmic reticulum. The form of endoplasmic reticulum found in muscle cells, specialized for the transmission of nervous excitation to the contractile filaments. *See also* excitation-contraction coupling.

satellite DNA. A fraction of DNA that separates from the bulk of the genomic DNA of an organism during centrifugation. DNA of mitochondrial, chloroplast, centromeric, and ribosomal types may all be recovered from centrifuged samples as distinct satellites, especially when the DNA is run through gradients of sucrose or caesium chloride.

Saurischia. An extinct order of reptiles of the subclass Archosauria containing dinosaurs with a triradiate (i.e. typically reptilian) pelvic girdle. They were the dominant reptiles of the Jurassic and Cretaceous. The suborder Theropoda were bipedal carnivores with birdlike feet, small grasping forelimbs, and simple sharp teeth; it includes *Tyrannosaurus*, 14.5 metres long and nearly 6 metres tall. The suborder Sauropoda contained the largest known tetrapods, notably *Apatosaurus (Brontosaurus)* (18.5 metres long) and *Diplodocus* (27.7 metres long and 30 tonnes in weight). Sauropods were semiaquatic quadrupedal herbivores with heavy limbs of equal size and weak teeth restricted to the front of the jaws. *Compare* Ornithischia.

Sauropterygia. An extinct order of the Synaptosauria containing aquatic and amphibious reptiles of the Triassic and Cretaceous. There are three suborders: the *Nothosauria, *Placodontia, and *Plesiosauria.

scalariform thickening. A type of secondary wall formation in xylem vessels and tracheids in which the wall material forms a continuous layer over the primary cell wall except for narrow transversely elongated *pits, which are often arranged one above the other like the rungs of a ladder. It is characteristic of many modern pteridophytes. *Compare* annular, spiral, reticulate, and pitted thickenings.

Scaphopoda. A small marine class of the Mollusca containing the tusk shells (e.g. *Dentalium*), characterized by a tubular shell open at both ends. The foot is pointed and reduced for burrowing in the sand and the head bears prehensile tentacles for food collection. Gills are absent (the mantle functions in respiration) and the posterior aperture of the shell serves for both inhalent and exhalent respiratory water currents.

scapula. A cartilage bone of the dorsal region of the *pectoral girdle of teleosts and tetrapods. It articulates with the humerus at the glenoid cavity and is the main site for the attachment of the muscles of the forelimb.

schizocarp. A multiovular *fruit that breaks up into one-seeded fragments (*mericarps*) at maturity.

schizogeny (in botany). The formation of any structure by the separation of the cells along their middle lamellae, as in the formation of intercellular spaces and certain resin ducts of tropical Leguminosae and conifers. *Compare* lysogeny.

Schizomycetes (Schizomycophyta). Bacteria (used in classifications that include the bacteria in the Fungi).

Schizophyta. A group comprising the bacteria and Cyanophyta (blue-green algae): used in certain classifications by authorities who regard the Cyanophyta as organisms too primitive to include in the Algae.

Schultze's solution. *See* staining.

Schwann cell. A glial cell of the vertebrate nervous system that is responsible for the formation of the *myelin sheath.

scion. *See* graft.

sclereid. Any sclerenchyma cell other than a fibre. Sclereids exist in a variety of forms, including *brachysclereids* (*stone cells* or *stereids*), which are roughly isodiametric; *macrosclereids*, rod-shaped cells occurring in seed coats, etc.; and *astrosclereids*, which are star-shaped. They may be formed singly (as in the leaf of *Trochodendron aralioides*), in groups (as in such fruits as the pear), or in continuous layers (as in the shells of nuts).

sclerenchyma. A plant tissue consisting of thick-walled cells whose function is mainly to give mechanical support. The sclerenchyma cell wall may or may not be lignified and at maturity the cells have frequently lost their living contents. Sclerenchyma is classified into *fibres (elongated cells with tapering ends) and *sclereids (all other sclerenchyma cells).

scleroprotein. One of a group of simple proteins that are insoluble in most solvents and form important components of animal skeletal and connective tissue. The group includes *keratin, *collagen, and *elastin.

sclerotic (sclera). The most external layer of the eye of vertebrates and cephalopods, forming a complete sheath around the eye (*compare* choroid, retina). Tough and fibrous, it maintains the shape of the eye and is specialized anteriorly to form the cornea.

sclerotium. A hard-walled resting body produced by some fungi as a means of overcoming adverse conditions. It is formed vegetatively from the mycelium or plasmodium by the outer layers hardening and forming the resistant wall. *Claviceps purpurea*, an ascomycete fungus parasitic on rye, produces sclerotia known as *ergots* in place of the ovary of the host grass flower. These ergots contain alkaloids that are responsible for outbreaks of the disease ergotism; however, they are also a source of the drug *ergotamine*, which is used to assist childbirth, etc. Ergots are overwintering structures that germinate the following spring to produce stalked stroma in which the perithecia are formed.

sclerotome. *See* mesoderm.

scolex. The head of a tapeworm (*see* Cestoda), which usually bears hooks and/or suckers for attachment to the gut wall of the host but lacks a mouth and sense organs.

Scorpiones. The order of the Arachnida that contains the scorpions, e.g. *Scorpio*. These large arachnids live in hot climates and are protected against excessive moisture loss by a layer of wax in the cuticle. Scorpions have three-jointed chelicerae and large pincer-like pedipalps. The last abdominal segments form the tail and the terminal appendage, the *telson*, bears the sting. Scorpions are ovoviviparous, the eggs hatching within the female.

scorpion flies. *See* Mecoptera.

scrotum. *See* testis.

scutellum. A part of the embryo of Gramineae (grasses) that is appressed to the endosperm and acts as an absorptive organ. It may represent the cotyledon, part of the cotyledon (together with the coleoptile), or the completely reduced embryonic axis (the plumule being an axillary bud). *See also* epiblast, mesocotyl.

scyphistoma. The sedentary polyp-like stage in the life cycle of the Scyphozoa. It develops from a planula and undergoes transverse fission (*see* strobila) to produce a number of free-swimming medusoid *ephyrae*, which grow into adult jellyfish.

Scyphozoa. The class of Cnidaria containing the true jellyfish, in which the medusa is the dominant or only form and the polyp, when present, is restricted to a small larval stage (*see* scyphistoma). The medusae are highly organized, with the coelenteron divided into four pouches and containing a canal system (*gastrovascular cavity*) for food distribution. The diameter of jellyfish varies from about 70 mm (e.g. *Aurelia*) to about 2 metres (e.g. *Cyanea*).

sea anemones. *See* Anthozoa.

sea cucumbers. *See* Holothuroidea.

seals. *See* Pinnipedia.

sebaceous gland. A lobed exocrine gland that secretes sebum, one or more of which open into each hair follicle near the skin surface in mammals. The cells of the glands are derived from the epidermal Malpighian layer and contain large fat granules. They release their entire contents by holocrine *secretion, a process that appears to be independent of nervous control. Sebaceous glands are absent from the palms and soles of the feet, although they are present in other hairless areas, such as the lips. The activity of the sebaceous glands increases during puberty and declines in pregnancy.

sebum. A mixture of fatty material and cellular debris produced by the sebaceous glands in the skin of mammals. The fatty portion of sebum consists of a mixture of triglycerides, fatty acids, waxes, steroids, etc. It lubricates the hair and, more importantly, provides a thin protective medium over the skin, which prevents desiccation and acts as a barrier against moisture entering the skin.

secondary growth (secondary thickening). Growth that gives rise to the *secondary plant body, i.e. growth from a cambium. Secondary growth in vascular tissues that arises by a means other than a normal vascular cambium is termed *anomalous*. In this type of growth the vascular cambium may arise in an unusual place (e.g. in the phloem); it may give rise to a different distribution of tissues (e.g. in the monocotyledon *Dracaena* the cambium cuts off entire vascular bundles to the inside); or there may be more than one cambium (e.g. one between the xylem and phloem and an additional one in the phloem).

secondary plant body. The parts of a plant consisting of tissues derived by secondary growth, i.e. by meristematic activity other than that of the embryo and apical meristems. The chief sources of secondary growth are the vascular cambium (*see* vascular tissue) and the phellogen (*see* periderm) but diffuse secondary growth from cells of the ground tissue may occur, for example, in some monocotyledons. *Compare* primary plant body.

secondary sexual characteristic. A characteristic of an adult animal that is restricted to one sex but does not include the gonads or their associated ducts and glands. Most secondary sexual characteristics develop under the influence of steroid hormones produced by the gonads (e.g. androgens and oestrogens). Examples include antlers in stags, the bright plumage of male birds, the mane of lions, and in humans enlargement of the breasts (women) and growth of beard (men).

secondary structure. That aspect of macromolecular structure dependent on *hydrogen bonds, e.g. the helical arrangement of a polynucleotide chain and the alpha-helix and beta-pleated sheet structures in *protein.

secondary thickening. *See* secondary growth.

secretin. A straight-chain polypeptide hormone of 27 amino acid residues synthesized and secreted by the duodenal mucosa when acidified food leaves the stomach. It stimulates the release of relatively enzyme-free pancreatic juice (further enzyme release occurs with stimulation of the vagus nerve). Secretin was the first substance shown to be a hormone, by the classic studies of Bayliss and Starling in the early 1900s, but it was not until the mid 1960s that it was characterized and synthesized and found to resemble glucagon.

secretion. The discharge or extrusion of intracellular molecules into the surrounding medium. The term is also applied to the molecules that are secreted, which include ions, enzymes, hormones, glycoproteins, fluids, inorganic molecules, etc. There are three principal mechanisms of secretion. *Exocytosis* (*merocrine* or *eccrine secretion*) is the most common type and involves the release of small membrane-bound granules of the secreted substance by a complex process in which the granule membrane fuses with the plasma membrane. Neurotransmitter is released from nerve endings by exocytosis. *Apocrine secretion* involves the loss of the apical plasma membrane, resulting in the release of the secretory product and some cytoplasmic constituents. It occurs in the glands around the anus. *Holocrine secretion* involves the loss of the entire cell in releasing its secretory product; it occurs in the sebaceous glands. The secretion of fluids such as sweat and small ions, often against osmotic or electrochemical gradients, is complex and requires energy, usually in the form of nucleotides.

seed. The structure that develops from an ovule after fertilization or, in some plants, by agamospermy. It comprises the testa (formed from the integuments), the nucellus (occasionally obliterated), the endosperm (occasionally absent), and the embryo sporophyte. Externally it bears a hilum and usually a micropyle; additional structures, such as a caruncle or an aril, may also be present. The seed habit first occurred in Carboniferous plants and has probably arisen more than once in evolutionary history. It is regarded as having evolved from a heterosporous diplobiont ancestor by a number of steps involving changes in the megasporangium and female prothallus to produce the ovule and in the male prothallus to produce the pollen grain. The steps included (1) a reduction in the size of the microspore; (2) the retention of the prothalli within the spore walls (i.e. endosporic development replaced exosporic); (3) a reduction in the number of megaspores in the megasporangium to one (with the abortion of the other three nuclei in the tetrad). Two further steps were involved in true ovule formation: (1) the loss of dehiscence of the megasporangium (the megaspore thus remaining completely enclosed) and (2) the development of one or more protective envelopes (integuments) around the megasporangium. In most living seed plants the male gametophyte is reduced to between two and six cells within the pollen grain (microspore) and on dehiscence (pollen-grain germination) usually produces a pollen tube.

Seed plants are divided into two major groups: the Gymnospermae and Angiospermae. The advantages of seed production to a plant are that the independence of water for fertilization greatly increases the range of available habitats and that the sporophyte is protected and nourished during its early vulnerable stages and is provided with a food store after its release from the parent plant.

seed ferns. *See* Cycadopsida.

seed plants. *See* Spermatophyta.

segmentation. *See* metameric segmentation, cleavage.

segregation. The separation of a pair of alleles on homologous chromosomes during meiosis, so that only one member of each pair is present in the gametes. For example, in the allelic pair *Aa*, segregation results in equal numbers of gametes containing *A* and *a*. *See* Mendel's laws.

seismonasty. Nastic movement in response to shock. *See* haptonasty.

Selachii. The order of the Elasmobranchii that contains the sharks: fast aggressive predators with a streamlined torpedo-shaped body tapering into a well-developed heterocercal tail. The mouth has a wide gape and numerous sharp teeth and the spiracle and gill slits are situated laterally. The Selachii includes small bottom-living sharks such as *Scyliorhinus* and *Squalus* (dogfishes) and larger pelagic sharks such as *Cetorhinus* (basking shark). The *Batoidea are sometimes included in this order.

Selaginellales. *See* Lycopsida.

selection pressure. The force of *natural selection acting on a population.

self-replicating (of *plasmids and other extrachromosomal DNA and RNA molecules). Able to control the timing and rate of their own synthesis rather than being under the same control as chromosomal DNA.

self-sterility. The condition in hermaphrodite plants and animals in which male gametes cannot fertilize female gametes of the same organism. It occurs in flowering plants in which an *incompatibility mechanism operates.

semen. A fluid, produced by the male of animals with internal fertilization, consisting of spermatozoa and secretions from various accessory sex glands (in mammals, these include the prostate gland and seminal vesicles). Semen is transferred from the male to the female during coitus.

semicircular canals. The organ of vertebrates that detects the rate of movement of the head. It consists of three semicircular tubes within the inner ear, each connected at both ends to the utriculus and set at right angles to each other. A swelling (*ampulla*) at one end of each canal contains a receptor (*see* crista). Movement produces currents in the endolymph that fills the canals and each crista registers a change in the rate of turning movement in the plane of its canal.

semiconservative replication. *See* replication.

seminal receptacle. *See* spermatheca.

seminal vesicle. 1. An organ of lower vertebrates and some invertebrates that stores spermatozoa.
2. One of a pair of glands of male mammals that opens via a duct into the vas deferens and secretes most of the alkaline fluid component of semen.

seminiferous tubules. *See* testis.

senescence. The phase in the life of an organism or part of an organism that precedes natural death, usually characterized by net degradation. Some organisms, however, never entirely cease growing (*see* growth) and senescence may be more generally defined as the group of effects that lead to a decreasing life expectancy with increasing age. Senescence of discrete parts of organisms (e.g. older leaves on growing plants) is often part of normal development and is, ultimately, genetically con-

trolled. It often involves the activity of lysosomes. Similarly, the rapid senescence of annual and biennial plants and of some herbaceous perennials (e.g. *Agave americana*) after flowering, and the death of some animals after reproduction, are probably genetically programmed. However, there is no commonly accepted mechanism for the ageing of most woody perennials (e.g. trees) and animals. Theories fall into two main categories, depending on whether ageing is envisaged as a genetically programmed event or as a slow accumulation of errors in metabolism to a disastrous level. The latter theory usually invokes genetic damage (e.g. by radiation) or accumulation of errors in genetic expression via the transcription or translation stages of protein synthesis.

sense organ. A collection of sensory *receptors that, with associated structures, are specialized to respond to one class of stimulus.

sensitization. The process of increasing the specific reactivity of an organism or cell to an antigen or hapten. In animals it may occur naturally or be induced artificially, e.g. by administration of an initial dose of antigen to provoke a stronger response to a second dose. *See also* anaphylaxis.

sepal. One of the structures in a flower that form the outer whorl of the *perianth. Known collectively as the *calyx*, the sepals are usually green and leaflike and protect the flower bud. Occasionally sepals are brightly coloured and petaloid and attract insects for pollination, either as well as or instead of the petals.

septicidal. *See* dehiscence.

septum. A dividing wall or partition in a plant or animal structure.

seral community (seral stage). Any one of a series of stages in the colonization of an uninhabited area. *See* sere.

sere. A completed *succession of plants and animals, ending in the establishment of a climax community. It is made up of a series of *seral communities* (or *stages*). A *primary sere* (or *prisere*) is one that has become established in an area never before inhabited; a *secondary sere* occurs in a region previously occupied by established communities, such as an abandoned cropland. A secondary sere usually takes a much shorter time to be completed than a primary sere, because the nutrients are already available and conditions are more favourable to colonization. Seres developing in different environments can be specified; for example, a *hydrosere* develops in an aquatic environment, a *halosere* in a salt marsh, a *xerosere* in a desert, etc.

serine (ser). An amino acid, $CH_2OHCH(NH_2)COOH$, one of the 20 common *amino acids found in proteins. Serine functions as a precursor of sphingosine.

serology. The study of *in vitro* reactions between antigens and antibodies. The three main serological tests are *agglutination reactions, the *complement fixation test, and precipitation reactions such as the *precipitin reaction.

serotonin (5-hydroxytryptamine). A compound with neurotransmitter properties that is released from certain neurones and is associated with the control of mood. Serotonin is concentrated in the hypothalamus region of the brain, where it is localized in granular synaptic vesicles in the nerve endings. Serotonin nerve terminals are also found in nuclei of the parasympathetic and sympathetic nervous system and in the pineal body. Serotonin is synthesized in the brain from the amino acid tryptophan. *See also* LSD.

serous membrane. The layer of mesothelium and underlying fibroelastic connective tissue lining many vertebrate internal cavities that are not continuous with the external environment. It occurs in the peritoneal, pleural, and pericardial cavities. *Compare* mucous membrane.

Sertoli cells. *See* testis.

serum. *See* blood serum.

sesamoid bone. A bone that develops in the tendons of vertebrates at a point of potential friction, for example where a tendon passes over a bony ridge. Sesamoïd bones, e.g. the patella, are common in mammals.

sessile. 1. Designating animals that live attached to a substratum, e.g. a rock, the shell of another animal, etc. Sponges, corals, tunicates, and many other invertebrates are sessile.
2. Designating an organ or part, such as the leaf of a plant or the eye of a crustacean, that lacks a stalk, being attached directly to the main body of the organism.

seta. 1. (in botany). Any stiff bristle-like structure, especially the stalk of the sporophyte of bryophytes.
2. (in zoology). A hairlike structure in invertebrates. Setae occur in many invertebrate groups, including annelid worms, in which they are solid cuticular outgrowths (*see* chaeta), and insects, in which they are hollow projections of the cuticle enclosing part of an epidermal cell.

Sewall Wright effect. *See* genetic drift.

sex chromatin. *See* Barr body.

sex chromosome. Any chromosome that is associated in some way with *sex determination. There are two types: the *X chromosome* and the *Y chromosome*. X chromosomes are similar in appearance to the other chromosomes, whereas the Y chromosome is usually much smaller. In diploid organisms, sex chromosomes are represented as XX in the homogametic sex and XY in the heterogametic sex. In some cases the Y chromosome is missing and the heterogametic sex is XO. The determination of sex by these chromosomes is somewhat variable. In some cases, as in man and many other mammals, XX is the female sex and XY is the male and the Y chromosome is important in sex determination. In *Drosophila*, however, although XX is female and XY is male, the loss of the Y chromosome does not result in an abnormal male. In this case the dosage of X is more important in sex determination and the Y chromosome is practically inert; thus XX is female and X is male. In some organisms the Y chromosome has been lost in the course of evolution; the female of certain grasshoppers is XX and the male is XO, while in caddis flies the female is XO and the male is XX. In lepidopterans, birds, and some fishes the homogametic (XX) sex is male and the heterogametic (XY) sex is female. Most plants are hermaphrodite. Of the few unisexual groups, *Melandrium dioicum* (campion) and *Salix* (willows) have an XX/XY mechanism of sex determination. In all methods of sex determination involving sex chromosomes, equal numbers of males and females are produced.

The sex chromosomes also contain genes concerned with processes other than sex determination, which results in the phenomenon of *sex linkage.

sex determination. Any of the methods by which sex is determined in an organism. One of the most common methods is by means of *sex chromosomes, with a homogametic (XX) sex and a heterogametic (XY or XO) sex, which results in equal numbers of males and females. Less commonly, a single gene with two alleles is concerned with sex determination. The gene exists in a homozygous recessive condition (*mm*) in the homogametic sex and in the heterozygous (*Mm*) condition in the heterogametic sex. This system is found in mosquitoes, where *mm* is the female and *Mm* the male; a similar method occurs in *Asparagus*.

Another method of sex determination involves haploidy and diploidy, where the male is haploid and the female diploid. This system is found in many members of the Hymenoptera, including bees: the queen controls the sex of the eggs she lays by fertilizing them to produce females and not fertilizing them to produce males. This method, of course, does not produce equal numbers of each sex. There is no known case in which the female is haploid.

An unusual method of sex determination is that of environmental control. It is based on the ability of one sex to change into the other; whether or not it does so depends on whether it can find a mate. For example, *Crepidula* snails go through stages of development from asexual to male to female. If a male finds a mate it remains male, if not it transforms into a female. Environmental control, which is also found in certain marine worms and fish, does not produce equal numbers of both sexes.

sex factor. *See* F factor.

sex-limited gene (sex-limited character). A gene, or the character produced by it, that has its effect in only one sex. The gene may be on any chromosome, but because of the influence of certain sex hormones or other sex-determining factors, it is expressed in only one sex. The genes for secondary sexual characteristics, such as breast development and milk production in women and deep voice and growth of beard in men, are sex limited. *Compare* sex linkage.

sex linkage. The presence of one or more genes on a sex chromosome, usually the X chromosome, resulting in certain characteristics appearing in only one sex. In those species in which there is no crossing over between X and Y chromosomes, the genes on the X chromosome are permanently linked there. When there is crossing over, or when the Y chromosome is not inert, only the unpaired part of the X chromosome contains sex-linked genes. These genes are present in duplicate only in the homogametic sex (XX); in the heterogametic sex (XY), sex-linked genes are present singly. If a gene is recessive, and therefore usually deleterious, it is more likely to show up in the heterogametic sex. In man, several sex-linked diseases are due to sex-linked recessive genes, such as *haemophilia and red-green *colour blindness. A woman is more likely to be heterozygous for the recessive and therefore will not show the disease, although she will carry it and pass it on to her sons. A man with the disease cannot pass it on to his sons but his daughters will become carriers. Women with sex-linked diseases are rare, since the recessive must be present on both sex chromosomes. Sex-linked genes in other organisms include the gene for ginger coat colour in cats (it is more usual for ginger cats to be toms) and that of white eye colour in *Drosophila*. *Compare* sex-limited gene.

sex ratio. The proportion of males to females in a population, often expressed as the number of males per 100 females.

sexual reproduction. Any form of reproduction in which two haploid cells (*gametes) or nuclei fuse to produce a diploid cell that develops into a new organism. The gametes (or nuclei) are typically of two kinds, male and female, and may be derived from one individual or from separate male and female organisms. Sexual reproduction permits genetic recombination and therefore results in greater variation in the offspring, on which natural selection can act, than is possible in *asexual reproduction.
Certain types of reproduction, notably *parthenogenesis and *apomixis, involve the development of individuals from female gametes without fusion taking place. These are usually regarded as special types of sexual reproduction.

sexual selection. A subsidiary mechanism bringing about some aspects of evolution according to Darwinism. Sexual selection is thought to be the cause of exaggerated secondary sexual characteristics in one sex, typically the male. Females of the species are assumed to prefer to mate with such males, whose characteristics are therefore inherited by their male progeny. Sexual selection is said to have accounted for the evolution of brilliant plumage of male birds, courtship behaviour, large antlers in

stags, etc. The importance of sexual selection in evolution is probably less than Darwin supposed, as the less brilliantly marked males of many species usually do find a mate.

Shannon–Wiener index. See diversity.

sharks. See Selachii.

shoot. The part of a vascular plant comprising the stems, leaves, buds, and inflorescences. Morphologically, stem and leaf are regarded as a unit (see telome theory) but functionally they are regarded as separate organs (see leaf, stem). The apex of a shoot is normally an *apical meristem from which the leaves and their axillary buds are initiated, the buds later forming lateral shoot systems themselves. Shoots are sometimes classified on their patterns of growth into long shoots and short shoots. *Long shoots*, which include the majority, have apical meristems that continue to function indefinitely. In *short shoots* the apical meristem ceases to function after a limited period. Examples of short shoots are stem thorns, as in *Ulex* (gorse) and *Crataegus* (hawthorn), and the very short axis bearing the needles in *Pinus* (pines).

short-day plant. See photoperiodism.

shoulder girdle. See pectoral girdle.

shrews. See Insectivora.

sialic acid. One of a group of amino sugars all derived from a nine-carbon compound containing nitrogen, *neuraminic acid*. Sialic acids occur in glycoproteins and glycolipids.

siblings (sibs). Two or more organisms having the same parents, i.e. brothers and sisters.

sickle-cell anaemia. A human disease affecting Black Africans in which the red blood cells have a tendency to assume a spiked or sickle-like shape when the blood is deprived of oxygen. The disease results from the inheritance of a defective allele coding for β-globin, which results in the production of an abnormal type of haemoglobin, *sickle haemoglobin* (*HbS*). Affected blood cells are removed from the circulation, leading to anaemia.

sieve element. An enucleate conducting cell of the phloem, responsible for the translocation of dissolved nutrients (e.g. sugars). There are two types of sieve element: *sieve cells*, which have *sieve areas*, and *sieve-tube elements* (or *sieve-tube members*), which have *sieve plates*. Both sieve areas and sieve plates are equivalent to primary pit fields (*see* pits) and grade into each other. The sieve areas are the least specialized, bear small pores (a fraction of a micrometre (µm) in diameter), and are randomly arranged on the cell wall. Sieve plates are more specialized, have larger pores (up to 15 µm or more in diameter), and are frequently arranged transversely on the end walls of the cells. A vertical series of sieve-tube elements constitutes a *sieve tube*. In angiosperms the sieve elements have associated *companion cells.

sieve tube. A tubular conducting element of phloem, consisting of a vertical series of sieve-tube elements (*see* sieve element).

sigma factor. A protein molecule that is one of the five distinct subunits of RNA *polymerase in prokaryotes. Sigma factor plays a crucial role in enhancing the preference of the enzyme for *promoter regions at the initiation end of gene sequences. RNA polymerase without sigma is referred to as *core enzyme*; that with sigma is *holoenzyme*.

silicula. A short flat bilocular fruit, a type of *siliqua, produced by some Cruciferae.

siliqua. A long thin *fruit produced by some Cruciferae, developed from a bilocular ovary with two parietal placentae and a false septum developed between them. On dehiscence the walls of the loculi break away from the placentae and septum and hang from the apex of the fruit. The two placentae

thus form a frame, the *replum*, which subtends the septum and upon which the seeds also hang. *See also* silicula.

Silurian. The third period of the Palaeozoic era, extending from 440 to 400 million years ago. It was named after a Celtic tribe that lived in the region of Wales where rocks of the period were first recognized. Silurian fossils consist of many marine invertebrates, including bryozoans, trilobites, crinoids, and corals. In some Silurian rocks scales and spines of ostracoderms (jawless fish) have been found. *See also* geological time scale.

Sinanthropus. See *Homo.*

single-cell protein. A protein produced by fermenting microorganisms with petroleum hydrocarbons. Some microorganisms, such as the yeast *Candida* and the bacteria *Nocardia* and *Pseudomonas*, are able to convert petroleum hydrocarbons to protein in the presence of air and suitable aqueous nutrients. The protein is nutritionally acceptable and a potential food source if large-scale production were to be undertaken.

sinoatrial node. *See* pacemaker.

sinus. 1. (in zoology). A cavity, recess, dilation, or indentation, usually an anatomical space such as a lymphatic sinus, nasal sinus, etc.
2. (in botany). A notch between two lobes of a flattened organ, especially of a leaf.

sinusoid. One of the minute blood vessels that replace capillaries in some tissues, e.g. the liver and adrenal glands. They differ from capillaries in the irregularity of their lumen, by the presence of macrophages within their walls, and by the absence of a surrounding layer of connective tissue, which allows a more intimate relationship between the tissue and the blood with which it is being supplied.

sinus venosus. A thin-walled chamber of the primitive vertebrate heart, draining venous blood from the Cuvierian ducts.

It becomes absorbed in the left atrium in amniotes.

siphonaceous. *See* coenocyte.

Siphonaptera. An order of small wingless endopterygote insects, the fleas, all of which are ectoparasites of mammals and birds. The body of a flea is laterally compressed, which eases movement over the host's body, and the mouthparts are modified for piercing and sucking. The legs are adapted for jumping and clinging to the host. The grublike larvae feed on organic detritus in the nest of the host. Many fleas transmit serious diseases, notably the rat flea (*Xenopsylla cheopis*), which carries bubonic plague.

siphonostele. *See* stele.

Siphunculata. *See* Anoplura.

Sipunculoida (Sipunculida). A small phylum of burrowing unsegmented wormlike marine invertebrates, formerly included in the Annelida. They have a U-shaped gut, with the anus opening anteriorly, and the mouth is surrounded by tentacles or lobes for catching food. The anterior part of the body is retractile.

Sirenia. The order of the Eutheria that contains the sea cows, e.g. *Manatus* (manatee) and *Dugong* (dugong): aquatic herbivorous mammals of warm coastal waters and tropical rivers. Sirenians have a streamlined hairless body with no hind limbs, large paddle-like forelimbs, and an expanded tail for swimming; there is a single pair of pectoral mammary glands (hence the mermaid legend).

sister chromatid exchange. Exchange of pieces of DNA molecules between sister chromatids prior to mitosis. Unlike crossing over in meiotic chromosomes, no genetic recombination is involved; sister chromatid exchange is revealed simply as a phenomenon appearing in autoradiography of chromosomes following DNA radio-labelling during the S phase of the cell cycle. *See also* harlequin chromosome.

SI units (Système International d'Unités). A system of units used, by international agreement, for all scientific purposes. It is based on the metre-kilogram-second (MKS) system and replaces both the centimetre-gram-second (cgs) and Imperial (fps – foot, pound, second) systems. It consists of seven base units and two supplementary units (see Table 1). Measurements of all other physical quantities are made in derived units, which consist of combinations of two or more base units. Seventeen of these derived units have special names (see Table 2). Base units and derived units with special names have agreed symbols, which are used without a full stop.
Decimal multiples of both base and derived units are expressed using a set of standard prefixes with standard abbreviations (see Table 3). Where possible a prefix representing 10 raised to a power that is a multiple of three should be used (e.g. mm is preferred to cm).

skates. *See* Batoidea.

skeletal muscle. *See* striated muscle.

skeleton. *See* endoskeleton, exoskeleton.

skin (cutis). The layer of epithelial cells, connective tissue, and associated structures that covers almost the entire body surface of vertebrates. It consists of two layers: (1) the *epidermis, an outer layer of epithelial cells derived from ectoderm; and (2) the *dermis (corium), an underlying layer of connective tissue derived from mesoderm. The skin is attached to the body organs by loose *subcutaneous tissue, which allows it to move easily over the underlying structures.
The skin has many important functions, particularly in protecting the body from injury and desiccation and in acting as a generalized sensory organ (it contains sensory receptors for pressure, temperature, pain, etc.). The skin of fishes and amphibians contains many glands that secrete a protective mucus; protective dermal plates or scales are present in

Table 1. Base and Supplementary SI Units

physical quantity	name of SI unit	symbol for unit
length	metre	m
mass	kilogram(me)	kg
time	second	s
electric current	ampere	A
thermodynamic temperature	kelvin	K
luminous intensity	candela	cd
amount of substance	mole	mol
*plane angle	radian	rad
*solid angle	steradian	sr

*supplementary units

Table 2. Derived SI Units with Special Names

physical quantity	name of SI unit	symbol for SI unit
frequency	hertz	Hz
energy	joule	J
force	newton	N
power	watt	W
pressure	pascal	Pa
electric charge	coulomb	C
electric potential difference	volt	V
electric resistance	ohm	Ω
electric conductance	siemens	S
electric capacitance	farad	F
magnetic flux	weber	Wb
inductance	henry	H
magnetic flux density (magnetic induction)	tesla	T
luminous flux	lumen	lm
illuminance (illumination)	lux	lx
absorbed dose	gray	Gy
radioactivity	becquerel	Bq

Table 3. Decimal Multiples and Submultiples to be used with SI Units

submultiple	prefix	symbol	multiple	prefix	symbol
10^{-1}	deci	d	10^{1}	deca	da
10^{-2}	centi	c	10^{2}	hecto	h
10^{-3}	milli	m	10^{3}	kilo	k
10^{-6}	micro	μ	10^{6}	mega	M
10^{-9}	nano	n	10^{9}	giga	G
10^{-12}	pico	p	10^{12}	tera	T
10^{-15}	femto	f	10^{15}	peta	P
10^{-18}	atto	a	10^{16}	exa	E

SI units

the skin of fishes and some reptiles and sebaceous glands occur in the skin of mammals. In warm-blooded animals the skin is important in temperature control: birds have an epidermal covering of feathers and mammals have hair or fur and sweat glands. The outermost layer (*stratum corneum) of terrestrial vertebrates is variously modified as spines, nails, claws, beaks, etc.

sliding growth (in botany). Growth in which newly formed cells slide over previously formed cells, independently of them and without causing any disruption in their organization. *Compare* intrusive growth, symplastic growth.

slime fungi (slime moulds). *See* Myxomycophyta. Two slime moulds are widely used as research organisms in biology and biochemistry: *Physarum*, an acellular or plasmodial organism belonging to the *Myxomycetes; and *Dictyostelium*, a cellular slime mould, belonging to the *Acrasiales.

sloths. *See* Edentata.

small intestine. *See* intestine.

smooth muscle (involuntary muscle). Muscle that has no obvious ultrastructure and produces slow long-term contractions. Vertebrate smooth muscle is autonomically controlled and occurs in sheets around hollow organs such as blood vessels and intestine. It consists of mononucleate spindle-shaped cells containing actin and myosin, often polymerized in irregularly arranged filaments or masses, which allow flexible patterns of contraction.

smuts. A group of basidiomycete fungi belonging to the order Ustilaginales. They are normally parasitic (though not obligate) and cause much damage to crops, including grains. The life cycle is basically as follows. A basidiospore infects the host and produces a mycelium with one nucleus per cell. When it encounters another mycelium of a different strain the two fuse to form a dikaryon. This then produces binucleate

unicellular teleutospores (*see* teleutosorus), also called *brand spores*. Within the spore karyogamy occurs, followed a few days later by germination to form a small *promycelium*, which produces basidia.

snakes. *See* Squamata.

sodium pump. The *active transport system in a neurone membrane, which moves sodium ions out of the cell against the concentration gradient. Sodium ions continuously enter the cell due to the membrane's slight permeability in the resting state and increased permeability during the passage of an *impulse. The action of the sodium pump therefore maintains the separation of ions required to produce a *resting potential across the cell membrane.

solenocyte. *See* flame cell.

solenostele. *See* stele.

Solo man. *See Homo.*

somatic. Relating to nonreproductive cells and cell divisions.

somatic hybridization. The fusion of diploid cells from different species in tissue culture; for example, a mouse cell and a human cell. The technique can be used to map human genes, since a hybrid cell that immediately after fusion contains a full complement of (for example) human and mouse chromosomes progressively loses the human chromosomes. Thus, loss of particular traits can often be ascribed to loss of a particular chromosome.

somatic motor nerve. A peripheral motor neurone of vertebrates that supplies striated muscle.

somatomedin (plasma growth factor). A polypeptide (molecular weight about 4000) in mammalian plasma that is released from the liver (and possibly the kidneys) by growth hormone, most of whose actions it is thought to mediate. Its activity was first demonstrated in 1957.

somatotrophin. *See* growth hormone.

somite. *See* mesoderm.

soredium. A vegetative diaspore of certain lichens, consisting of a few algal cells closely invested in fungal hyphae. Soredia originate in the medulla and erupt through the cortex of the thallus to form delimited masses known as *soralia*.

sorocarp. An asexual sporangium, often minute, produced by the Acrasiales (cellular slime fungi). It consists of a base, a stalk, and a sporogenous head and is produced from a single pseudoplasmodium (*see* plasmodium).

sorosis. A composite *fruit formed from a spike whose axis (as in the pineapple) or perianth (as in the mulberry) becomes fleshy.

sorus. A small area on the abaxial surface of a fern lamina concerned with sporangia production. It consists of a small cushion of tissue (the *placenta* or *receptacle*) from whose superficial cells the sporangia are produced. It is often covered by a small flap of tissue, the *indusium*, and is usually associated with a vein ending, which provides its nutrients. Sori in which the sporangia ripen simultaneously are known as *simple*; those in which the sporangia at the middle ripen first are *gradate*. When the different stages of development are randomly distributed over the placenta, the sorus is *mixed*. Mixed sori are regarded as the most advanced; simple sori the most primitive. Several sori may merge, usually with the loss of their indusia, to form a *coenosorus*.
The term sorus is also used for other types of sporangial masses, such as those of the rust and smut fungi.

Southern blotting technique. A widely used method in gene manipulation invented by Ed Southern in 1975. An agarose gel containing denatured DNA fragments is placed between buffer-saturated filter paper and a cellulose nitrate filter. The DNA is eluted from the gel onto the cellulose nitrate filter, to which it binds strongly. This filter can then be used for complementary nucleic acid hybridization, which reveals the identity of the sequences in the blotted filter and thus in the original agarose gel. Other similar techniques, which have been given the jargon names of 'Northern' blots and 'Western' blots, are used for elution of RNA fragments from gels.

spacer DNA. DNA that is located between genes and may or may not be transcribed by RNA polymerase. Spacer DNA is found, for example, between the cistrons coding for 18S and 28S ribosomal RNA in most eukaryotic organisms.

spadix. A raceme in which the flowers are small, inconspicuous, and sessile and are borne on a swollen fleshy axis and surrounded by a spathe, as in arum lily. *Compare* spike.

spathe. A large bract that entirely or partially encloses a spadix in flowers of the Araceae family, such as the arum lily.

Special Creation. The doctrine, opposed to *evolution, stating that each species (or genus, family, etc.) of organisms was created in its present form, rather than developing gradually from ancestral types.

specialization. 1. The evolution of a special adaptation to suit an organism to a particular environment. An organism with such an adaptation is less capable of evolving in other directions, and this could result in extinction of the species if the environment were to change considerably.
2. *physiological* (*biological*) *specialization.* The existence in a population of forms (*physiological forms*) that, although identical in appearance, differ biochemically from one another. It is especially important in plant pathology, when a parasite attacks only one form of a species or variety.

speciation. The formation of new species, usually occurring by one of two mechanisms. *Sympatric speciation* occurs within a single population to produce two or more different species. It requires the operation of behavioural or ecological differences to permit speciation to occur. It is also commmon in plants that undergo allopolyploidy (*see* polyploidy) and in organisms that reproduce asexually or consistently self-fertilize. *Allopatric speciation* is the formation of new species from populations that are geographically isolated from each other. It occurs in species that have sexual reproduction and cross-fertilization, i.e. in most animal species. In order that two separate species may develop, the two populations must evolve some sort of sexual and/or genetic isolating mechanism so that they do not interbreed if they come into contact again. *See also* isolating mechanisms.

species. A unit used in the *classification of plants and animals. Ideally a species is defined as a group of organisms that interbreed with each other to produce fertile offspring. Members of different animal species do not normally interbreed; if they do, the progeny are sterile. Hybrids of two plant species are usually sterile but may occasionally be made fertile by allopolyploidy (*see* polyploidy). Members of the same species usually resemble each other closely, but when species are subdivided into *subspecies, *clines, or cultivated *varieties, the members of these subgroups often differ from one another in appearance. Not all species have been tested for the breeding definition, and this definition cannot be applied to specimens studied from dead or preserved material only or to species that habitually self-fertilize or have only asexual reproduction. Such species can be defined only in terms of observable similarities between their members. Each species has a *holotype, which was used in the original naming and description of the species, and two names (*see* binomial nomenclature).

Species can be designated according to the criteria used in defining them. The *taxonomic species*, the unit in general use, satisfies all possible criteria and meets the requirements of the International Rules of Nomenclature. The *morphospecies* is a species named only on morphological evidence, for example from herbarium or preserved specimens. These species must often be modified if live material becomes available. The *palaeospecies*, an extinct group, is named from fossil material only; such species often have to be modified as more fossil material becomes available. A *biospecies* is a species that fulfils the breeding requirements of the definition. The term can therefore be applied only to species with sexual reproduction and cross-fertilization and in practice only to species that mature quickly and breed fairly frequently. The *agamospecies* consists of a group of organisms that reproduce only asexually and must therefore be treated as morphospecies since the breeding definition cannot be applied. *See also* coenospecies.

sperm. *See* spermatozoon, antherozoid.

spermagonium. *See* spermogonium.

spermatheca (seminal receptacle). A cavity or sac in the body of some female and hermaphrodite animals in which spermatozoa received from the male (or hermaphrodite partner) during copulation are stored until required for fertilizing the ova.

spermatid. A haploid cell of the animal testis produced by the second meiotic division of a spermatocyte (one spermatocyte produces four spermatids). The spermatid then matures and changes shape to form a spermatozoon.

spermatium. A minute spherical non-motile male gamete produced by the red algae and by certain fungi, including some Pyrenomycetes (a subdivision of the Ascomycetes) and the Uredinales (*rusts).

spermatocyte. A cell within the seminiferous tubules of the testis that undergoes meiosis to form a spermatid with a haploid nucleus. Typically a *primary spermatocyte* undergoes the first division to form two *secondary spermatocytes*, which each undergo a second division to form two spermatids.

spermatogenesis. The formation of spermatozoa from precursor cells (*see* spermatocyte, spermatid).

spermatogonium. *See* testis.

spermatophore. A mass of spermatozoa bound together by a gelatinous substance, produced by some animals having internal fertilization. It is usually deposited by the male directly into the body of the female, as in cephalopods and insects, but in salamanders and newts the male sheds the spermatophore into the water, from which it is taken into the cloaca of the female.

Spermatophyta. The plant group containing the seed-bearing plants, i.e. the *Gymnospermae and *Angiospermae. The seed ferns, usually included in the Gymnospermae, are sometimes separated into a group of equal rank, the Pteridospermae. Spermatophytes are sometimes called *phanerogams*.

spermatozoid. *See* antherozoid.

spermatozoon (sperm). The small motile male gamete formed in the animal testis and released in large numbers to fertilize the female gamete during the process of sexual reproduction. It generally comprises a head region (*acrosome*) containing a compact haploid nucleus, a middle region containing mitochondria, and a tail region (often a flagellum).

spermine. *See* polyamines.

spermogonium (spermagonium). A flask-shaped reproductive structure of certain fungi, including the *rusts. It consists of two kinds of uninucleate hyphae: the *spermatiophores*, which abstrict sporelike *spermatia* from their tips (*see* sperma-

tium); and others, which are branching and receptive.

S phase. A phase of the *cell cycle.

Sphenodon. *See* Rhynchocephalia.

Sphenopsida (Arthrophyta, Articulatae). A large group of pteridophytes that reached its peak in the Carboniferous and now has only one surviving genus, *Equisetum* (horsetails). Sphenopsids are characterized by the possession of roots, stems, and leaves, the latter being *microphylls borne in whorls. The sporangia are thick-walled and borne reflexed on whorled peltate sporangiophores. Some extinct tree forms, e.g. *Calamites*, had secondary thickening and were co-dominants (with the lepidodendrids) in the forests that formed the Carboniferous coal seams.

spheroplast. A *protoplast that retains some cell wall material. Spheroplasts are spherical and osmotically labile. The term protoplast is often loosely used for what are, strictly, spheroplasts.

spherosome. An organelle of eukaryote cells, bounded by a single membrane, that stores and synthesizes lipids (fats and oils). Derived from the endoplasmic reticulum, it measures up to 1 μm in diameter and is usually spherical.

sphincter. A band of circular smooth muscle surrounding a hollow or tubular organ, such as the anus (*anal sphincter*) or pylorus (*pyloric sphincter*). By contracting, it can partly or wholly occlude the lumen of the organ.

sphingolipid. One of a group of lipids containing one fatty-acid residue, one sphingosine residue, and one base residue per molecule. The most abundant

$$CH_3(CH_2)_{12}CH:CHCHOH$$
$$|$$
$$CHNH_2$$
$$|$$
$$CH_2OH$$

Sphingosine

sphingolipid is sphingomyelin (*see* phospholipids).

sphingomyelin. *See* phospholipids.

sphingosine. A lipid alcohol consisting of a long hydrocarbon tail and a polar head (see formula). It is a component of the sphingomyelins (*see* phospholipids), gangliosides, and cerebrosides.

spiders. *See* Araneae.

Spike

spike. A type of raceme in which the flowers are sessile (see illustration). The flowers may be small and individually inconspicuous, such as the plantain, or large and conspicuous, as in acanthus. *Compare* spadix, catkin.

spinal column. *See* vertebral column.

spinal cord. The part of the vertebrate central nervous system that is enclosed within the vertebral column. Derived from the embryonic neural tube, it consists of an H-shaped core of grey matter, which surrounds a narrow central canal and gives rise, by dorso-lateral and ventro-lateral roots, to paired segmentally arranged spinal nerves. These carry sensory and motor information to and from the central nervous system. Reflexes, which form the basis of simple coordination of bodily activities, are mediated by synapses in the grey matter of the spinal cord. Surrounding the core are tracts of nerve fibres, the white matter, which carry information up and down the cord and increasingly thicken as the spinal cord becomes subordinate to the brain in overall coordination of nervous activity.

spinal nerves. A series of segmentally arranged paired nerves arising laterally from the vertebrate spinal cord via a dorsal afferent and a ventral efferent *root. The roots commonly fuse close to the cord to form mixed nerves, which constitute the major part of the *peripheral nervous system. *Compare* cranial nerves.

spindle. A structure formed within the cytoplasm during mitosis and meiosis. It is shaped like two cones joined at their bases and is made of longitudinally arranged contractile protein microtubules or fibres. Chromosomes come to be orientated on the equatorial plate of the spindle by their centromeres. The spindle microtubules are of different types: some are continuous between the poles (*interpolar microtubules*); some are discontinuous and involved in attaching to the centromeres (kinetochores) of the chromosomes (*kinetochore microtubules*). The precise mechanism by which the spindle microtubules accomplish movement of the chromosomes to the spindle poles during anaphase remains unclear. Organization of the spindle is associated with activity of the centrioles in the cells of animals and some lower plants. Higher plant cells lack centrioles but still generate spindles, and there is no evidence that the presence of centrioles is essential for spindle formation even in higher animal cells.

spindle attachment. *See* centromere.

spine (in botany). A sharply pointed rigid structure formed from a modified leaf or stipule, as in *Berberis aggregata* (barberry), in which the leaf and two stipules form a tripartite spine. *Compare* prickle, thorn.

spinneret. A cylindrical or conical organ on the abdomen of spiders (*see* Araneae) perforated at the tip by numerous tiny spinning tubes through which fluid silk issues, hardening on contact with the air. The spinning tubes are connected to various types of silk gland in the abdomen, which manufacture different kinds of silk used for lining the nest, for constructing an egg cocoon, for wrapping captured prey, or for building a web to trap prey. Spiders usually have six spinnerets, which are thought to represent the vestiges of abdominal limbs.

spiracle. **1.** The gill slit in fish lying between the mandibular and hyoid arches. It is reduced in size and function because of the involvement of the hyomandibular bone in jaw support. In some elasmobranchs it serves as a channel for the inflow of water but in most teleosts it is closed. In tetrapods the spiracular gill pouch develops into the middle ear cavity.
2. The external opening of the tracheae in insects. It contains valves that control the entry and exit of respiratory gases.

spiral thickening (helical thickening). A pattern of secondary wall formation in primary xylem vessels and tracheids in which the wall material is laid down in spiral bands. It is usually the second type of thickening to appear in the primary xylem and occurs mainly in the protoxylem. *Compare* annular, reticulate, scalariform, and pitted thickenings.

spiral valve. **1.** A complex spiral fold of the epithelium of the intestine of all fish except teleosts, developed to increase the area of the secretory and absorptive surface.
2. A valve in the conus arteriosus of lungfish and amphibians that aids the separation of oxygenated and deoxygenated blood.

spirochaetes. A group of spiral bacteria that lack a rigid cell wall and move by flexions of the cell. These are achieved by contraction of a bundle of fine fibrils, the *axial filament*, wound spirally around the protoplast. Some spirochaetes occur in water; others, including *Treponema* (syphilis bacterium), are parasites of man and cause disease.

splanchnocranium (viscerocranium). The part of the vertebrate skull surrounding the oral cavity and forming the jaws. It is made up of both cartilage bone, derived from the two anterior visceral arches (mandibular and hyoid), and membrane bone. *Compare* neurocranium.

spleen. A large lymphoid organ in the intestinal mesentery of most vertebrates, lying in the course of the blood vascular system (*see* lymphoid tissue). It consists of a network of venous sinuses lying in a loose connective tissue meshwork, which is interposed with globular masses of lymphocytes. While having similar functions to lymph glands, i.e. filtering foreign bodies and producing lymphocytes, the spleen is also thought to be concerned with the destruction and storage of blood cells.

splicing. The enzyme-catalysed joining of conserved sections of messenger RNA, following excision of the intron sequences. The term is also used for the joining of fragments of DNA in *genetic engineering. The enzymes effecting both types of splicing are known as *splicing enzymes*.

sponges. *See* Porifera.

spontaneous generation (abiogenesis). The doctrine that living organisms arise from nonliving material. Until the middle of the 17th century it was widely believed that microorganisms arose in this way, from rotting meat, infusions of hay, etc. However, the work of bacteriologists, especially Pasteur (1822–95), proved that microorganisms are always present in the air and merely undergo rapid growth and reproduction when they come into contact with a suitable substrate. *Compare* biogenesis.

sporangium. A reproductive structure in plants, formed asexually, within which asexual spores (*sporangiospores*) are produced. The stalks that bear the sporangia are called *sporangiophores*.

spore. A small, usually microscopic, reproductive unit consisting of between one and several cells. Spores are produced by plants, Protozoa, and bacteria;

the different types are indicated by a prefix, e.g. *megaspore, microspore, zygospore, monospore, endospore*. More than one kind of spore may be produced by a single organism, each being specialized to perform a different function. For example, many spores serve as a means of rapid vegetative spread; others form a resistant resting stage in the life cycle. *Sexual spores* are those that take part in sexual reproduction, i.e. they behave as gametes (sometimes the term sexual spore is used for a spore formed by a sexual process). *Asexual spores* are not involved in sexual reproduction, before or after formation.

spore mother cell (sporocyte). A diploid cell within a sporangium that undergoes meiosis to produce one to four haploid spores.

sporocarp. A spore-producing structure characteristic of the water ferns (Marsileales and Salvineales), consisting of a sorus that is completely enclosed by the indusium. The term sporocarp is sometimes used synonymously with *ascocarp.

sporocyst. 1. One of the cysts produced in the Sporozoa by multiplication of the zygote, in which numerous spores are formed.
2. A sac produced by endoparasitic flukes (*see* Trematoda) that develops from the *miracidium larva in the secondary host, a snail, and in which the next larval stage, the *redia, is produced asexually. *See also* cercaria.
3. A structure produced by some plants that contains mature spores and usually forms a resistant phase of the life cycle. Sporocysts are formed by certain algae (including some Xanthophyceae) and fungi.

sporocyte. 1. *See* spore mother cell.
2. The spore-containing structure of the Acrasiales (cellular slime moulds).

sporogonium. The sporophyte phase of the Bryophyta, which is developed from a fertilized archegonium and comprises the *capsule* (producing the asexual spores), the *seta* (stalk), and the *foot* (embedded in the gametophyte tissue).

sporophore. Any spore-bearing structure, particularly the fruit body of the Basidiomycetes.

sporophyll. A sporangium-bearing leaf on the sporophyte of vascular plants. *See also* microsporophyll, megasporophyll.

sporophyte. The generation in the life cycle of a plant that bears the asexual spores. It forms the small semiparasitic capsule in bryophytes and is the dominant phase in vascular plants.

sporopollenin. A highly polymerized cyclic alcohol related to suberin and cutin but more durable than either. It occurs in the walls of many spores, including fungal spores and pollen. The durable nature of sporopollenin allows the outer layers of spores to survive sometimes millions of years virtually unchanged and thus provides the basis of *palynology. *See also* perispore.

Sporozoa. A class of parasitic Protozoa having a complex life cycle involving the alternation of sexual and asexual reproduction and the production of numerous spores. They have no locomotory structures and food is usually absorbed over the whole body surface. The class contains *Plasmodium* (malaria parasite).

sport (rogue). An organism produced by a naturally occurring mutation.

springtails. *See* Collembola.

Squamata. The order of the Lepidosauria that contains the most successful living reptiles – the lizards and their descendants, the snakes. Lizards typically have a long tail; four limbs (some, e.g. *Anguis* (slow worm), are limbless); a movable quadrate bone providing a flexible joint between the upper jaw and the skull, which increases the jaw gape; and teeth fused to the jaws. Snakes, unlike lizards, lack an ear drum and movable eyelid; their eyes are covered by transparent eyelids. Snakes are

Common stains for plant and animal tissues

material stained	dye	solvent	colour
bacteria	Bismarck brown	alcohol	red
	carbol-fuchsin	alcohol	red
	methylene blue	alcohol	red
blood	methyl blue	usually alcohol	
blood cells	Leishman's stain	methyl alcohol	red-pink
cellulose	Bismarck brown	alcohol	red
	eosin Y	water or alcohol	red
	light green	alcohol or clove oil	red
	*Schultze's solution (chlor-zinc-iodine)	water	blue or violet
connective tissue	Van Geison	water	red
cytoplasm	eosin Y	water or alcohol	pink
	picro-carmine	water	yellow
DNA	Feulgen	water	purple
epithelium	Van Geison	water	yellow
fungi	aniline (cotton) blue	lacto-phenol	red
	carbol-fuchsin	alcohol	red
fungal hyphae	Congo red	water	red
lignin	*aniline sulphate or hydrochloride	water	yellow
	*phloroglucin + conc. HCl	alcohol	red
	safranin	alcohol	red
	*Schultze's solution	water	yellow
muscle	Van Geison	water	yellow
nucleus	Bismarck brown	alcohol	pink
	borax carmine	alcohol	pink
	gentian violet	water or alcohol	pink
	haemalum	water	blue
	haematoxylin:		
	Delafield	alcohol	blue
	Ehrlich	alcohol	blue
	methyl blue	usually alcohol	
	methyl violet	water or alcohol	
	methylene blue	alcohol	
	picro-carmine	water	red
	safranin	alcohol	red
protein	*Schultze's solution	water	yellow
sieve plates	aniline blue	alcohol	
starch	*Schultze's solution	water	blue
suberin	safranin	alcohol	red
white blood cell nucleus	Leishman's stain	methyl alcohol	blue

*temporary stain

characterized by an elongated limbless body, a deeply forked protrusible sensory tongue, and an extremely wide jaw gape, made possible by the loose articulations of the skull bones. The prey is swallowed whole. Primitive snakes, e.g. *Python,* suffocate their prey; the more advanced forms use fanglike teeth. Some snakes, e.g. *Vipera* (viper), inject fast-acting poisons through their fangs.

squamosal. A membrane bone in the cheek region of the vertebrate skull. In mammals it articulates with the dentary of the lower jaw.

staining. A process used in the preparation of temporary or permanent microscope slides of organisms or tissues. In light microscopy the specimens are coloured by adding solutions of dyes, so that they become visible under the microscope. The different dyes used for temporary and permanent preparations are shown in the table. The stain solvent is usually either water or alcohol, and it is necessary to know which has been used if dehydration is to follow, in the making of permanent preparations. Some stains are general and colour any nucleus or cytoplasm, while others are specific and are taken up by certain tissues only. Several specific stains can be used in sequence, a process known as *counterstaining* or *double* (or *triple*) *staining.* For example in animal tissues, haematoxylin or haemalum can be counterstained with Van Geison stain; in plant tissues safranin can be counterstained with light green. Stains are described as *acidic, basic,* or *neutral*; this refers to the coloured radicals of the molecules, not to the pH of the solution. In acidic stains the actively staining part is an anion, which is usually combined with a metal; in basic stains the actively staining part is a cation, which is usually combined with an inorganic acid. Acidic stains colour the cytoplasm and collagen while basic stains colour the nucleus (and also the cytoplasm to some extent) because they are taken up by nucleic acids. Materials

that stain strongly with basic dyes are known as *basiphilic* (or *basophilic*); those that stain strongly with acid dyes are termed *acidophilic. Metachromatic* stains produce colours in certain tissues or cells that are different from the colour of the stain solution. For example, methyl violet (violet-blue) becomes purple or reddish. *See also* vital staining.

stamen. The *microsporophyll of angiosperms. Commonly it consists of a pollen-producing structure (*anther*) borne upon a thin stalk (*filament*). However, a whole spectrum of forms exists between the anther-filament type of stamen and a flattened leaflike structure bearing the pollen sac on its adaxial surface, which is regarded as phylogenetically more primitive. Some species (e.g. *Nymphaea odorata*) exhibit this spectrum in each flower. The stamens of a single flower are known collectively as the *androecium.*

staminode. A sterile stamen in which the anther is not developed.

standing crop. The total quantity of organic matter available at any level in a food chain at a given time and place; it usually represents potential energy for food or fuel. The standing crop is usually expressed as the *biomass of a particular trophic level (the *standing crop biomass*).

stapes. An *ear ossicle in mammals, homologous with the hyomandibular bone of fish and columella auris of amphibians, reptiles, and birds. It is the innermost of the three ossicles and is attached to the fenestra ovalis.

Staphylococcus. A genus of spherical nonmotile Gram-positive bacteria. Streptococci form short chains or clusters and do not produce spores. They cause a variety of suppurative infections in man, including abscesses, wound infections, and meningitis. Some strains produce a toxin and can cause food poisoning.

starch. A widely distributed plant polysaccharide that functions as a store of carbohydrate. It occurs in the form of granules in the *amyloplasts of roots, tubers, and other storage organs. Starch consists entirely of D-glucose units joined by glycosidic links and exists in two forms, α-amylose and amylopectin. *α-amylose*, which comprises about 25% of most starches, is made up of long unbranched glucose chains; *amylopectin* consists of branched glucose chains and comprises about 75% of most starches. The hydrolysis of starch into maltose and glucose is catalysed by the *amylases*: *α-amylase*, occurring in saliva and pancreatic juice, and *β-amylase*, found particularly in malt (partly germinated dried cereal grains). Short-chain polysaccharides formed as intermediate products during amylase action are termed *dextrins*.

starch sheath. A layer one to several cells thick, endodermal in origin, that surrounds the stele in some leaves and dicotyledonous stems. It contains more starch grains than adjacent cells and remains parenchymatous, although the cells may later develop *Casparian strips. *See also* endodermis, bundle sheath.

starfish. *See* Asteroidea.

statoblast. An internal bud, enclosed in a chitinous shell, that is produced asexually by certain ectoprocts and is capable of surviving adverse conditions (freezing, drought) on the death of the parent colony and later of giving rise to a new colony.

statocyst (otocyst). A receptor occurring in many invertebrates, including the Crustacea, that detects the position and movements of the body (or parts of the body) in relation to gravity. It consists of a fluid-filled sac lined with hairs, some of which support a *statolith*. This is a ball of lime, sand, etc., either of foreign origin or secreted by the animal; angular displacement of the hairs by the statolith stimulates sensory neurones,

resulting in reflex righting movements of the limbs. Statocysts closely resemble the *macula of the vertebrate inner ear in structure and function.

statolith. 1. One of a number of large starch grains that consistently lie on the lowermost side of certain plant cells. Because of this and the fact that they occur in the cells of gravity-sensitive organs, statoliths are thought to function in geotropism.
2. *See* statocyst.

stearic acid. *See* fatty acid.

Steinheim skull. *See Homo*.

stele. The primary vascular tissue of the Tracheophyta, comprising the xylem and phloem together with the pericycle and endodermis, arranged either in discrete bundles or in a continuous cylinder. There are a number of types of stelar arrangements (see illustration). Steles can be divided into two fundamental groups: those with leaf gaps and those without.
Steles without leaf gaps are called *protosteles*, of which there are five basic types (Figs. 1–5). Steles with leaf gaps are of two basic types (Figs. 6 and 7), both of which are in the form of a cylinder of vascular tissue surrounding a central medulla of nonvascular tissue. One (or both) of two variations may occur in any of the above types. In a *polycyclic stele* two or more steles occur one within the other (Figs. 8 and 9). The *leaf trace may originate solely from the outer stele or be formed from any or all of the inner steles. In a *polystele* two or more parallel vascular systems occur together, anastomosing only occasionally, as at branch junctions (Fig. 10). Occasionally medullated protosteles and solenosteles are grouped together under the term *siphonostele*. Steles that possess gaps not associated with leaves are said to be *perforated*.
The stelar structure that occurs in dicotyledons and gymnosperms, consisting of a ring of discrete primary vascular bundles all within a single ring of endoder-

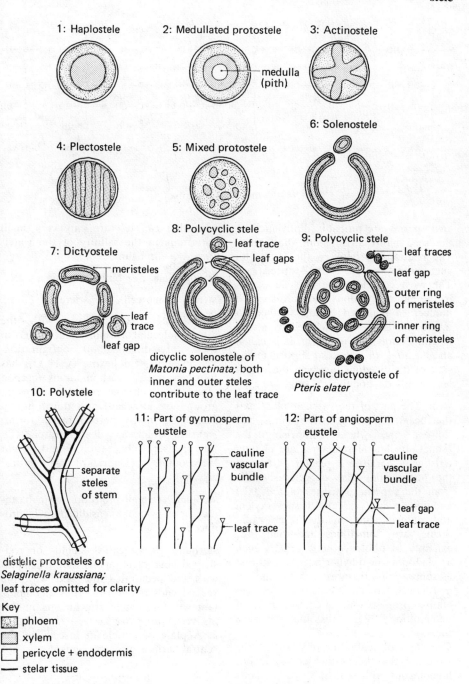

1: Haplostele

2: Medullated protostele

medulla
(pith)

3: Actinostele

4: Plectostele

5: Mixed protostele

6: Solenostele

7: Dictyostele

meristeles

leaf
trace

leaf gap

8: Polycyclic stele

leaf trace

leaf gaps

dicyclic solenostele of
Matonia pectinata; both
inner and outer steles
contribute to the leaf trace

9: Polycyclic stele

leaf traces

leaf gap

outer ring
of meristeles

inner ring
of meristeles

dicyclic dictyostele of
Pteris elater

10: Polystele

separate
steles
of stem

distelic protosteles of
Selaginella kraussiana;
leaf traces omitted for clarity

11: Part of gymnosperm
eustele

cauline
vascular
bundle

leaf trace

12: Part of angiosperm
eustele

cauline
vascular
bundle

leaf gap

leaf trace

Key
phloem
xylem
pericycle + endodermis
stelar tissue

Stelar types

mis and pericycle, is termed a *eustele*. (Fig. 12) is based on a stele with leaf
The gymnosperm eustele (Fig. 11) lacks gaps. This indicates that the ferns and
leaf gaps but the angiosperm eustele gymnosperms and the gymnosperms and

```
   CHO          CHO          CHO          CHO          CHO          CHO          CHO          CHO
   |            |            |            |            |            |            |            |
H—C•—OH    HO—C—H      H—C—OH    HO—C—H      H—C—OH    HO—C—H      H—C—OH    HO—C—H
   |            |            |            |            |            |            |            |
H—C•—OH     H—C—OH    HO—C—H    HO—C—H       H—C—OH     H—C—OH   HO—C—H      HO—C—H
   |            |            |            |            |            |            |            |
H—C•—OH     H—C—OH     H—C—OH     H—C—OH   HO—C—H     HO—C—H    HO—C—H      HO—C—H
   |            |            |            |            |            |            |            |
H—C•—OH     H—C—OH     H—C—OH     H—C—OH     H—C—OH     H—C—OH     H—C—OH      H—C—OH
   |            |            |            |            |            |            |            |
  CH₂OH        CH₂OH        CH₂OH        CH₂OH        CH₂OH        CH₂OH        CH₂OH        CH₂OH

 D-allose     D-altrose    D-glucose    D-mannose    D-gulose     D-idose    D-galactose    D-talose
```

• asymmetric
carbon centre

D-forms of aldohexose

angiosperms are probably diphyletic, i.e. the seed habit arose more than once. The relationship between the ferns and angiosperms has yet to be deduced.

The most complex type of stele occurs in the monocotyledons and consists of a number of scattered bundles embedded in ground tissue and encircled by a ring of endodermis and pericycle. It is called an *atactostele* (a term also applied to the stele of dicotyledons in which the vascular strands do not form a single ring).

stem. The part of the vascular plant axis that bears the leaves, axillary buds, and flowers, the whole comprising the *shoot. Its lateral structures are characteristically borne in a regular pattern at the nodes and arise exogenously (i.e. from the superficial tissues of the axis) and its primary vascular tissues (xylem and phloem) are on the same radii. Stems are sometimes modified, for example as photosynthetic organs such as cladodes and phylloclades; as thorns; as supporting structures such as tendrils; as runners, stolons, offsets, etc., for vegetative propagation; and as organs of perennation (e.g. rhizomes, corms, tubers).

The stem of leafy bryophytes (i.e. the structure that bears the leaves) is not homologous with that of vascular plants as it is part of the gametophyte. It lacks true vascular tissue and the regular arrangement of leaves on the stem reflects their origin from the apical cell.

stenohaline. Designating aquatic organ-

isms that can tolerate only very small variations in the salinity of the water. *Compare* euryhaline.

stenopodium. *See* biramous appendage.

stereid (stone cell). *See* sclereid.

stereoisomers. Compounds with the same molecular formula that differ in their three-dimensional configuration. For example, aldohexose ($C_6H_{12}O_6$) has four asymmetric carbon atoms (carbon atoms to which four different atoms or groups are attached) and it can therefore exist in 16 stereoisomeric forms, eight of which are dextrorotatory (D-forms; see illustration) and eight laevorotatory (L-forms) (*see* optical activity).

sterigma. A small projection on a basidium upon which a basidiospore is produced.

sternum. 1. A ventral shield- or rod-shaped bone of tetrapods that articulates with the pectoral girdle and with the ventral ends of the ribs. It is an important site for muscle attachments in flying vertebrates. *See* keel.
2. A plate of cuticle in insects on the ventral surface of each segment.

Steroid nucleus

steroid. One of a large group of complex lipids characterized by a 17-carbon (perhydrocyclopentanophenanthrene) nucleus (see formula). The group contains many important physiologically active compounds, including the sterols, corticosteroid (adrenocortical) hormones, sex hormones (oestrogen, androgen, progesterone, etc.), and vitamin D.

sterols. A group of steroid alcohols that includes cholesterol, the most abundant animal steroid, and ergosterol.

stick insects. *See* Phasmida.

sticky ends. Self-complementary single-stranded ends of double-stranded DNA molecules produced by a *restriction endonuclease cutting the DNA at specific points in its recognition sequence.

stigma. 1. The receptive surface of a *carpel, to which pollen grains adhere (see illustration at *ovule). It is usually borne on a style but in some plants is sessile. The stigmatic epidermis exudes a sugary fluid that stimulates the pollen grains to germinate.
2. *See* eyespot.

stimulus. An aspect of the internal or external environment of an organism that provokes a response in the organism. The energy of the response is not derived from the energy of the stimulus. *See also* irritability.

stipe. A stalk, particularly (1) the stalk of fungal fruiting bodies such as mushrooms and toadstools and (2) the stalk of the larger Phaeophyta (brown algae), whose basal end bears a *hapteron and whose distal end bears the *lamina.

stipule. An outgrowth from the base of a leaf (phyllopodium). Its form varies; for example, it may be leaflike, functioning in photosynthesis, or it may form a tendril or a spine.

stock. *See* graft.

stolon. 1. An organ of vegetative propagation in plants, consisting of a horizon-tal stem that grows along the surface of the ground and takes root at the nodes, where a new shoot arises. Long rapidly elongating stolons that root only at the tip are called *runners* (e.g. strawberry); short stolons are called *offsets* (e.g. houseleek).
2. A branched stemlike structure in some invertebrates. In colonial organisms such as hydrozoan coelenterates it is the part from which new individuals develop; in some urochordates it is a stalk from which budding takes place.

stoma (*pl.* **stomata**). One of a large number of small pores or apertures in the epidermis of the aerial parts of leaves, stems, and flowers (and in some underground rhizomes and aquatic plants) through which the exchange of gases takes place and water is lost by transpiration. Each pore is surrounded by a pair of *guard cells, which control its opening and closing. The term stoma sometimes includes the pore together with the surrounding guard cells.

stomach. A dilation of the anterior region of the alimentary canal, developed primarily for the storage of food and secondarily specialized for its mechanical and chemical treatment. In vertebrates food is broken up by the churning action of the muscular walls of the stomach. Glandular cells in the stomach mucosa secrete gastric juices containing hydrochloric acid, which acidulates the food, and pepsin, which initiates protein digestion. A pyloric sphincter at the posterior end of the stomach regulates the passage of food into the duodenum.
The stomach is often compartmental: in birds the posterior end forms the gizzard; in herbivores there are several chambers to facilitate the digestion of cellulose by bacteria.

stomium. A weak area for dehiscence in the walls of certain plant structures. A stomium is present in anthers and in fern sporangia (where it may be associated with an *annulus).

stomodaeum. An anterior invagination of the ectoderm of the embryo that opens into the archenteron. It gives rise to the regions of the alimentary canal specialized for the reception of food, e.g. the buccal cavity of vertebrates and the foregut of arthropods.

stone cell (stereid). *See* sclereid.

stoneflies. *See* Plecoptera.

stratum corneum. The outer layer of cells of the *epidermis of terrestrial vertebrates. It consists of clear dead denucleated cells whose cytoplasm has been entirely replaced by keratin and which become increasingly flattened (*squamous*) as they approach the surface of the skin. It is particularly thick on the palms and soles of the feet and is continually being sloughed off as a result of frictional contact. *See* cornification.

Strepsiptera. A small order of endopterygote insects containing the stylops, e.g. *Stylops melittae*. Both females and larvae are endoparasites of bees, wasps, and other insects; the white larva-like females lack wings, legs, and eyes. The short-lived males are active fliers, having large membranous hind wings, forewings modified as knoblike balancing organs, and degenerate mouthparts. The order is sometimes included in the Coleoptera.

Streptococcus. A genus of spherical nonmotile Gram-positive bacteria that form long chains. Streptococci do not form spores. Many are haemolytic (i.e. they

destroy red blood cells) and are responsible for a variety of diseases, including throat infections, puerperal fever, scarlet fever, and rheumatic fever.

streptomycin. An aminoglycoside antibiotic that kills susceptible bacteria by binding to the small subunit of bacterial ribosomes and causes misreading of codons in protein synthesis. Streptomycin is obtained from a filamentous fungus-like bacterium, *Streptomyces griseus*.

striated muscle (skeletal, striped, or voluntary muscle). Muscle responsible for the voluntary movement of skeletal parts and therefore of great importance in locomotion. In vertebrates it consists of elongated multinucleate cells (*muscle fibres*) with a characteristic transverse banding pattern. The fibres contain many longitudinal fibrils (*myofibrils*), and the banding pattern reflects the structure of the *sarcomere* units of which these myofibrils are constructed. The sarcomeres contain protein filaments, which form the contractile apparatus of the muscle (see illustration). The I filament is composed of *troponin* and *tropomyosin*, which regulate contraction, and *actin*. The A filament is polymerized *myosin*, and the head of each myosin molecule projects from the filament to form a cross-bridge. When muscle is stimulated, the two filaments interdigitate, causing the sarcomeres to shorten. This is brought about by the cyclical activity of the cross-bridges, which attach to actin and undergo a conformational change accompanied by the release of energy, thereby exerting a pulling force. They then detach and split a molecule of ATP to recharge with energy before they are ready to reattach. The *excitation-contraction coupling system allows synchronous sliding in all filaments so that contraction of the whole muscle is rapid and powerful.

stridulation. The production of sound by an insect, usually by rubbing one part of the body, modified as a hard ridge or knob (the *scraper*), against another part, modified as a series of ridges or projec-

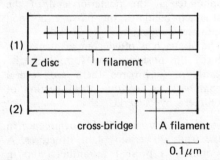

(1)

Z disc　　I filament

(2)

cross-bridge　　A filament

0.1 µm

Cross-section of two sarcomeres, contracted (1) and relaxed (2)

tions (the *file*). For example, crickets stridulate by rubbing together modified veins on their forewings but other insects use elytra, legs, the abdomen, etc. Cicadas stridulate by vibrating a membrane at the base of the abdomen, which produces a series of clicks. The majority of insect sounds are used in sexual behaviour but they may also be used in the maintenance of territory, for warning, etc.

striped muscle. *See* striated muscle.

strobila. 1. The body of a tapeworm (*see* Cestoda), consisting of numerous proglottides (segments) that are budded off from the scolex (head). *See* proglottis.
2. A stage in the life cycle of the Scyphozoa (jellyfish) consisting of a *scyphistoma in the process of transverse fission.
The processes of budding in the tapeworm and transverse fission in the scyphistoma are both termed *strobilation*.

strobilus. 1. A spike of fertile appendages borne at the tip of a shoot in small-leaved pteridophytes (horsetails, club mosses, etc.) and in gymnosperms. Each appendage consists of a sporophyll (fertile bract, scale, or leaf) together with the sporangium or sporangia associated with it. In gymnosperms and in some advanced pteridophytes two types of strobilus are formed: the *microstrobilus* (or *microsporangiate cone*), concerned with microspore production, and the *megastrobilus* (or *megasporangiate cone*), concerned with megaspore production. In gymnosperms the microstrobilus consists entirely of microsporophylls, but in the megastrobilus each megasporophyll has an associated *bract scale* in whose axil it is produced. Also called: **cone**.
2. A dry composite *fruit developed from an inflorescence, consisting of an axis plus a number of bracts surrounding the flowers. The true fruits are achenes.

stroma. 1. The colourless matrix of a *chloroplast, which surrounds the lamellar system of photosynthetic membranes.
2. A compact vegetative mass of fungal hyphae within or from which reproductive structures develop.
3. The network of connective tissue or intercellular material that forms the framework of an animal organ, e.g. the mammalian ovary.

stromatolites. Laminated calcareous structures formed by blue-green algae in intertidal zones of warm waters, such as those of the Bahamas. In the last two decades interest in stromatolites has been aroused by the discovery of similar structures in Pre-Cambrian rocks nearly 3.0×10^9 years old. *See* origin of life.

style. A sterile apical prolongation of a *carpel that bears the stigma (see illustration at *ovule). In syncarpous ovaries the styles are either free (or partly so) or united to form a single functional unit.

stylops. *See* Strepsiptera.

subarachnoid space. The space between the arachnoid mater and the pia mater meninges of the tetrapod brain and spinal cord. It is filled with cerebrospinal fluid and communicates with the ventricles through foramina in the hindbrain.

subclavian artery. A blood vessel supplying oxygenated blood to the forelimbs of tetrapods. In many groups its origin from the aorta is closely associated with that of the carotid artery. *See also* innominate artery.

subcutaneous tissue (hypodermis). The layer of loose connective tissue that lies directly beneath the dermis of vertebrate skin. It usually contains fat cells (*see* adipose tissue), which are present to varying degrees depending on the species; large blood vessels; and nervous tissue.

suberin. A fatty substance similar to *cutin. It occurs in the Casparian strip in young roots and certain stems and also forms a protective layer on the primary cellulose walls of cork cells.

subhymenium. The tissue layer between the hymenium and the trama in certain fungal fruiting bodies.

sublittoral. 1. Designating the zone of a lake or large pond between 6 and 10 metres in depth. The sublittoral zone is dominated by plankton but also contains large populations of molluscs and crustaceans. *Compare* littoral, profundal. **2.** Designating the zone of a sea between the seashore and the edge of the continental shelf (i.e. down to a depth of about 200 metres). Sublittoral organisms form part of the benthos.

subsidiary cell (accessory cell). One of the epidermal plant cells that surround the *guard cells. They can be distinguished structurally from guard cells and unspecialized epidermal cells and their function is to aid the guard cells when the stoma is opening and closing.

subspecies. A unit of *classification that is a subdivision of a species. Subspecies have certain characteristics in common and tend to breed with each other rather than with other members of the species, usually because of geographical isolation. The name of a subspecies is written in italics after the specific epithet. For example, the British pied wagtail and the continental white wagtail are subspecies of *Motacilla alba*; the pied wagtail is *Motacilla alba yarrellii* and the white wagtail is *Motacilla alba alba*. The term subspecies may be written into the name, as in *Motacilla alba* subsp. *alba*. Subspecies will eventually become new species if the isolation is maintained, but if there is a zone where they overlap, they grade into each other.

succession. The establishment of a sequence of different communities in a particular area over a period of time. *Primary succession* occurs during the colonization of an uninhabited area, such as a recent lava flow or a sand dune. Algae and lichens are usually the first plants to be established and they consti-

tute the *pioneer community*. They are followed by mosses and, as the soil develops, higher plants, eventually resulting in a completed succession of plants and animals – the *sere. Secondary succession* is the establishment of communities on sites previously occupied by well-developed communities, such as a cleared forest or a burnt patch of soil.

succus entericus. The secretion of the glands of the walls of the small intestine of vertebrates. It contains digestive enzymes including amylase, enzymes that release free monosaccharides, lipase, enteropeptidase, and proteases that release free amino acids.

Sucrose

sucrose (cane sugar). A disaccharide of glucose and fructose (see formula) widely distributed in plants, its principal sources being sugar cane and sugar beet.

sugar. Any carbohydrate that has a sweet taste and is soluble in water and usually crystalline. Sugars include the *monosaccharides and *disaccharides.

sulphatide. *See* cerebroside.

Sulphanilamide

sulphonamides. A group of drugs, derived from the dye sulphanilamide (see formula), that inhibit the growth of bacteria (i.e. they are bacteriostatic). It is thought that they act by preventing sulphonamide-sensitive bacteria from utilizing para-aminobenzoic acid, which they require for synthesizing folic acid. Bacteria that do not require folic acid or can utilize preformed folic acid are not affected by the drugs.

summation. 1. The synaptic phenomenon of the linear addition of separate post-synaptic responses elicited by stimuli that are adjacent in time or space. Excitation of a synapse evokes a graded potential change in the postsynaptic membrane (an EPSP, EPP, or IPSP; *see* synapse), which may be below the threshold required to trigger an impulse. However, if two or more such potentials are evoked either approximately simultaneously at different synapses on the same neurone (*spatial summation*) or in rapid succession at the same synapse (*temporal summation*) the summed response may be sufficient to trigger a postsynaptic impulse. Summation may occur between two excitatory potentials, between two inhibitory potentials, or between an excitatory and an inhibitory potential. It is one of the principal mechanisms of nervous *integration. *Compare* facilitation.
2. *See* synergism.

superior. Designating an angiosperm gynoecium with the other flower parts inserted below it, i.e. the gynoecium of a hypogynous or perigynous flower. *Compare* inferior.

supernormal stimulus (in animal behaviour). A stimulus that has a greater effect in producing the typical response than the normal stimulus has. A herring gull presented with eggs of different sizes will attempt to brood the largest in preference to any smaller egg, even though its own egg may be one of the smaller ones.

supination. *See* pronation and supination.

suspension culture. A tissue-culture system in which single cells and small cell clumps are grown in suspension in an agitated liquid medium. Suspension cultures are used to study cell division, cell differentiation, and the regulation of cell metabolism both in microorganisms and in isolated plant cells. Plant suspension cultures are obtained by adding fragments of friable callus tissue to the medium. Under appropriate conditions single plant cells may develop into embryos and subsequently into complete plants.

suspensor. *See* embryo.

suture. A line of junction or fusion. Sutures in plant organs are often lines of weakness along which dehiscence may occur; the *ventral suture* of a carpel represents the line of fusion of the margins of the megasporophyll.
In animals sutures may occur between bones (especially the bones of the skull), between the cuticular plates of insects, and between adjacent chambers of a nautiloid or ammonoid shell (in ammonites the patterns made by the suture lines on the external shell become increasingly complex during the evolutionary history of the group).

S value. *See* Svedberg unit.

Svedberg unit (Svedberg, S value). Symbol: S. The rate of sedimentation of a particle in an ultracentrifuge is expressed as the sedimentation coefficient (s) and is a function of its weight and shape. A Svedberg unit is a sedimentation coefficient of 1×10^{-13} seconds. Since sedimentation depends also on the solvent properties, it is usual to express S values for the solvent water at $20°C$ (S_w^{20}). S values are quoted as indicators of size or molecular weight when comparing cellular particles and macromolecules. For example 70S ribosomes have 30S and 50S subunits, containing 23S, 16S, and 5S RNAs.

SV40 virus. A small animal virus, belonging to the papovavirus group of double-stranded DNA viruses. The name is short for Simian Virus 40: the virus was originally isolated from cell cultures derived from an African green monkey. The virus has been widely used in research and is noted both for its ability to induce cellular *transformation and for the fact that its genome consists of a *minichromosome of chromatin. The entire genome of SV40 virus has been sequenced and is now known to consist of only six genes.

Swanscombe skull. *See Homo.*

swarm spore (swarm cell, swarmer). A zoospore that may act as an asexual or a sexual spore. It is produced particularly by the fungal groups Myxomycetes and Plasmodiophorales.

sweat. The watery fluid produced by sweat glands in mammals, which is hypotonic with respect to blood plasma. It contains about 0.5% solid material, mainly sodium and chloride ions with smaller quantities of urea, lactate, and calcium. Its ionic constituents (particularly sodium and chloride ions) vary in concentration with age and gland activity. Sweat is produced in response to increased body temperature (man begins to sweat at about 34.5°C), and its evaporation on the skin assists in cooling the body surface.

sweat gland. An exocrine gland in the skin of mammals that secretes sweat. It consists of a tube of cuboidal cells, the secretory portion of which is coiled and embedded in the dermis. From this a duct runs to the surface of the skin through which the sweat is discharged. Sweat glands occur over almost the entire body surface of man and higher primates but only to a limited extent in other mammals, usually being found only on the pads of the feet. The activity of the glands is controlled by fibres of the sympathetic nervous system; these fibres are unusual in that they release acetylcholine rather than noradrenaline as a neurotransmitter.

swim bladder (air bladder). The hydrostatic device of actinopterygian fish: an air-filled bladder derived from the lungs of ancestral fish and homologous to the tetrapod lung. The air pressure in the bladder, and hence the specific gravity of the fish, can be adjusted by taking in air either through a duct from the pharynx or by the extraction of gas from the blood in a special capillary bed. In some teleost fish the bladder is utilized for the reception of sound waves, by transferring vibrations to the inner ear either directly or through a chain of *Weberian ossicles. In some groups it is readapted as a lung.

switch plant. A xeromorphic plant that produces normal leaves in its younger stages or during the early part of a growing season that are quickly shed, their photosynthetic function being taken over by another organ, such as a phyllode or cladode.

syconus (synconus, synconium, synconum). A composite *fruit in which the inflorescence is a hollow capitulum, inside which the flowers and true fruits develop. The capitulum forms the succulent flesh at maturity. An example is the fig.

symbiosis. Any close relationship between two different types of living organisms, including parasitism (*see* parasite), *mutualism, and *commensalism. The term is sometimes restricted to mutualism, in which the relationship is mutually beneficial (the two organisms being known as *symbionts*).

Symmetrodonta. An extinct order of late Triassic and early Jurassic mammals, e.g. *Spalacotherium*, characterized by molar teeth with three cusps arranged in a symmetrical triangle. Unlike all later mammals, the lower molars lacked a heel (*talonid*). Symmetrodonts were probably small insectivores and carnivores. They are variously regarded as a side-branch of early mammal stock or as ancestors of the Pantotheria.

sympathetic nervous system. The part of the vertebrate *autonomic nervous system that has adrenergic peripheral nerve endings. It is concerned mainly with homeostasis and emergency activities.

sympathin. *Adrenaline or *noradrenaline in their role as neurotransmitters.

sympatry. The occurrence of populations in the same geographical area. *See* (sympatric) speciation. *Compare* allopatry.

symphysis. A type of joint in which the articulating surfaces of the bones are bound together by collagen fibres to minimize movement at the joint and to confer rigidity upon the structure. It occurs between the centra of the vertebrae.

symplast. The system of interconnected protoplasts in a plant. Protoplasts of adjacent cells are linked by means of plasmodesmata through the cell walls, forming a continuous system of protoplasm throughout the plant.

symplastic growth (in botany). Cell growth in which adjacent cell walls remain in contact and grow in unison. *Compare* intrusive growth, sliding growth.

sympodium (in botany). A branching system in which the apex of the primary axis stops growing (for example at the end of a growing season) and its function is taken over by the apices of one or more lateral branches. This type of branching is sometimes called *definite* (or *cymose*) branching and is characteristic of a *cymose inflorescence. *Compare* dichotomy, monopodium.

synangium. A spore-producing structure of some ferns, e.g. many Marattiales and Ophioglossales, that is formed by the fusion of sessile sporangia and represents a single sorus.

synapse. The area of functional contact between one neurone and another or between a neurone and an effector, at which information is transferred from cell to cell by means of a chemical *neurotransmitter. Synapses are generally made between the fine terminal branches of the axon of one cell and the dendrites of the next. In the region of the synapse the plasma membranes of the two cells become closely apposed, separated by a narrow synaptic cleft. Small vesicles in the synaptic region of the presynaptic cell (*synaptic vesicles*) contain the neurotransmitter. An electrical impulse in the presynaptic cell stimulates the simultaneous discharge of many vesicles with the transitory emission of neurotransmitter into the synaptic cleft. The postsynaptic membrane is not obviously structurally differentiated but it does contain protein receptor molecules. Neurotransmitter molecules in the synaptic cleft combine with the receptor molecules to produce specific changes in the ionic permeability of the membrane and hence graded local changes in membrane potential. Depolarizing changes at excitatory synapses and neuromuscular junctions (termed *excitatory postsynaptic potentials* and *endplate potentials* respectively) may initiate an impulse in the postsynaptic cell. At inhibitory synapses and neuromuscular junctions the permeability changes produce either a hyperpolarizing potential (*inhibitory postsynaptic potential*) or serve to clamp the membrane potential at its resting value; both mechanisms attenuate or inhibit ongoing excitation.

synapsid. Designating a condition of the amniote skull in which the roofing of membrane bones is pierced by one opening in the cheek, allowing greater room for jaw musculature and resulting in improved jaw function. This condition is found in mammals and their fossil reptile antecedents (*see* Synapsida).

Synapsida. The extinct subclass of mostly carnivorous reptiles from which the mammals evolved. They were common from the Upper Carboniferous to the Triassic and were characterized by a *synapsid skull. There are two orders: the *Pelycosauria and the more advanced *Therapsida.

synapsis. *See* pairing.

synaptonemal complex. An organelle or molecular structure that can be observed by electron microscopy between homologous chromatids of meiotic chromosomes. It is presumed to play an important role in mediating movement of DNA and its fissure and rejoining during meiotic *chiasma formation.

Synaptosauria (Euryapsida). A subclass of extinct reptiles most of whose members were secondarily adapted for a marine or estuarine life. First appearing in the Triassic and common during the Jurassic and Cretaceous, they were characterized by a *parapsid* skull, i.e. one with a single pair of temporal openings high up on the cheek. *See also* Sauropterygia. *Compare* Ichthyopterygia.

syncarpy. The state of an angiosperm gynoecium of having its carpels fused together to a greater or lesser extent, as in *Delphinium* (fused at base); *Stellaria* (ovaries fused, styles free); primrose (complete fusion of carpels). *Compare* apocarpy.

synchronous culture. A culture of cells, either microorganisms or tissue cells, in which cell division is synchronized, i.e. each cell is at the same stage of mitosis at any one time. This synchrony is achieved by various techniques, including varying the temperature and limiting the nutrients, but is lost after a few generations because of random variations in the generation times of the cells of the population.

synconus (synconium, synconum). *See* syconus.

syncytium. An animal tissue consisting of a mass of protoplasm containing many nuclei and bounded by a plasma membrane. Syncytia occur in many animal groups; for example they form the epidermis of nematodes, the body wall of rotifers, and the fibres of striated muscle.

synecology. The ecology of a group of plants and animals making up a natural community, such as those of a freshwater pond, beech wood, etc. *Compare* autecology.

synergida (synergid cell). A cell forming part of the egg apparatus in certain *embryo sacs.

synergism. The interaction of two or more substances (e.g. drugs, hormones, plant growth substances) having a similar effect in a given system to produce an effect that is greater than the sum of the effects of the substances acting in isolation. This interaction is also termed *potentiation* to distinguish it from *summation*, the synergistic action of two substances to produce an effect greater than either is capable of in isolation. *Compare* antagonism.

syngamy. *See* fertilization.

syngraft. *See* isograft.

synovial membrane. The lining of the sacs (*synovial sacs*) that enclose the joint cavities of movable joints. It is composed of mesothelial cells and connective tissue and is involved in absorption from the *synovial fluid* bathing the joint cavity. This fluid is clear, yellow, and viscous and owes its viscoelastic properties to its content of hyaluronic acid. Synovial fluid plays a part in nourishing the cartilage covering the articulating surfaces of the bones and is thought to act as a lubricant.

synthetase. *See* ligase.

syntype. *See* holotype.

syrinx. The sound-producing organ of birds, resembling the *vocal cords but situated at the base of the trachea.

systematics. The study of the diversity of plants and animals and of the relationships between them, including their identification, classification, and nomenclature. It is sometimes used as a synonym for *taxonomy. *See also* biosystematics.

systemic arch. The fourth aortic arch of tetrapod embryos. In adult land-living tetrapods it passes blood via the aorta to the trunk and hind limbs. Amphibians and reptiles retain both arches, birds only the right one, and mammals only the left one.

systole. The contractile phase of the beating of the heart, when blood is expelled into the aorta and pulmonary artery. The term normally implies contraction of the ventricles, i.e. *ventricular systole*, and should be distinguished from *atrial systole*. In man ventricular systole lasts for about 0.3 seconds.

T

2,4,5-T.   2,4,5-trichlorophenoxyacetic acid: a synthetic *auxin widely used as a herbicide.

tactic movement. *See* taxis.

tailing. The modification of some nuclear RNA molecules after transcription by the addition of 10–20 adenosine residues to the 3′ end of the RNA. Most *messenger RNA (mRNA) is tailed, the adenosine residues being added to the *HnRNA precursor and surviving the removal of any intron sequences in the processing of the HnRNA to form mRNA.

tannin. One of a heterogeneous group of plant phenol derivatives (molecular weight 500–3000) that can all combine with animal hide to form leather. They are astringent to taste and are widely distributed in higher plants in vacuoles, cytoplasm, and occasionally cell walls. They sometimes occur in specially enlarged cells (tannin cells or sacs) or systems of cells, which are visible as granular masses or yellow, red, or brown bodies. Tannins are common in leaves, vascular tissues, bark, unripe fruits, galls, and seed coats; they are used in tanning, dyeing, and the preparation of ink.

T-antigen. A protein produced by poly-omaviruses (*see* virus) soon after infection, so called because it is present in cells *t*ransformed (i.e. made into tumour cells) by these viruses. T-antigen binds to the viral DNA and is necessary for replication of the viral genome.

tapetum. **1.** A layer of guanine crystals or shiny connective tissue fibres either within or internal to the choroid of the eye of nocturnal and deep-sea vertebrates. It reflects light back onto the retina, thus improving visual sensitivity at the expense of acuity.
2. A layer of cells in a sporangium of a vascular plant that provides nourishment for the developing spores. The tapetum may represent the inner layer of the sporangium wall (as in *Lycopodium*), sterile sporogenous tissue (as in *Selaginella*), or a combination of the two (as in microsporangia of angiosperms). It is either *plasmodial*, the cell walls breaking down so that the protoplasts intrude between the spores (as in *Equisetum* and in angiosperm pollen sacs), or *secretory*, in which the cells remain intact and secrete nutritive substances (as in *Lycopodium* and *Selaginella*).

tapeworms. *See* Cestoda.

Tardigrada. A phylum of minute aquatic invertebrates, the water bears, e.g. *Macrobiotus*. The body is covered with a cuticle of thin plates, giving the animal a segmented appearance, and there are four pairs of clawed legs. Tardigrades are widespread, particularly in temporary pools of water, and are highly resistant to desiccation. They were formerly classified with the Arthropoda.

tarsal bones. The bones of the proximal part of the foot of the tetrapod rear limb. The primitive arrangement of twelve bones in three rows has been modified in many species by reduction, fusion, and repositioning of the bones. *See also* pentadactyl limb.

tarsus. The complex of tarsal bones, forming the ankle in man.

taste bud. The receptor for taste in vertebrates, consisting of a group of sense cells usually located on a papilla.

In terrestrial vertebrates the taste buds are restricted to the epithelium of the mouth, especially the tongue, but in aquatic vertebrates they may occur anywhere on the surface of the body. There are four populations of structurally indistinguishable taste buds, which discriminate sweet, salty, bitter, and sour tastes, respectively.

TATA box (Hogness box). A sequence of homology found some 20–40 bases from the initiation site of many gene sequences in DNA. The TATA box is so called because the homologous sequence is TATAA (T = thymine; A = adenine). This sequence has the property of binding RNA polymerase and so seems to function as a *promoter region. A similar sequence of homology is prokaryotes is known as the *Pribnow box.*

taurine. A sulphonic-acid-containing *amino acid, $H_2NCH_2CH_2SO_2OH$, that is a component of the bile salt taurocholate and has a hyperpolarizing action on certain neurones of the central nervous system.

taxis (tactic movement). A locomotory movement of an organism or cell in response to, and directed by, an external directional stimulus. Taxes are specified according to the type of stimulus. For example, *phototaxis* is the response to variation in light intensity and direction; many phytoflagellates, e.g. *Euglena*, and the chloroplasts of higher plants are positively phototactic (i.e. they move towards the light); some insects, e.g. cockroach, are negatively phototactic (they move away from the light). *Chemotaxis*, the response to a chemical concentration gradient, occurs in the antherozoids of liverworts, ferns, and mosses in response to chemicals secreted by the archegonia. *Aerotaxis*, the response to variation in oxygen concentration, is found mainly in aerobic bacteria. *See* paratonic movements. *Compare* kinesis, tropism.

taxon. A unit of classification of any rank in the hierarchical scale.

taxonomy. The study of the theory, procedure, and rules of classification of organisms according to the similarities and differences between them. There are several subdivisions of taxonomy, which are based on the different methods used in determining taxonomic positions. The most widely used method is that of *classical taxonomy*, which uses morphological, serological, and biochemical data in classifying, describing, and naming organisms. *Cytotaxonomy* is a specialized method of classification based on the characteristics (size, shape, and number) of the chromosomes in somatic cells. *Numerical taxonomy* uses mathematical methods and such aids as computers in grouping similarities and differences and forming taxa. In *experimental taxonomy*, breeding and other experiments are used to clarify the relationships between organisms and to define evolutionary units. The term experimental taxonomy is often used synonymously with *biosystematics, and the term taxonomy with *systematics.

tectum. An enlargement of the visual regions of the midbrain. It is prominent in amphibians, reptiles, and birds, in which it receives and integrates all sensory information and issues motor commands. In mammals this function is taken over by the *cerebral hemispheres, and the tectum becomes a reflex centre.

teeth. Modified dermal papillae whose surfaces are covered by a layer of calcified tissue, present in the oral cavity of vertebrates and used for biting and masticating food, fighting, and general manipulation. In fish, amphibians, and many reptiles the teeth are widely distributed on the palate; they arose in the Chondrichthyes as modified placoid scales. In crocodiles and mammals the teeth are less numerous and are confined to the jaws.

Two distinct anatomical parts of teeth can be distinguished: the exposed surface (*crown*), which is covered with *enamel derived from the epithelium, and the *root*, inside the gum, which fits into a cleft in the jaw bone (*alveolar cavity*) and is coated with *cement. The bulk of the hard portion of the tooth consists of *dentine, derived from connective tissue, which encloses the internal *pulp cavity.

Mammals possess four distinct types of teeth: *incisors, *canines, *premolars, and *molars, whose size and number vary in different species. The number and form of the teeth of a species is expressed by its *dental formula. In man and most mammals two successions of teeth occur, the *deciduous (milk) teeth, which are fewer in number and are later replaced by the *permanent teeth. A few mammals acquire only one set of teeth, which remain in active growth throughout life, while in most other vertebrates the teeth are continuously replaced. *See also* dentition.

teichoic acid. One of a group of linear polymers of either glycerol phosphate or ribitol phosphate. Ribitol teichoic acids are one of the two characteristic constituents of the cell wall of Gram-positive bacteria (the other being mucopeptide); glycerol teichoic acids are associated with the bacterial cell membrane.

telegony. The theory that the progeny of one mating can be influenced by a male that has previously mated with their mother. It was proposed by Weismann in the 19th century, but although certain stockbreeding regulations in force today suggest that there is still some belief in this theory, there has been much evidence to disprove it and it is no longer generally accepted.

teleology. The theory that all organisms or their parts have evolved for a particular purpose.

Teleostei. The largest group of bony fishes, belonging to the subclass Actinopterygii. They have a completely ossified endoskeleton, thin rounded bony scales, a symmetrical (homocercal) tail, and shortened jaws with reduced cheek bones, which allows the mouth to gape widely. The more primitive teleosts, e.g. the Clupeiformes (herrings, salmon, etc.), have soft flexible fin rays and the pelvic fins are towards the rear of the body. In the more advanced, and majority, of teleosts, e.g. the Perciformes (perches), the fins are supported by a few strong movable spines and the pelvic fins are at the anterior end of the body, where they assist the pectorals. The swim bladder is typically completely hydrostatic in function, which confers great manoeuvrability and is a major contribution to the success of the group. Teleosts first became abundant in the Cretaceous, since when they have become adapted to most types of aquatic habitat, showing considerable variation in form.

teleutosorus (telium). A sorus of sporogenous hyphae that produce *teleutospores* (or *teliospores*), occurring in the Heterobasidiomycetes, notably the *rusts and *smuts. The teleutospores are produced on dikaryotic hyphae (*see* heterokaryosis) and are one- or two-celled. At maturity the nuclei of each cell undergo karyogamy to produce a single nucleus per cell; the spore is then released and overwinters. On germination each cell undergoes meiosis and produces a single basidium with four basidiospores.

telocentric. *See* centromere.

telomere. The end of a chromosome. The molecular structure of telomeres has recently been studied and it has been shown that the chromosomal DNA molecule forms a loop (i.e. the sugar–phosphate backbone is continuous, as in the hairpin loops in *transfer RNA molecules).

telome theory. The theory, expanded by Zimmerman from a suggestion made by Lignier (1903), that the *megaphyll originated from a stem structure, i.e. that it is fundamentally a cladode. Zimmerman suggested that primitive plants consisted of a system of dichotomizing axes whose ultimate divisions he termed *telomes*, which either bore sporangia (*fertile telomes*) or were sterile (*phylloids*). The megaphyll evolved from the phylloid-bearing axes.

telophase. The final stage of *mitosis and *meiosis.

telson. A single appendage on the last abdominal segment of certain arthropods. It is present in some crustaceans – it forms part of the tail fan of *Astacus* (crayfish) – and in scorpions, in which it forms part of the sting. A telson is absent in adult insects.

temperate phage. A bacteriophage that can become integrated into the chromosome of its bacterial host instead of immediately reproducing and causing lysis of the host cell. *See* lysogeny.

temperature coefficient (Q_{10}). The ratio by which the velocity of an enzyme-catalysed reaction increases for a rise in temperature of 10°C. The velocity of many biological reactions approximately doubles for a 10° rise in temperature, i.e. $Q_{10} = 2$.

temperature-sensitive mutation. A mutation giving a normal phenotype at one temperature but a mutant phenotype at another. This effect is usually due to a heat-labile mutant gene product.

template. The structure that directs accurate synthesis of a macromolecule. For example, a DNA strand serves as the template for synthesis of the complementary strand.

tendon. An almost inextensible band of white fibrous connective tissue that attaches a muscle to a bone and helps to concentrate the muscle pull on a small area. Tendons consist of closely packed bundles of collagen fibres interposed with rows of fibroblasts.

tendril. A helical climbing organ in plants that is modified from any part of the shoot system and shows haptotropism (response to mechanical contact by twining and clinging), especially in its young stages. Some tendrils are little altered from the normal structure, as in the twining petioles of *Tropaeolum* (nasturtium), but in most plants the modification is extensive. Stem tendrils are seen in *Vitis* (vines) and *Passiflora* (passionflower); leaf tendrils occur in *Gloriosa*, *Mutisia*, and in *Pisum sativum* (pea). Where the whole lamina is used up in tendril production, photosynthesis may be taken over by another structure, e.g. by laminate stipules in *Lathyrus aphaca* (yellow vetchling). In some plants the stipules may form the tendrils.

teratogen. An agent that damages or interferes with the normal development of unborn young. An example is thalidomide, a drug formerly prescribed to prevent nausea during pregnancy, which was found to prevent development of the limbs of the foetus. X-rays, which cause chromosome damage, are also teratogenic.

teratology. The study of animal or vegetable monstrosities (morphological abnormalities). It is often used to speculate on possible ancestral types and relationships.

teratoma. A tumour of embryonic origin, normally containing a number of different differentiated cell lines within it. An embryonic tumour that retains an invasive stem-cell population of relatively undifferentiated cells is known as a *teratocarcinoma*.

tergum. The plate or cuticle covering the dorsal surface of a body segment of an arthropod.

terminalization. The movement of chiasmata towards the ends of homologous chromosomes in metaphase I of *meiosis.

termites. *See* Isoptera.

terpenes. Lipids made up of five-carbon monomers, i.e. isoprene units ($-CH_2-C(CH_3):CHCH_2-$). The smaller molecules are found in plants and are responsible for the characteristic odours of geranium, mint, etc. Larger terpene molecules include phytol (a component of chlorophyll), vitamin A, squalene and lanosterol (precursors of cholesterol), carotenoids, and rubber.

territory. The particular part of a habitat that is held and defended by an animal or sometimes a group of animals of the same species. Territories ensure adequate spacing, food, and shelter for family groups and are usually most vigorously defended during or prior to the breeding season. Territorial behaviour, characterized by threatening displays and the attacking of intruders, is shown by some species of most classes of vertebrates, notably fish and birds, and by some arthropods.

Tertiary. The first period of the Cenozoic era, extending from 70 to 1 million years ago. It is the first period in which mammals are the dominant fauna and modern families of angiosperms are the dominant flora. The Tertiary is subdivided into the following epochs: Palaeocene, Eocene, Oligocene, Miocene, and Pliocene. The mammal fossils of these epochs show a gradation from primitive to advanced forms, and the angiosperms show increasing specialization.
The *Palaeocene* extended from 70 to 60 million years ago. Placental mammals appeared in such primitive forms as the creodonts (primitive carnivores) and condylarths (primitive herbivores).
The *Eocene*, extending from 60 to 40 million years ago, saw the appearance of the true ungulates and the first type of horse, eohippus (*Hyracotherium*), which was a small browser.
The *Oligocene* extended from 40 to 25 million years ago. The fossil fauna of this epoch is much more modern and archaic groups have disappeared. In many groups of mammals there is a trend to increased size and complexity. In the evolution of the horse, eohippus had evolved to the larger *Mesohippus* and *Miohippus*.
The *Miocene* extended from 25 to 11 million years ago and is characterized by a general drying of the climate,

which is reflected in the fossil fauna in many groups. For example the horses, such as *Merychippus*, were faster moving larger grazers compared with their small broad-footed ancestors. Many groups that could not adapt to the drier environment died out.
The *Pliocene* extended from 11 and 1 million years ago and ended with the onset of the Pleistocene Ice Age. Pliocene fossils are similar to modern types. *See also* geological time scale.

tertiary structure. The three-dimensional folding of a *protein molecule.

testa. The outer protective coat of the seed formed from the integument(s) of the ovule after fertilization or agamospermy. It is frequently sclerotic or fibrous.

test cross. The mating of an F_1 hybrid with a double recessive, often its double recessive parent. *See* back cross.

testis. The main reproductive organ of male animals. In vertebrates there is a pair of testes, which produce both spermatozoa and steroid hormones under the control of the pituitary *gonadotrophins.
In mammals and most other vertebrates the testis is composed of *seminiferous tubules*, which are lined with a *germinal epithelium* containing cells (*spermatogonia*) that produce haploid spermatozoa by meiosis (*see* spermatocyte, spermatid). The seminiferous tubules also contain larger *Sertoli cells*, which are thought to facilitate the development of the spermatozoa. Between the tubules lie *interstitial cells of Leydig*, which are the major androgen-producing cells of the testis. The endocrine function of the testis was first demonstrated in 1849, when Berthold showed that a capon (castrated cock) with a testis transplanted into its abdomen redeveloped male characteristics and behaviour. In most mammals the testes are found within a pouch of skin (*scrotum*) outside the abdominal cavity. This helps to maintain them at the optimal temperature (lower than

body temperature) for their development.

Testosterone

testosterone. The main natural *androgen produced and secreted by the mammalian testis (see formula); it was first isolated from bull testes by Laqueur in 1935. Testosterone is also an intermediate in the biosynthesis of oestrogens.

Tethys Ocean (Tethys Sea). The ancient ocean that surrounded Pangaea and later separated Gondwanaland and Laurasia. *See* continental drift.

tetracyclines. A group of antibiotics that includes tetracycline and chlortetracycline. They are derived from *Streptomyces* bacteria. Tetracycline molecules bind to the small subunit of bacterial ribosomes and block the binding of aminoacyl transfer RNAs, thus halting protein synthesis.

tetrad. The group of four haploid cells that is formed by meiosis of a diploid cell.

tetrad analysis. Analysis of the products of meiotic division, especially in haploid phases of such fungi as *Neurospora* and *Sordaria*. Such fungi produce an ordered sequence of spores within a long capsule, the position of the spores in a group of four representing the arrangement of chromosomes at the earlier meiotic division. Thus analysis of the genetic characteristics of the ordered spores can be used to reveal information about *crossing over during meiosis.

tetrahydrofolic acid. *See* folic acid.

tetraiodothyronine. *See* thyroid hormone.

tetraploid. (Designating) a nucleus, cell, or organism having four times the haploid chromosome number. If the haploid number is *n*, the tetraploid is 4*n*. Tetraploids can be produced by auto-polyploidy (*autotetraploids*) and by allo-polyploidy (*allotetraploids*) by doubling the diploid chromosome number. *See* polyploidy.

tetrapod. A member of the group of vertebrates having four limbs, i.e. the amphibians, reptiles, birds, and mammals. Tetrapods are primarily terrestrial animals and the tetrapod limb evolved as a walking leg. In some groups, however, the limbs have become secondarily specialized as flippers, wings, etc. *See also* pentadactyl limb.

tetrasporophyte. An independent asexual generation produced by some red algae, which develops from the carpospore (*see* carpogonium) and may be haploid or diploid according to species. It produces cells known as *tetrasporangia*, each giving rise to four *tetraspores* (by meiosis in diploid plants), which germinate to form the sexual haploid generation (*see also* Chantransia stage). Tetraspores may also be formed on the haploid sexual plants and are also produced by algae of other groups, such as the brown algae Dictyotales, as a means of asexual reproduction.

tetrose. A *monosaccharide with four carbon atoms, e.g. erythrose.

thalamus. 1. An elaboration of the grey matter of the posterior part of the forebrain of higher vertebrates, surrounding the third ventricle. It is concerned with the relay of sensory information to higher centres and with consciousness. *See also* hypothalamus.
2. *See* receptacle.

Thallophyta (in some classification schemes). One of the two major sub-kingdoms of plants (*compare* Embryophyta), including all those forms not differentiated into roots, stems, and leaves, i.e. whose plant body is a thallus. It comprises the bacteria, algae, fungi, and lichens.

thallus. A plant body that is not differentiated into roots, stems, and leaves and lacks a true vascular system. The term is applied to the plant body of the Thallophyta and also to parenchymatous and pseudoparenchymatous structures in higher plants, such as the pteridophyte gametophyte.

Thecodontia. An extinct order of reptiles of the subclass Archosauria that contains the earliest archosaurs, which appeared at the beginning of the Triassic and were extinct at its close. The suborder Pseudosuchia (e.g. the carnivorous *Euparkeria*) was a widespread and varied group with a definite trend towards bipedalism. It evolved into the later archosaurs, including the dinosaurs, and the birds. The suborder Phytosauria, whose members resembled crocodiles, were the dominant reptiles of the Upper Triassic.

Therapsida. An order of the Synapsida containing advanced mammal-like reptiles of the Permian and Triassic. The Anomodontia (Dicynodontia), e.g. *Moschops* and *Dicynodon*, were heavy herbivorous forms. The more advanced Theriodontia, from which the mammals evolved, contained a variety of active omnivorous and carnivorous reptiles, e.g. *Cynognathus* and *Thrinaxodon*, with teeth, limbs, and many other skeletal features resembling those of mammals. The Ictidosauria so closely resembled primitive mammals (the genus *Diarthrognathus* had both reptilian and mammalian types of jaw articulation) that they are sometimes classed as mammals.

thermal denaturation. Loss of structural conformation of a molecule induced by heating. Proteins and nucleic acids can be readily denatured by heating (as, for example, when the white of an egg hardens on boiling). Thermal denaturation of nucleic acids is used in technology involving hybridization and also in

determining *Cot values. *See also* denaturation.

thermonasty. Nastic movement in response to temperature. *See* nyctinastic movements.

thermophilic. Designating microorganisms that require an optimum temperature of 55–75°C for growth, with a minimum of 35–40°C. *Compare* mesophilic, psychrophilic.

therophyte (in *Raunkiaer's classification). A plant in which the dormant winter bud is situated inside the seed, the parent plant being dead. Annual plants are therophytes.

Thiamine

thiamine (vitamin B_1). A water-soluble vitamin (see formula), part of the *vitamin B complex, that serves as a precursor of the coenzyme *thiamine pyrophosphate*, which is involved in decarboxylation in carbohydrate metabolism. Most vertebrates and many microorganisms are unable to synthesize thiamine and it therefore has to be supplied from an external source. A deficiency of this vitamin in the diet of man leads to the disease beriberi.

thigmotropism. *See* haptotropism.

thoracic duct. A dorsal longitudinal lymphatic vessel that collects lymph from most of the body and empties into the posterior vena cava (or an associated vessel) close to the heart. The thoracic duct provides the main route by which lymph enters the bloodstream. It is single in mammals and paired in birds. In man it is about 0.5 metres long and extends up through the thorax close to the thoracic vertebrae, joining the bloodstream via the left innominate vein at the base of the neck.

thoracic vertebrae. The rib-bearing bones of the upper back region of the *vertebral column.

thorax. 1. The part of the body cavity of vertebrates in which the heart, lungs, and associated structures are suspended (*compare* abdomen). In mammals it is separated from the abdomen by the diaphragm.
2. The part of the body of arthropods that lies anterior to the abdomen. In insects it consists of three segments to which the wings and legs are attached. In crustaceans and arachnids it is often fused with the head to form the *cephalothorax*.

thorn. A sharply pointed rigid structure formed from a modified shoot (or root) whose apex is used up in its production, as in hawthorn. A whole branch system may become modified to form thorns so that the main axis, whose apex is a thorn, bears lateral branches that are also thorns, as in gorse. *Compare* prickle, spine.

thread cell. *See* cnidoblast.

threonine (thr). An amino acid, $CH_3CH(OH)CH(NH_2)COOH$, one of the 20 common amino acids found in proteins and an *essential amino acid for man.

threshold. The critical stimulus intensity that is just sufficient to initiate a response in an irritable tissue.

thrips. *See* Thysanoptera.

thrombin. A proteolytic enzyme, present only in blood removed from the circulation, that catalyses the conversion of fibrinogen to fibrin during *blood clotting. It is formed from an inactive precursor, prothrombin, which is present in normal plasma; the conversion is highly complex and requires many cofactors, the most important of which are calcium ions, thromboplastin, and platelets. The absence of thrombin in normal

blood appears to be the means by which its fluidity is preserved, as intravenous injection of thrombin results in immediate clotting.

thrombocyte. The former name for a *platelet, which was originally incorrectly thought to be a true cell.

thromboplastin. A protein that is responsible, together with certain other substances, for converting prothrombin into *thrombin during blood clotting. Thromboplastins are normally present in the brain, lung, placenta, testis, and other tissues and are formed in blood that has been removed from the circulation (usually by injury).

thylakoid. One of a number of flattened fluid-filled sacs that form the photosynthetic lamellar system of *chloroplasts, photosynthetic bacteria, and blue-green algae (*see* lamella). The thylakoid membranes contain the components of the light reactions of photosynthesis, including chlorophylls and other *photosynthetic pigments.

thymidine. A *nucleoside consisting of D-ribose and thymine linked with a β-glycoside bond.

Thymine

thymine. A pyrimidine base (see formula) that is an essential constituent of *DNA. *See also* nucleotide, nucleoside.

thymus gland. An irregular two-lobed gland that develops ventrally in the lower neck region of vertebrates from the third gill pouch. In mammals it consists primarily of epithelial cells, large numbers of rapidly dividing lymphocytes, and cells of suspected endocrine function. The thymus specifically controls cell-mediated immunity, homograft rejection, and hypersensitivity (or allergic) aspects of the immune response of the animal. Such effects were first clearly demonstrated in the early 1960s using mice that had been thymectomized at birth. Certain lymphocytes are either derived initially from the thymus or require its mediation (possibly via a hormone) before they are immunologically competent. Following sexual maturity the gland atrophies and is active only if the established lymphocyte pool is depleted.

thyrocalcitonin. *See* calcitonin.

thyroglobulin. *See* thyroid hormone.

thyroid gland. A paired endocrine gland of vertebrates that is formed in the embryo from ventral endoderm of the pharynx and is concerned primarily with regulation of the metabolic rate by the secretion of thyroid hormone. It probably evolved from the endostyle of protochordates and occurs as diffusely scattered tissue in some lower vertebrates (e.g. teleost fish). In mammals it consists of two lobes on either side of the trachea, joined anteriorly by an isthmus of tissue. Histologically it is composed of follicles of variable size that are lined with secretory epithelium, contain a colloidal substance, and are embedded in vascular connective tissue. The mammalian thyroid also contains *C-cells, which secrete calcitonin. Normal growth of the gland and secretion of thyroid hormone requires trace amounts of iodine in the diet and stimulation by *thyrotrophin.

HO—⟨benzene ring⟩—O—⟨benzene ring⟩—CH_2—CH—COOH with NH_2

Thyroxine

thyroid hormone. Either (or both) of two iodine-containing amino acid hormones secreted by the follicles of the vertebrate thyroid gland. Thyroid hormones are synthesized from a large precursor protein, *thyroglobulin*, in the colloidal substance of the follicles. Thyroglobulin is hydrolysed into various *iodotyrosines*, some of which are coupled together by specific enzymes to form *iodothyronines*, which are secreted. Of these, only *thyroxine* (*tetraiodothyronine*; see formula) and *3,5,3'-triiodothyronine* have biological activity. Evidence suggests that triiodothyronine is the active form and thyroxine is metabolized to this form in the target tissues. Both hormones produce a large number of metabolic effects on many tissues; in particular they increase oxygen consumption and energy production (they probably interact synergistically with growth hormone, adrenal corticosteroids, and adrenaline in producing these effects). Thyroid hormone also stimulates developmental changes, such as moulting and metamorphosis; its effect on precocious metamorphosis in the amphibian tadpole has been known since 1912. Thyroid hormone effects involve RNA and protein or enzyme synthesis.

thyrotrophin (thyroid-stimulating hormone, TSH). A glycoprotein hormone, secreted by the pars distalis of the mammalian pituitary gland and homologous tissue of other vertebrates, that stimulates the growth of the thyroid gland, its uptake of iodine, and the secretion of its hormones. It consists of two large peptide subunits, one of which is similar to those of the glycoprotein pituitary gonadotrophins (LH and FSH).

thyroxine. *See* thyroid hormone.

Thysanoptera. The order of exopterygote insects that contains the thrips. These tiny insects, universally distributed, have piercing and sucking mouthparts and mostly feed on plant sap. They are serious plant pests, both damaging plants and transmitting diseases. The eggs, which are either attached to the surface of the plant or inserted in the tissues, hatch into nymphs that also suck sap.

Thysanura. An order of primitive wingless insects of the subclass Apterygota, the three-pronged bristletails. They are characterized by a tapering body often covered with scales, long antennae, biting mouthparts, and three long tail bristles. The order includes the silverfish (*Lepisma saccharina)* and firebrat (*Thermobia domestica*), which inhabit houses and bakeries, feeding on starch.

tibia. 1. The main supportive bone of the lower section of the tetrapod rear limb. *See also* pentadactyl limb.
2. The fourth segment from the base of an insect's leg.

ticks. *See* Acari.

tight junction. *See* junctional complex.

tissue. A collection or aggregation of adherent cells and associated intercellular substances that is specialized to perform a particular function or functions. Combinations of tissues make up the organs of multicellular organisms. The cells comprising a tissue may be of the same type, e.g. the neurones of nervous tissue, or of mixed type, e.g. the fibroblasts, histiocytes, mast cells, macrophages, etc., of connective tissue.

tissue culture (explantation). The growth in a suitable medium of pieces of tissue removed from a living animal or plant. The medium is often *Ringer's solution supplied with oxygen and nutrients and kept free of microorganisms. A similar medium is used for the culture of organs.

titre. An assessment of the amount of antibody present in serum. It is estimated from the highest dilution of the serum at which agglutination by antigen-antibody reaction will still occur to a detectable extent and is expressed as the reciprocal of this dilution.

TMV. *See* tobacco mosaic virus.

toads. *See* Anura.

tobacco mosaic virus (TMV). A rodshaped plant virus consisting of a helical array of 2130 identical protein molecules in which is wound a single-stranded RNA molecule, 6500 nucleotides long. TMV was the first virus to be discovered.

tocopherol. *See* vitamin E.

tone (tonus). The state of partial contraction of a muscle, maintained by reflex activity. Tonic reflexes constitute the basic mechanism of posture control.

tonoplast. The bounding membrane of plant cell *vacuoles. Usually 5–7 nm thick, it is often thinner and stronger than the plasma membrane.

tonsils. Small bodies of dense lymphoid tissue, found in many vertebrates, that are situated at the rear of the mouth (*palatine tonsils*), the back of the tongue (*lingual tonsils*), and at the rear of the nose (*pharyngeal tonsils*). Histologically they appear as deep indentations of the surface epithelium (crypts), which are surrounded by diffuse lymphatic tissue and dense lymphatic nodules. Tonsils participate in the production of lymphocytes and are situated at the beginnings of efferent lymphatic vessels.

tornaria. The planktonic larva of the Hemichordata, which resembles the bipinnaria larva of the Asteroidea (*see* dipleurula) in having pre- and postoral ciliated bands for feeding, but differs in having an additional lower band around the anus for locomotion. As in echinoderms, cleavage is radial and the coelom arises from hollow mesodermal pouches. These similarities in development indicate a relationship between the chordates and echinoderms.

tortoises. *See* Chelonia.

torus. 1. A thickening on the pit membrane of pit pairs (*see* pits) in certain gymnosperms. It forms part of the primary wall structure and is slightly larger than the internal aperture of the pits. The thinner margin round the torus formed from the rest of the pit membrane is termed the *margo*. On death or injury to the tracheid on one side of the pit pair, the loss of pressure causes the torus to be displaced and to block the aperture on that side. This prevents loss of water to dead cells and helps prevent the spread of disease.

2. *See* receptacle.

totipotent. Designating embryonic cells at a stage before they become irreversibly differentiated. A totipotent cell has the capacity to develop into any differentiated cell of the organism it belongs to if suitably stimulated.

TPN (triphosphopyridine nucleotide). The former name of NADP. *See* NAD.

trabecula. A slender bar of tissue or other material across a cavity in plant or animal tissues and organs. Among plants, trabeculae include the multicellular bars that stretch across the sporangial lumen in *Isoetes* and the bars of wall material extending between the tangential walls in the lumina of certain gymnosperm tracheids. In animals, trabeculae, in the form of a pair of cartilaginous bars, constitute the anterior part of the floor of the embryonic vertebrate cranium. Trabeculae also form the meshwork of spongy bone.

trace element. An element required in minute amounts by an organism for healthy growth (i.e. a *micronutrient*). A total lack of certain elements (*essential trace elements*) eventually causes death. These elements are required mainly as components of enzymes or for activation of enzymes. Essential trace elements of plants include copper, zinc, molybdenum, manganese, and boron. *Compare* macronutrient (essential element).

tracer. *See* radioactive labelling.

trachea. 1. The windpipe of vertebrates. It consists of a single tube leading from the larynx and carrying air through the neck region to the lungs, where it divides to form the bronchi. It is supported by incomplete rings of cartilage and lined with a ciliated mucous membrane. In birds the posterior end is specialized to form the *syrinx.

2. One of the branching invaginations of the body wall in insects through which air diffuses directly to the tissues. Larger tracheae are supported by rings of chitin. Each trachea opens to the exterior by a *spiracle and terminates in fine fluid-filled *tracheoles*, which ramify among the tissues. Transport of oxygen through the tracheae occurs by diffusion; in larger insects this is assisted by active pumping of the abdomen and longitudinal connections between the tracheae may permit circulation of the air. Tracheae may also occur in some other terrestrial arthropods, e.g. arachnids.

3. A xylem vessel (*see* vessel elements).

tracheary elements. Certain lignified cells in the xylem. Strictly the term refers only to the tracheids and vessels (from the type of secondary wall thickening they show), but now it is commonly used to include fibres, fibre-tracheids, tracheids, and vessel elements. Because of the gradation in form between fibres, fibre-tracheids, and tracheids, these are sometimes grouped together as *imperforate tracheary elements*.

tracheid. An elongated empty lignified *tracheary element with somewhat tapered ends and bordered pits that forms part of the vertical system of the xylem and is concerned with water conduction and mechanical support. It is regarded as the fundamental cell of the xylem from which fibres, fibre-tracheids, and vessel elements have evolved, and in more primitive tracheophytes it forms the only type of water-conducting and mechanical cell in the wood. Cells termed *ray tracheids*, which have very thick lignified walls but are otherwise similar to the ray parenchyma cells, occur in the medullary rays of some plants.

Tracheophyta. Vascular plants: one of the two groups of *Embryophyta. They are characterized by the possession of specialized *vascular tissue (xylem and phloem) for the translocation of substances around the plant body. The sporophyte is always the dominant generation and the one in which the vascular tissues are developed. The group contains four subdivisions: the *Psilopsida (which includes the earliest tracheophytes), *Lycopsida, *Sphenopsida, and *Pteropsida (which, in its broadest sense, includes the Pterophyta (ferns), Gymnospermae, and Angiospermae).

trait. A characteristic, particularly the phenotypic manifestation of a single gene.

trama. The hyphal tissue in a basidiomycete fruit body that forms the pileus and bears the hymenium.

$$\text{aspartate} + \underset{\text{glutarate}}{\alpha-\text{keto}} \underset{\overset{\longrightarrow}{\underset{\longleftarrow}{\text{phosphate}}}}{\overset{\text{pyridoxal}}{}} \text{oxaloacetic} + \text{glutamic acid acid}$$

$$
\begin{array}{llll}
CH_2COOH & CH_2COOH & CH_2COOH & CH_2COOH \\
\; \mid \underset{}{\diagup}COO^- & \; \mid & \; \mid & \; \mid \\
C & CH_2 & C \!-\!\! COOH & CH_2 \\
\; \mid \diagdown_H & \; \mid & \; \parallel & \; \mid \\
NH_3 & C \!-\!\! COOH & O & CH \\
& \; \parallel & & NH_2 \diagdown COOH \\
& O & &
\end{array}
$$

A representative transamination

transamination. The enzymic transfer of an amino group $(-NH_2)$ from an amino acid to a keto acid with the production of a second keto acid and amino acid. The coenzyme for all transaminase enzymes is *pyridoxal phosphate*. The amino group is transferred to the coenzyme to form pyridoxamine phosphate, which in turn transfers the amino group to the keto acid. A representative transamination catalysed by glutamate transaminase is illustrated.

trans **configuration.** The location of two alleles on different chromosomes, thus permitting complementation in the *cistrans test.

transcriptase. An RNA *polymerase. *Compare* reverse transcriptase.

transcription. The transfer of information in the form of nucleotide sequences from DNA to RNA. A single strand of DNA acts as a template for the synthesis of a complementary RNA sequence, the synthesis being catalysed by DNA-dependent RNA polymerase. Genes coding for ribosomal RNA or transfer RNA are transcribed into a precursor RNA, which is modified to yield the final RNA. DNA sequences coding for protein, i.e. structural genes (*or* *cistrons) are transcribed initially into heterogeneous nuclear RNA (*HnRNA), which is processed after transcription by removal of introns to yield the final product, *messenger RNA. Transcription involves no elementary change to the coding language, i.e. the sequence of bases is the coding information. This contrasts with the process of *translation, which involves conversion of the nucleotide code to a radically different amino acid code.

transduction. The transfer of DNA from one bacterium to another by a bacteriophage. Some of the host's DNA becomes incorporated into the viral DNA of the phage, which is released on lysis of the host cell. On infecting another bacterial cell, the transducing phage introduces this bacterial DNA, which may be incorporated into the new host's genome. In *generalized transduction* the vector phage is likely to carry a randomly selected piece of the host cell DNA; in *specialized transduction* the phage carries a specific gene or group of genes from the host cell DNA. *See also* abortive transduction.

transect. A line marked off within an area undergoing an ecological survey. By measuring the composition of the organisms (usually plants) at different points along the line, variations in the flora and fauna of the whole area can be determined.

transfection. The introduction of naked DNA into recipient cells, which may be mammalian cells in tissue culture or bacterial cells.

transferase. One of a group of enzymes that catalyse reactions in which substances other than hydrogen are transferred. This group forms one of the main groups used in *enzyme classification; it has the code number E.C.2.

transfer cell. A plant cell whose secondary walls, and hence also plasma membrane, are greatly increased in surface area by extensive, often branched, ingrowths. The significance of transfer cells is related to their wide occurrence at sites of absorption or secretion, where high rates of flow of solutes over short distances are required. For instance, they probably participate in the unloading of xylem vessels and the loading of phloem sieve elements in certain leaves and stems and they often feature in exchange between embryo and parent in flowering plants. They may also be secretory, as in nectaries and other glands (e.g. glands of insectivorous plants). Various cell types can function as transfer cells, which typically contain numerous mitochondria and a well-developed endoplasmic reticulum.

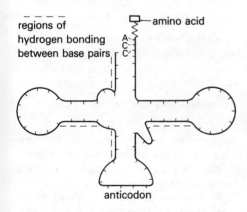

General structure of a tRNA molecule

transfer RNA (tRNA, soluble RNA, sRNA). A type of RNA, 70–80 nucleotides long, that acts as an adaptor for matching an amino acid to its correct codon in messenger RNA during *translation. Each amino acid combines with a specific amino-acyl tRNA synthetase in a reaction requiring ATP; the activated synthetase complex then reacts

with a specific tRNA molecule giving amino-acyl tRNA. tRNA has a sedimentation value of 4S and a three-dimensional structure resembling a clover leaf (see illustration). All tRNAs have three regions of common nucleotide sequences: a terminal sequence (adenine-cytosine-cytosine) to which the specific amino acid is attached, a sequence that is believed to interact with the ribosome, and a centrally located complementary anticodon that pairs with the appropriate codon of messenger RNA during translation on the ribosome.

transformation. 1. A permanent genetic change in a cell following its acquisition of new DNA. The process was originally observed in bacteria: the classic experiment of Griffith in 1928, in which living nonvirulent bacteria acquired the property of virulence from dead bacteria in the same culture, was the first recognized example of transformation. In 1944 Avery, MacLeod, and McCarty demonstrated that the 'transforming principle' was DNA. Cells other than bacteria can also be transformed, but less easily than bacteria.
2. A permanent inherited change in a cell or cells in tissue culture. It is seen as a change in properties of growth and adhesiveness to neighbouring cells in culture and it involves changes similar to those associated with tumour formation. Some transformed cells are clearly malignant. Transformation is often associated with the growth of viruses in the tissue culture cells but may also result from the action of other agents.

transition. A mutation in which one purine or pyrimidine is converted into another, leading to a AT↔GC base-pair change. *Compare* transversion.

transition zone. *See* hypocotyl.

translation. The conversion of the sequence of nucleotides in a molecule of messenger RNA (mRNA) into a corresponding sequence of amino acids in a polypeptide chain, a stage in *protein synthesis. The process occurs on the ribosomes, several to many of which are usually attached to a single molecule of mRNA, forming a polysome. Each triplet of nucleotides (*codon) in the mRNA determines a single amino acid. Each amino acid is bonded to a specific molecule of *transfer RNA (tRNA); base pairing occurs between the appropriate codon of the mRNA and the anticodon of the tRNA, during which the amino acid is added to the growing polypeptide chain on the ribosome.

translocation. 1. The movement and circulation of substances within multicellular plants via conducting tissues (xylem and phloem in vascular plants). The xylem conducts mainly water, mineral salts, and organic nitrogen (mostly as amino acids and amides), principally from the roots to the aerial organs in the transpiration stream (*see* transpiration). Inorganic nitrogen taken up by the roots from the soil is mostly converted to organic nitrogen in the roots before translocation. Phloem conducts relatively large quantities of sugar as sucrose, which is made in photosynthetic tissues, mainly leaves (the *source*), and is translocated to growth or storage regions (the *sinks*). Phloem also conducts sugar phosphates, some organic nitrogen, vitamins, growth substances (e.g. auxin), and some inorganic ions. Rates of movement in phloem are relatively rapid (up to 100 cm per hour is common), but the mechanism of this translocation is still uncertain (*see* mass flow).
2. A type of chromosome mutation in which a section of chromosome breaks off and is replaced in an abnormal position, either on the same chromosome or on a different one. For example a translocation in a chromosome containing the genes ABCDEFGH might lead to section CDE breaking off and either being transferred to the end of the chromosome, resulting in the gene sequence ABFGHCDE, or being attached to a different chromosome.

transmitter. *See* neurotransmitter.

transpiration. The loss of water vapour from the surface of a plant. It occurs mainly through the stomata of leaves (usually from the walls of turgid mesophyll cells lining spaces called *substomatal cavities*), but can also occur slowly through cuticles (*cuticular transpiration*). Water loss results in movement of water through the plant in the *transpiration stream*, since water is continuous throughout the plant, from the soil via the roots and xylem to the transpiring organs. Water moves down gradients of *water potential, from high potentials in the soil and roots to low potentials in the leaves and surrounding atmosphere. Transpiration is influenced by environmental conditions and, providing stomata are open (necessary for gaseous exchange), is inevitable. This can lead to deleterious effects when transpiration is rapid (e.g. with low humidities, high temperatures, air turbulence) and water loss exceeds water uptake from the soil: wilting and eventual death may occur. Stomata usually close in response to wilting. *Compare* guttation.

transplantation. The transfer of a tissue or organ from one individual either to another part of the same individual or to a different individual. *See* graft.

transplantation antigen. *See* histocompatibility antigen.

transposon. A DNA element that has the ability to insert itself into other DNA sequences; plasmids and the genomes of bacteria and some eukaryotic cells are known to harbour transposons. Most transposons possess special insertion sequences (*see* insertion element), which facilitate entry into another DNA sequence. Transposons often carry genes that are involved in the insertion process, but their most significant effect is that of disturbing the expression of the genes with which they become associated.

transverse process. A lateral projection on each side of the neural arch of the vertebrae in tetrapods on which the rib, if present, articulates.

transversion. A mutation in which a purine is converted to a pyrimidine or *vice versa*, resulting in an AT↔TA, GC↔CG, or AT↔CG base-pair change. *Compare* transition.

Trematoda. A class of parasitic platyhelminths, the flukes, in which the body is covered with a thick cuticle, bears suckers for attachment to the host, and has a forked gut. The Trematoda contains the orders Monogenea: ectoparasites with only one host and a rapid life cycle, and the Digenea, e.g. *Schistosoma* (blood fluke) and *Fasciola* (liver fluke): endoparasites with a complex life cycle (*see* cercaria, miracidium, redia) and more than one host. These orders are sometimes regarded as separate classes.

Triassic (Trias). The first period of the Mesozoic era, extending from 225 to 180 million years ago. It was named after the German strata of this period, which are divided into three groups. In many places the Triassic system grades into the Permian and the two can be considered as a single system: the *Permo-Triassic* (or *Permo-Trias*). *See* Permian.

tribe. A unit used in the classification of plants as a subdivision of the subfamily (*see* family). It is used only in very large families. The name of the tribe ends in -eae and is derived from one member of the tribe. In the Compositae, for example, the subfamily Carduoideae consists of ten tribes; one of these is the Astereae, which contains the genera *Aster*, *Bellis* (daisy), *Erigeron* (midsummer daisy), etc.

tricarboxylic acid cycle. *See* Krebs cycle.

trichogyne. An elongated protuberance for the reception of the male gamete, produced from the female sexual organs of the red algae and some ascomycete fungi (including most Discomycetes and the Laboulbeniales).

trichome. A specialized epidermal outgrowth of vascular plants. It includes all hairs and derivatives of hairs, such as glands, papillae, and prickles. Trichomes are entirely epidermal in origin and have no vascular supply.

Trichoptera. An order of endopterygote insects, the caddis flies (e.g. *Phryganea*). These mothlike insects, which are found near fresh water, differ from the Lepidoptera chiefly in their wings, which are covered with hairs (rather than scales). The mouthparts are reduced and the adults of many species do not feed. The aquatic larvae (*caddis worms*) are herbivorous or carnivorous and have biting mouthparts. Most caddis worms build protective cases around themselves of sand, pebbles, leaves, etc.; some spin silken webs to trap their prey.

Triconodonta. An extinct order of late Triassic to Cretaceous mammals containing both small mouse-sized insectivores and larger types such as *Triconodon*, which was probably a true carnivore. Triconodonts had long jaws with numerous teeth, including shearing molars bearing a row of three strong conical cusps.

tricuspid valve. A valve comprising three membranous flaps between the atrium and ventricle of the right side of the mammalian heart.

trigeminal nerve. *See* cranial nerves.

trigger plant. A plant whose stamens, on the alighting of a visiting insect, suddenly bend so that the insect is tapped with the anther and covered in a layer of pollen. A certain amount of time must elapse for the stamen to recover its erect position before it will respond again.

triglyceride (triacyl glycerol). A fatty-acid ester of glycerol that is the major component of plant and animal fat. *See* glyceride.

triiodothyronine. *See* thyroid hormone.

Trilobita. A class of extinct marine bottom-dwelling Arthropoda, abundant from the Cambrian to the Silurian. The oval flattened body was divided longitudinally into three lobes and transversely into a head, thorax, and abdomen. The head bore a pair of compound eyes, a pair of antennae, and four pairs of jointed forked appendages with a inner projection used as an aid in feeding. There were numerous similar paired appendages on the body. Trilobites are thought to have been closely related to the ancestors of other arthropods, particularly the Crustacea.

triose. A *monosaccharide with three carbon atoms, e.g. glyceraldehyde.

triploblastic. Designating animals with three embryonic cell layers: ectoderm, endoderm, and mesoderm. All the Metazoa are triploblastic with the exception of the Coelenterata, which are diploblastic.

triploid. (Designating) a nucleus, cell, or organism having three times the haploid chromosome number. If the haploid number is n, the triploid is $3n$. Triploid organisms are usually ·sterile. See polyploidy.

trisomy. The condition in which one or more chromosomes are represented three times in a nucleus, cell, or organism, so that the diploid chromosome complement is $2n + 1$, where n is the haploid number. *Down's syndrome in man is caused by chromosome 21 being present three times, resulting in a chromosome number of 47 rather than 46. See also aneuploidy.

tritium (^{3}H). An unstable *isotope of hydrogen with an atomic mass of 3 (the atomic nucleus contains 1 proton and 2 neutrons). Tritium has a half-life of 12.26 years and undergoes radioactive decay to yield a stable helium isotope, ^{3}He, with the emission of a beta particle:

$$^3_1H \rightarrow \; ^3_2He + \beta-$$

Tritium is of particular use in autoradiography since the beta emission is of very low energy and electrons cannot travel far from the point of their origin in a photographic emulsion.

trochanter. 1. One of several knobs on the proximal end of the tetrapod femur to which the extensor and flexor muscles of the leg attach.
2. The second segment from the base of the leg of an insect.

trochlear nerve. See cranial nerves.

trochophore. The planktonic larva of the Polychaeta, Mollusca, and some other invertebrates. It is spherical, with a mouth on the equator and an L-shaped gut with the anus underneath. Two main bands of cilia encircle the body above and below the mouth and there is often a third band around the anus. The cilia are used in feeding and for locomotion, producing a spinning movement. Cleavage is spiral and the coelom arises as splits in the mesoderm.

trophic level. See food chain.

trophoblast. A layer of extraembryonic nutritional epithelium formed around the blastocyst of mammals. It forms the outer layer of the chorion (see extraembryonic membranes), attaches the ovum to the uterine wall, and absorbs nutrients for the early embryo.

tropism (tropic movement). A directional growth movement of part of a plant in response to a directional stimulus (one that comes from a particular direction or is greater from one direction than another). It is one of the three types of *paratonic movements. A growth curvature is brought about by relatively faster growth on one side of the organ. Growth towards the stimulus (i.e. the side nearest the stimulus grows more slowly) is a *positive tropism*; the opposite response is a *negative tropism*. If, at equilibrium, the organ is aligned with the stimulus, the organ is *orthotropic*; if at an angle to the stimulus, it is *plagiotropic*. Tropisms are of necessity confined to younger actively growing organs. Sedentary animals sometimes exhibit tropisms. *See* chemotropism, geotropism, haptotropism, hydrotropism, phototropism.

troponin and tropomyosin. Proteins occurring in the I filament of *striated muscle cells. They inhibit contraction in the absence of calcium. *See also* excitation-contraction coupling.

trypsin. A protease of the vertebrate gut, secreted by the pancreas as the inactive form, trypsinogen, which is activated by *enteropeptidase.

trypsinogen. A low-activity protease secreted by the pancreas. Removal of a length of polypeptide by the enzyme *enteropeptidase converts trypsinogen to the high-activity form, trypsin.

Tryptophan

tryptophan (trp). An amino acid (see formula), one of the 20 common amino acids occurring in proteins and an *essential amino acid for man. Tryptophan is a precursor of indole compounds such as IAA (indoleacetic acid) and serotonin.

TSH (thyroid-stimulating hormone). *See* thyrotrophin.

tuatara. *See* Rhynchocephalia.

tube feet. Elongated outgrowths from the body wall of all members of the phylum Echinodermata. Tube feet can be protruded or retracted by alterations in the fluid pressure of the water vascular system (part of the coelom), with which they are continuous. The Crinoidea (feather stars) and Ophiuroidea (brittle stars) normally have pointed tube feet used for feeding while the Asteroidea (starfish), Echinoidea (urchins), and Holothuroidea (sea cucumbers) possess mostly suckered tube feet for locomotion. Tube feet also serve other functions, such as burrowing, mucus production, sensation, and respiration.

tube nucleus. *See* pollen tube.

tuber. An organ of perennation and vegetative propagation in plants. A *stem tuber*, such as the potato, is the swollen food-storing underground end of a stem, at the tip of a thin rhizome. One old tuber produces at least one plant from its terminal bud, which grows using the food stored in the tuber; at the end of the season this plant produces many tubers, each of which can produce at least one plant: thus reproduction has occurred. In some cases several buds on one tuber grow to produce plants. A *root tuber* is a swollen food-storing adventitious root, as in dahlia and lesser celandine. The plant dies down over winter and grows the following season from a terminal bud on the stem borne at the tip of the root tuber. Vegetative reproduction occurs if several buds grow, but these are usually buds on the stem, not on the root itself.

Tubulidentata. An order of the Eutheria containing a single genus, *Orycteropus* (aardvark or African anteater), a nocturnal burrowing termite-eating mammal. *Orycteropus* has a long narrow head and snout, with nostrils that can be closed; a long tongue for collecting termites; large salivary glands; and strongly clawed feet for digging. Incisors and canines are absent and the remaining peglike rootless teeth are of unique composition.

tumour (neoplasm). A swelling in an organism resulting from the abnormal or uncontrolled proliferation of cells. Tumours that do not invade and destroy other parts of the body are described as *benign*; those that do are termed *malignant* (*see* cancer).

tunica-corpus theory. The theory of Schmidt (1924) proposing that the *apical meristem of vascular plants consists of two parts, each with its own separate initials: an outer *tunica* of one or more layers, characterized by anticlinal cell divisions, and an inner *corpus*, in which cell division occurs in various planes. Since Schmidt first put the theory forward it has been modified a number of times, and as more plants are studied it has become more difficult to define and delimit the two parts. However, the terms are still used in describing apex growth patterns.

Tunicata. *See* Urochordata.

Turbellaria. A class of small free-living mostly aquatic and bottom-living Platyhelminthes, the planarians, in which the body is covered with cilia for locomotion and the mouth and pharynx are on the ventral surface. The most primitive order is the Acoela, in which a gut and excretory system are absent. In the Rhabdocoela the gut is straight and unbranched; in the Tricladida it is three-branched; and in the Polycladida it has many branches.

turbidimetry. The measurement of *turbidity, used to estimate cell numbers in bacterial cultures.

turbidity (of liquid bacterial cultures). The degree of cloudiness, determined by the concentration of bacteria present. A bacteriophage plaque may be turbid if many bacterial host cells remain intact, as is normally the case for a temperate phage.

turgor. The state of maximum turgidity of a plant or prokaryote cell when it cannot expand further through admission of water. Such a cell is said to be *turgid*. When water enters the cell by osmosis the cell volume increases. The outwardly directed pressure exerted by the swelling protoplast against the cell wall is called the *turgor pressure*; the equal and opposite counter pressure exerted by the wall on the protoplast is the *wall pressure*. Turgor pressure builds up rapidly because the cell wall is only slightly elastic and is soon stretched rigid. Entry of water ceases when the turgor pressure compensates for the difference in *water potentials of the cell

solution and the solution outside it. The osmotic pressure of the cell remains virtually constant since little water is required for a large increase in turgor pressure. Turgor pressure is necessary for maintenance of form and mechanical support of succulent plant parts such as leaves, flowers, and young stems; for expansion of growing cells; and opening of stomata and of many flower parts. It probably also plays a role in phloem translocation by causing mass flow of solutions.

turion. An organ of perennation found in many water plants. It is a winter bud, typically covered in mucilage, that detaches from the parent plant and spends the winter at the bottom of a pond. *Compare* bulbil.

Turner's syndrome. A syndrome involving reduced stature, webbing of the neck, infertility, and some degree of mental retardation in the human female, resulting from a *sex chromosome anomaly. Affected individuals have a sex chromosome constitution of XO, rather than the normal XX, and lack a *Barr body. This would seem to indicate that the Barr body of normal females must play a role in normal development and is probably not heterochromatic (*see* heterochromatin) in embryonic life.

turtles. *See* Chelonia.

tusk shells. *See* Scaphopoda.

tylose. A ballooning of a parenchyma cell via the pit pairs into the lumen of a tracheary element, occurring when the latter becomes inactive or following injury. Tyloses may be abundant enough to block the lumen of the element and their walls may remain thin or become lignified. Their production is probably mechanical, due to a decrease of pressure in the tracheary lumen, but they appear to be functional; for example, they prevent the spread of fungal and other infections.

tympanic cavity. *See* middle ear.

tympanum (tympanic membrane, ear drum). A thin membrane, consisting of fibrous tissue bounded by epithelia, that stretches across the external opening of the tetrapod *middle ear and vibrates in response to sound waves.

type specimen. *See* holotype.

tyrosine (tyr). An amino acid, $(OH)C_6H_4CH_2CH(NH_2)COOH$, one of the 20 common *amino acids occurring in proteins. Tyrosine is important as a precursor of noradrenaline, adrenaline, melanin, thyroid hormone, isoquinoline alkaloids (e.g. papaverine), and opium alkaloids (e.g. morphine).

U

ubiquinone. *See* coenzyme Q.

ubiquitin. An acidic protein that is widely distributed in different types of cells and organisms. It has a highly conserved amino acid sequence and an affinity for histones and chromatin. Ubiquitin is a small globular protein and may have a universal role in the structure of chromatin and chromosomes.

ulna. One of the two long bones of the lower region of the tetrapod forelimb (*compare* radius). It carries many muscle attachments, notably those for the forelimb extensors, on the olecranon process. It bears little weight and in some species is fused with the radius. *See* pentadactyl limb.

ultimobranchial bodies. A pair of glandular bodies in lower vertebrates that are derived from *C-cells and secrete calcitonin.

ultracentrifuge. An instrument in which solutions or tissue homogenates can be subjected to carefully controlled and intense centrifugal forces of several hundred thousand times gravitational force. The effect of this high-speed centrifugation is to sediment cells, subcellular particles, and macromolecules rapidly according to their size, shape, density, and molecular weight. Molecular weights of proteins and nucleic acids may be determined from the rate of sedimentation of the molecule, especially by the use of density gradients in which the molecules under study can be sedimented to an equilibrium position in the gradient, equivalent to the precise density of the molecular species (*see* density gradient centrifugation). The first ultracentrifuge was constructed by Svedberg in 1925.

ultramicrotome. *See* microtome.

ultrastructure (fine structure). The structure of a cell or tissue at the molecular level or at the microscopic level using resolutions unobtainable with the visual spectrum, e.g. as observed using an electron microscope.

ultraviolet fluorescence microscopy. *See* microscope.

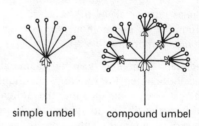

simple umbel   compound umbel

Umbels

umbel. A type of racemose inflorescence in which the flowers occur in flat-topped clusters with their pedicels arising from the same point on the main axis, like the spokes of an umbrella. The oldest flowers in the inflorescence are to the outside and the youngest are in the centre. This type of inflorescence is found mainly in the family Umbelliferae. Many umbels are compound, and the stalks that bear the flower clus-

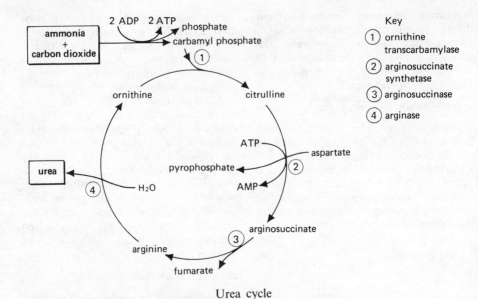

Urea cycle

ters themselves arise from the same point on the main axis, e.g. carrot, cow parsley, hogweed (see illustration).

umbilical cord. The connection between the embryo and the placenta in pregnant mammals. It consists of mesodermal connective tissue enclosing arteries and veins of the allantois but also includes part or all of the yolk sac. It is surrounded by the amnion. *See* extraembryonic membranes.

ungulate. A hoofed grazing mammal, typically adapted for running. The limbs and feet are elongated and the animal walks on the tips of its digits, which are reduced in number. This type of locomotion is called *unguligrade*. The molars have ridged cusps and are specialized for grinding vegetation. The Ungulata, a group no longer in taxonomic use, formerly included a wide variety of mammals that had evolved independently and were probably not closely related. The term is now usually restricted to the orders *Perissodactyla (odd-toed ungulates) and *Artiodactyla (even-toed ungulates).

unguligrade. Designating a gait of mammals in which the weight of the body is borne on the tips of the digits. It is characteristic of the *ungulates. *Compare* digitigrade, plantigrade.

unicellular. Designating organisms or parts that consist of one cell only. Unicellular organisms include the Protozoa and some algae.

unisexual. (Designating) a plant or animal species that bears either male or female reproductive organs but not both. *Compare* hermaphrodite.

Uracil

uracil. A pyrimidine base (see formula) that is an essential constituent of *RNA. *See also* nucleotide, nucleoside.

urea. A nitrogen-containing water-soluble organic compound, H_2NCONH_2, that is the main nitrogenous excretory product of the catabolism of amino acids in *ureotelic animals. Urea is produced in the liver via the *urea* (or *ornithine*) *cycle* (see illustration).

uredium. A sorus of sporogenous hyphae producing unicellular *uredospores* (*brand spores*), occurring in some Heterobasidiomycetes, including the *rusts and *smuts. Uredospores are produced on dikaryotic hyphae (*see* hetèrokaryosis) and serve as asexual diaspores.

ureotelic. Designating animals that excrete most excess nitrogen, derived from the catabolism of amino acids, in the form of urea. Ureotelic animals include elasmobranchs, amphibians, and mammals. *Compare* uricotelic.

ureter. The duct draining the metanephric kidney of amniotes. It is formed from an evagination at the junction of the cloaca and Wolffian duct that enters the metanephros and discharges excretory matter into the cloaca (in reptiles and birds) or bladder (in mammals).
The term is also applied to the kidney duct of other vertebrates.

urethra. The duct of mammals that conveys urine from the bladder to the exterior. In male mammals it is also connected to the vasa deferentia and serves as a channel for both urine and spermatozoa (*see* penis).

uric acid. An end product of purine degradation, also the main nitrogenous excretory product of the catabolism of amino acids in *uricotelic animals. It is almost insoluble in water. Persons suffering from gout usually have abnormally high levels of uric acid in the blood; in these cases the uric acid precipitates out in various parts of the body, notably around the joints of the fingers and toes, which become painful and swollen.

uricotelic. Designating animals that excrete most excess nitrogen, derived from the catabolism of amino acids and nucleic acids, in the form of uric acid. Birds are uricotelic. *Compare* ureotelic.

uridine. A *nucleoside consisting of D-ribose and uracil linked with a β-glycoside bond.

urine. The liquid produced in the kidneys and excreted through the urethra or cloaca. Urine typically consists of a solution of nitrogenous excretory products (mainly urea or uric acid), cations (e.g. sodium, calcium, magnesium), and anions (e.g. chloride, phosphate, and sulphate). Many other substances occur in the urine in smaller quantities, including the yellow pigment *urochrome*, amino acids, and purine bases.

uriniferous tubule (kidney tubule). A narrow convoluted tube forming part of the unit (*nephron*) of the vertebrate *kidney. Substances filtered from the blood at the Malpighian body pass down the tubule and are concentrated (by selective reabsorption) into urine, which drains into the Wolffian duct or ureter. The long hairpin-shaped portion of the tubule in reptiles, birds, and mammals is known as the *loop of Henle*.

Urochordata (Tunicata). A marine subphylum of the Chordata in which the chordate characteristics of notochord, dorsal tubular nerve cord, and pharyngeal gill slits are clearly seen only in the free-swimming larval (*tadpole*) stages. In the adults the gill slits are modified for filter feeding (*see* endostyle) and respiration, and the notochord and nerve cord are resorbed and reduced, respectively. The coelom is reduced to the pericardial cavity. The body is enclosed within a protective test (*tunic*) with two openings, an inhalent mouth and an exhalent atriopore. The class Ascidiacea (sea squirts, e.g. *Ciona*) are colonial or solitary sessile forms. The Thaliacea are pelagic and include the salps (e.g. *Salpa*) and *Doliolum*. The Larvacea, e.g. *Oikopleura*, are also pelagic and retain the larval notochord and nerve cord throughout life.

Urodela. The order of the Amphibia (subclass *Lissamphibia) that contains the newts and salamanders, which live almost entirely in the northern hemisphere. They are characterized by a long body with short limbs and a long tail. Most urodeles are largely or wholly aquatic but some, e.g. *Triturus* (newt), are terrestrial, although confined to damp environments. The aquatic larvae resemble the adults and metamorphosis is slight. Partial or complete neoteny is common, as in *Ambystoma* (Mexican axolotl), in which the larval gills are retained in the adult and the lungs tend to atrophy.

urophysis. A concentration of neurosecretory neurone terminals at the posterior end of the spinal cord of teleost and elasmobranch fish that closely resembles the mammalian neurohypophysis (*see* pituitary gland). First described in 1955, it produces polypeptide factors that are thought to influence osmoregulation and the contraction of smooth muscles.

urostyle. A rod-shaped bone of anurans that is formed by fusion of the caudal vertebrae and, with the ilium, transfers the thrust of jumping from the legs to the body.

uterus (womb). A muscular expansion of the midregion of the *Müllerian duct of female mammals (except the Monotremata) that contains the developing embryo and (later) foetus during pregnancy. In most mammals it is a paired structure (it is single in humans), connected anteriorly to the two Fallopian tubes and posteriorly to the exterior via the vagina. The uterus has an internal lining of glandular cells that, under the control of the reproductive hormones, fluctuates in form and function during the *oestrous cycle in nonpregnant females (*see* endometrium) and grossly increases in size during pregnancy (*see* decidua). The smooth muscle also grows rapidly throughout pregnancy to become large and powerful enough to expel the foetus and placenta at parturition.

utriculus. The dorsal chamber of the vertebrate membranous labyrinth, from which the *semicircular canals arise. *See also* inner ear.

vaccination. The administration of antigens for the purpose of inducing active *immunity, by establishing adequate levels of antibody and lymphocytes carrying cell-bound antibody. Antigens are injected or ingested in the form of *vaccines*. These may be toxins derived from pathogenic bacilli, dead pathogenic bacteria or viruses, or attenuated organisms (*see* attenuation).

vacuole. A fluid-filled often spherical membrane-bound compartment within a cell. Mature parenchyma cells of plants commonly have a large central vacuole bounded by a membrane, the *tonoplast*. The vacuolar solution (or *cell sap*) may contain salts, sugars, organic acids, oxygen, carbon dioxide, pigments (e.g. anthocyans), and waste products such as calcium oxalate in the form of single crystals or raphides, tannin in tannin cells, latex in laticifers. The vacuoles control *turgor of plant cells by osmotic exchange of water. Plant vacuoles probably also have a lysosomal function; there is a growing tendency to describe all lysosomes as types of vacuole, with all vacuoles having similar origins. Vacuoles are also formed during *endocytosis, particularly in animal cells, as in the formation of food vacuoles in Protozoa. Many freshwater unicellular organisms and sponges possess *contractile vacuoles, which function in osmoregulation.

vagina. The fused lower part of the Müllerian ducts of female mammals. It forms a muscular tube, lined with stratified nonglandular epithelium, that connects the uteri to the exterior and receives the penis of the male during copulation. In most mammals it is a single medial structure, but in some marsupials it is paired. The differentiation and turnover of the lining cells fluctuates during the oestrous cycle, under the control of the reproductive hormones.

vagus nerve. The tenth cranial nerve of vertebrates, which arises from the medulla oblongata of the hindbrain. It contains sensory fibres from the viscera and parasympathetic motor fibres serving the heart, lungs, and viscera. *See also* autonomic nervous system.

valine (val). An amino acid, $(CH_3)_2CHCH(NH_2)COOH$, one of the 20 common amino acids found in proteins and an *essential amino acid for man. Valine functions as a precursor of pantothenic acid.

vallecular canal. An air-filled canal occurring in the cortex of some sphenopsid pteridophytes, such as *Equisetum* (horsetails).

van der Waals forces. *See* hydrophobic interactions.

Van Geison. *See* staining.

variation. The differences in characteristics between members of a population or of a species. Variations are due to environmental influences, the genetic constitution of the individual (genotype), or to interactions between the two. Genetic variations are due to recombination of the genes during sexual reproduction or to mutations. These inherited variations are the raw material on which *natural selection acts and are the basic cause of the evolution of species. *Continuous variation* (*quantitative inheritance*) is brought about by the action of many genes (*polygenes*), each having a small effect and causing a gradual change in a characteristic of the species. Examples are the height and weight variations in man.
Discontinuous variation (*qualitative inheritance*) is brought about by one or a few major genes, which may be present in the population in two or more allelic

forms. These alleles give rise to alternative characteristics in the phenotype that differ sharply from each other, with no intermediates between them. Examples are the different blood groups in man, normal and vestigial wings in *Drosophila*, and round and wrinkled seed coats in peas.

variety. A unit of classification that is a subdivision of a *species. The term is usually applied loosely to a number of a groups within the species. It is most often used for a cultivated form of a plant, usually produced vegetatively, but is sometimes applied to a new breed of animal. The name of a variety is usually added after the name of the species in the style *Salix repens* var. *fusca* (a variety of creeping willow), or simply as *Salix repens fusca*. Cultivated varieties produced in horticulture are known as *cultivars*. Cultivars have English names, rather than Latin ones, and the specific epithet is often omitted from the name (as in *Gypsophila* 'Bristol Fairy').

varve dating (geochronology). A *dating technique that gives the absolute age of a sediment and therefore of the fossils it contains. Varves are finely stratified clays, formed especially in Scandinavia during the retreat of ice in the Pleistocene. Each varve is thought to be seasonal and to represent the yearly melting of the ice. In some places, varve formation has continued until the present day; by counting varves it has been possible to establish an absolute chronology for northern glaciated Europe that goes back to the end of the Pleistocene (i.e. to 20 000 years ago).

vascular bundle. A discrete longitudinal strand of *vascular tissue. The arrangement of the elements of the bundle varies (*see* bicollateral bundle, centric bundle, collateral bundle).

vascular cambium (fascicular cambium). The lateral meristem of the *vascular tissue.

vascular plants. *See* Tracheophyta.

vascular system. 1. Any series of fluid-filled vessels or spaces in animals, e.g. the *blood vascular system or the *water vascular system.
2. The system of *vascular tissues in plants.

vascular tissue (fascicular tissue). A composite tissue in vascular plants consisting principally of water- and food-conducting elements (the *xylem and *phloem respectively) but also containing strengthening elements (sclerenchyma, mainly in the form of fibres) and parenchyma cells. The first formed or *primary vascular tissue* develops from the procambium and its arrangement is very varied (*see* stele). The *secondary vascular tissue* is formed in plants with secondary thickening, from a special secondary meristem, the *vascular cambium* (or *fascicular cambium*). This originates from undifferentiated cells between the primary xylem and phloem, presumably dormant meristematic cells from the procambium. These resume their meristematic activity and cut off cells on their inner and outer periclinal faces. In plants with primary vascular tissue as a ring of *vascular bundles*, the meristematic activity spreads between the vascular bundles across the primary medullary rays as the *interfascicular cambium* and eventually joins up to form a complete ring. The cambium consists of two types of meristematic cells (initials): small isodiametric *ray initials*, which give rise to the secondary medullary ray cells; and larger vertically elongated tapering *fusiform initials*, which give rise to the cells of the vertical systems of the xylem and phloem (the conducting elements (i.e. *sieve elements, *vessel elements, and *tracheids), the axial parenchyma, and the strengthening cells, i.e. *fibres and *fibre-tracheids).
Types of secondary growth other than those described above are termed *anomalous* (*see* secondary growth).

vas deferens. One of a pair of muscular ducts of amniotes and some amphibians that conveys spermatozoa from the epididymis (via the medial urethra in mammals) to the exterior during coitus.

vas efferens. One of a number of ducts in vertebrates that convey spermatozoa from the testis to the epididymis. The vasa efferentia are derived from tubules of the embryonic mesonephros.

vasoconstriction. A reduction in the diameter of blood vessels, usually arterioles or capillaries, caused by contraction of the smooth muscle in their walls. It can be induced by the stimulation of vasoconstrictor nerve fibres (*see* vasomotor nerves), which innervate the blood vessel walls, or by the local injection of adrenaline or similar substances. Reflex vasoconstriction can occur in response to pain, loud noises, fear, a fall in blood pressure, and taking deep breaths.

vasodilatation. An increase in the diameter of small blood vessels caused by a decrease in the tone of the smooth muscle in their walls. It can be induced by the stimulation of cholinergic vasodilator nerve fibres, reduction of the sympathetic vasoconstrictor innervation, or by the injection of acetylcholine, histamine, or kinins. Vasodilatation can occur in response to a rise in blood pressure, exercise, high external temperature, and certain forms of stress, e.g. embarrassment.

vasomotor nerves. Autonomic nerve fibres that induce an alteration in the diameter of blood vessels. The *vasoconstrictor nerve* fibres, which are sympathetic, arise from the thoracic and upper lumbar regions of the spinal cord and receive impulses from the medulla oblongata (*see* vasconstriction). *Vasodilator nerve* fibres have been demonstrated in only a few instances and may be of sympathetic or parasympathetic origin (*see* vasodilatation).

vasopressin (antidiuretic hormone, ADH). A peptide hormone secreted by the pars nervosa of the mammalian pituitary gland (*compare* oxytocin, vasotocin). In 1895, Oliver and Schäfer first showed that pituitary extract caused vasoconstriction and increased blood pressure in the dog. The mammalian vasopressins were characterized and synthesized by du Vigneaud in the 1950s. The main effects of vasopressin are: (1) the stimulation of water re-uptake by the epithelial cells of the kidney distal tubules in higher vertebrates (antidiuretic effect), (2) stimulation of the permeability of skin and bladder cells in amphibians, (3) contraction of the smooth muscle in the walls of blood vessels (vasopressor effect), and (4) the regulation of the release of hormones from the adenohypophysis. These effects are all mediated by cyclic AMP. The secretion of vasopressin is stimulated by most emotional, systemic, or reflex stimuli and by osmotic and electrolyte factors in the blood. Purified posterior pituitary extracts containing vasopressin are known as *pitressin. See also* neurohormone.

vasotocin. A peptide hormone secreted by the posterior pituitary of most lower vertebrates and by the mammalian foetus and pineal gland. It was first identified in the chicken in 1958, but subsequent work has shown that the amphibian water balance principle described by Heller in 1941 was vasotocin. Its wide distribution has led to the hypothesis that vasotocin was a stem hormone in the evolution of the neurohypophysial hormones. Vasotocin structurally resembles and exhibits similar properties to *vasopressin and *oxytocin (see formulae) but its most characteristic action is to increase permeability in the skin and bladder of amphibians.

vector. 1. (in medicine) An animal, such as an insect or a tick, that harbours pathogenic microorganisms and conveys them to other animals or to humans, who thus become infected.
2. (in *genetic engineering) A *plasmid used to carry genes into recipient cells. For example, a plasmid vector that can replicate in both bacterial and mammalian cells can be used to carry a bacterial gene into mammalian cells, or *vice versa.*

vegetal pole (vegetative pole). The point on the surface of an animal ovum that is furthest from the nucleus and at which most of the yolk is concentrated. *Compare* animal pole.

vegetative. Designating any type of growth not involved with or resulting from sexual reproduction.

vegetative propagation (vegetative reproduction). 1. (in plants). Any method of nonsexual reproduction that involves the detachment of fairly large usually differentiated multicellular bodies from the parent plant. Organs of vegetative propagation include bulbs, corms, rhizomes, tubers, stolons, turions, and gemmae, some of which are also used in perennation.
2. (in animals). The production of nonsexual multicellular progeny, as by budding in *Hydra.*

vein. 1. A blood vessel that conveys blood from the capillary bed to the heart. Compared with the arteries, veins have a larger lumen and thinner walls, in which much of the muscular and elastic tissue has been replaced by white fibrous tissue. Most veins contain valves

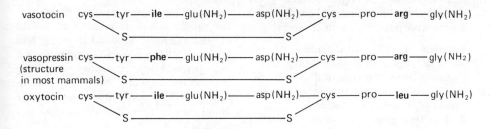

Amino acid sequences of peptide hormones of the neurohypophysis

that direct blood flow towards the heart and prevent backflow.
2. One of the vascular bundles of a leaf.
3. One of the chitinous tubes that strengthen and support the wing of an insect.

velamen. The outer layer of the aerial roots of certain epiphytic monocotyledons, such as some orchids, and of certain soil-rooting ones, such as *Asparagus*. It is composed of several layers of dead empty cells with perforated walls and acts as a water-retaining spongy tissue, being equivalent to a multiple epidermis. It is bound internally by an exodermis.

veliger. The second planktonic larval stage of most molluscs. It develops from a trochophore and has two large ciliated lobes (*velum*) used for locomotion and feeding. The velum increases the ciliated area so that a greater weight can be supported and the larva no longer rotates but can direct its movements. Adult organs such as the shell, mantle, and foot are present.

vena cava. Either of two main veins, the *anterior* (or *superior*) *vena cava* (*precaval vein*) or the *posterior* (or *inferior*) *vena cava* (*postcaval vein*). The anterior vena cava is a single or paired vein of adult tetrapods that returns deoxygenated blood from the head and forelimbs to the right atrium of the heart. It is homologous to the anterior and common cardinal veins of fish. The posterior vena cava, a single main vein of adult tetrapods and lungfish, returns deoxygenated blood from the trunk and rear limbs to the right atrium. It is derived from the primitive hepatic, renal portal, and posterior cardinal veins.

venation. 1. The arrangement of the veins in an insect's wing. Many insect groups have a constant and characteristic venation, which provides a useful means of identifying species.
2. The arrangement of vascular bundles in the blade of a leaf. For example, in dicotyledons the veins form a network

(*reticulate* or *net venation*); in most monocotyledons there are several parallel veins of equal size (*parallel venation*).

venter. The part of an *archegonium containing the oosphere.

ventral. 1. Designating the surface of prostrate organisms or structures, such as flatworms and fern prothalli, that is nearest to the substrate (the *lower* surface).
2. (in botany). *See* adaxial.
3. Designating the surface of a chordate that is furthest from the notochord. *Compare* dorsal.

ventral aorta. The artery of tetrapod embryos that carries deoxygenated blood forward from the ventricle of the heart and divides to form the six paired *aortic arches. In adult tetrapods it is represented by the ascending section of the aorta.

ventricle. 1. The thick-walled muscular contractile chamber of vertebrate and molluscan hearts. In primitive vertebrates it receives blood from the atrium and pumps it through the conus arteriosus into the arterial system. During the evolution of air-breathing forms it has become progressively divided; in birds and mammals it is anatomically and functionally separated so that the left ventricle pumps oxygenated blood to the tissues and the right ventricle pumps deoxygenated blood to the lungs.
2. One of a series of four or five cavities within the brain of vertebrates. They are derived from the central cavity of the neural tube and are filled with *cerebrospinal fluid. *See also* choroid plexus.

venule. A small vein situated adjacent to the capillary bed. It consists of a tube of endothelium surrounded by a thin layer of collagen fibres. Venules have a high permeability, sometimes surpassing that of the capillary bed, thus permitting the diffusion of substances from the blood into surrounding tissues, and vice versa.

vermiform appendix. *See* appendix.

vernalin. *See* vernalization.

vernalization. The exposure of certain plants to a period of cold, which in these plants is either required before flowering will occur or induces earlier flowering than usual. Flowering is usually subsequently controlled by *photoperiodism. Winter varieties of rye, oats, and wheat, unlike spring varieties, require vernalization before flowering within one year. Therefore they are usually sown in autumn for vernalization during winter. Alternatively, the partially germinated seed is vernalized in cold storage, a technique perfected in Russia where severe winters would kill seedlings. Many biennials, which require a winter before flowering, can be induced to flower in the first year by vernalizing the young plants. Treatment with gibberellins can sometimes substitute for the cold period. Some perennials, e.g. wallflower, require annual periods of low temperature before flowering. The low-temperature stimulus is perceived by the apical bud, or sometimes by the leaves, and transmitted to the floral apex. The bud-perceived stimulus can also be transmitted across a graft to a second plant. A hormone, *vernalin*, has been postulated as being responsible, but has not been isolated.

vernation. The way in which young leaves unfold from the bud and their subsequent appearance and relationships, which are all dependent on their *ptyxis. For example many ferns have a *circinnate vernation*, in which the fronds unroll from base to apex.

versatile. Designating an anther fixed by its back to the tip of the filament, so that it swings freely. *Compare* basifixed, dorsifixed.

vertebra. One of the individual bones of the *vertebral column.

vertebral column (backbone, spinal column). A series of closely apposed bones or cartilages (*vertebrae*) that runs dorsally from the skull to the tail in vertebrates. It replaces the primitive notochord as the main longitudinal strengthening element of the body and surrounds and protects the spinal cord. In fish the vertebral column serves as a flexible compression member for resisting the contraction of the myotome muscles. Hence the individual vertebrae lie intersegmentally, receiving attachments from adjacent muscle blocks. Fish vertebrae consist of a massive *centrum, a dorsal *neural arch* enclosing the spinal cord, and, in the tail region, a ventral *haemal arch* protecting the main blood vessels. Vertebrae are linked by *symphyses between the centra. In tetrapods the vertebrae show increasing development of *zygapophyses* – paired lateral processes by which adjacent vertebrae articulate – which provide increased rigidity and resistance to torsion. Tetrapod vertebrae also bear *transverse processes, on which the ribs articulate. The vertebrae themselves become increasingly regionally differentiated. Anteriorly, the *atlas and the *axis permit independent movement of the head on the body. The *cervical vertebrae* of the neck have reduced ribs, *thoracic vertebrae* have full ribs, and *lumbar vertebrae* have no ribs. *Sacral vertebrae* and their ribs are more-or-less fused and specialized for attachment of the pelvic girdle. The *caudal vertebrae* of the tail are ribless and may be specialized (*see* autotomy, coccyx, urostyle). The vertebral column of birds is largely fused to confer the rigidity necessary for flight.

Vertebrata (Craniata). The most important subphylum of the Chordata, containing the fishes, amphibians, reptiles, birds, and mammals. Typically they possess an endoskeleton of cartilage or bone, a dorsal vertebral column (the backbone) enclosing the tubular nerve cord (the spinal cord), and a complex nervous system with a well-developed brain, which is housed in the cranium (skull). The blood and digestive systems are located below the vertebral column. All but the most primitive vertebrates have jaws, formed from the anterior pair of visceral arches. There are nine classes: the *Agnatha, *Placodermi, *Acanthodii, *Chondrichthyes, *Osteichthyes, *Amphibia, *Reptilia, *Aves, and *Mammalia.

verticillaster. A type of inflorescence found in the family Labiatae (deadnettle, mints, etc.). The flowers are arranged in two dichasial cymes, one on each side of the stem, but they are so crowded that they appear to be arranged in dense whorls.

vessel (trachea). A long tubular water-conducting element of xylem, consisting of a vertical series of *vessel elements.

vessel element. A specialized lignified xylem cell occurring only in angiosperms and characterized by the possession of *perforation plates (*see also* tracheary elements). The most primitive type of vessel element is long and thin with oblique perforation plates and is very similar to a tracheid. The most advanced are short and wide with horizontal perforation plates. A gradation exists between the two types. A vertical series of vessel elements constitutes a *vessel* (or *trachea*). Vessels, together with tracheids, form the water-conducting system in plants possessing them.

vestibulocochlear nerve. *See* cranial nerves.

vestigial organ. An organ that has become reduced because the organism possessing it evolved in such a way that it was no longer required. Vestigial organs are important in that they show evolutionary relationships. For example, the skeleton of a snake shows that it possesses vestigial limbs, which cannot be seen in the external form but indicate that snakes evolved from limbed lizard-like ancestors.

viable count. A count of the proportion of cells in a sample (e.g. of bacteria, yeasts, or cells in a tissue culture) that are able to grow and reproduce.

vicariad. A group of species produced by allopatric speciation from one common ancestor.

villus. A finger-like projection, usually developed to increase the surface area of a tissue or organ. *Intestinal villi* project from the superficial layers of the intestinal wall. They have a core containing blood vessels and a lacteal, into which the products of digestion are absorbed, and a muscular strand that permits movement of the villus. *Chorionic villi* develop from the chorion of the mammalian placenta, providing an extensive area of contact between the uterus and placenta. *See also* microvillus.

virion. *See* virus.

viroid. A factor similar to a virus but with an even simpler organization, since it exists simply as a closed circle of single-stranded RNA (partially base-paired). Some viroids are believed to be pathogenic agents in higher plants, e.g. potato spindle tuber viroid.

virulence. The capacity of a parasitic microorganism for causing disease.

virulent phage. A *bacteriophage that always causes lysis of the host cell soon after infection. *Compare* temperate phage.

virus. One of a group of minute infectious agents, formerly defined as unique obligate intracellular parasites. Since this is also a property of certain bacteria and the rickettsiae, viruses are now distinguished by their simple organization and structure and mechanism of replication. Many viruses cause disease in their hosts; they are metabolically inert outside the host cell and are no more alive than the pieces of nucleic acid used in transformation. A mature virus, known as a *virion*, is much smaller than a bacterium, with a diameter ranging between 20 and 400 nm. It consists basically of a shell or tube of protein subunits (*capsomeres*), the *capsid*, around a centrally located nucleic acid. Any particular virus contains only a single type of nucleic acid, RNA or DNA, as its genetic material. Some virus capsids resemble an icosahedron (a polyhedron of 20 triangular faces with 12 corners) and are called *icosahedral virions*; others have a cylindrical form with a helical structure and are called *helical virions*. Virus particles lack ribosomes, transfer RNA, ATP-generating systems, and biosynthetic enzymes. The virus genome contains no information for synthesizing ATP-generating systems. The virus shows a specificity for its host not shown by naked viral nucleic acid.

After the virus attaches to its specific host cell, the viral nucleic acid enters the cell, directs the synthesis of virus-specific proteins, and undergoes replication. The protein subunits of the virus coat are then assembled around the new copies of the viral genome to give complete virions. These are released by the dissolution of the infected cell either as *naked virions* or as *enveloped virions*, which acquire additional coats from the host cell envelope during release. Some viruses show other types of growth and development that do not necessarily cause dissolution of the host cell (*see* lysogeny, transduction).

Viruses can be divided into four groups according to the types of organism they infect, i.e. animals, plants, insects, and bacteria (*see* bacteriophage). The host range depends both on the capsid and the specific receptors it interacts with on the host cell surface. Viruses can also be grouped into highly specific morphological types but the number of these is too small for adequate classification. The type of nucleic acid of the viruses can also be used for classification. Some important animal viruses are classified below.

Viruses containing double-stranded DNA
1. papovaviruses: naked icosahedral viruses causing tumours. There are two types: *papillomaviruses*, about 550 Å in diameter, which include the viruses causing warts; and the smaller *polyomaviruses*, about 450 Å in diameter, which include *SV40 virus.
2. *adenoviruses*: naked icosahedral viruses causing acute respiratory diseases in man. Adenoviruses possess a small genome of double-stranded DNA associated with up to 12 different kinds of protein molecule. Like some other types of eukaryotic virus, adenoviruses have messenger RNA molecules that are mosaics of *exon sequences spliced together after transcription.
3. *herpesviruses*: enveloped icosahedral viruses responsible for herpes and chickenpox. This group includes the *cytomegalovirus*, which, if present in pregnant women, may cause congenital handicap in the foetus. *See also* latent virus.
4. *poxviruses*: enveloped helical capsid viruses causing smallpox, cowpox, and myxomatosis.

Viruses containing single-stranded RNA
1. picornaviruses: naked icosahedral viruses, including the enteroviruses of man (such as those causing poliomyelitis), the rhinoviruses (responsible for colds), and the agents of foot-and-mouth disease in cattle.
2. *arboviruses*: enveloped viruses causing such diseases as yellow fever and encephalitis.
3. *myxoviruses*: enveloped helical capsid viruses responsible for influenza, mumps, measles, rubella, and rabies.

visceral arch. 1. One of a series of bars of tissue in the lateral walls of the pharynx of fish and tetrapod embryos, separating the mouth from the spiracle, the spiracle from the first gill slit, and subsequent gill slits from each other. It provides support for the gill apparatus. **2.** The bony or cartilaginous skeleton supporting a visceral arch, usually consisting of four elements on each side, the most ventral of which articulate medially. The first arch is modified to form jaws (*see* mandibular arch) and the second is modified to form jaw-supporting elements (*see* hyoid arch). The third and subsequent arches (*branchial arches*) support the gills.

visceral pouch and cleft. See gill pouch.

viscerocranium. *See* splanchnocranium.

visual purple. *See* rhodopsin.

vitalism. The theory that living organisms contain a unique *vital force* that distinguishes them from nonliving things. The vital force (*élan vital*), thought to be a form of energy, was proposed by the French philosopher H. Bergson (1859–1941) as being responsible for the evolution of living organisms, rather than the action of natural selection proposed by Darwin.

vital staining. The process of staining cells while they are still alive. Some vital stains are specific, e.g. Janus green stains mitochondria. *Supravital staining* involves the immersion of cells in basic stains, e.g. methylene blue stains axons. In *intra-vitam staining*, acidic stains are injected into animals and taken up by their cells, e.g. trypan blue is taken up by macrophages.

vitamin. An organic substance required in small quantities for the maintenance of vital metabolic functions. Vitamins are known as *micronutrients*, in contrast to *macronutrients*, e.g. amino acids, carbohydrates, and fats, which are required in larger amounts. Higher animals and some microorganisms are unable to synthesize vitamins, which must then be obtained from plants, microorganisms, or other animals as part of the diet. Dietary deficiency of a vitamin results in a specific vitamin deficiency disease (*avitaminosis*). For example, the absence of thiamine (vitamin B_1), ascorbic acid (vitamin C), or vitamin D from the diet of man results in the diseases beriberi, scurvy, and rickets, respectively.
Vitamins are divided into water-soluble and fat-soluble groups. The water-soluble vitamins include the *vitamin B complex and *ascorbic acid. The former function as coenzymes (or the precursors of coenzymes) and the latter as a cofactor in several enzyme reactions. All the other vitamins, i.e. *vitamin A (retinol), *vitamin D, *vitamin E (tocopherol), and *vitamin K, are fat-soluble and have less well established mechanisms of action.

Certain other substances have vitamin-like activity and were formerly regarded as vitamins; however they can be synthesized in adequate amounts and are not required in the diet. These substances, which include *choline, *inositol, *carnitine, and *lipoic acid, were formerly regarded as part of the B complex.

Vitamin A

vitamin A (vitamin A_1, retinol). A fat-soluble vitamin derived from plant carotenes and occurring in most vertebrates (see formula). It is stored in the liver and is particularly abundant in fish-liver oil. A deficiency of this vitamin results in night blindness and, in the long term, to growth impairment. The physiologically active form of vitamin A is its aldehyde, *retinal* (or *retinene*), which takes part in the visual cycle of the rods of the retina (*see* rhodopsin).
A similar vitamin, *vitamin A_2*, differing only in having an extra double bond in the ring at the 3,4 position, occurs in the tissues of freshwater fish.

vitamin B complex. A large group of water-soluble vitamins that are obtained from similar sources, such as yeast and liver, and function as coenzymes or precursors of coenzymes. The group includes *thiamine (*vitamin B_1*), *nicotinic acid, *riboflavin (*vitamin B_2*), *pantothenic acid, *pyridoxine (*vitamin B_6*), *biotin, *folic acid, and *cyanocobalamin (*vitamin B_{12}*).

vitamin C. *See* ascorbic acid.

vitamin D. A fat-soluble vitamin consisting of a group of closely related steroids, *vitamins D_2* (or *calciferol*) and D_3 (see formula) being the most important. A deficiency in this vitamin leads to rickets in children, failure in calcifica-

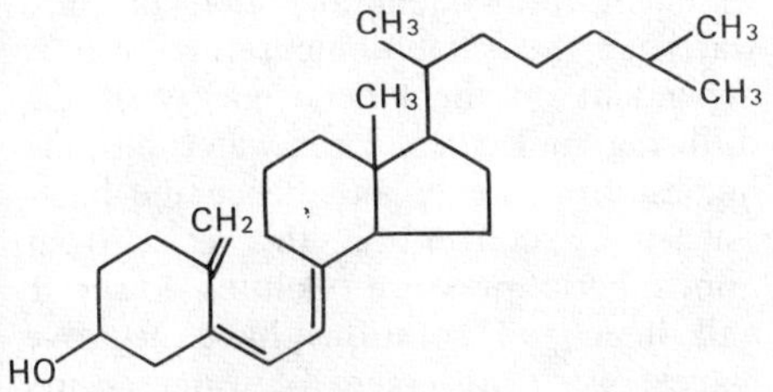

Vitamin D$_3$

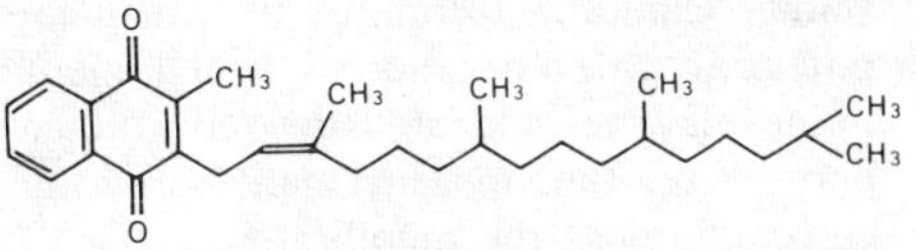

Vitamin K$_1$

n 6, 7, or 9

Vitamin K$_2$

tion of the bones causing skeletal abnormalities. The precursors of vitamins D$_2$ and D$_3$, obtained from plant sources, are ergosterol and 7-dehydrocholesterol respectively: these substances are converted to the vitamins in animal tissues in the presence of ultraviolet radiation. Vitamin D acts by increasing calcium and phosphate absorption from the small intestine.

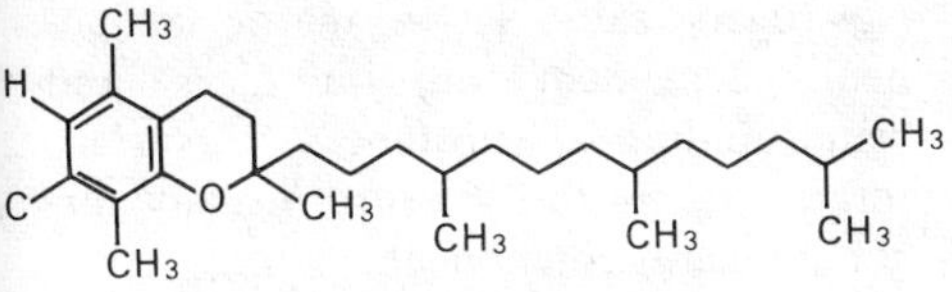

α-tocopherol

vitamin E (tocopherol). A fat-soluble vitamin consisting of a group of closely related compounds, the most common forms being α-, β-, and γ-*tocopherol* (see formula). A nutritional deficiency in vitamin E leads to sterility and atrophy in rodents and it is thought that this vitamin is necessary for healthy reproduction in all vertebrates. Vitamin E has powerful antioxidant properties and may act by stabilizing membranes, preventing oxidation of the unsaturated fatty acid components. It occurs in wheat germ and some vegetable leaves.

vitamin K. A fat-soluble vitamin required in the diet of most vertebrates. A deficiency of vitamin K leads to an inability to synthesize prothrombin and hence to defective blood clotting. The two main forms are *vitamins K$_1$ and K$_2$* (see formula), the former occurring in

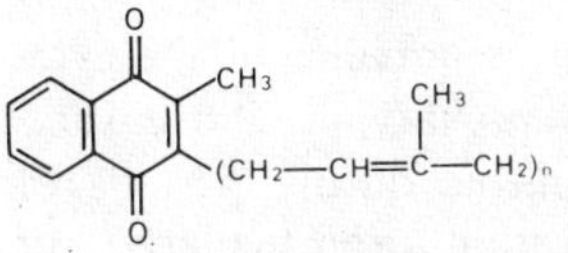

plants, particularly in leafy vegetables, and the latter being synthesized by bacteria, including those in the gut.

vitelline membrane. *See* egg membrane.

vitreous humour. The transparent semigelatinous substance that fills the cavity behind the lens of the vertebrate eye.

viviparity. 1. A type of reproduction in animals in which the embryo(s) develop within and derive nourishment from the maternal organism. Viviparity is characteristic of all placental mammals; it also occurs in some snakes, lizards, sharks, and invertebrates. *Compare* oviparity, ovoviviparity.
2. The process by which certain plants bypass the shedding of spores or seeds, producing instead small plants similar to themselves. For example, in *Selaginella apoda* (a lycopsid) the spores germinate on the parent plant so that the gametophyte phase is passed in the sporangium and an embryonic sporophyte plant is released.

vocal cords. A pair of elastic fibres stretched across the *larynx in amphibians, reptiles, and birds. The cords, which lie parallel to the glottis, vibrate as air is expelled, producing vocal sounds. Movement of the cartilages of the larynx regulates the stretch of the cords, and hence the pitch of the sound. *Compare* syrinx.

voltage clamp. A technique by which the potential difference across a cell membrane may be held at a desired voltage, permitting the measurement of ionic currents across the membrane.

voluntary muscle. *See* striated muscle.

volutin. A polymer of inorganic phosphate occurring as granules in the cytoplasm of many prokaryotic and eukaryotic microorganisms during periods of nutrient starvation (particularly of sulphate). Volutin forms an intracellular reserve of phosphate that rapidly disappears when the nutrient limitation is relieved.

W

Wallace's line. The hypothetical line, running along the deep strait between the islands of Bali and Lombok, near Java, that divides the Oriental and Australasian zoogeographical regions. These regions, and the positioning of the line, were worked out by A. R. Wallace (1823–1913) in the 19th century.

warm-blooded. *See* homoiothermy.

warning coloration (aposematic coloration). The brilliant and striking patterns of colours occurring in some animals, especially insects. It often occurs in species that are predator resistant, as in being distasteful, poisonous, or stinging, and results in a predator learning to avoid the species. Warning coloration is also adopted by some harmless or palatable species in some forms of *mimicry. *Compare* cryptic coloration.

water potential. Symbol: Ψ. A measure of the *free energy status of water in a system, e.g. soil, a cell, or an organ. Ψ is the difference between the *chemical potential* (which is a thermodynamic concept related to free energy) of the water in the system and that of pure water at the same temperature and is dependent on the kinetic energy of the diffusing molecules. Pure water has the highest free energy and hence the highest Ψ; by convention this is zero at atmospheric pressure. Solutes lower Ψ and hence all solutions have negative values of Ψ. Movement of water occurs along gradients of free energy from higher to lower Ψ, i.e. from pure water or solutions of higher Ψ to solutions of lower Ψ. The tendency for water to enter a plant cell, organ, etc., can be expressed in terms of differences in Ψ. The total Ψ of soils, cells, tissues, etc., has various components, summarized in the following equation:

$$\Psi_w = \Psi_s + \Psi_m + \Psi_p,$$

where Ψ_w = the total water potential of the system; Ψ_s = the osmotic component, dependent on solute concentration, e.g. sugars, salts; Ψ_m = matric component, dependent on interfaces and water-binding substances (surface forces); Ψ_p = the pressure (usually turgor pressure) component.

The terms are usually measured in pressure units (commonly atmospheres) rather than energy units. Ψ_w is increased by pressure (Ψ_p positive) and temperature and decreased by solutes (Ψ_s negative) and surface forces (Ψ_m negative). Ψ_w varies from zero in a turgid cell to a value equal to Ψ_s in a flaccid cell. In cells Ψ_m is usually negligible and therefore ignored. Hence, in a cell:

$$\Psi_w = \Psi_p + \Psi_s \text{ or } \Psi_w = TP - OP,$$

where TP = turgor pressure; OP = osmotic pressure.

Water moves through plants because water potential gradients exist from the soil (high Ψ) into the roots, through the plant, and out of the leaves (low Ψ) into the atmosphere. Movement of water along these gradients is a purely physical process, the only energy required being used in the maintenance of the osmotic properties of the cells. *See also* osmosis, turgor.

water vascular system. A system of fluid-filled tubes forming part of the coelom of the Echinodermata. It typically opens to the exterior by a sieve plate, the *madreporite*, and provides fluid for the operation of the *tube feet.

waxes. Esters of fatty acids with long-chain alcohols, often with free hydrocarbon, fatty acid, and alcohol groups. Waxes are produced by both plants and animals, commonly serving as an outer protective covering. Beeswax, a constituent of the honeycomb of bees, contains the wax myricyl palmitate (formed from palmitate and myricyl alcohol). In plants, waxes form additional water-repellent layers on the cuticles of many leaves, fruits, and seeds; wax from the leaves of *Copernicia cerifera* (Brazilian wax palm) is the carnauba wax of commerce. The microscopic pattern of the wax is often characteristic of the species. Waxes are particularly common in xerophytes, in which they reduce transpiration.

Weberian ossicles. A chain of three modified vertebrae in some fishes that transfer sound waves from the swim bladder to the labyrinth of the inner ear.

whalebone. *See* baleen.

whales. *See* Cetacea.

white blood cell (white blood corpuscle, leucocyte). One of various types of nucleated blood cells, found in most vertebrates, that are involved in protecting the body against toxins and bacterial infection. They contain no respiratory pigments and all possess some degree of amoeboid movement. They may be subdivided anatomically into two groups: those with granular cytoplasm, the *polymorphs (neutrophils, eosinophils, and basophils), and those with agranular cytoplasm, the *lymphocytes and *monocytes. In man there are normally between 5000 and 10 000 white blood cells per cubic millimetre of blood, although stress or vigorous exercise can double this number.

white matter. The outer region of the vertebrate *central nervous system. It consists of tracts of medullated nerve fibres, carrying information to and from the higher centres, together with glia and blood vessels. *Compare* grey matter.

wild type. The type of individual (or the genotype or phenotype it possesses) that is most common in wild populations. For example in *Drosophila*, the wild type has normal wings, a grey body, and red eyes. Each of these genes is dominant to any other allele for that gene. Wild-type alleles are often represented as + rather than by a letter. Thus an insect homozygous for wild-type wings would be represented as + +. If a recessive gene becomes, by natural selection, the wild type, its status is modified so that it becomes dominant.

Wolffian duct. A kidney duct of vertebrates, arising as the duct of the pronephros and becoming the duct of the mesonephros. It is therefore the functional kidney duct of adult fishes and amphibians and of embryo amniotes. In male anamniotes it is a urinogenital duct, conveying spermatozoa from the testis as well as urine from the kidney. In adult amniotes, in which the metanephros is the functional kidney, the Wolffian duct is functionally replaced by the ureter; in males, parts of it become modified as the epididymis and vas deferens.

womb. *See* uterus.

wood. The secondary *xylem of dicotyledons and conifers (the term is sometimes used (incorrectly) for both primary and secondary xylem, which are then called *primary wood* and *secondary wood*, respectively. The secondary growth of monocotyledons does not form the compact tissue known as wood, although they and other plants forming tough, fibrous, or rigid structures may loosely be termed woody. Several types of wood are recognized.

(1) *hardwood and softwood*. Hardwoods are derived from dicotyledons; softwoods from conifers. Both contain tracheids and parenchyma, but hardwoods also contain fibres and vessels. Being terms that originated in carpentry but have since taken on specific botanical meanings, they are generally true indicators of hardness but not absolute; for example, balsa (*Ochroma lagopus*), the softest of all woods, is termed a hardwood.

(2) *sapwood (alburnum) and heartwood (duramen)*. In the mature tree the outermost (youngest) wood conducts water and dissolved substances; hence it is called sapwood. Being wet, it cracks and warps on drying and is not valuable timber. The older crushed central heartwood is not conducting and is drier; it is often impregnated with tannins and other metabolic waste products, which preserve it and render it darker in colour. It provides the more valuable timber. *See also* growth ring.

woodlice. *See* Isopoda.

X

xanthophore. *See* chromatophore.

Xanthophyceae. Unicellular, colonial, filamentous, or siphonaceous chrysophyte algae that possess only chlorophylls a and b and β-carotene and produce oil, chrysolaminarin, and glycogen as storage products. The cell wall is mainly pectin and composed of two equal or overlapping pieces. Motile cells or spores are biflagellate, with one whiplash and one tinsel *flagellum. Sexual reproduction is rare and usually oogamous.

xanthophyll. *See* photosynthetic pigments.

X chromosome. *See* sex chromosome.

xeroderma pigmentosa. A human disease involving excessive sensitivity of the skin to sunlight and an increased incidence of cancer of the skin. Affected individuals have a defect in the enzymes responsible for *DNA repair.

xeromorphic. Designating the characters of *xerophytes.

xerophyte. A plant that inhabits dry regions and can survive long periods of drought. Xerophytes are adapted to a dry environment by possessing *xeromorphic* characters, such as hairs, water-storage cells, rolled leaves, stomata in grooves, etc. Examples of xerophytes are *Ammophila* and cacti.

xerosere. *See* sere.

X-ray diffraction analysis (X-ray crystallography). A technique for determining the arrangement of atoms in a crystalline substance by analysing the diffraction patterns produced when a narrow beam of X-rays is passed through the substance. The substance may be examined as a single crystal (used for detailed protein structure) or as a more-or-less randomly orientated mixture of crystals, as with powders and whole cell walls. X-ray diffraction has contributed to the elucidation of structure of many biological molecules, including some important macromolecules, e.g. DNA, haemoglobin, myoglobin. It is particularly useful for determining the tertiary and quaternary structure of proteins; the structure of myoglobin, for instance, has been determined at a resolution of less than 0.2 nm.

xylem. The principal water-conducting tissue in plants, which together with the phloem forms the *vascular tissue. The first xylem to be formed is the *primary xylem*, which develops from the procambium of a primary meristem and consists of *protoxylem and *metaxylem. Secondary wall formation in primary xylem starts with annular and spiral thickenings, which allow greatest flexibility and occur in the earliest protoxylem elements, and proceeds via scalariform thickening to the heavy reticulate and pitted thickenings, which are the least flexible and occur in the latest metaxylem elements. *Secondary xylem* is formed in plants with secondary thickening, from the vascular cambium (*see* wood).

Xylem is a composite tissue with several cell types. The *vessel elements (present in angiosperms) and *tracheids are the water-conducting elements and they, plus the *fibre-tracheids and *fibres, are all lignified and therefore contribute to the mechanical support of the plant (*see also* tracheary elements). By maturity, all these cells have lost their living contents, the functions of the cell being carried out by the cell wall alone. The living cells of the tissue are the parenchyma cells: in secondary xylem these are in the form of horizontal *medullary rays and vertical axial parenchyma.

Y

Y chromosome. *See* sex chromosome.

yeasts. *See* Ascomycetes.

yolk. The store of food material, mostly protein and fat, that is present in the eggs of most animals. The amount and distribution of the yolk varies in different groups: the eggs of oviparous animals contain a large yolk; those of mammals (except monotremes) contain very little yolk, which is evenly distributed in the cytoplasm.

yolk sac. *See* extraembryonic membranes.

Y-organ. One of a pair of glands in the antennary or maxillary segment of malacostracan crustaceans that histologically and functionally resembles the prothoracic gland of insects (*see* ecdysone).

Z

zeatin. *See* kinin.

Zinjanthropus. *See Australopithecus.*

zona pellucida. A glycoprotein membrane that surrounds the mammalian ovum and is secreted by the ovarian follicles.

zoogeography. The study of the distribution of animals, especially in relation to the continents they occupy. There are three main areas of distinct fauna: *Arctogea, *Neogea, and *Notogea, whose distributions can be explained by the theory of *continental drift.

The diversity of marsupials found in Notogea is due to the fact that Australia has been a completely separate continent since Cretaceous times: thus its marsupial fauna has avoided unsuccessful competition with the more efficient placentals. Neogea, too, has a very distinct fauna. It was isolated for much of the period of mammalian evolution, and during the Tertiary period a great variety of marsupials and primitive placentals evolved there, cut off from the more advanced placentals of North America. In late Tertiary times a land bridge connecting the two continents was formed, and many advanced placentals invaded from the north and have now replaced most of the native marsupials. The continents comprising Arctogea have only recently drifted apart. During much of the Pleistocene they formed one continuous land mass over which the animals freely moved. Thus many families, and even genera, of animals are today present on several of the continents. Once the continents had separated, climatic and other forces came into effect; the animals disappeared from some of the continents and evolved in different directions in others.

zooid. The part of a colony of *Ectoprocta or Entoprocta consisting of an individual animal (*polypide*) surrounded by its protective case.

zoology. The study of animals.

zooplankton. Animal members of the *plankton.

zoosporangium. A sporangium that gives rise to motile (flagellate) *zoospores.

zoospore. A flagellate spore produced by many algae and some fungi. Frequently a zoospore has the potential to behave either as an asexual disseminule or as a gamete, as conditions dictate. The sporangium in which it is produced is termed a *zoosporangium*.

Zoraptera. A small order of minute exopterygote insects found in decaying wood and humus.

zwitterion. An ion that bears both a positive and a negative charge. All amino acids, e.g. alanine ($CH_3CHNH_3^+COO^-$), can exist as zwitterions.

zygomorphic (in botany). Showing *bilateral symmetry. The term is applied particularly to flowers whose parts are arranged in bilateral symmetry on the receptacle. *Compare* actinomorphic.

zygospore. *See* zygote.

zygote. The diploid cell resulting from the fusion of two gametes. A zygote usually undergoes cleavage immediately but may occasionally develop a thick wall and become a resting *zygospore*.

zygotene. A stage of the prophase of the first division of *meiosis.

zygotic induction. Induction of bacteriophage proliferation and cell lysis in a nonlysogenic bacterial cell as a result of its *conjugation with a lysogenic bacterium containing an integrated prophage. The transfer of DNA during the conjugation process results in the acquisition of the prophage gene by the recipient bacterium. However, the nonlysogenic characteristics of this cell lead to breakdown of the prophage state, induction of phage replication, and eventual lysis of the recipient cell. Zygotic induction is the technique normally used to map the incidence and location of prophage genes.

zymogen. An inactive precursor of an enzyme. Large dense *zymogen granules* occur in the exocrine cells of the pancreas (i.e. those cells lining the branches of the pancreatic duct). They comprise a mixture of proteins (the precursors of the pancreatic juice enzymes carboxypeptidase, trypsin, and chymotrypsin), which are synthesized on the endoplasmic reticulum and concentrated in Golgi vesicles prior to release into the pancreatic duct.